AMERICAN

The First Patent in America

Jenkes mo-
nopolye

At a generall Courte at Boston
the 6th of the 3th m⁰ 1646
The Co^rt consid^ringe y^e necessity of raising such manifactures of
engins of mils to go by water for speedy dispatch of much worke
with few hands, & being sufficiently informed of ye ability of ye peti-
tion^r to pforme such workes grant his petition (y^t no oth^r p-
son shall set up, or use any such new invention, or trade for
fourteen yeares w'hout ye licence of him ye said Joseph Jenkes)
so far as concernes any such new invention, & so as it shalbe
always in ye pow^r of this Co^rt to restrain ye exportation of such
manifactures, & ye prizes of them to moderation if occasion so require.

SCIENCE AND INVENTION

A PICTORIAL HISTORY

THE FABULOUS STORY OF HOW AMERICAN DREAMERS, WIZARDS, AND INSPIRED

TINKERERS CONVERTED A WILDERNESS INTO THE WONDER OF THE WORLD BY

MITCHELL WILSON

SIMON AND SCHUSTER, NEW YORK

FOR MY DAUGHTERS—ERICA AND VICTORIA

MANUFACTURED IN THE UNITED STATES OF AMERICA BY UNION LABOR. PRINTED BY
KIPE OFFSET PROCESS COMPANY, INC. SET IN TIMES ROMAN BY WESTCOTT & THOMSON,
INC. TEXT PAPER BY CROCKER BURBANK PAPERS INC. AND BINDING SIDES BY
PENINSULAR PAPER COMPANY, TO SPECIFICATIONS OF THE WHITAKER PAPER COMPANY.
BOUND WITH A BACKSTRIP OF ALBERT D. SMITH AND COMPANY'S BANCROFT BUCKRAM
BY H. WOLFF BOOK MANUFACTURING COMPANY.

PUBLISHED BY SIMON AND SCHUSTER, INC. ROCKEFELLER CENTER, 630 FIFTH AVENUE, NEW YORK 20, N. Y.
FIRST PRINTING
LIBRARY OF CONGRESS CATALOG CARD NUMBER: 54–9812
DEWEY DECIMAL CLASSIFICATION NUMBER: 973

CONTENTS

PART THREE

Bright Dream—Dark Fulfillment PAGE 90

The Tools of War PAGE 178

The New Era PAGE 212

FOREWORD

The "civilized man" may be defined as someone who is at home in his own time and place; it is my belief that to be a civilized American today one must be as aware of the mainspring of contemporary America—its technology—as Americans of a hundred years ago were aware of the soil.

Americans today—whether they earn their livings in offices, factories, stores or farms—either make machines, plan new machines, sell the raw material for machine-made products, or feed, represent, amuse, educate, heal, or bury the people who work on or with machines. Nor does this American-living-with-machines end with the end of the working day. I am not talking here about the machines and mechanisms used in the American home, but about the social rules, the social aims, the social strifes that are developed in a society based on machinery and mass production. These we live with twenty-four hours a day. This history of American science and invention is the story of how all this came about.

A few years ago, when I wrote Live with Lightning, *a novel about the life of an American physicist at the present time, I remember trying to explain to John K. Hutchens of the* New York Herald Tribune *that I considered myself a "regional" novelist in that the area of American living to which I felt most closely attuned was this core of technology, which seemed to me to be so central in our society. I knew our scientists—I used to be one; I knew our engineers—I used to work with them in their laboratories and over their drawing boards. I knew how salesmen, advertising men, executives and bankers looked when seen from that center.*

Just as a novelist who has lived much of his life in the mountains, and knows mountain people, and how their very nearness to the mountains has affected their lives, finds a history of his region an exciting field of study, so I found this history of American science and invention one of the most enthralling tasks I ever undertook. If I am right in my contention that American technology is the center of contemporary American living—a center from which millions of threads emanate—then a great many other American men and women will find in this book new insights into the way they live, the things they believe and how these things came to be.

Let me say right now that on reading over my book, I find it an extremely personal story. I find nothing in it with which I would seriously quarrel, which means that I have written not the perfect history but the perfect representation of my own prejudices, biases, enthusiasms, and angers. It could not have been different. No man can encompass all of truth. The only truth he can tell is the statement of his own opinions. I have written this book not as an historian—which I am not—but as the two other fellows I really am: a novelist and a scientist. It was the novelist in me who told the personal stories, who enjoyed the dramatic detail, who tried to bring to life the men and values of gone time. It was the physicist in me, the worker in various laboratories, who appraised and explained the work of these men.

Because this book is a collaboration between my two professional selves, the result is a compromise. When I found a man whose personality was interesting, the novelist insisted on giving him room to act out his human story, even though the physicist kept protesting that the man's work didn't entitle him to that much space. On the other hand, the physicist would just as strongly insist on the inclusion of a brilliant and crucial piece of research when the novelist could not truly get the feeling of the man.

I can see now, too, that many of my judgments were colored by this attitude on my part: how would it feel to work with this man? I have been singularly fortunate in that at one time or another I did research in the laboratories of outstanding physicists like I. I. Rabi and Enrico Fermi. In applied science, I worked for several years with Wallace Cohoe, who is today almost a legendary figure to the leading scientists of the American chemical industry, for he was himself one of their pioneers. I have sat in seminar rooms with hundreds of other scientists, and every man has his style.

With this personal experience, I could say to myself about the men in this book that I would have enjoyed knowing Franklin in his forties; I would have been frightened, charmed and impressed by Count Rumford but I wouldn't have worked either for him or with him. I think I would have misjudged John Fitch if I had met him, but I would have found Fulton an altogether impressive man. Cyrus McCormick, who could out-father Father Day, I would have avoided, although I would have come again and again to listen to stories about him from some caustic but fond relative. Charles Goodyear would have left me speechless with rage—that a man so completely unequipped could manage to weather so many adversities and still succeed. I see him as a Chaplinesque figure in a story that is both heartbreaking and outrageously funny in its sight-gags. In my desk, I actually have a partially completed movie script which I intend to finish some day.

Alexander Graham Bell must have been a delightful man to know and an exasperating one to work with. I have the feeling that I know him intimately, and every time I think of him I find myself smiling, the way one does about an old friend. On the other hand, Thomas Edison was on the grand scale of classic American success and tragedy. I really knew very little about him—his sensitivity, his disguises, his unrestrainable creativity—until I began to work on this book. For him, too, I have notes on a fictionalized biography. The Wright brothers, as human beings, belong in the same class. Their story is truly moving and tragic in a particularly American way because the goals of their time confused them. They wanted to be considered as creative scientists—which they really were—but they also wanted to be rich men.

My feeling for Joseph Henry and Willard Gibbs is admiration, both for their work and for them as human beings. I would have liked to work with Henry but Gibbs would have paralyzed me with awe, however kindly he might have meant to be. His personality was exactly suited to his destiny.

I could go on like this about every man mentioned in the book and I express my regrets in particular that so little room was given to Henry Rowland and so much to George Mortimer Pullman. But historical balance insisted that Pullman's effect on American living of his time and after was greater than Rowland's. I must also point out that there are many gaps in this book because there are certain fields of science so rich that justice could not be done in the brief space that was available. What I have written about mostly is American physical science and mechanical invention.

No one is more aware than I of the mass of material that has been left out. All I can say is that, given my theme and premise, this is the book to be expected from a man with my background, my experiences in life, my temperament, my weaknesses and my talents.

Nothing is to be taken as the last and final word, for that will never be written. You are reading history only as it appears this year. In my discussion of scientific theories—particularly those of recent times—be aware, too, that these must be as transient as older theories that served their time and then were discarded. The caloric theory of heat seemed to answer many questions to scientists once upon a time and our present vocabularies are filled with terms that date back to it. The electromagnetic theory of light was truth for half a century before Michelson and Einstein found its flaws. The quantum theory of matter which has given so much information to our own contemporaries must, in the very nature of man's mind, be eventually superseded by a still closer approximation to objective reality. We know no scientific truth that is not a truth by definition—just as one and one is two only by definition—and definitions are not permanent. Only of one thing can we be reasonably sure: the climate of man is change.

This is the story of American change; how the very nature of the Colonies determined a particular kind of science and invention; how this science and invention reacted on American life to change it; how this changed America made new and different demands on science and invention and was again changed, until after one hundred and seventy-five years of this interplay of action and reaction, of constant change, we find ourselves here today. We look at each other, some of us satisfied, some of us not, and wonder how we got that way. This book is my answer to that question.

M. W.

August, 1954

London, 1776

Paris, 1776

Philadelphia, 1776—The America that declared its independence from England was poor, sparsely settled, and backward. American artisans and mechanics had low standards of workmanship, little talent, and poor training. The tradition of American mechanical know-how did not begin until forty years later. In France, on the other hand, a mass of ingenious craftsmen supported the aristocracy in fabulous luxury. The same conditions existed to a lesser extent in London, where more people lived than in all the states of America combined.

PART ONE

Giants
in the
Wilderness

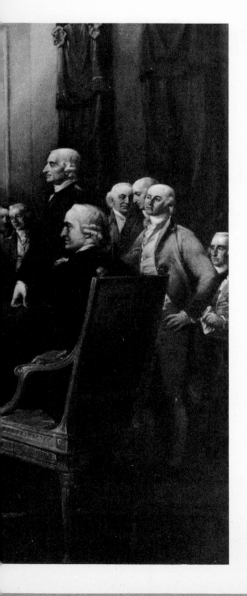

The Philadelphia summer day in 1776 was stiflingly hot. The fifty-six men had become tired, worn, and contentious. They were men of widely different station, background, and opinion. They distrusted themselves, each other, and their mission. By any sane standard they were committing open treason. But each one was to affix his signature to the document on the table—and an idea so new existed in the world that the world itself was different. They were proclaiming the high importance of each individual man, his dignity, and his inalienable right to life. Beginning with that as their premise, they were shaping an American society whose first purpose was to proclaim the inviolability of every member of the human race.

Yet, if this Declaration of Independence were not such an outrageous insult to His Britannic Majesty, George III, the gesture would have been ludicrous. For who—and where—was this "one people" who were clamoring "to take their equal station among the nations of the earth . . ."?

That particular summer day occurred one hundred and fifty years after the first permanent landings of the English in New England—one hundred and fifty years during which seven generations of men and women had been born, had multiplied, and died—and the "American Colonies" were still nothing but the sparsest fringe of seacoast settlements separated by swamps, desolation, empty beaches, and primeval forests of terrifying silence, stretched out in a thin line for a thousand miles from Maine to Georgia. The innermost penetrations were rarely more than one hundred miles from where the Atlantic surf seethed up on the sand. Deeper than one hundred miles was a forested land of silence in which only stealthy shadows moved; a region as remote as the moon, as terrifying as the blackest nightmare. It was called simply, the Wilderness.

In the thousand miles of settled beach-head were scattered some two and a half million people, most of them clustering around the few small towns. One third of the total number lived in the several New England commonwealths. Another tenth were scattered on Long Island, in New York City, and the Hudson Valley as far north as Albany; but only seventeen miles west of Albany, Fort Schenectady was an outpost against the Indians. Maryland had more people than all of New York, and Pennsylvania had more than Maryland. More Presidents were to come from Virginia during the first half century of the Republic not because Virginia possessed any magic, but because, compared to any other region, it contained the most men, including the richest and the poorest, the most educated few and the most backward many.

Yet the new country was unique because nobody was really very poor and nobody was very rich. Only five men out of the two and a half million spent more than ten thousand dollars a year on themselves and their families. In Massachusetts, almost half the towns had schools, and each father was fined twenty shillings if he neglected his children's education. But in Virginia, illiteracy was as prevalent as in the most backward parts of Europe and deliberately kept that way. There were colleges; yet they contained fewer than three hundred students altogether, graduating less than fifty a year.

The New Englanders distrusted the Albany Dutch and were distrusted in turn because each suspected the other of dealing secretly with the Indians. The Germans in Pennsylvania disliked the English of New York and were disliked in turn because each thought the other stiff-necked and cruel. The Virginians looked down on everyone and were resented in return. And yet these were the "one people" who were clamoring.

Along the thousand miles, there was community in only three things: they had farms that were rich to European eyes; they hated the oppression of the Crown; and they all lived in deep fear of the Wilderness.

THE BOUNDARIES
OF AMERICA

The line of outposts pressing against the Wilderness was called the frontier, or more generally by another word that was to carry, like the aftertones of a bell, the meaning of heroism and violence—the West. America began as a country of Westerners.

The earliest settlements were situated on a lip of land at the mouth of a river; and the West was half a mile upstream in the quiet of the watching forest.

First through the thicket went the wild game to water-holes and salt licks. Behind them, silently, went the Indians. In the trail of the Indians, and almost as savage, were hunters, trappers, and white traders exchanging beads and firearms for the pelts which the Indians caught. Returning traders told of open meadows; and the settlements drove out their cattle and horses to graze. This opened land to the pioneer farmer who built a shack and tilled the soil until the earth was exhausted.

The silent parade of game, savage, hunter, trader, farmer, townsman, and merchant moved slowly across Massachusetts and Virginia. A century later, the same file was passing across the black plains of Ohio into Wisconsin.

The West carried along with it, like the foam on the edge of a tide, the habits of roughness and violent democracy. Most of the men who signed the Declaration of Independence, like Thomas Jefferson, had been born on the edge of the frontier.

The awareness of the Wilderness colored every strand of American life. The immensity of the Wilderness was an ever-present nightmare reducing human beings to insignificance. The war against this terror determined the national character. Americans became more pragmatic than any other people since the Romans; yet the purpose of their science and invention was to safeguard and exalt the rights of the individual. Science became a strategy for exploring and settling the unknown world; invention became the way to give twelve hands to a man beleaguered in his struggle to clear the continent.

This fear of the outer darkness and the American anger at the British were enough to bring men together to Philadelphia from their colonial diversity. The paper they signed on that August day was their desperate outcry against the Crown, and in a few short years Americans won their military vindication.

Their other war, however—the war of science and invention against the outer darkness—was to continue all their lives and for seven generations thereafter.

NORTH

Lake Winnipesaukee in New Hampshire was deep in Indian territory. To the settlers in eastern Massachusetts, this spot was a remote corner of the West.

WEST

The Albany patroons refused to break up their million-acre estates, and immigrants were excluded. The eastern Genesee valley was still in the frontier.

SOUTH

Charleston, in the Carolinas, was the hub of the South. Rice, their single crop, was ruining the soil, and even then general pauperization loomed.

Portsmouth, at the mouth of the Piscatagua River in New Hampshire, was the northernmost community of any size. It was the colonial outpost of Boston.

The blockhouse marked the frontier; but as the frontier moved westward, so did the farms and mills, into territory still half occupied by Indians.

Rich, populous Philadelphia had the freest atmosphere. Nevertheless, when Franklin came to America's richest city, he found only two printers.

Pennsylvania was wealthy largely because of the diverse religious sects, who were devoted to their communities, and who were industrious and gentle.

Deserted rice plots and cross-laid nailless snake fences marked the face of the Carolinas. Americans were forbidden to make nails for sale to others.

Florida was on the Indian side of the frontier. The frontier was legally defined as the region containing one white person per ten square miles.

TRADES IN AMERICA

1. WHALING AND FISHING

Science and invention developed in the colonies as Americans learned to use tools. In the thousand mile fringe of seaside towns lived a seafaring people, and most of their handicrafts were related to the sea. While no edict issued by the Crown ever expressly forbade Americans to improve the tools by which they earned their livelihood, the same effect was achieved by the body of law which restricted Americans to only certain fields of activity, and Adam Smith saw the evil. In 1776, he wrote: "To prohibit

Eighteenth-century fishermen used draggers . . .

. . . and a variety of stationary traps.

The cooper's art was important in whaling.

American whalemen at work

a great people from making all that they can of every part of their own produce, or from employing their stock and industry in a way that they judge most advantageous to themselves, is a manifest violation of the most sacred rights of mankind."

Tools and methods for net-making

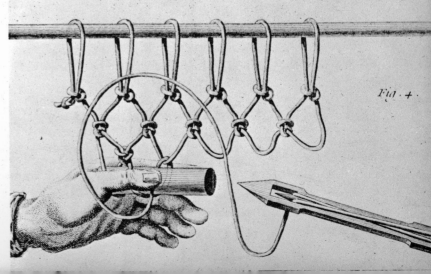

2. A COMPARISON BETWEEN AMERICAN AND EUROPEAN TRADES

In the eighteenth century, science and invention had purely utilitarian goals. The Royal Society had been founded in England over one hundred years before the American Revolution for the purpose of perfecting the useful arts and increasing man's useful knowledge. This was simply putting into words the basic human instinct to make the world a safer place in which to live. *Knowledge is Power* is more than a precept; it is a description of the way in which this instinct works.

Advances in science sprang from man's impulse to increase his power over the world by understanding it. Advances in invention came when he used this new knowledge to create better tools. A hoe gave man control over the soil beneath his feet and forced it to grow an edible grain instead of a weed. An oar and a sail gave him power over water in one way; while a wooden trough gave him control in another for he could use the trough as a conduit to make water go where he wished.

In America, though, these were far more than the tools of husbandry—they made up the American arsenal in the war against the Wilderness, the war for the defense of the rights of the individual, not only within the State, but within the larger domain of the physical universe.

Building in America

Building in Europe—Some of the most exquisite building in Europe was done in the 18th century. Most houses in America were built either of logs or clapboard, yet large scale building was to be an American innovation.

Farming in America

Farming in Europe—European farming methods were improving rapidly in the 18th century. The American farmer was careless with his land because he could always move farther on when his soil was exhausted.

English and American science and invention had the same roots in the eighteenth century, but later, the two paths diverged because the needs and tempers of the two countries were different. Even by the time of the Revolution and the founding of the Republic there were marked differences in the level of handicraft because of the English Mercantile Theory.

The stated policy of the British government demanded that its colonies be *only* sources of raw materials to be shipped home to England in English ships. Local manufactures were discouraged except for what was made either within the home or the colony.

By and large the colonists accepted this mercantile theory, for among the twenty-seven specific complaints made in the Declaration of Independence, there was not one mention of this restraint of manufacture. During the first years of the Republic, the question of manufactures was hotly debated. But just as twenty centuries of man's belief that the world was flat did not to one degree affect the roundness of the planet, so all the words in the world could not stop the growth of an American technology once the need was made manifest.

American industry was primitive and based mostly on hand operations.

Glassblowing in Europe—18th-century European houses enjoyed an abundance of glass windows. Glass in America was a comparative luxury, yet America was eventually to turn out more glass of all kinds than any other nation.

Glassblowing in America

Papermaking in Europe—Benjamin Franklin helped introduce papermaking to America. During the Revolution paper was scarce; yet the time was to come when the American paper industry would consume the great forests.

Papermaking in America

HAT MAKER

"Hats, Manufactured by the Advertiser, to exceed, in Fineness, Cut, Colour and Cock; to turn rain, and prevent the Sweat of the Head damaging the Crown. Nesbitt Deane. Aside the Coffee-House Bridge, New-York."

SAWYER

"Blake, Carpenter and Joiner, in John-Street near the Golden-Hill, Takes this Method of informing the Publick, that he undertakes Carpenter's & Joiner's Work by Measure, or makes Estimates before he begins to work."

PEWTERER

"Joseph Leddel, Pewterer, who for many Years had liv'd at the Sign of the Platter in Dock-Street, opposite to Mr. Franks's, is now removed to the lower End of Wall-Street near the Meal Market."

3. THE AMERICAN CRAFTSMAN

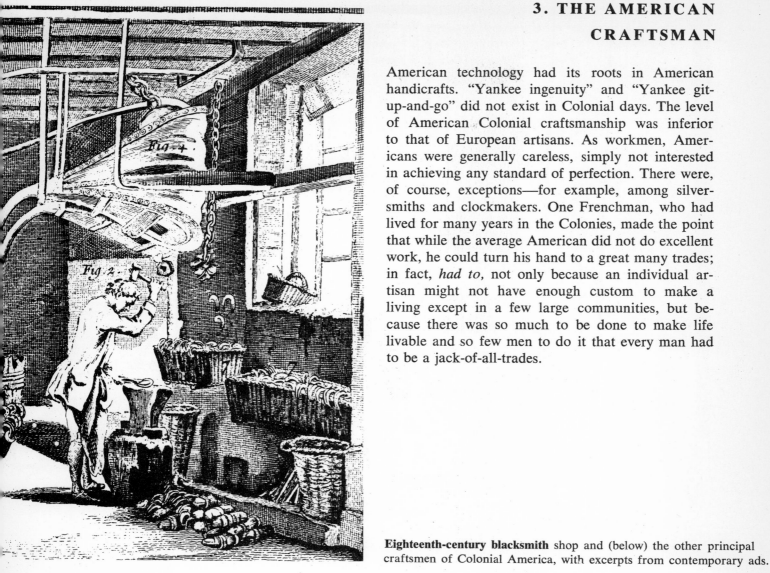

American technology had its roots in American handicrafts. "Yankee ingenuity" and "Yankee git-up-and-go" did not exist in Colonial days. The level of American Colonial craftsmanship was inferior to that of European artisans. As workmen, Americans were generally careless, simply not interested in achieving any standard of perfection. There were, of course, exceptions—for example, among silversmiths and clockmakers. One Frenchman, who had lived for many years in the Colonies, made the point that while the average American did not do excellent work, he could turn his hand to a great many trades; in fact, *had to,* not only because an individual artisan might not have enough custom to make a living except in a few large communities, but because there was so much to be done to make life livable and so few men to do it that every man had to be a jack-of-all-trades.

Eighteenth-century blacksmith shop and (below) the other principal craftsmen of Colonial America, with excerpts from contemporary ads.

TANNER

"Hugh Hughes informs the Public that he has a Tan-Yard, and Currying Shop, in Ferry-Street, near Peck's Slip, where the Business is carryed on as usual. A good Price is given, by said Hughes, for good Hides, Bark, Oyl and Tallow."

CANDLE MAKER

"All sorts of Sope and Candles, made and Sold by John Ditcher, living in the House of Mr. Jacobus Roosevelt's. Said Ditcher has his Tools well fix'd after the London Manner. He would be glad of a Partner with a little Cash."

PRINTER

"Mr. John Zenger, Printer in this City, being lately deceased: This is to give Notice, that the Printing Press and Materials lately occupied by him, will be exposed to Sale at publick Vendue, on Tuesday the 30th of this Instant July."

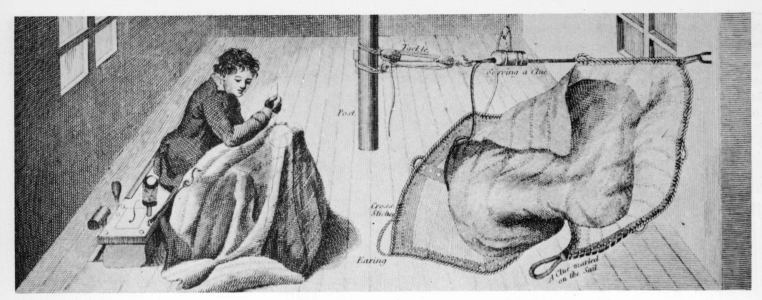

Well-equipped sail lofts were in every Colonial seaport. The American sailmaker was one of the very few artisans who competed on equal terms with the European. Every stitch was made with palm and needle.

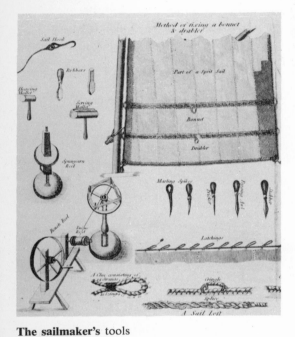

The **sailmaker's** tools

Three 18th-century ships: a brig, a bark, and a sloop.

The men who fashioned the Yankee Clippers learned their trade building for the British.

4. THE CRAFTS OF THE SEA

Georgian England had been stripped of forests to supply wood for the iron foundries. Timber had to be imported from the American colonies, and could be carried more cheaply in ships built in American ports. Shipyards were erected all along the American coast. With them went ropewalks, sail lofts, blockmaking; and all the associated arts and trades. By the time of the Revolution, one third of all British vessels had been built in America.

The first American nautical invention was the schooner—a fast, easily handled rig, more suitable to American waters and weather than the ketch which the English had designed for traffic in their stormy channels.

American ropemakers supplied the rigging for many British vessels. A half-century later, Americans were to be the first to twist wire strands into cable for long-span suspension bridges such as the world had never before seen.

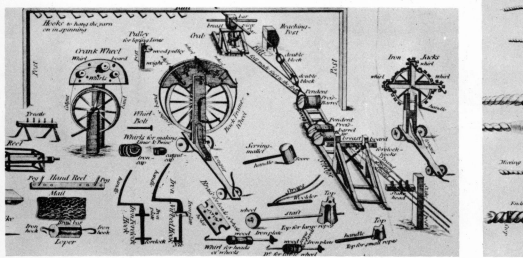

The ropemaker's tools

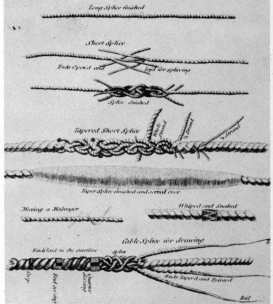

Splicing—A ropemaker's art

With the outbreak of the Revolution, American shipyards began to build fast privateers to beat the British blockade. There were 2,000 of these ships, employing 90,000 men—equal to the total number of soldiers in the Army. The new American government had no regular men-of-war, and did not commission any for almost twenty-five years thereafter, because the young Republic believed that an armed force was the hallmark of tyranny. But just as the Whiskey Rebellion proved the need for a national Army, the Tripolitan pirates created a United States Navy.

For decades the general level of American mechanical workmanship remained extremely low. Thirty years after the signing of the Declaration of Independence, Robert Fulton was able to find only one mechanic in the entire city of New York sufficiently skilled to build a time-fuse torpedo.

American-made fittings
for
His Majesty's ships

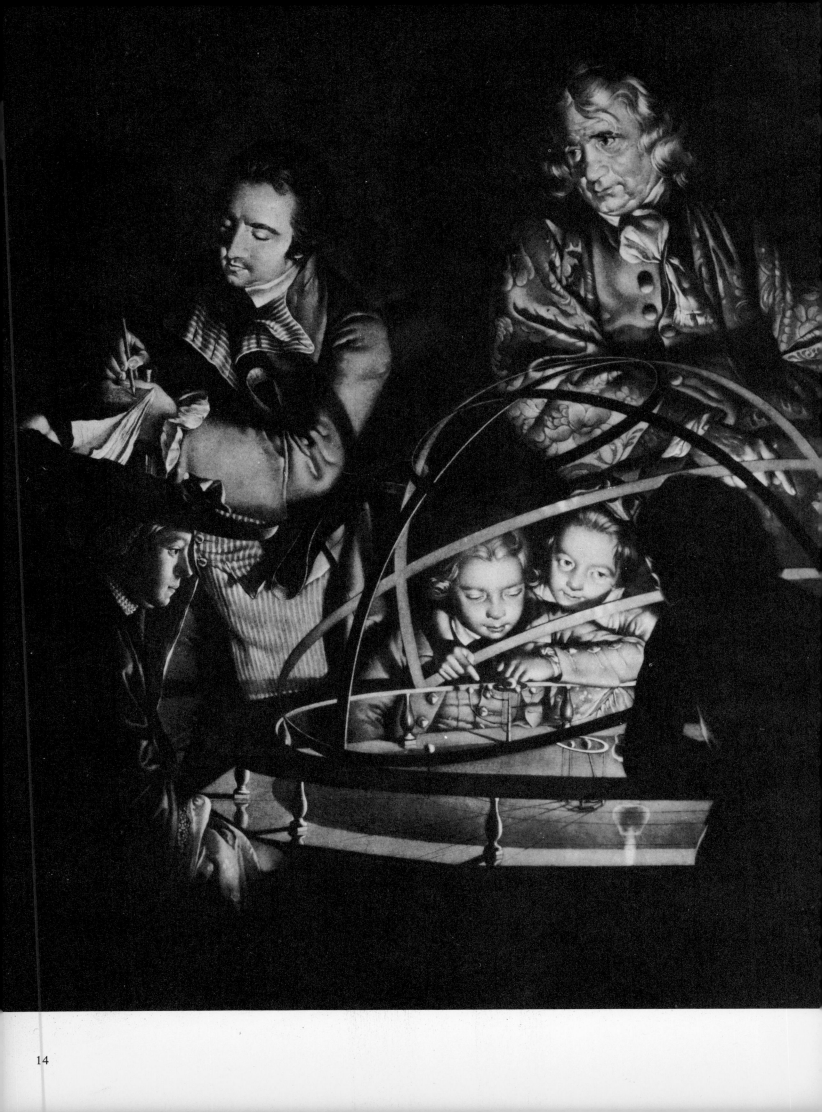

THE NATURAL PHILOSOPHERS

Two great revolutions were started in the year 1620. One began when a band of stubborn religious dissenters, in flight from King James, made a landfall on the sandy cape off the savage New England shore, to dwell with high heads in the wilderness rather than submit to tryanny. The second revolution began when Bacon published early in 1620 the first statement of an attitude that was to change the shape of man's world, the way he lived in it, and the way he thought. Bacon claimed that the object of true knowledge was the relief of man's estate and the furtherance of man's power over nature. Only with a new understanding of the physical world could man make himself master of his fate.

A century and a half after the Pilgrims landed, their political revolution against the Crown finally burst out into violence. Within the same time span, Francis Bacon's disciples had effected so profound a change in English science and technology that later generations were to refer to the great events of the third decade of the eighteenth century not as "the time of the American Rebellion," but as the years of England's Industrial Revolution.

The followers of Bacon formally banded themselves together in 1662 and founded the Royal Society of London, "to promote the welfare of the arts and sciences." Two of the foremost of the original members were Isaac Newton and Robert Boyle. Had the English Civil Wars ended differently, Boyle and the Royal Society would have emigrated to the American province of Connecticut because it was governed by the father of one of the Society's prominent members—John Winthrop, who corresponded with such men as Tycho Brahe, Kepler, John Milton, Newton, Robert Boyle and Galileo. His grandson was known for his contribution to mineralogy. The third John, the most famous, taught astronomy and science at Harvard and became a member of the Royal Society in 1766.

However, except for the handful of men who were members of the Society, which included Cotton Mather, there were few Americans familiar with science. Certainly no Colonial made a career of science.

Science made advances as more men made practical applications of its teachings. Because of the British mercantile theory, Americans were forbidden to engage in arts and crafts based on natural phenomena; and this lack of experience in turn deprived Americans of the incentive for speculation and experiment. American scientific activity was more concerned with trying to keep up with European advances than adding to the body of knowledge. The two exceptions are Benjamin Franklin and Benjamin Thompson, later Count Rumford—both of them were men who would have risen to their separate genius at any place and at any time. No background explains them—such men can only be described.

The Orrery—An 18th-century planetarium as painted by Joseph Wright.

Benjamin Franklin at forty

BENJAMIN FRANKLIN

1. THE PERSONALITY

Late in the autumn of the year 1732 an old man came to life as a character on paper. The author who created him was tall, young, with a swimmer's shoulders and supple build. His face, even in the deceptive repose of creation, was saturnine, amused, and worldly. His style had been taken from Addison; his polish had been achieved from living in London; but his humor was native American. At the age of twenty-seven Franklin was the most successful and amusing American writer of his day.

He took up a quill and, in the words of his character, wrote with sly solemnity:

"I might in this place attempt to gain thy favour by declaring that I write almanacs with no other view than the public good; but in that I should not be sincere, and men now-a-days are too wise to be deceived. . . . The plain truth of the matter is, I am excessive poor, and . . . the printer has offered me considerable share of the profits. . . ."

The bumbling old savant (on paper) half starv-ing, ridden by a shrewish wife, giving out pious sentiments on thrift along with bawdy oglings at the girls, achieved a popularity far beyond the author's expectations. His creation was so successful that *Poor Richard* went into several printings within three weeks after its appearance on December 19, 1732.

Ironically, the comic, half-pompous creature of the almanac was given such reality in the minds of his readers that succeeding generations confused the dashing Franklin with his own creation. To enhance the false impression, his most popular pictures were painted in his late years when his athlete's muscularity had become portliness, his chestnut hair was gone in baldness, and the Mephistophelean smile had softened.

In his own lifetime, however, no one who ever knew him made the mistake in identity—neither merchants, scientists, princes, nor, most particularly, pretty women. Always gay, disarming, and plausible, he was the charmer supreme, the intellectual *beau ideal* of his time.

Since the Renaissance, no other man has proven so variously accomplished as Franklin or so many sided in personality. He was a brilliant man of business, a diplomat, a writer, an acute observer of nature, and a lover who was too persuasive for his own good.

To call him diffuse is to be blind to the deeper talent: Franklin's adaptability to each new man and each new situation. He understood everyone he met so intuitively that he could not only be like them, but even surpass them at their best accomplishments. To see him simply as an intellectual phenomenon is to see only half. Without his human adaptability, his intellect would have missed its highest stimulation. Without his intellect, his adaptability would have been merely that of a sensitive actor in a thousand roles.

His intellect could penetrate through a morass of detail to the one underlying simplicity. Of all human talents, it is the most uncommon, even though men flatter themselves by calling it common sense. It led to his remarkable career as a scientist and a statesman, but it also meant that he was without illusions. He was outside his own time, and therefore he was outside all time. That is why Franklin's autobiographical writings seem so modern. In the same way they will seem modern to readers two thousand years from now, just as they would have seemed contemporaneous to Chaucer, and before him, to Cicero, and before him, to David ben Jesse, the King of the Jews.

Most men consider themselves lucky if they have forty years of useful work to contribute out of their lifetimes. Franklin possessed his full intellectual vigor twice as long as most men. At eighty-three he invented bifocal glasses; his last political act was the framing of the Constitution of the United States. He must be rated one of the giants of human history.

1—Franklin was born in Boston in 1706. He said his earliest memory was of the time he bought a penny horn and made such a racket that even his indulgent father couldn't stand it. In general, his childhood was happy.

2—Franklin was apprenticed to his brother James, a printer. At sixteen, he wrote an anonymous weekly column which became popular. When he was found out, he was congratulated by everyone but his jealous brother James.

3—Disgruntled, Franklin violated his apprenticeship and made his way to Philadelphia. He made a strange sight as he wandered with only a loaf of bread in his pocket. A girl who laughed later became his wife.

4—He soon found work with one of the two printers in Philadelphia. He made such a reputation for his wit that Governor Keith visited him and suggested, in front of the flabbergasted owner, that he go to England.

5—Keith, famous for his unfulfilled promises, let Franklin think that, after two years in London, he would set the young man up in business. When he got there, he knew the Governor would do nothing.

6—He returned to Philadelphia broadened and with cosmopolitan tastes. He set up his own print shop and newspaper with borrowed money, and organized the Junto, which opened the first library in America.

7—The famous kite picture is full of errors. He never wore a fur hat until he was quite old. At forty-six he was slim and athletic. His son was a full-grown man of twenty. The leyden jar is held in the wrong hand.

2. FRANKLIN AS A SCIENTIST

Some twelve to fourteen years after Franklin started his own printing establishment, he had expanded his business interests to the point where he was able to retire at the age of forty with an income of a thousand pounds a year. This was the same as the salary being paid to the Royal Governor, the most exalted personage in the Province of Pennsylvania— equal today to some thirty thousand dollars annually. To a man of Franklin's vigorous temperament, retirement simply meant withdrawing from one absorbing activity in order to plunge himself into another. Science—or natural philosophy as it was then called—had been challenging him for years.

His scientific fame does not rest on the spectacular kite experiment as most people assume. Actually, the kite episode was the least of his contributions, and was made after his world reputation was established. He achieved greatness in science because the experiments he performed or suggested were completely original and crucial. He was never content merely to amplify someone else's results. Before he began work in 1747, electricity was a mass of uncoordinated observations and confusing theories couched in confusing terms. Franklin unified what was then known, and added enough original information so that he was able to present a new and simple theory that has since stood the test of time.

An eighteenth-century electrical experiment

3. ELECTRICITY BEFORE FRANKLIN

In the 1740's Franklin's attention was first drawn to electricity. This is all that was known at the time:

When certain substances such as glass were rubbed, they mysteriously attracted light objects like feathers or pieces of paper. The feather would be drawn gently onto the surface of glass, actually touching it, and then

Greatest among his contributions, however, was his experimental approach. His procedure was brilliantly analytical and objective. Standards of experimental science advanced a long step with him. Moreover, his theorizing was of the kind that Einstein calls "operational." Those of his contemporaries who had the wit to perceive that his approach was different considered him remarkable. The very vocabulary of modern electricity originated with him—words like *battery, condenser, conductor, charge, discharge, armature, electric shock, electrician, positive* and *negative* electricity and concepts of *plus* and *minus* charge.

His first fame in Europe was neither that of a successful merchant nor the wittiest writer in America, but as a scientist. On his diplomatic missions years later, he was received with respect only because his scientific contemporaries were calling him the Newton of Electricity. Magic surrounded his name, and that was exactly why he was sent as American Agent. In 1777, Horace Walpole wrote: "The natural philosophers believe that Dr. Franklin has invented a machine of the size of a toothpick case, and materials that would reduce St. Paul's to a handful of ashes."

The man who earned that reputation was not the dumpy, stringy-haired figure of the Currier and Ives lithograph done almost a century later; but a vigorous, dashing, Rabelaisian athlete just entering his forties.

The electrostatic machine on the left was described in Joseph Priestley's book on electricity which was written at Franklin's suggestion. The machine on the right is the one which Franklin used in performing his experiments.

a very surprising thing would happen: the feather was violently repelled back into the air. It was as if an invisible wind had blown the feather onto the glass and then miraculously reversed itself to blow the feather away again. Also a thin blue flame or spark could be made to leap from the rubbed glass to the tip of a man's outstretched finger. Depending on the intensity of the spark, the experimenter might feel a slight tingling or a powerful shock. Moreover the spark was accompanied by a crackling noise.

These were the basic facts.

There were a large variety of ways to duplicate the sparking, but the very variety only served to make matters look more complicated. There was a long list of substances besides glass—sulphur was another—which could be made to act this way. Altogether a mass of detail and no order. Two other things were definitely known: the new phenomenon was *not* magnetism, and it was certainly not gravity. It was a completely new kind of force.

The first observation had been made by a Greek philosopher named Thales who described the attractive powers of amber when rubbed. For the next twenty centuries these observations lay unnoticed. Then William Gilbert of Colchester, England, physician to Queen Elizabeth, in 1600 took up the subject and showed that many other substances besides amber could be made to exhibit the same property. It was he who coined the word *electrica* from the Greek *elektron*, for amber.

After Gilbert, the next important name belonged to the 300-pound German burgomaster, Guericke, who invented the first electrostatic machine: a sphere of sulphur rotating on a shaft through its center. The sphere could be charged electrically by a man holding his hand against it as it spun. Not until a few years after Franklin was born was glass substituted for sulphur by Hawkesbee. In Hawkesbee's machine, an iron chain touched the spinning globe and carried the electric charge up to a suspended gun barrel. At the other end of the gun barrel, another chain carried the charge to the experimenter.

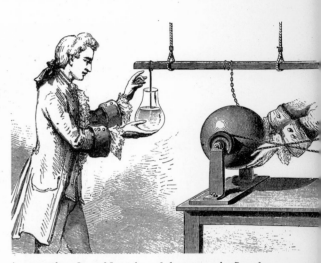

A sensational accident in a laboratory in Leyden attracted popular attention the year before Franklin began work. Cuneus, a student, was using a Hawkesbee machine to electrify water in a flask which he was holding in his hand. When the charging had been going on for some time, he tried with his free hand to remove the chain which hung down through the neck of the bottle into the water. On touching the chain, he received a shock so intense that he almost died. Never before had there been so large an accumulation of electric charge.

In July, 1750, Franklin wrote: "To determine the question whether the clouds that contain lightning are electrified or not, I would propose an experiment. On top of some high tower . . . place a kind of sentry box big enough to contain a man and an electrical stand (*a platform that was insulated*). From the middle of the stand let an iron rod rise and pass bending out of the door, and upright twenty or thirty feet pointed very sharp at the end. If the electrical stand be kept clean and dry, a man standing on it when such clouds are passing low, might be electrified and draw sparks, the rod drawing fire . . . from a cloud . . ."

Franklin was first to prove that a spark generated heat. The discharge of a Leyden jar across the gap, F-G, raised the reading on thermometer, *a*.

4. FRANKLIN'S LEYDEN JAR EXPERIMENTS

The news of the "Leyden Jar" was so startling that it spread all over Europe, and the experiment was repeated everywhere. For the edification of the French Court, the experiment was performed on a line of one hundred and eighty guardsmen, all holding hands. The shock made all one hundred and eighty leap simultaneously into the air as if attempting to parade in the sky. At the Couvent de Paris, seven hundred monks joined hands and tried the same experiment. Like an explosion of brown leaves, all seven hundred went whirling in one convulsion. Public exhibitions were given with the audience freely offering themselves to be shocked. Electricity became the most popular show of the day. Franklin saw such an exhibition in Boston, and this was what aroused his interest.

Franklin wrote to England for electrical apparatus in the autumn of 1746 and began his experiments in the following spring. With very little more information than was outlined above, Franklin set to work.

Lightning rod hats were a 1778 Paris fashion.

The "Leyden Jar" as it came to Franklin was simply a stoppered bottle of water. Through the cork stopper, a metal rod hung down into the liquid. Some experimenters wrapped the outside of the bottle in metal foil.

Franklin set himself the task of answering a question which no one else had thought of asking: exactly what was it in such an apparently simple arrangement of glass, metal, and water that allowed for such enormous accumulations of electricity? Was it due to the wire, the water, or the bottle? Or what combination? In Franklin's day, no one even knew, once the question had been asked, how to go about finding the answer. Actually, to ask the same question two centuries after Franklin would leave an embarrassingly large number of people looking blank. Franklin's step-by-step approach had the simplicity of genius:

"To analyze the electrified bottle, in order to find wherein its strength lay, we placed it on glass and drew out the cork and wire. . . . Then taking the bottle in one hand, and bringing a finger of the other near the bottle's mouth, a strong spark came from the water . . . which shewed that the force did not reside in the wire."

And so one possibility was completely eliminated.

"Then to find if it resided in the water . . . which had been our former opinion, we electrified the bottle again." This time, Franklin and his assistant removed the cork and wire as before, and then in addition decanted the water from the electrically charged flask into another flask which had not been electrified. If the electric charge actually was in the water alone, then the new flask should give a spark. It did not.

"We judged then, that it must be lost in decanting or remain in the first bottle. The latter we found to be true, for that bottle on trial gave the shock, though filled with fresh, electrified water from a teapot."

Now, having come this far, not one man in a hundred thousand would have gone on to the next question, which was this: did the electrical charge reside in the bottle because it was *shaped* like a bottle or because it was made of glass? Again, one may well ask how could that be tested? Franklin took glass of a completely different shape: a simple pane of window glass. On either side of the glass, he placed a thin sheet of lead. This arrangement was electrified. Then, one at a time, the sheets of lead were slid away and tested. Neither, when isolated, gave off any spark. The glass pane, standing alone, being touched, gave off a multitude of sparks. Franklin then concluded that "The whole force and power of giving a shock is in the *glass itself* . . ."

This proof that the seat of electrostatic action is in the material which insulates a conductor laid the foundation for Maxwell's work a century later when he developed the theory of electromagnetic waves which in turn led to radio. In this one experiment alone, Franklin had invented the electrical condenser, one of the most useful elements in circuit theory, a device that was to be used in every radio, television set, telephone circuit, radar transmitter, cyclotron and cosmotron.

Until Franklin, the prevalent theory had been that there were two different kinds of electricity vaguely distinguished by unanalytical names as *resinous* and *vitreous*. He claimed that there was only one kind; that electricity was neither created nor destroyed either by friction or by any other means, but that electricity was simply redistributed throughout matter. Moreover, he stated that electricity had to be composed of "subtile particles" that could penetrate the interior of metals as easily as gas diffused through the atmosphere. J. J. Thomson who later discovered the electron and laid the foundations of modern electron theory paid tribute to Franklin as generously as Franklin's own contemporaries.

FRANKLIN'S VINDICATION

Franklin planned to perform the lightning experiment after the completion of the spire on Christ Church, in Philadelphia. In the meantime, his book was published in France and made a deep impression. A scientist named D'Alibard made a secret trial of the sentry box experiment near Paris on May 10, 1752. There was a peal of thunder and the iron shaft sparkled blue with charge pouring into a Leyden jar, proving that the cloud was electrified. Eight days later, the experiment was repeated for the King in Paris.

The King himself wrote to the Royal Society of London, complimenting their member, Franklin. Early in July, his experiment was performed in London. By the time the news reached him in September, he had been world famous for months. Instead of waiting for the completion of the spire, he had meanwhile performed the kite experiment himself, but he ungrudgingly gave D'Alibard credit for having been first to "draw lightning from the skies." However, the world knew that Franklin had suggested the experiment; and the awe with which people looked upon lightning was now added to Franklin's name. He became a figure of magic, a demigod.

5. FRANKLIN'S BROAD INTERESTS AND WIDE INFLUENCE

THE FRANKLIN STOVE

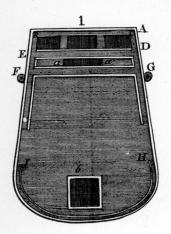

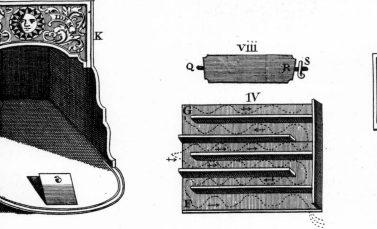

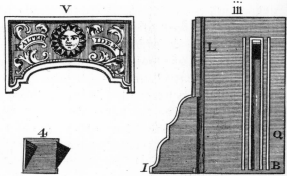

Franklin's famous stove was designed just before he began his electrical experiments. The important feature was the flue, which doubled back and formed a sort of radiator, around which room air circulated.

A Russian scientist, Richmann, was killed while trying to duplicate Franklin's lightning experiment. Richmann's apparatus was not grounded. The true story of Franklin's work on lightning is further proof of his superiority to all other eighteenth-century electricians. For almost half a century before him, men had been suggesting the identity of lightning and the electric spark. However, no one had ever worked out a means of proving it. Franklin not only suggested an actual experiment, but he was able to explain lightning in rational terms and not as an awesome supernatural manifestation.

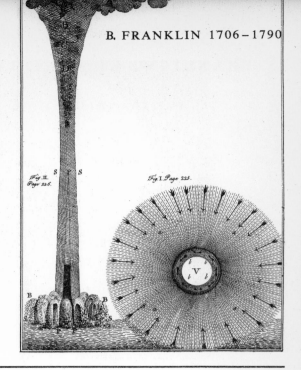

HE WAS AN EARLY AMERICAN METEOROLOGIST

During a partial eclipse of the moon, observers in Philadelphia were able to see only the beginning of the transit because of clouds which blew in from the northeast. Days later, Franklin noticed an oddity in a newspaper from Boston: the sky there, too, had become overcast by a northeast storm, but at a much later hour of the night, even though Boston was northeast of Philadelphia. Franklin immediately sent for newspapers from all the colonies in the path of the eclipse. Sure enough, all of them mentioned a northeast storm. But in the southern colonies, the storm had risen during the afternoon. In other words, even though the wind had been blowing from the northeast, the path of the storm had been from southwest to northeast. Franklin was the first to notice this prevailing weather pattern and was the first to offer an explanation in terms of air mass circulation. The concepts of high and low pressure in the atmosphere originated with him, and his explanation of the water spout has never needed revision. His diagram shows how a column of warm air is forced upward by the cool, heavier air from the surrounding region.

FRANKLIN WAS ALSO A PHYSICIST

The boiling point of water, 212° F, was considered to be one of the unchanging constants of nature, but Franklin claimed that the evidence showed that the boiling point of water depended on the atmospheric pressure. It had long been known, for example, that eggs took longer to cook when boiled on a mountain. Franklin proved his theory by partially evacuating a flask of water and demonstrating that he could find a new boiling point for every stage of evacuation. When the pressure within the flask was too low, water boiled spontaneously at room temperature. The experiment illustrated here uses the same principle as the bubbling glass Christmas tree bulbs, which are filled with a colored fluid that boils continuously when the lights are on. He also experimented with surface phenomena. Once he observed how an oil slick kept waves from breaking, and years later in London, he performed a control experiment on a pond ruffled by the wind. He poured a measured volume of oil on the surface and made a good guess as to the thickness of the resulting film. He came very close to stating that he had created a monomolecular layer.

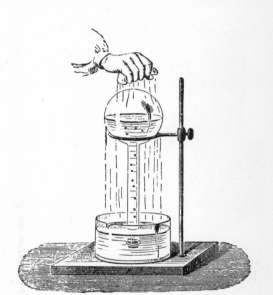

BUT HE WAS NOT ALWAYS RIGHT

When Franklin was a young man in Boston, the town was threatened by an epidemic of smallpox. The one man who stood out in support of inoculation was Cotton Mather, more famous for his fanatical witch-hunting. Mather had heard of the practice of inoculation from a slave, and induced a local physician, Boylston, to carry it out as widely as possible. Most of Boston rose up in arms, and Mather, rather than Boylston, was the target for Boston's anger. Franklin joined the ignorant attack on Mather. Later, Franklin's beloved son Francis died of smallpox because he had not been inoculated and Franklin sorrowfully confessed his error. After that he urged that inoculation be made a general practice.

Cotton Mather, a member of the Royal Society in London, had a great effect on Franklin's youth because Mather was one of the most widely-informed men in the colonies and one of the first to realize the importance of Isaac Newton's work. His great fault was not religious bigotry, but intellectual arrogance: whatever he believed *must* be right. That was one quality Franklin never shared. Franklin had the true humility of a man who learned about human weakness by observing his own frailties.

Cotton Mather, 1663–1728

Gainsborough's portrait of young Thompson

BENJAMIN THOMPSON

COUNT RUMFORD

1. KNIGHT OF THE GARTER

If Benjamin Franklin was the intellectual *beau ideal* of his time, then Benjamin Thompson was the century's personification of picaresque reality. His scientific achievements were of the highest rank, yet they were merely incidental to a life of fantastic adventure, duplicity, and intrigue.

Thompson was born in 1753 in the small, complacent Massachusetts town of Woburn, through which no coach had ever rumbled, when there were fewer than a hundred family coaches in all of America, and travelers thought nothing of a twenty-mile walk. England was the mother country, yet six generations of American-born Englishmen had lived and died without ever seeing London. Thompson's boyish ideas of magnificence were measured by the affluence of the local squire.

His father died when he was an infant, and his destitute mother remarried a man equally poor. The boy received what local schooling there was, and no one suspected that he was brilliant.

Young Thompson, red-headed, handsome, tormented with impossible dreams of being a famous soldier, friend of princes, Lord Mayor of a City of Dreams, became an apprentice storekeeper, first in Salem, then in Boston. He wrote a neat hand, but he was a poor storekeeper. Thompson at seventeen spent his time in a most un-apprentice-like way; teaching himself to speak French, to dress like a gentleman,

The Bloody Massacre in Boston occurred when Thompson was seventeen years old. He later claimed to have been a witness.

to fence, and in the study of natural philosophy. He read prodigiously; and he still had no idea by which road he would reach the magnificence that plagued his dreams.

The incredible began to happen in his nineteenth year when he became schoolmaster in Portsmouth, the provincial capital of New Hampshire. Within a few months, dressed like a gentleman in the one suit he possessed, he devastated the heart of the richest heiress in town—the thirty-two-year-old widow of Colonel Rolfe. Sarah Rolfe married Thompson, clothed him magnificently, and gave him her thousand acres to manage. His father-in-law gave him an introduction to Governor Wentworth, and Governor Wentworth gave him a majority in the Second Provincial Regiment of New Hampshire.

Having been touched by the fairy wand, he was now destined to get the dirty end of the stick. This was 1774. The patriots were forming their Committees of Correspondence. They had little love for Governor Wentworth, less for his friends, and none at all for the upstart stranger of nineteen who had become the local squire. Within a year, Thompson was charged with corresponding with General Gage in Boston, and with having returned to him four British deserters. He talked his way out of the accusations but satisfied no one. A mob started for his house to burn it down. Just in time, he escaped and fled to Woburn, leaving his family behind. They were unmolested.

For a year, he wandered around Boston trying to secure a commission in the Colonial Army. In the meantime, he was arrested once more for being in touch with the British, but was dismissed for lack of evidence. However, he was unable to get a commission under Washington because New Hampshire officers, who could not hang him, refused to serve in the same army with him.

Boston in 1775 was neither the time nor the place to be neutral. Simply to stay alive, he had to choose a side. So 1776 found him in Boston behind the British lines. When Gage retreated from Boston, an important commission of four men sent back to London to explain the British withdrawal, surprisingly enough included Benjamin Thompson.

The meteoric rise had a simple explanation.

From the very beginning, Thompson actually *had* been in correspondence with Gage, actually *had* returned the four deserters, and for two years before 1776, he *had* sent continual and brilliant intelligence to the British in Boston. The truth is that Thompson from the very first had been loyal to the Crown. He, like many others, considered himself an Englishman —but no one except the British War Ministry had proof of his actions for one hundred and sixty-one years.

Bunker's Hill became the scene of the first major battle of the Revolution. Benjamin Thompson was gambling on a decisive victory for the Crown. The painting is by John Trumbull.

2. THOMPSON
AND
LORD GERMAINE

When he set sail for England on this important mission, in his early twenties, he had no idea what lay in store for him. He was ambitious and knew that his military reports had proved his military genius as well as his shrewdness. He had absolute confidence in his ability to handle any situation that might arise and turn it to his own advantage. However, waiting for him in London was a man ten times as shrewd, and a thousand times more sinister: Lord George Germaine, His Majesty's Colonial Secretary, the man in charge of prosecuting the war.

Germaine's career makes no sense unless one realizes that in his own time patriotism was a word that many people used to describe an emotion that very few people felt. It was a time for the purest opportunism.

Lord George had begun his career in the Army, and by the time he was fifty, had risen to the rank of general without ever once having seen action. However, when he finally did get out on the field, his conduct was so disgraceful that he was cashiered for cowardice. To Lord George this was only a temporary setback; he then set himself for a career in politics, and acquired an army of private spies so that within ten years he was able to blackmail his way up to the Secretaryship of Colonial Affairs. He was utterly ruthless; and in addition he was a degenerate homosexual.

In 1776, Gage's letters of praise about Thompson impressed Germaine. He looked forward to meeting a young man whom he could use in his band of informers; what he met was a young man with whom he fell in love. Within a few months, Thompson was not only installed as a member of Lord George's household, he was also made Undersecretary in the Ministry for Carolina and Georgia. He was twenty-two years old at the time.

3. BALLISTICS,
STATISTICS,
AND ESPIONAGE

Now Thompson was far more than an ordinary courtier who would be content to use his post merely to help rifle the government treasury. He was basically interested in the science of warfare. He undertook a research in the explosive force and fire-power of gunpowder to standardize and improve the explosives he was sending to the American colonies in his jurisdiction. He devised a small vertical mortar into which could be put a measured charge of powder. Over the muzzle of the mortar, he placed successively heavier weights until he reached a point where the mass could no longer be lifted by the explosion. The weight was then exactly equal to the lifting force of the charge. To avoid the escape of gases through the usual touch hole, he ignited his charge by conduction from a red-hot rod. He was also the first to fire a shot into a pendulum and use the swing to measure the bullet's momentum. He later refined the experiment by mounting the cannon as another pendulum so that he could measure the explosive power through the recoil. The whole modern science of ballistics is traceable directly to Thompson at this stage of his career, and much of the apparatus still bears his name.

He continued his ballistic experiments when he took a cruise in 1779 with Sir Charles Hardy's fleet: 60 ships, 3,260 guns, and 26,544 men. He made a wide acquaintance among the captains and studied the tactics of fleet and battle formation. At no time did he permit his researches to interfere with the business side of his position, and since he was responsible for making all the purchases for the provincial army, his share of the bribes came to almost seven thousand pounds a year. This was at a time when Benjamin Franklin was considered a rich man on one-seventh of that annual income. Within a few short years, up to 1781, Thompson must have earned and spent the modern equivalent of a million dollars.

In 1781, all this came to an end because Thompson had secretly been playing for still higher stakes. His naval cruise had a motive in addition to scientific curiosity. He had made a deal to sell his naval information

18th-century mortar

to the French who were to pay one-eighth of the prize money when they captured Governor Johnstone's fleet. Thompson was to have shared this with two confederates: one named Lutterloh, who became the government's witness against the third conspirator, a Frenchman named La Motte. La Motte was hanged, drawn, and quartered, but Thompson's name was never mentioned in the public trial; Lord George Germaine protected him by blackmailing the Lord of the Admiralty, Lord Sandwich, by simply threatening to have Sandwich removed from the Ministry. Sandwich apparently reasoned that since he had been made in God's image it was his religious duty to take care of his own power and incomes, patriotism being merely devotion to lesser institutions. He satisfied himself with La Motte. Nevertheless, London was suddenly too hot for Thompson who had himself appointed Lieutenant Colonel of a company of horse dragoons in America, an unusual demotion for one of the heads of the Ministry. His public explanation was that he could no longer restrain his taste for action.

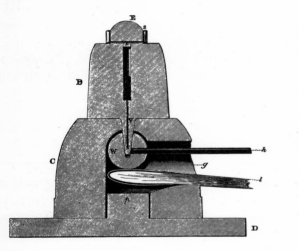

Thompson invented a device for measuring the power of gunpowder (left). Weights, such as the heavy cannon (right), were stacked over the top of the vertical bore to measure the force of the explosion. To avoid pressure leakage through a touch hole, Thompson ignited the powder by conduction from a red-hot poker (*h*).

Thompson fought as a cavalry officer with the British Army during the Revolutionary War. He had been run out of London because he had been spying for the French. By the time he got to America, the British were surrendering on every front. Above is the encampment of the defeated British Army at Charlottesville.

Thompson became an expert artillerist and founded the science of modern ballistics. He was accepted as a member of the Royal Society at the age of twenty-six.

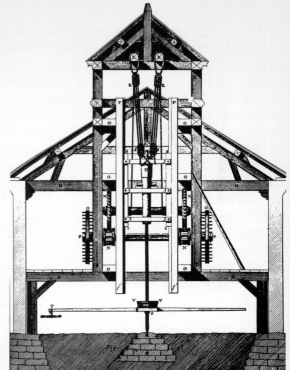

After the American War, Thompson attracted the attention of the Duke of Bavaria for whom he did his famous work on heat while perfecting the science of artillery.

Great heat of friction was developed when cannon barrels were bored. The heat was greater than the caloric theory permitted. He studied heat only to make better cannon.

4. THE PRACTICAL MAN

Before Franklin, the science of electricity was contradictory. Before Thompson, the accepted theory of heat seemed to explain most of the known phenomena. Expressions like "heat flow," "specific heat," and "latent heat" are all vestiges of the day when men believed in a substance called "caloric"—the embodiment of heat. It was an invisible atmosphere that surrounded every molecule in the same way that air surrounds our planet. Caloric was assumed to have the property of repelling other caloric. Two molecules surrounded by caloric would attract each other due to gravity, but the atmospheres of caloric would keep the molecules from fusing into a single mass. When a solid was heated, more caloric was added to the atmosphere of each molecule, forcing them to move farther apart, expanding the substance. With enough heat, the attractive force of gravity was completely overcome and the solid became liquid. That was the caloric explanation.

Moreover, when two solids were rubbed together, the surface molecules were compressed and caloric was squeezed out. Which was why friction created heat. This was the caloric theory before Benjamin Thompson blew it apart with his experiments on cannon boring.

Besides his experiments on heat, Thompson was busy with diplomacy. He had become Minister of War, Minister of the Interior, and Royal Scientist to the King, and all this time, he had been a spy for the British. He had actually been put into his position by British intrigue; he had been knighted by George III, who loathed him, simply as a cover for his espionage activities. Sir David Keith had engineered the entire operation, and was the man to whom Thompson sent detailed secret reports on Bavarian activities.

In 1785, Thompson had found his new position in Bavaria so much to his liking that he decided to break with Keith. The British, unable to expose him, had to wait for revenge.

Thompson's penchant for complicating his life with intrigue contrasted with his passion for order. He hated waste, whether it was human energy or time, and he hated poverty, certainly for himself, and in others because it seemed unnecessary waste. Private philanthropy drew his contempt because it solved nothing. Munich, with a population of 60,000, had 2,600 beggars. To Thompson, so much idleness was scandalous. Accordingly, he created a Society for the Amelioration of the Condition of the Poor, made his Army charter members, and sent them out to drive all the mendicants into newly organized Houses of Industry. The Bavarian Electors boasted that within twenty-four hours beggary disappeared from the streets of Munich.

The Houses of Industry made clothing and supplies for the Army. They were fed on a community basis and given lodging. Thompson began to lay the foundation of his second fortune. He was made a Count

Thompson's theory of heat was demonstrated by rotating a test tube full of water within wooden paddles. The water boiled due to friction. The heat of friction is unlimited.

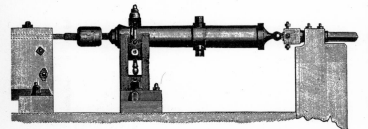

Thompson's apparatus was a small replica of the cannon-boring process. He came to the conclusion that heat of friction is due to increased motion of molecules.

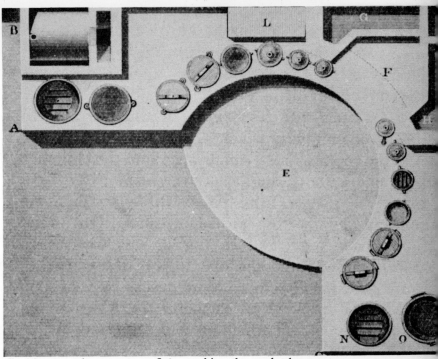

Cooking was done on open fires, cooking the cook along with the roast, until Thompson's work. He was the first to enclose the fire within a range to conserve the heat.

of the Holy Roman Empire in 1791. He was famous throughout Europe because of his scientific achievements, his military genius, and particularly because of his new Houses of Industry. However, one particular House of Industry was very little publicized.

Ladies of the Bavarian aristocracy occasionally found themselves with child without husbands. Count Rumford set up a special house where they could conveniently disappear for several months at a time. The children, when born, became the wards of Count Rumford to grow up and work in the Houses of Industry. They were housed and fed and educated so that they could be better workers. Schooling was necessary, so he instituted the first public schools, and the Bavarian treasury paid the bills.

However, he was responsible for feeding large numbers of people, and his passion for efficiency along with his interest in heat led him to undertake the first exhaustive study of kitchen equipment.

To his contemporaries, one of his most important experiments was his demonstration that heat could pass across a vacuum. It was inconceivable that caloric could flow through nothingness. The apparatus Thompson used for that experiment turned out to have great importance. He placed one glass flask within another and evacuated the space between. Light was shone through the glass to heat water in the inner container. He pointed out that if the glass surfaces were silvered, no heat at all could flow either in or out. Today such a device is in everyday use under the name of thermos bottle.

Pots, kettles, and pans of the most modern design were made by Thompson to be as efficient as his stoves. In his own time, these designs were laughed at.

Drip coffee pots were also among Thompson's inventions. He had a Yankee love for coffee which he tried unsuccessfully to introduce to Europe.

5. THOMPSON,
HEATING ENGINEER
AND DECEITFUL DIPLOMAT

In 1795, Count Rumford, now a distinguished diplomat and scientist, made a visit to England, ostensibly to present his collected papers to the Royal Society, but actually to sound out the British Government's feeling about him. On his first day there, he was robbed of the one trunk that contained all his private papers. The British Government professed all the sympathy in the world, but neither the thieves nor the trunk were ever found, and certain British officials suddenly seemed familiar with all his private business.

In England, he lived the life of a visiting scientist, published several books of essays, and presented the famous paper in which he announced his discovery of convection currents.

Thompson was the first to explain correctly why clothing keeps the human body warm: the fibers keep body-warmed air in tiny cells so that convection cannot carry it away from the skin.

At the end of the year he returned to Munich, a man of fifty, dapperly distinguished, of medium height, and with a dry, almost testy manner.

By this time, Rumford had become the Bavarian Prime Minister with unlimited power and enemies. After two years, they had so organized against him that he had to flee, pausing only long enough to sign his own appointment as Minister to Great Britain.

To his intense disappointment he found that the British Government refused to accept him as Bavarian Minister and gave the gravely diplomatic reason that His Majesty could not receive one of his own subjects as an ambassador from a foreign prince.

Thompson immediately turned to Rufus King, the United States Minister to St. James, and suggested to him that he would like to set up an American Academy for Army Officers such as he had instituted in Bavaria. The U. S. War Department, authorized by President Adams, offered Count Rumford the appointment as the first Superintendent of a new Military Academy to be erected at West Point—with suitable rank and emoluments. Time was spent haggling because Thompson wanted to be sure that his rank would be the equivalent of Washington's. In the meantime, Rufus King made a routine check on Thompson. The British Government now took belated revenge for Thompson's double dealings and told King all about Thompson's unpublicized espionage activities.

The United States Government found itself in a state of official embarrassment. Rufus King put the matter to Rumford in blunt words: it was now impossible for the U. S. to make the appointment. To state the reasons publicly would expose Thompson, but it would also make the U. S. look foolish. There was only one way out. The U. S. would make him a handsome offer; in return, Thompson must guarantee to refuse. Thompson, an old hand at direct propositions, was sensible enough to accept at once. West Point came into being under a different management, and Rumford suddenly decided to throw himself

The modern fireplace and flue were designed by Thompson after he had discovered convection currents. The "smoke shelf" kept down drafts from puffing smoke into the room.

Thompson, as Count Rumford, visited London in 1795, and gave a thousand pounds to the Royal Society, an equal sum to the American Academy of Arts and Sciences. Later, he

into a new project for scientific research to be called the Royal Institution.

In two years, however, he left London forever, and settled in Paris where he was extravagantly admired by Napoleon, who had developed his military theories of mobile artillery from the Count's precepts. In the model of the Bavarian Military Academy, St. Cyr was founded. The French Government made him one of the eight foreign members of the French Institute on the same date that it elected Thomas Jefferson, then the President of the United States. Many of Count Rumford's later papers were presented before this body.

And so he was beginning to feel, at sixty, that he had finally come home. To give stability to his life, he married the fascinating widow of the great chemist Antoine Lavoisier. Madame Lavoisier was a personage in her own right. Her salon was famous, she was rich, she was a countess, and between them she and Rumford knew everybody worth knowing. Their marriage was the union of two of the most glamorous figures of the day.

During the years of his marriage, he performed further experiments attacking the caloric theory. He also made the first experiments standardizing light, invented the first photometer to measure light intensities, and invented the term *candle-power* to have a standard for measurement. He also invented the steam-heated radiator, and installed the first central heating systems in the world—one in the Royal Institution and the other in the French Institute. They were among the wonders of the world.

The marriage with Mme. Lavoisier, from which so much had been hoped, was a total failure. The Countess loved parties, the Count loved order and quiet. After four years they separated, and the Count was financially comfortable once again, with half of Mme. Lavoisier's fortune.

His only son, in fact his only child to live to maturity besides a daughter Sarah by his American wife, was born during this marriage. The mother was Mme. Lavoisier's gardener's daughter.

After the separation he lived quietly while the Napoleonic wars raged about him. Great Britain and Bavaria continued to pay him his pensions even though they were Napoleon's enemies. In 1814, Rumford died, a bitter and disappointed man—nothing had ever gone right for him, through no fault of his own, as far as he could see.

After his death, the Royal Institution flourished and produced the greatest English researchers of the nineteenth century. A Harvard professorship which he had endowed became one of the greatest scientific honors. His discoveries made possible the greatest human advances in comfortable living in centuries. Against that, one weighs the deceit, dishonor, and nastiness revealed by a few sheets of paper that came to light a century and a half later. The people he betrayed are dead, the causes he defiled are either forgotten or survived in spite of him. To measure the good against the bad and draw a moral therefrom would appear to be an antisocial act; but the fact remains that the world is better off that Benjamin Thompson lived.

founded the Royal Institution. Gillray's caricature of Rumford shows him standing prudently at the right of Sir Humphry Davy during a demonstration of laughing gas.

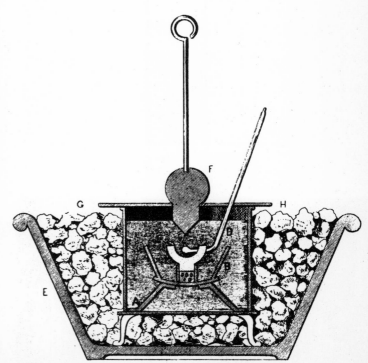

Thompson discovered that water at 41° F was denser than water at 32° F. Life was possible, he said, only because under every sheet of ice was a warmer reservoir.

Priestley's main concern always was religious and political freedom. He had no scientific interests until he met Franklin.

JOSEPH PRIESTLEY : 1

THE HONEST HERETIC

THE

HISTORY

AND

PRESENT STATE

OF

ELECTRICITY,

WITH

ORIGINAL EXPERIMENTS,

By JOSEPH PRIESTLEY, LL.D. F.R.S.

Caufa latet, vis eft notiffima.
Ovid.

LONDON,

Printed for J. DODSLEY in Pall-Mall, J. JOHNSON and B. DAVENPORT in Pater-nofter Row, and T. CADELL (Succeffor to Mr. MILLAR) in the Strand. MDCCLXVII.

In one year of research and writing, Priestley produced the 18th century's definitive book on electricity.

Chemistry, still suffering from the burden of a general belief in alchemy, was Priestley's next interest. His friend Josiah Wedgewood made porcelain apparatus as a gift.

On Thursday morning, June 5, 1794, the New York paper, the *American Daily Advertiser,* carried this intelligence:

"Dr. Priestley, with about one hundred other passengers, are on board the *Samson* which may be hourly expected."

Two days later, the newspaper stated:

"The name of Joseph Priestley will be long remembered among all enlightened people; and there is no doubt that England will one day regret her ungrateful treatment to this venerable and illustrious man . . ."

Priestley's desperate flight across the ocean to America actually began thirty years earlier in the teeming London of fogs, highwaymen, and industrious apprentices. He had come to London to meet Franklin. In that year Priestley was thirty-one. He was slender, of less than middle height, with delicate, almost feminine features. For an ordained minister, he dressed with worldly elegance. He had gaiety, wit, and enjoyed his growing reputation as a writer on religious matters. He had a genteel poverty that he took for granted; he also had a moral courage that was so incorruptible that he was to die of it.

Priestley had been born the son of a woolen cloth dresser in the small town of Fieldhead. His parents died when he was very young and he was adopted by an aunt who adored the boy and raised him in an atmosphere of free religious discussion. Because of his aunt's influence, he studied for the ministry, became a teacher, and married a sympathetic, intelligent woman when he was twenty-eight. He was considered a young man of advanced ideas, his writings were popular, and he lived among congenial friends. His "Essay on Government" in 1768 inspired Bentham's classic definition of democracy: "The greatest happiness for the greatest number." No one was less suited to the role of traitor and Antichrist that was to be fastened on him over the years to come.

His visits with Franklin marked a turning point of his career that did not change his destiny, but made him only the more marked for it. Quite casually he suggested that he write a popular book on electricity, and because Franklin approved, Priestley turned to it as merely another essay in his expanding interest in popular education.

The book took only a year to write and went into five editions during his lifetime. When it appeared, in 1766, he was made a member of the Royal Society.

Joseph Priestley, therefore, was a man who could within one year do enough original research to write a serious book on an abstruse subject that was to be the authoritative work for years to come. His gaiety and charming manner were merely ribbons disguising an iron lance of purpose.

A Philosopher Shewing an Experiment on the Air Pump, by Joseph Wright, reveals the spirit of the 18th-century research on gases. When Priestley came to America, he explained his techniques to Americans in just this informal spirit.

A few years later, he turned to chemistry. His work in chemistry was again started by accident. In Leeds he lived next to the public brew-house of Jakes and Nell. The odors of fermentation permeated his house and became the object of his first researches.

At that time, it was commonly thought that sea-scurvy was due to an insufficient supply of "fixed air" in the human system. Priestley worked out a method for producing a gas from chalk and sulphuric acid and leading it directly into water. This was the invention of soda water. The Royal Society was so impressed with Priestley's achievement that it awarded him the Copley medal, its highest honor in chemistry. This was only two years after he began his chemical researches.

Priestley was the true pioneer in gas chemistry— "pneumatic" chemistry it was called. He explained that the word *gas* was a corruption of the German *geist*—meaning spirit. The collected work was eventually to be called *Experiments and Observations on Different Kinds of Air*. Priestley was a master experimentalist. The apparatus he devised had the elegance of true simplicity.

His first discovery, for which he is famous, was his greatest: the production and isolation of pure oxygen. In this experiment, he heated what was then called *mercurious calcinatus* (mercuric oxide). On heating the salt, the mercury level within the flask was sufficiently lowered to show that the solid matter had given off four to five times its own volume of gas. Through a series of cocks and tubes, the gas could be led off to other sealed containers for testing. In one enclosed flask, a candle was burning. When a sample of the gas generated from the mercury salt was fed into this flask, the candle ". . . burned in this air with a remarkably vigorous flame . . . I had got nothing like this remarkable appearance from any (other) kind of air . . . the candle burned with splendor . . . and a piece of red-hot wood *sparkled* in it . . . and consumed very fast . . ."

Later he reported that mice lived in such an atmosphere very much longer than mice which were kept in a closed container of the same size which had been filled with ordinary air.

Priestley focused sunlight to get heat for experiments enclosed in glass. His technique was widely copied. The burning glass shown above was designed for his scientific rival, Antoine Lavoisier, who bitterly opposed Priestley's theories.

2. PRIESTLEY'S DISCOVERY OF OXYGEN

It had already been demonstrated that when animals were kept in a closed container they eventually died. Also, a candle left burning in a closed container would lose its flame long before the wax was consumed. A burning candle and an animal "injured" air in the same way. Indeed, no animal could live long in an atmosphere where a candle had burned out. Priestley realized that he had discovered a way to "restore" the element which had been removed from the air which, of course, was oxygen.

His next important discovery was nature's method of maintaining the vital element in air. The chapter title is "Air in Which Candles Have Burned."

"I have been so happy as by accident to have hit upon a method of restoring air injured by candles, and to have discovered one of the restoratives which Nature employs. It is *vegetation*.

"On the 17th of August, 1771, I put a sprig of mint into a quantity of air in which a wax candle had burned out, and found that on the 27th of the same month, another candle burned perfectly well in it. This experiment I repeated without the least variation in the event, not less than eight or ten times in the remainder of the summer . . ."

Priestley, as a conscientious researcher, elaborated the experiment to remove many extraneous details.

"This remarkable effect does not depend on anything peculiar to mint, which was the plant that I always made use of until July 1772, for on the 16th of that month I found a quantity of this kind of air to be perfectly restored by sprigs of balm which had grown in it from the 7th of the same month.

"That this restoration of air was not owing to any aromatic effluvia of these two plants not only appeared by the essential oil of mint having no effect of this kind, but from the equally complete restoration of this vitiated air by the plant called groundsel, which is ranked among the weeds and has an offensive smell.

". . . Plants, instead of affecting air in the same manner with animal respiration, reverse the effects and tend to keep the atmosphere sweet and wholesome when it is become noxious in consequence of animals either living and breathing, or dying and putrefying in it."

Besides oxygen and carbon dioxide, Priestley also generated and isolated for the first time ammonia, nitrogen, nitric oxide, carbon monoxide and a host of other substances. Ammonia he called *alkaline air;* hydrochloric acid vapor was named *marine acid air;* sulphur dioxide was *vitriolic acid air.*

3. FLIGHT TO AMERICA

During the years of the American Revolution, Priestley's openly expressed sympathies were with the Colonists although he himself remained an undeviating monarchist.

In 1788, Franklin wrote from America to one of Priestley's pupils:

"Remember me affectionately to the honest heretic, Dr. Priestley . . . . Do not, however, mistake me. It is not to my good friend's heresy that I impute his honesty. On the contrary, 'tis his honesty that has brought upon him the character of heretic."

At the time this letter was written, the contagion of the American Revolution had spread to France. Just as Priestley supported the American cause he, like many liberal Englishmen, supported the French struggle for freedom.

Bastille Day, 1791, was celebrated in many English communities. In Birmingham, however, a five-day campaign accused all those who planned to attend the anniversary dinner of being traitors. Priestley was singled out as the main target.

After some discussion, Priestley and his friends met at noon in a private dining room and no attempt was made to interfere with them. That evening, however, hysteria ran like a malignant fever through Birmingham. A mob collected and the two dissident churches were set afire. The mob's avowed purpose was to go on to Priestley's, to burn his house and lynch him and his family.

With only a few minutes to spare, the Priestley family was bundled into a coach and sent off into the night, but the house was looted, the papers scattered, the walls were battered down, while several thousand voices yelled their drunken delight at the sight of the flames.

Two years in London saw the situation worsen. He resigned from the Royal Society after his fellow members began to cut him dead. His sons could not be placed and the young men sailed to America. At length, Priestley decided to follow them to Pennsylvania.

He became a welcome visitor of Washington in retirement; he preached to a congregation that included Vice-president and then President Adams, and became a close friend of Jefferson. The University of Pennsylvania offered him a professorship, and later he was asked to head the school.

Franklin influenced the generations that followed him, but the path of that influence is marked by Joseph Priestley who taught his marvelous experimental techniques to Woodhouse, Maclean, and Robert O'Hare, through whose efforts chemistry became another means of assaying the wealth of America.

DOCTOR PHLOGISTON,
The PRIESTLEY politician or the
Political Priest.

Attacks on Priestley were bitter because of his defense of religious freedom. He was a Unitarian. He almost sailed as chaplain with Captain Cook, but the Church stopped him.

Priestley studied gases in glass containers inverted in a mercury trough. If the chemicals generated gas, the mercury level was lowered. He studied the effect of oxygen on life.

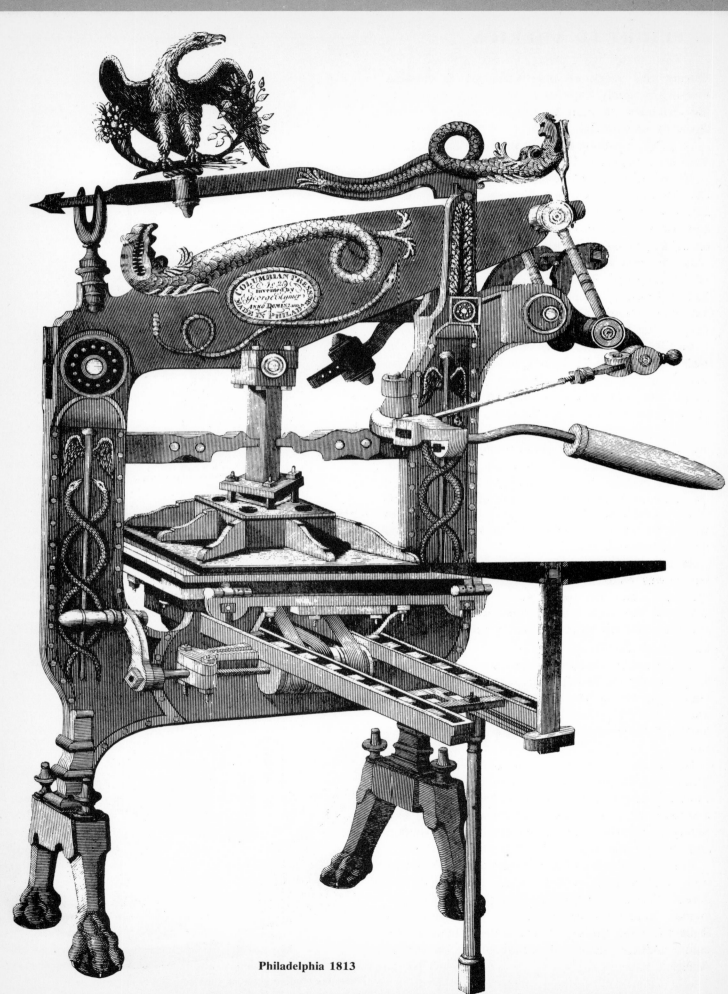

Philadelphia 1813

36

Political chaos was complete in the republic's early years. The Federalists under Adams fought the emerging Republicans at every turn; at one point physical violence broke out even on the floor of Congress when Republican Matthew Lyon of Vermont and Connecticut Federalist Roger Griswold fought it out with cane and fire tongs. The typical cartoon at the top shows the Republicans consorting with the devil. Such an atmosphere was anathema to scientific and mechanical progress. There was just no need, nor the money to pay for inventions. There was always a market for an improved printing press, however, since this was the main political weapon. The ornate machine at the left could have been made only in America. With its large eagle and serpents, and small cornucopia, it aptly symbolized the ominous presence of the Wilderness and the pitiful condition of the floundering new country.

PART TWO

The
Shock
of
Freedom

The years following the war were a time of confusion, despair, and rebellion. Whatever commerce had existed before was now in a state of ruin. Independence was what the colonies had sought; and now the deserted mother country gave it in full measure. The British mercantile theory had stated that the Empire was composed of the heart and stomach—the British Isles, to be fed by the limbs, the colonies. The limbs in turn were to be nourished by the blood and wealth pumped to them from the heart. One limb had severed itself. Now, said the British, let it shift for itself.

Until the war, most American merchants had merely been agents for British goods. After the Treaty of Paris, the Americans were foreigners in British ports, as foreign as the French or Spanish, and had no price privileges at all. Before the war, American goods had been guaranteed ready markets in London. After the break, the British turned to their other colonies for the same products, and Americans sailed west to China, east to the Baltic Seas, looking for new markets.

American Colonials had once petitioned the Crown for the right to issue their own money. When they had won that right, they mismanaged the business so badly that money was worthless. Vast improvements were needed to change a string of colonial settlements into a nation; but there was nothing with which to pay for them. Americans fell back on barter, and trade was conducted in terms of Spanish and French coins, because American overseas trade was the first to recover from the effects of the war. The enormous increase in shipping—124,000 tons in 1784 to 981,000 in 1810—ended disastrously with the War of 1812, but until then it was the Spanish dollar which was America's standard money, not anything either minted or printed at home.

They had asked for their own government. When they got it, they mistrusted, abused, defied and laughed at the very men they had sent to represent them. The Articles of Confederation, drawn up during the war, were useless as instruments of power once the individual states became divided and engaged in fratricidal struggles.

A new agreement was needed. A Constitution was drafted, this time by men more conservative than the extremists who had drawn up the Declaration of Independence. The Constitution framers were men of property who considered themselves to be leaders and respected at home. But no sooner had they finished their series of compromises and political horse-trades to make the new agreement palatable to all the dissenting factions, than they too were subjected to the same abuse as their predecessors. And they in turn responded with the same bad-tempered show of force. The excesses of the Sons of Liberty were now exceeded by the bullying of Federalist judges who handed down lynch law justice based on the sleazy legality of the Alien and Sedition Act, under which it was a crime to criticize the government.

Tempers ran high, constructive ideas ran low; the jails were full, and the exalted words of the Declaration of Independence were empty. A dozen generals of the Army were in the pay of foreign powers, a vice-president planned treason, the best people of the most conservative towns preached secession. Insurrection was in the air, repression was the order of the day. The shock of freedom seemed unbearable.

Yet within three more decades, the American mood changed so sharply that the backward, sluggish people—devoid of any ability or interest in mechanical arts—the American artisan whose slogan seemed to have been "half-finished is all finished"—were so exuberantly optimistic that they were developing a new article of faith—"Any American can do anything better than anyone else."

From despair to Yankee brag in forty years, and the new nation was firmly entrenched, its commerce sought after, its example a beacon of hope to the entire world. What had happened in that time? Who were the men who made these things happen?

The premise of America had been the rights of man; and on that premise a republic had been erected whose sole function was to enhance, protect, and widen these rights against the opposition of a hostile world. But while the political pioneers like Jefferson, Hamilton, Clay, Calhoun, and Webster shaped a national destiny out of words, there was another class of men who more lastingly shaped the face of America, men who had no name for themselves.

A poet knows he is a poet, a farmer knows he is a farmer; but in the years following the founding of the republic there were no words in the American vocabulary to describe what later came to be called the engineer, the scientist, the inventor. And just as there was no name for these men, there was no place for them.

Young men grow up and fit themselves into one or another of the molds offered to them by their society. Whatever talents they possess which do not fit the mold are rarely developed. Only when the excess talent is so compelling, so explosive that no mold can contain its energy, does the man smash out of the confinement and become gloriously what he feels he must be. For such a Promethean, the way is hard, and the end is death under the beaks of the eagles.

In the early days of the republic, only such driven men could come to the fore. Others, perhaps as talented, but lacking the drive and the energy, remained within the molds and came in time to fit them so securely that they too laughed and jeered at what they had once known in their hearts must be true. Men like Robert Fulton, John Fitch, Oliver Evans, Eli Whitney, and John Stevens were of extraordinary stature, and they thrived on diets of disappointment. Those who died happy were those who died prematurely. Another week, or another year, and their hearts too would have been broken.

These and some others were the men who had no name for themselves; yet what they did in the first decades of the republic so securely shaped the face and lifted the heart of America that their most enduring monument was what came after them—a century of American self-confidence.

FROM DESPAIR

TO YANKEE BRAG

IN FORTY YEARS

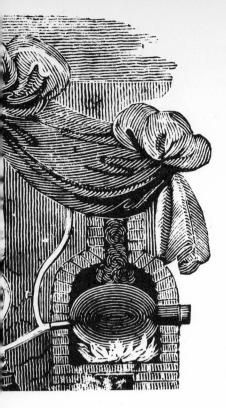

Gas lamps were a laboratory novelty at the beginning of the 19th century. Gas was made by heating wood or coal in an airtight container. Pressure was equalized by a floating tank, exactly as it is today, in huge steel storage tanks.

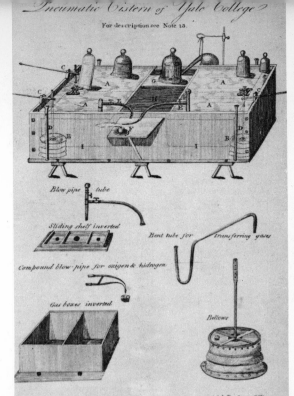

Chemical apparatus built for Professor Silliman of Yale showed improvements stimulated by Priestley after his emigration from England.

Fourth of July in Centre Square, by John Lewis Krimmel: Philadelphians around the steam engine water works—imported from England.

Captain Lewis

Captain Clark

1

SURVEYORS
OF A
CONTINENT

"A civilized man," runs one definition, "is a man who is at home in his own time." By that exacting standard, Thomas Jefferson was such a man. The eighteenth century was as productive of the highest forms of philosophy, art, and science as any period after the cessation of the Religious Wars; Jefferson was not only acquainted with the best thought of his time, but he made his own original contributions to it. He was most powerful as a political thinker; and he had the intellectual resilience to alter his ideas to fit the realities which he met while President.

Jefferson's vision was so large that he was not appalled by the vastness of land to the west of the thirteen states. When he became President, he interrupted the vacation of his Minister to France, Robert Livingston, who was at home conducting steamboat experiments, and sent him back to Paris to buy from Napoleon the city of New Orleans at the mouth of the Mississippi. Most Americans thought of the Mississippi as an infinitely distant

river in a semi-mythical land. To frontiersmen, however—and Jefferson had been raised near the Virginia frontier—the Mississippi was within the foreseeable future of the republic; but New Orleans, as a Spanish city, was closed to Americans.

In 1800, Napoleon, by a secret deal, received the Louisiana territory from the Spanish. Two years later, he decided to garrison New Orleans with a massive military force of 28,000 men shipped aboard one of the greatest fleets ever assembled. However, the expedition first landed in Haiti to suppress the native uprising for independence under Toussaint L'Ouverture. Jungle war and yellow fever laid waste almost the entire French force. Livingston landed in Paris within sixty days of the disaster and offered two million dollars for the city that had become Napoleon's liability. Napoleon made a counter proposition. He would sell the entire territory, over a million square miles, for fifteen million dollars, New Orleans included. It was a take-it-or-leave-it-and-talk-fast proposition. Livingston, by then assisted by James Monroe sent over for that purpose, had no authorization to negotiate nor any means for getting such a sum of money in time. Fifteen million dollars in 1803 was a fantastic price even in wealthy France—it would sound astronomical to poverty-stricken America. Nevertheless, on their own initiative and with their hearts in their throats, the two Americans agreed.

In spite of the most terrifying warnings, Jefferson backed them up, and eventually so did Congress. New England was in a rage. America was suddenly two and a half times its original size. The boundary had flown west two thousand miles to the foothills of the legendary Stony Mountains, as they were then called, to the Pacific Ocean through the territory of Oregon.

No white man had ever traveled across the plains or climbed the terrible mountains. It was a land of nightmare emptiness inhabited by wild men who did not even know that a civilized white race existed. Jefferson himself believed that the plains might be the habitat of woolly mammoths and other monsters long extinct elsewhere.

The Senate ratified the purchase October 21, 1803. Within a few weeks, Jefferson asked Congress to appropriate $2,500 for an expedition to explore the new territory. Jefferson selected a twenty-nine-year-old Army officer who had once been his private secretary, Captain Meriwether Lewis. As co-leader, he appointed another officer, thirty-three-year-old William Clark. To them were assigned fourteen soldiers who volunteered for the service and nine young frontiersmen from Kentucky. In addition, there were three French voyageurs and Captain Clark's servant, a Negro slave.

Their mission was to find the headwaters of the

Fossilized bones of a mastodon were discovered near Newburgh, N. Y., in 1801. Peale built the machinery to exhume the remains and later painted this picture. The find fascinated President Jefferson. Two years later, he directed Lewis and Clark to search newly purchased Louisiana for similar specimens and unknown species.

Messowrie River (as the Missouri was then called), to cross the continent, to find a pass through the Stony Mountains and search for the headwaters of the Columbia River which had been discovered by a seal-hunting Salem sea captain only a short time earlier. Once the upper reaches of the new western river were explored, the party was to proceed downstream to the Pacific.

On a cold Monday morning in May, 1804, the expedition's keel boats set sail up the Missouri, making little progress against headwinds. Four days later, they reached the outermost white settlement—the seven primitive houses of La Charette where Daniel Boone at seventy had settled in his final poverty and disillusionment with white men.

From that point on, the trip back to prehistoric time began. They met no woolly giant elephants or dinosaurs, but they did meet human beings who lived just as the white men had lived eons earlier when mammoths and saber-toothed tigers actually had roamed Europe. Although the names of these Stone Age people have since become part of our western lore, to Lewis, Clark, and their contemporaries, the tribes were as new as races from another planet. In expedition journals, the tribes call themselves Mahars, Canseze, and Scouex. Later the names were standardized into Omahas, Kansas, and Sioux.

In the unknown land, the party found species of animals they had never seen before. They saw, shot, and examined a "goat," swift, with grayish hair, a white mark on the rump, and short pronged horns that pointed backwards: the American antelope. A four-acre tract of flatland was covered with mysterious small holes. Seated at the entrance of each hole was a "small dog in some particulars, although they have points of similarity to the squirrel. The head resembles the squirrel in every respect, except that the ear is shorter; the toenails are long, the fur is fine, and the long hair is gray." They weighed about three pounds. These were the prairie dogs.

41

2. THE LEWIS AND CLARK EXPEDITION OF DISCOVERY

When the party reached the Black Hills, mention begins of a "white bear," a frightful beast eight feet high, weighing a quarter of a ton. In order to define the peculiar color of the pelt, the word "grizzly" appears: a highly descriptive pun—"grisly"—became the Latin name—*Ursus horribilis*. They discovered the big-horned "Rocky Mountain Sheep," and what they called the "calumet bird" or golden eagle. They met a new species of wolf: "These wolves are rarely if ever seen alone, not being able singly to attack a deer or antelope. They sally out in a body against any animal which they think they can overpower, but on the slightest alarm retreat to their burrows making a noise exactly like that of a small dog." This was the coyote.

They discovered rivers, mountains, the terrible alkali poison that corrupted the ground and water, a pass through the Rockies; and in July, 1805, the principal sources of the Missouri River. Then they happened on a marvelous piece of good luck: just across the divide were the springs that fed the streams which fell into the Columbia River and the Pacific Ocean.

The journals are full of complete accounts and descriptions of the various tribes. In an age when one of the deepest needs of America was manpower, it never occurred to anyone that these Stone Age men could be assimilated and enrolled in the development of the continent, as the paint-bedaubed German, Gallic, and Celtic aborigines had been absorbed by the Romans fifteen centuries earlier.

The woodcut prints in the outside columns of these pages are from the journal kept by Patrick Gass, a member of the expedition; the water colors in the center columns, by George Catlin, who later went out and lived with the Indians.

Lewis and Clark understood the importance of friendship with the Indians. The journey began with a council. This meeting place became known as Council Bluffs.

The Mandans, with whom the expedition wintered, later were wiped out by an epidemic of smallpox. Their appearance and customs were preserved by artist George Catlin.

Winter quarters had to be built at the end of the first six months because of bad weather. The expedition settled near one of the villages of the Mandan tribe.

With a hook in his chest, a Mandan warrior stared all day into the sun to prove his bravery. Life with the Mandans led Clark to return later and begin the western fur trade.

Feasting and dances proved the Mandans' friendliness for the white men. Lewis and Clark convinced them that the American white men would bring them everlasting peace.

The grizzly bear was unknown to white Americans before Lewis and Clark. The grizzly looked as monstrous as the mastodon and mammoth Jefferson expected them to find.

Stone Age ancestors of Lewis and Clark would have felt at home with the Mandans. European aborigines were absorbed by more civilized races. American aborigines were killed.

For three years, the expedition traveled through the West. On their return, most of their specimens, notes, and fossils were lost when a canoe was sunk by a floating tree.

The Mandan way of life was unchanged thirty years later when Catlin lived with them. Their wars still raged. They still waited for the white man's promises to be filled.

Strict military discipline was observed by the expedition. Flogging was the penalty for disobedience; shooting, the sentence for stealing. Here, Lewis shoots an Indian.

Nathaniel Bowditch, by Gilbert Stuart

1

SURVEYOR
OF THE SEA

One of the first casualties of the War for Independence was the American merchant fleet. For the first few years, as privateers, Yankee skippers won fantastic prizes; but when the full weight of the British Navy was brought to bear, the towering seventy-fives bottled up the Yankee schooners in the Colonial ports for the rest of the war.

After the war, when American vessels were free to sail again, they found their old ports of call closed to them; but of all the American trades, the sea-traders were the first to recover.

Only three months after the British formally withdrew their occupation from New York, the *Empress of China* cleared Sandy Hook for a trip around Cape Horn to Canton. Her cargo was the ginseng root, of enormous value to the Chinese. Almost immediately after, the sloop *Enterprise* made the same trip. The voyage, begun in 1784, took a year, and the profits were staggering.

Five years later, the China trade had become of such enormous importance to the republic that eighteen American vessels were riding in the Canton harbor. The American ships were very small com-

pared to the huge British East Indiamen—an average of seventy tons against fifteen hundred; but the Americans were fast, daring, and able.

Most of the China trade was centered in the small seacoast town of Salem. Within fifteen years after the end of the Revolution, the town had streets of beautiful mansions, and its wealth was enormous. Fortunes were being made by boys of eighteen and nineteen who thought nothing of sailing off for years of trading and any young man who did not follow the sea was considered to be a plain damned fool. It was no wonder, then, that Nathaniel Bowditch never once thought of becoming a mathematics teacher. He did what every other Salem boy did—signed up as supercargo in 1795 when he was twenty-two, and retired eight years later as a man of means.

During those eight years, Bowditch performed such a masterwork of applied mathematics that he was elected to the American Academy of Arts and Sciences. Fortunately there was plenty of time for reading Newton, Leibnitz, Descartes, and Lacroix. He was particularly impressed by the elegance of Laplace. Bowditch, with very little formal education, had taught himself six languages by comparing six different translations of the New Testament.

The science of navigation, until his time, had been fairly crude. Usually, captains found their way by dead reckoning, but this was full of risks. For example, in 1790, the *Massachusetts,* out of Boston, spent three weeks wandering around the Indian Ocean without knowing its position. Latitudes were fairly simple; but finding a longitude in days before the general use of chronometers was something very different.

It was only natural for Bowditch to turn his mathematical skill to navigation. The standard book on the subject was J. H. Moore's *The New Practical Navigator,* first published in London in 1772. Bowditch found it to be full of errors, as he did many charts and tables of navigation. By 1799, Bowditch had compiled a great mass of information and in that year he had a Newburyport printer bring out a new edition of Moore's book with his corrections.

Bowditch was thirty when he retired as a sea captain; and he was offered the presidency of the Essex Fire and Marine Insurance Company. Statistics replaced astronomy so successfully that during the twenty years of his presidency the stock paid an average dividend of ten per cent.

His greatest contribution was his annotated translation of Laplace's *Mécanique Céleste* into English. The five volumes were published at his own expense since there was no American public for such an advanced work. Another work that attracted international attention was his contribution to the theory that meteors were of cosmic origin. In the late eighteenth and early nineteenth centuries, meteors and

Crowninshield's Wharf in wealthy Salem was one of the world's busiest in the early part of the 19th century.

planets were extensively studied because they could be so easily treated by Newtonian mechanics. The paths of meteors could be calculated, but their origins were mysteries. The theory that their origin was in outer space was first stated by the German, Ernst Chaldni, in 1794. Few scientists were willing to accept it. Thirteen years after Chaldni's statement, in 1807, a huge meteor swept over New England and crashed finally in Weston, Connecticut. Bowditch collected all the information he could from its first appearance near Rutland, Vermont, until its final explosion. He published his results after eight years of study: the meteorite had been moving at a height of eighteen miles at a velocity of 3.5 miles per second. Its original mass must have been six million tons.

When Bowditch was fifty, he left Salem and became the director of the Massachusetts Hospital Life Insurance Company at a salary of $5,000 a year, a figure that few mathematicians would be able to match for over another century. That he was a success in American terms was proven by an accolade even more convincing than all his honorary degrees—for the austere, pinch-faced little savant was made the title hero of a biography in the Horatio Alger tradition—*Nat the Navigator*.

The Prudent was typical in the China trade—small and with shallow draft for seal hunting on the Pacific coast.

The China trade centered in Canton. Round trip from Salem took about a year, and the profits were enormous.

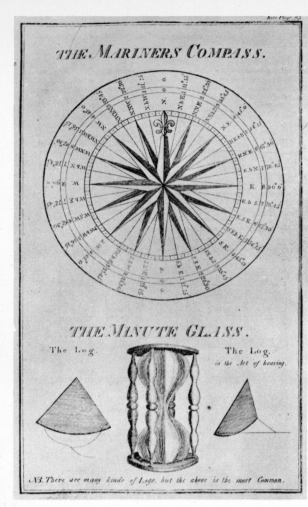

Compass and log were used in dead reckoning navigation. The speed of sailing was multiplied by the time a given course was held. Such determinations were subject to error.

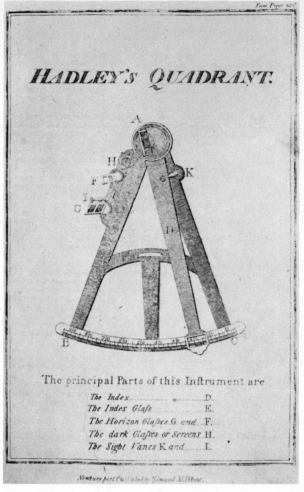

The quadrant measures the angular distance between celestial bodies and the horizon. These angles vary according to latitude or time of day observation is made.

2. THE NEW AMERICAN PRACTICAL NAVIGATOR

The first edition of Bowditch's *New American Practical Navigator* appeared in 1802. This contained a new method of calculating longitudes by means of "lunars" —using a sextant to measure the angular distances from the moon to certain fixed stars.

The Commissioners of Longitude in England published annual tables giving the distances for every three hours calculated for the meridian of Greenwich. Bowditch explained how these tables were to be used by navigators. His explanation begins:

"There are only nine stars from which the distances are computed on the Nautical Almanac; and as it is of the greatest importance to be able to discover them easily, I shall here add a number of remarks which will be found useful to that purpose."

One of the very serious errors in Moore which Bowditch corrected was the tabulation of 1800 as a leap year. A number of fatal shipwrecks could be traced directly to this miscalculation. The year after Bowditch's book appeared, he was awarded an honorary degree by Harvard. The book went through sixty editions and quickly became the sailor's bible. Its fame was international.

THE NEW AMERICAN

PRACTICAL NAVIGATOR

BEING AN

EPITOME OF NAVIGATION;

CONTAINING ALL THE TABLES NECESSARY TO BE USED WITH THE

NAUTICAL ALMANAC,

IN DETERMINING THE

LATITUDE;

AND THE

LONGITUDE BY LUNAR OBSERVATIONS;

AND

KEEPING A COMPLETE RECKONING AT SEA:

ILLUSTRATED BY

PROPER RULES AND EXAMPLES:

THE WHOLE EXEMPLIFIED IN A

JOURNAL,

KEPT FROM

BOSTON TO MADEIRA,

IN WHICH ALL THE RULES OF NAVIGATION ARE INTRODUCED:

ALSO

The Demonstration of the most useful Rules of Trigonometry: With many useful Problems in Mensuration, Surveying, and Gauging: And a Dictionary of Sea-Terms; with the Manner of performing the most common Evolutions at Sea.

TO WHICH ARE ADDED,

Some General Instructions and Information to Merchants, Masters of Vessels, and others concerned in Navigation, relative to Maritime Laws and Mercantile Customs.

FROM THE BEST AUTHORITIES.

ENRICHED WITH A NUMBER OF

NEW TABLES,

WITH ORIGINAL IMPROVEMENTS AND ADDITIONS, AND A LARGE VARIETY OF NEW AND IMPORTANT MATTER:

ALSO,

MANY THOUSAND ERRORS ARE CORRECTED,

WHICH HAVE APPEARED IN THE BEST SYSTEMS OF NAVIGATION YET PUBLISHED

BY NATHANIEL BOWDITCH,

FELLOW OF THE AMERICAN ACADEMY OF ARTS AND SCIENCES.

ILLUSTRATED WITH COPPERPLATES.

First Edition.

PRINTED AT NEWBURYPORT, (Mass.) 1802,

BY

EDMUND M. BLUNT, (Proprietor)

FOR JACOB RICHARDSON, NEWPORT.

SOLD BY EVERY BOOK-SELLER, SHIP-CHANDLER, AND MATHEMATICAL INSTRUMENT-MAKER IN THE UNITED STATES AND WEST INDIES.

To find the Latitude by one Altitude of the Sun, having your watch previously regulated.

RULE.*

ADD together the log. co-fine of the latitude by account, (Table XXV.) the log. co-fine of the declination, (Table XXV.) the logarithm in the column of rifing (Table XXI.) corresponding to the time from noon when the obfervation was taken, rejecting 20 in the index ; the natural number of the remainder (found in Table XXIV. and) added to the natural fine of the obferved altitude (Table XXII) will give the natural fine of the meridian altitude, from which the latitude may be obtained by the common rules.

If the computed latitude differs confiderably from the latitude by account, it is beft to repeat the operation, ufing the latitude laft found inftead of the latitude by account. This method of finding the latitude by a fingle altitude of the fun, may be applied to any other celeftial object.

EXAMPLE I.

Being at fea in latitude 49° 50′ N. by account, when the fun's declination was 20° S. at 11h. 28m. per watch well regulated, the fun's correct central altitude was 19° 41′ to the fouthward of me. Required the true latitude.

Lat.	49° 50′	Co-fine	9.80957		
Decl.	20 0	Co-fine	9.97299	Mer. alt.	20° 3′
Time from noon 0h. 32m.		Log. rifing	2.98820	Zen. dift.	69 57 N.
				Decl.	20 0 S.
		590 Nat. num.	2.77076		
Obf. alt. 19°41′ Sine 33682				Latitude	49 57 N.
Mer. alt. 20° 3′ Sine 34272					

EXAMPLE II.

At fea in latitude by account 60° N. when the fun was on the equator at 1h. 0m. P. M. per watch well regulated. The fun's correct central altitude was 28° 53′ to the fouth of me. Required the latitude.

Lat.	60° N.	Co-fine	9.69897		
Decl.	0	Co-fine	10.00000	Mer. alt.	30° 0′
Time from noon 1h. log. rifing			3.53243	Zen. dift.	60 0 N.
				Decl.	0 0
		1704 Nat. num.	3.23140		
Obf. alt. 28° 53′ Sine 48303				Lat.	60 0 N.
Mer. alt. 30 0 Sine 50007					

* In calculating by this rule, it is neceffary to have your watch well regulated ; this may be done by an obfervation taken the preceding morning, or in the evening following the obfervation ; it being impoffible to regulate the watch and determine the latitude by a fingle altitude without other data ; though Moore (in his Epitome, page 217, 218, Edition 14) feems to think it may be done ; for all his examples are calculated on that fuppofition.

EVERYTHING A GOOD SEAMAN SHOULD KNOW

Description and Ufe of the QUADRANT OF SEXTANT of REFLEXION.

MR. JOHN HADLEY was the firft publifher of the defcription of the *Quadrant of Reflexion,* for meafuring angular diftances ; and the inftrument ftill bears his name, although it has been afcertained that Sir Ifaac Newton invented a fimilar inftrument many years before, but never made it public : one of our countrymen, Mr. Thomas Godfry, of Philadelphia, had alfo contrived an inftrument on the fame principles fome time before Hadley made known his difcovery.

In the adjoined plate we have given a figure of the quadrant ; the principal parts of which are, the graduated arch BC, the index D, the vernier, the index glafs E, the horizon glaffes G and H, the dark glaffes or fcreens H, and the fight vanes K and I.

The graduated arch BC contains only 45°, but is to be efteemed as 90°, and fo divided, becaufe by the double reflexion the angle is doubled. Each degree is divided into three parts of 20 minutes each ; and the arch is numbered from the right to the left, beginning at 0° and ending at 90°. The index D is a flat bar moveable round the centre of the inftrument, where is fixed the index glafs E ; at the other end is fixed the vernier fcale : from the bottom of the index a piece of brafs turns up againft the back of the inftrument, with a fcrew to it, ferving to faften the index againft any divifion. The vernier is a fmall narrow flip of brafs or ivory, fixed to that part of the index which flides over the graduated arch ; its ufe is to fub-

---

To find the LONGITUDE at SEA, by the LUNAR OBSERVATIONS.

AMONG the various methods propofed for finding the longitude at fea, none has been more juftly celebrated, nor is of greater utility, than that by meafuring the diftance of the moon from the fun or a fixed ftar, ufually called the LUNAR OBSERVATIONS. To facilitate this method, a work is annually publifhed by the Commiffioners of Longitude in England, which contains the diftance of the moon from the fun or a fixed ftar, for every three hours, calculated for the meridian of Greenwich. An obfervation of thefe diftances being made in any place, the time at Greenwich may be deduced therefrom, which compared with the apparent time of obfervation, will give the difference of meridians.

The diftances of the moon from the fun and proper ftars, are generally given in the Nautical Almanac from one object on each fide of her, to afford a greater number of opportunities of obfervation, and to enable the obferver to correct, in a great degree, the errors of the inftrument, or of the adjuftments, or a faulty habit of obferving the contact of the limbs ; becaufe the errors have a natural tendency to correct each other, in taking the mean of obfervations made with ftars on different fides of the moon. Previous to making the obfervation, the Nautical Almanac muft be examined, to fee from what objects the diftances are computed, and it is from them only the diftances muft be meafured.

There are only nine ftars from which the diftances are computed in the Nautical Almanac ; and as it is of the greateft importance to be able to difcover them eafily, I fhall here add a number of remarks which will be found ufeful for that purpofe.

THE MEN
WHO INVENTED
THEMSELVES

At the end of the eighteenth century most of America was living one hundred years behind Europe. That particular century had been a time of great material advance for the Continent. Great networks of barge canals covered France and England. French machinists had so much more skill than their society demanded of them that the surplus of their ingenuity went into the making of "genius toys"—tiny music boxes, chess-playing machines, fantastically intricate watches. The same ingenuity that made the toys also made the first silk looms.

In England, steam engines designed by Newcomen ponderously pumped water from coal mines, newly opened as the last of the English forests were stripped. English coal also meant an increase in the production of English iron. By the time of the American Revolution, the English had also begun to adopt the factory system. The expanding English economy accelerated so much in the third quarter of the century that the loss of the American colonies made no difference at the moment.

In the century-long change that was taking place in Europe, the position of the inventor was no longer that of a lunatic. He was beginning to have a place in the society; and if his invention could be proved to have some immediate use, the inventor was awarded the same respect as a successful merchant.

The word *engineer* was undergoing a change. Originally, it had only a military meaning—the man who erected and worked the intricate engines of war: the catapult, the storming towers, the fortifications of camps. In eighteenth-century Europe, the meaning was expanded and given a civil application—builders of canals, bridges, and wharves were also engineers. However, engineering was still not considered a learned profession but rather a highly skilled craft. The meaning was still not expanded to what would later be called mechanical engineering—although books had been written on certain mathematical aspects of machinery. The study was called *mechanical philosophy*. A man who invented and built new machines was called a mechanic. Joseph Bramah, one of the greatest tool and machine designers who ever lived, was called a mechanic, though his shops and inventions made him rich and respected. Among his apprentices were most of the great names of nineteenth-century mechanical science.

Vastly different was the situation in America at the turn of the century. Americans who could accept the need for political revolution were blind to the slightest change in either agriculture, road-building, travel, or mechanical appliances. If a man could use tools to repair implements that had broken, that was well and good. If a man used tools to make something familiar in a new way profitably, that too was welcomed because a rich shop was its own justification. But if a man wanted to make something that no one before had heard of, no matter how reasonable it might sound—there, friends, was a lunatic.

There were no real wharf, canal, or highway engineers. There were so few mechanics that when Robert Fulton returned to America in 1805 and wanted to build one of his clockwork torpedoes which had been of such interest to both the British and French, he could find only one mechanic in New York who could follow his plans, Henry Frasse—a Frenchman who barely spoke English. His account book reads: "26th May 1810, à Fulton, répare un turpedos, le grand ressort, volant et rone, 4.50."

Apathy toward new mechanical devices was so deep that when the first and only steam engine was installed in the colonies, people who lived two days' walk distant still had not heard about it *seventeen*

James Watt, instrument maker, studied Newcomen's steam engine and added ten improvements during the years of the American Revolution. A timid man, he changed the world more radically than two and a half million colonists in revolt.

years later. The engine had been set up in 1753 in the Schuyler copper mines in Belleville, New Jersey. Oliver Evans, who was destined to become the James Watt of America, was born two years later. During his boyhood, he became fascinated with the idea of using steam to drive a piston without knowing that such an engine had already been invented, that such an engine had been pumping every day of his life not fifty miles away.

Long before Robert Fulton sent the *Katherine of Clermont* up the Hudson to Albany, a small steam-driven launch went shuddering in and out of a little harbor in Hoboken. Two loungers watched in silence from the New York side. Finally, one said:

"That's Jack Stevens."

"Lively feller, ain't he?"

In the first years of the republic, most of the men who should, through their interests and talents, have become engineers were lost to their country. No work was offered them, there was no place for them; yet they were the very men who were most sorely needed.

The inventors of these early years pioneered not only in their respective fields and in making a place for themselves in their society, but also in ways of doing business. The right to a patent had been written into the first Article of the Constitution, but patent grants were hit-or-miss affairs; and what was more serious, the general public resented a patent as an infringement on the right to general knowledge. Where did one man come off to keep his neighbors from using an idea just because he was the first one to think of it? That was plain monopoly; and Adam Smith writing in 1776, in *Wealth of Nations,* said monopoly was a bad thing.

Oliver Evans tried one way of working out a schedule of payments on his inventions, Eli Whitney tried another, and Robert Fulton tried still a third. All three had their ideas pirated right from under their noses and the courts were very little help. Whitney became so disgusted after his experience with the cotton gin patents that he never again applied for a patent on any of his subsequent inventions.

The men who changed America's mood from apathy to pride did so at a fearful price to themselves. In two decades they advanced America a century. In talent and achievement they were the peers of their counterparts across the Atlantic. In sheer courage and perseverance, they were incredibly heroic.

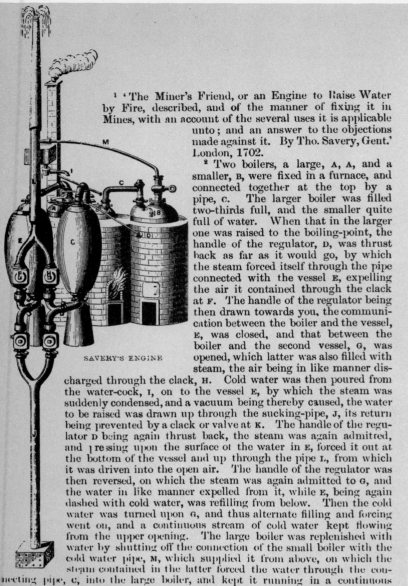

[1] 'The Miner's Friend, or an Engine to Raise Water by Fire, described, and of the manner of fixing it in Mines, with an account of the several uses it is applicable unto; and an answer to the objections made against it. By Tho. Savery, Gent.' London, 1702.

[2] Two boilers, a large, A, A, and a smaller, B, were fixed in a furnace, and connected together at the top by a pipe, C. The larger boiler was filled two-thirds full, and the smaller quite full of water. When that in the larger one was raised to the boiling-point, the handle of the regulator, D, was thrust back as far as it would go, by which the steam forced itself through the pipe connected with the vessel E, expelling the air it contained through the clack at F. The handle of the regulator being then drawn towards you, the communication between the boiler and the vessel, E, was closed, and that between the boiler and the second vessel, G, was opened, which latter was also filled with steam, the air being in like manner discharged through the clack, H. Cold water was then poured from the water-cock, I, on to the vessel E, by which the steam was suddenly condensed, and a vacuum being thereby caused, the water to be raised was drawn up through the sucking-pipe, J, its return being prevented by a clack or valve at K. The handle of the regulator D being again thrust back, the steam was again admitted, and pressing upon the surface of the water in E, forced it out at the bottom of the vessel and up through the pipe L, from which it was driven into the open air. The handle of the regulator was then reversed, on which the steam was again admitted to G, and the water in like manner expelled from it, while E, being again dashed with cold water, was refilling from below. Then the cold water was turned upon G, and thus alternate filling and forcing went on, and a continuous stream of cold water kept flowing from the upper opening. The large boiler was replenished with water by shutting off the connection of the small boiler with the cold water pipe, M, which supplied it from above, on which the steam contained in the latter forced the water through the connecting pipe, C, into the large boiler, and kept it running in a continuous stream until the surface of the water in the smaller boiler was depressed

SAVERY'S ENGINE

This steam engine was built by Thomas Savery in London in 1698. Apart from the valves, it had no moving parts.

A flask, heated at a tavern fireplace, sucked up wine as it cooled. This, so goes the story, started Savery off.

THE ATMOSPHERIC STEAM ENGINE

1

In the same decades that the seaboard fringe of colonies was stretching out north and south along the American beaches, the steam engine was clanking through its evolution in England.

For centuries, men had observed that when the spout of a steaming kettle was stopped up, the force of steam blew the lid off. Sometimes the same men noticed that when a bottle, partially filled with boiling water, was stoppered and set aside to cool, the stopper was sucked into the bottle when the steam condensed. These two observations—that boiling water expands explosively into steam, and that steam condensing back into water creates a vacuum—gave countless anonymous men the same idea.

The Marquis of Worcester, once a Royalist prisoner of Cromwell, wrote a book about a "Water Commanding Engine" which would use a vacuum to raise water from mines, but there is no evidence that he ever operated such a machine.

Twenty years later, in 1685, Dionysius Papin came to London and tried to give reality to Worcester's idea by having steam expand against a movable diaphragm in a cylindrical chamber. At the same time, an English Army officer named Captain Thomas Savery was trying to interest the Admiralty in a ship that could be propelled by side wheel paddles cranked by men. The Lord of the Admiralty practically kicked Savery out of his chambers as a lunatic and a meddler.

Savery then gave up his navigation scheme and built a pumping engine. This consisted of a chamber that was alternately filled with steam and then sprayed on the outside with a stream of cold water. The vacuum in the chamber sucked up water from a mine shaft through a pipe. Steam pressure then drove the water out of the chamber through another opening. The steam in the chamber was then condensed by the cold water to form a new vacuum which sucked up more water. He compared its work with that performed by a horse, and invented the term *horsepower*. However, he never thought of combining his engine with his first idea of paddle-wheel–driven vessels.

The idea did occur to Papin who in 1707 was in Germany. He actually built a small boat in which Savery's paddles were turned by a ratchet mechanism driven by Savery's steam engine. When he tried to transport his vessel for a demonstration on the Thames, he sailed as far as Münden where the river boatmen destroyed what appeared to them a monstrosity. He could never raise the money to build another.

Three years later, an English blacksmith named Newcomen saw one of Savery's engines and set out to build a better model. Newcomen succeeded so well over the next decade that his engine went unchanged for fifty years, when James Watt of Edinburgh refined it still further into a form that has gone practically unchanged until today. Unchanged, that is, with one important exception; and that missing step was supplied by an American, Oliver Evans, in the years when Thomas Jefferson was President.

Newcomen's engine was basically a simple affair. The main chamber was an upright cylinder about six feet high and a foot in diameter, open at the top. The bottom end was closed except for two spigots that opened into it—one to feed steam from a boiler, the other to feed a spray of cold water that could condense the steam. Sliding up and down in the cylinder was a piston that was attached to a long arm. The piston was counterbalanced so that its normal position was at the top of the open cylinder.

Steam was let into the cylinder, expelling all the air. The steam faucet was then closed, and the cold water faucet was opened. The cold spray made the steam condense within the cylinder, creating a sudden vacuum that brought the piston plunging down. The steamcock was again opened, filling the space beneath the piston with steam at atmospheric pressure, and the counterbalance then made the piston rise. A boy tending the faucets could make the engine go through five or six such cycles a minute. The "walking beam" drove a force pump that raised the water from the mine shaft. Working properly, the engine could develop about five horsepower.

An engine boy named Humphrey Potter grew bored with tending the petcocks. By an ingenious arrangement of strings and levers, he made the rise and fall of the piston open and close the faucets in the proper order, doubling the engine's speed.

By 1769, the Newcomen Atmospheric Engine, as is was called, was capable of raising two and a half tons of water one hundred feet for each bushel of coal burned. This was called the engine's "duty," and amounted to a half-million foot pounds per bushel.

It was just at that time that James Watt patented several improvements to use the heat more efficiently. Watt closed the top of the cylinder and did away with the counterweight by introducing steam first on one side and then on the other side of the piston. Instead of cooling down the cylinder with successive charges of cold water, he led the steam off into another chamber called the condenser. He introduced sliding valves, the flywheel to keep reciprocation uniform throughout the cycle, and the governor to keep the steam feed constant in spite of the load. These improvements more than quadrupled the engine's "duty."

Newcomen engines were ponderous contraptions which were used to pump water from English mines during the 18th century.

Automatic valves were invented by Humphrey Potter, a boy employed to tend the faucets on one of Newcomen's steam engines.

Dr. Dionysius Papin, of France, ran the first steamboat in 1707. Weser River boatmen destroyed it during trial.

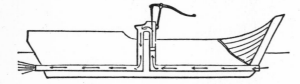

Benjamin Franklin suggested a jet-propelled boat, to be worked by hand pump. He had no faith in steam.

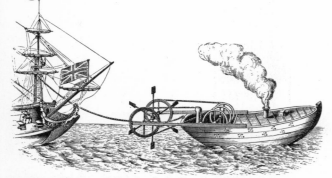

Jonathan Hulls, of England, built a model steam tug, driven by ratchets, in 1737. It was a failure.

Mr. Miller, of Scotland, built a twin-hull steamboat in 1788. Using ratchets, it went five miles an hour.

2. THE FIRST
STEAM-DRIVEN BOATS

Suggestions for using the atmospheric engine for driving boats and wagons were as old as the engine itself. No single individual invented either the steamboat or the locomotive. The main problem was always one of coupling the output of the Newcomen or Watt engine with some driving mechanism, either wheels or paddles—a problem that remained only partially solved for almost a century after the steam engine was accepted as standard equipment for mine work.

Because of the primitive conditions of the roads of the time, steam propulsion was applied to boats decades before any attempt was made to drive a wheeled vehicle. This work was done principally by Americans because the great rivers such as the Hudson and the Mississippi were ideally suited to steamboat travel.

Within the first five years after the founding of the republic, almost a half-dozen steamboats of various types were tried in the rivers along the Atlantic coast. At that time, hardly any attention was paid to these trials, and the few spectators of these ungainly and convulsive little boats only laughed; to a people who were practically without mechanical vision, the vague splashing efforts could hardly have inspired awe.

Nathan Reade of Salem, Samuel Morey of Fairlee, Vermont, William Henry of Lancaster, Pennsylvania, James Rumsey of Virginia, and John Fitch of Connecticut all built and successfully operated steam-driven vessels before 1790—almost twenty years before Robert Fulton achieved total success on the Hudson with his *Katherine of Clermont*.

Rumsey's design was based on a suggestion of Franklin's that if water were pumped through a vessel and ejected from the stern at high speed, the reaction of the expelled jet would force the boat forward. Rumsey demonstrated his craft before George Washington, who was sufficiently impressed to invest money for further work. Rumsey went to England where he met only discouragement. James Watt, by this time a famous engine builder with his partner Matthew Boulton, saw little future in steamboats.

Of this group of disappointed inventors, the best known was John Fitch, whose small steam launch ran two thousand miles as a ferry on the Delaware before he gave up.

In spite of the desperate need for improved methods of transportation, the new American republic was too poor to provide support for the immense amount of developmental work that was required. Through every story of the mechanical pioneers of the time runs the same refrain—American money was worth little more than a continental.

Fitch's early steamboat attempted to duplicate the action of human paddlers. Other inventors copied duckfeet.

FITCH'S LIFE—HIGH HOPES AND BITTER DISAPPOINTMENTS

Luck was against Fitch from the moment he was born; a tyrannical father, a dishonest master during his apprenticeship, a termagant wife, a plaguing idea twenty years ahead of its time, lifelong poverty—nothing was spared him. He made a trip to England for support, but met only with shrugs and polite contempt. His plans and models gone, he shipped back to America as a common seaman, and a few years later, in 1798, a confirmed alcoholic, he died—some said a suicide—in the frontier country of Kentucky. His fate is less obscure than that of the other early steamboat builders only because he left a journal; though almost illegible, it is nevertheless so full of the bitter humor of despair that it still makes gripping reading.

Sidewheels were also tried by Fitch. They used as much energy raising water on the upstroke as they used for propulsion. An Archimedean screw was tried as a primitive propeller.

Fitch's death, as imagined by a French artist. His life was one long disappointment, but his work was carried to success by John Stevens later.

OLIVER EVANS

1. SHOPKEEPER
AND MECHANIC

Water wheels drove 18th-century American mills. An ordinary mill required the hard labor of at least four men.

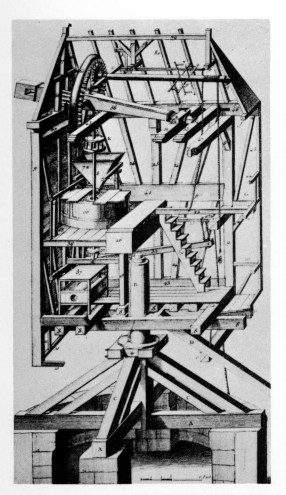

Windmills were favored in Europe. The British responded coolly to Evans' Improved Mill.

Like great puffing monsters, the engines of Newcomen and Watt did their feeble work. It is no wonder that men were unimpressed by the suggestion that one of these mammoths of brick oven, iron pots and pipes, and heavy oak beams could profitably be built into a wagon or a boat. They were suited only for permanent installation and then to do only one specific kind of work—pump water. Not until the size could be reduced and the power increased would there be any chance of mobility.

Yet the principles of Newcomen and Watt did not leave room for any modification of size. A smaller engine meant simply a less powerful engine. It remained for an American, Oliver Evans, to find the new principle. His Columbian engine delivered the same output as an atmospheric engine five to ten times its size, and thereby made it possible for a steam engine to transport a profitable cargo in addition to its own weight.

Perhaps there never was a great creative artist who was not also a markedly original personality. Oliver Evans, as original an inventor as America ever produced, was just such a man. He had the kind of tenacity that could make him hang on day after day in the face of the most discouraging of obstacles—the obtuseness of his fellow men—to hang on, to offer proof of a still more convincing kind, to build a still more advanced model, and everlastingly refuse to give up. He was no happy warrior who loved the excitement of struggle. Nor did he bear his disappointments with the sweet equanimity of a saint. Evans fought when he was attacked; he bellowed like a bull when he was hurt; he was a sarcastic diplomat of the sledge-hammer school—and he never gave up.

He was of medium height, inclined to portliness. His disposition was gentle and courteous, and while he was subject to periods of black depression, there was nothing neurotic about him. At one point, a Pennsylvania judge refused to uphold one of his most important patents on the ground that a patent was an infringement of public rights. His despair was not so much due to the loss of years of work, but rather to concern for his family.

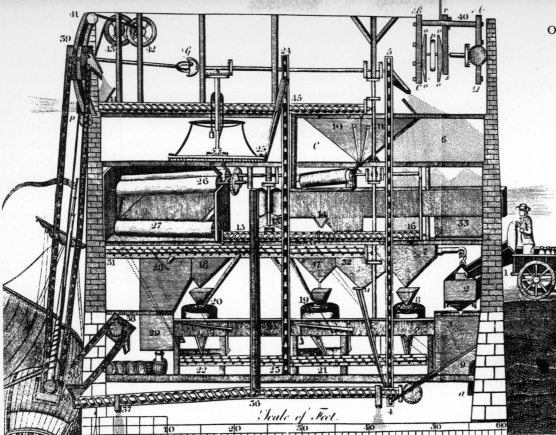

Evans' Improved Mill was automatic. Using bucket chains and Archimedean screws, it needed only one operator.

When he was fourteen, he was apprenticed to a wagon maker who begrudged him time at night for studies. Evans was forbidden to use candles, so he collected the wood shavings from the day's work, took them to the chimney corner, and studied by the flickering light. As a wagon maker, he began to dream of the various ways to make a horseless carriage. According to Evans, his brother told him about a game played with a gun barrel filled with water, stoppered at the ends, and thrown into a fire. The explosion was as good as gunpowder. That was all that Evans needed; but since he knew nothing of any previous experimentation, his mind began to improvise along entirely original lines.

Evans passion for machinery was unusual for his time and environment. He was the fifth of nine children, the only one with any interest at all in machinery or science. There were no technical books available to him; nor was there any machinery in use about him. It was as if, never having heard of poetry, he had one day written ten perfect Petrarchan sonnets.

He thought of using the force of steam, at fairly high pressures, to *push* a piston first in one direction and then in another. When someone finally gave him a book that contained a description of Newcomen's engine, his first remark was, "But he's doing it the wrong way!" He was amazed to discover that steam was so far not being used as a motive force at all—in the Newcomen engine the steam, at atmospheric pressure only, was used simply as a substance that could condense and thereby form a vacuum. Evans' plan made a vacuum entirely unnecessary. In a closed cylinder, an inrush of high-pressure steam would push the piston down. A valve in the bottom of the cylinder would be open so that no counter pressure was exerted against the falling piston. At the bottom of the stroke, the exhaust valve would be closed and another valve feeding high-pressure steam would drive the piston back up again. It meant that engines could be reduced in size in the same proportion as the pressure of steam was increased over atmospheric pressure.

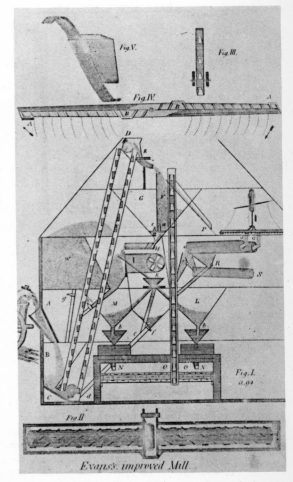

Five inventions allowed Evans to sift, grind and load grain from shafts driven by 1 water wheel.

2. OLIVER EVANS—INVENTOR AND BUSINESSMAN

Since no one in eastern Delaware was interested in steam engines, no one was interested in any improvement on one. No one was even capable of judging whether or not it was an improvement. Since Evans himself had so little learning, and no contact at all with the outside world, he put the idea aside and went to work on making a living. His experiments had convinced only himself, but he was sure that he had found a way to build a horseless carriage. This was in 1773.

He took a job making wool cards by hand. Raw wool came in tangles that had to be combed out. Such a comb consisted of a flat paddle of tough leather bearing iron teeth made of wire. When done by hand, the paddle had to be perforated with many holes, and the iron teeth, made one at a time, had to be inserted one at a time. Evans built a machine that would make three thousand teeth a minute, cut and bent into the proper shape. This is how Evans himself described his experience:

"In 1777 or '78, Mr. Evans began to manufacture wire from bar iron. . . . His father's family becoming acquainted with the circumstance, united argument with ridicule, to dissuade him from his visionary schemes. . . . The card manufacturers in Wilmington, having learnt the excellent qualities of this machinery, made offers for the secret; but so patriotic was Mr. Evans that he could not think of selling to individuals, to the exclusion of the public. . . . The legislature appointed a committee—to study his petition for financing. The committee, like the parson in the fable, lavished their eulogiums, but would lend no money."

He built the machine himself and agreed to allow a manufacturer to use it provided the machine was kept secret and that Evans was given a share of the profits. There were no patent laws, and no code of ethics for respecting such agreements. Evans realized only two hundred dollars, the down payment, for within a year the cardmaker had made the secret public, and other cardmakers infringed at pleasure.

When Evans was twenty-five, he opened a general store and married. He also went into the milling business with his brothers, having had his fill of cardmakers. The cardmakers were gentlemen and generous compared with what he now had to face. But Evans was Evans, and he could no more stop inventing than he could stop breathing. Within a few years, he worked out and installed five separate machines which, when combined, ran the mill without any human help. It was the first automatic plant in the world and cut labor requirements in half. One

THE ORUKTER AMPHIBOLOS OR AMPHIBIOUS DIGGER

This scow, thirty feet long, and weighing fifteen tons, was the first wheeled vehicle to move under its own power in America. It was the first amphibious steam-driven vehicle in the world. It was the first vehicle of any kind to use a high-pressure steam engine with success. To develop its full five horsepower it had a piston six inches in diameter, packed with hemp, which traveled through a stroke of ten inches. Under load, it made about thirty revolutions a minute. Steam pressure was thirty pounds. The two pictures of the scow above were made at different times; one shows the smoke stack at the front and the other at the rear, but the details of the engine in both pictures are the same as those of the Columbian engine at the right, which Evans built to grind plaster of paris and to saw marble.

of Evans' customers was an astute businessman and investor in the republic—George Washington.

Until this time, the only parts of a mill worked by power were the grinding stones. All of Evans' inventions were run by the same power source—wind or water. The five inventions were:

1. the elevator—an endless belt carrying wooden buckets that brought the grain continuously from the farmer's wagon to the top of the mill. This machine could handle three hundred bushels of grain an hour. Before Evans, this work was done by a man carrying a three-bushel sack on his back.

2. the hopper boy—a revolving rake twelve feet long that continually stirred the grain, aerating it and guiding it to the central chute leading to the stones. Usually a boy did this job erratically, mixing dust and dirt in with the raw grain.

3. the drill—an endless belt carrying rakes that moved the grain along a chute either horizontally or up a slight incline.

4. the conveyor—an Archimedes screw used for the first time to move solids rather than to raise water.

5. the descender—a belt on which the grain fell and was guided to whatever chute or loading place that was required. The belt was mounted on rollers and moved only under the weight of the grain.

None of these five inventions in itself was an original conception. What was original was the method with which Evans combined and applied them. Millers came and wondered at the marvelous performance of a mill that ran itself; but they refused to take any stock in anything Oliver Evans made, and millers from other states admitted that the inventions looked good but saw no reason to invest in machines when a man's nearest neighbors wouldn't buy them. Resistance took a long time to overcome; but finally the state promised to grant a patent if he could convince a committee that his work was really novel. Evans agreed and made his presentation. Seeing that the committee was impressed, he went on in his enthusiasm and described his plans for steam carriages. The committee then decided that he was a lunatic. They did grant his milling patent, but cautioned him to keep quiet about that other fantastic idea.

The income from the sale of his milling improvements was so slow at first that Evans moved to Philadelphia where he hoped to find less resistance.

In 1800, at the age of forty-five, he decided that since he could get no backing he would invest his savings in the work. He showed his plans for a high-pressure steam engine to Robert Patterson, professor of mathematics in the University of Pennsylvania, who said the principles were new to him but sound. He showed the plans to Benjamin Latrobe of the Philosophical Society who said they were absurd.

A doting father, Evans found time to make toys for the children, despite his business, his inventions, and his patents.

Evans' magnum opus was his *Young Steam Engineer's Guide*. The Whiskey Rebellion had drained the treasury, removing state support.

To raise money, Evans asked Philadelphians for twenty-five cents apiece to view the Orukter.

3. OLIVER EVANS, THE PRACTICAL DREAMER

Evans "commenced the construction of a small engine, for a mill to grind plaster of paris. The cylinder six inches in diameter and the stroke of the piston eighteen inches, believeing that with one thousand dollars, I could fully try the experiment. But, before I had done with experiments, I found that I had expended three thousand seven hundred dollars—all that I could command! I could break and grind 300 bushels of plaster of paris or twelve tons in 24 hours; I applied to saw stone in Market Street where the driving of twelve saws, sawing at the rate of a hundred feet of marble in twelve hours, made a great show. . . . I thought this was sufficient to convince the . . . spectators of the utility of my discoveries; but I frequently heard them inquire if the power could be applied to saw timber as well as stone, to grind grain, propell boats, etc.; and though I answered in the affirmative . . . they still doubted."

In 1804, he was finally given an order from the Philadelphia Board of Health for a steam engine to be used in dredging and cleaning docks. The engine, to be five horsepower, was to be mounted on a scow twelve by thirty feet long. The machine had to be built sixteen miles up the river in a shed a mile and a half from water. Evans decided that he would get the scow to town under its own power, using wheels and water paddles. When finished, the loaded scow weighed fifteen and a half tons. Slowly, the great scow moved over the rough ground with the wheels shrieking and swaying, then it rolled down the shallow muddy bank into the river where it floated idly for awhile until the drive belts were shifted to the paddle wheel. Then down the river went the steaming scow. The wind was dead against them, and as the sailing craft tacked endlessly from one shore to the other, the scow sailed straight ahead leaving them all behind.

At the Center Square Waterworks, the scow lumbered back on land again and slowly circled the drive before thousands of spectators. Again Evans thought he had given an unanswerable demonstration; but the public made no allowance for the crudeness of the machinery or that the load was all out of proportion to the feeble power of the engine.

Over the years, Evans' principles came slowly to be accepted; but his income which was considerable towards the end came exclusively from his store and his iron foundry; and only at the very end from his high-pressure engines. He died in 1819, a decade before the first railroads were introduced in America. Nevertheless, long before his death he had written, not as a visionary prediction, but as a sober report based on his own figures: "The time will come when people will travel in stages moved by steam engines, from one city to another, almost as fast as birds fly, fifteen to twenty miles an hour. Passing through the air with such velocity, changing the scene in such rapid succession, will be the most exhilarating exercise. A carriage (steam) will set out from Washington in the morning, the passengers will breakfast at Baltimore, dine at Philadelphia, and sup in New York on the same day. To accomplish this, two sets of railways will be laid, so nearly level as not in any way to deviate more than two degrees in a horizontal line, made of wood or stone, or smooth paths of broken stone or gravel, with a rail to guide the carriages so that they may pass each other in different directions, and travel by night as well as by day. Engines will drive boats ten or twelve miles per hour and there will be many hundreds of steamboats running on the Mississippi."

Colonel John Stevens of Hoboken

Robert Livingston Stevens

Commodore John Cox Stevens

James Alexander Stevens

Edwin Augustus Stevens

On May 23, 1768, the *New York Gazette and Weekly Mercury* announced the Commencement exercises of King's College. Nine young men, all eventually to become famous, were to receive degrees. One was John Stevens; another was his closest friend Robert Livingston. Both were sons of extremely wealthy families. They would in the following year become brothers-in-law whose tight friendship was to develop into an enmity that directly determined the future of steam engines and steamboats in America.

At stake were the immense fortunes to be gained from steamboat travel, and all the honors of first invention. As weapons, both men used their native wit, their family wealth, and their political power. Stevens was as powerful in New Jersey as Livingston was in New York.

An incidental gambit in this war was the draft by Stevens and passage of the first federal patent law, not so much to protect inventors as a class, but simply as an outflanking maneuver against Livingston and Livingston's nephew, Robert Fulton. After awhile, there were no rights or wrongs on either side as each faction shifted and exchanged position. Repeated attempts at reconciliation were blown up at the last minute simply by pride.

In the last analysis, the trouble was that both men knew, loved, had hurt and been hurt by each other far too deeply. Only death and Chief Justice Marshall made the final disposition of the struggle—and the judge's decision determined not only the future of steamboating but also the basic question of states' rights under the federal constitution.

ENGINEERING DYNASTY

1. THE STEVENS FAMILY

2. JOHN STEVENS— GENTLEMAN INVENTOR

John Stevens was born in New York when his fashionable parents were spending a winter in their town house. The Stevenses owned great estates in New Jersey and Pennsylvania, bought with the profits of shipping and royal favor. John grew up as one of the dandies of Colonial New York society. He studied law, but never practiced although many of his briefs were later to be submitted to the Constitutional Convention through his brother-in-law. In the Revolution, Stevens broke with his Loyalist New York friends and secured a commission with Washington.

In 1782, the year before the war ended, he married the great beauty Rachel Cox. She was a young woman with a fortune and a sense of humor. She called her husband "Mr. Stevens" for most of her life; and one morning in bed when Stevens awoke with a plan for a new engine, he sketched it out with his finger on her back. As she awoke and moved, he demanded impatiently, "Hold still! Don't you know what figure I am making?" "Yes, Mr. Stevens—the figure of a fool."

After the war, the wealthy young couple moved back to New York, snubbed by all their old Loyalist friends except the Van Cortlandts. Wanting a summer home, Stevens put in a bid for some property directly across the Hudson—the Indian name for the bluffs was Hopaghan Hackingh—in the post-Revolutionary days called Hoboke. The several estates together came to well over a thousand acres and cost almost twenty thousand pounds, an enormous piece of cash for a young man of thirty-five to pay in those years of acute national poverty.

Originally, he intended only to farm the land, but, becoming impatient with the delays of daily ferrying back and forth across the river, he bought the ferry

Stevens' first success was a twin-screw boat which he described to Dr. Robert Hare. Its speed was seven knots.

Boiler pressures of 100 pounds was Stevens' aim even though James Watt would build no engine requiring more than 3 pounds' pressure. The *Juliana's* boilers kept exploding, but Stevens believed in the future of high-pressure steam.

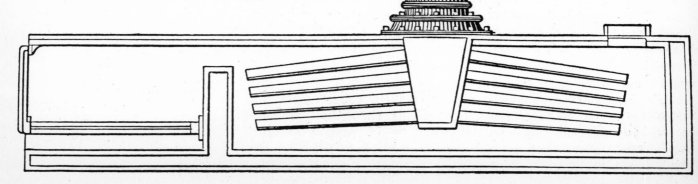

monopoly to insure better service for himself and his family. However, once he owned the company, he did everything he could to make it a paying proposition. His brother-in-law, Robert Livingston, first turned his attention to the steamboat experiments of Fitch and Rumsey. Livingston, besides being active politically, had a strong scientific interest and was continually directing Stevens to read the latest publications of Priestley and Count Rumford.

The brothers-in-law met Fitch and saw the trial runs. The worldly-wise New Yorkers knew that they were seeing ramshackle equipment put together by poverty-strained mechanics, but they were astute enough to realize that the future lay in steam power. The two men reacted with characteristic difference. Stevens went home to begin experimenting on his own. On the other hand, Livingston went home to buy up the unfulfilled patent grant to Fitch by the State of New York granting sole permission to run steamboats on the Hudson River providing that regular commercial service could be maintained between Albany and New York.

It was only natural for the two brothers-in-law, so closely tied by affection and interest, to become partners. Stevens could draw plans on paper, but he was no artist with his hands. A third partner was called in—Nicholas Roosevelt of New York, as skilled a mechanic as there was for those days.

From the first, Stevens appreciated the promise of high-pressure steam. Evans had preceded him, but Stevens, with an eye for detail, knew that the weak spot of the arrangement was in the boiler design. His progress was slow but steady, and while Livingston was becoming impatient, the wrangles over design were just good-natured squabbles between Livingston the man who considered himself the teacher and the erstwhile pupil Stevens who had begun to do practical work. Stevens' experimental boats, scows five or six feet wide and twenty feet long, running at four miles an hour, became a familiar sight to New Yorkers in the 1790's. However, he was still a long way from building a boat that would satisfy Livingston's charter, and the charter's time was running out.

At the end of the decade, Livingston was hurriedly sent to France to negotiate the purchase of the Louisiana territory while Napoleon was in a mood to sell; and while in France, Livingston came across a young American inventor named Robert Fulton. Fulton was at work on a submarine, but Livingston, anxious to fulfill his charter, interested him in steamboats. In an attempt to break the news gradually, Livingston's note home to Stevens mentioned Fulton, but did not state that Fulton was to be his new partner. For once, the astute diplomat Livingston underestimated his man: John Stevens was to prove a tougher adversary than Napoleon.

Their house on lower Broadway did not suit young John Stevens, though the family liked to spend winters in New York.

Across the Hudson was a delightful estate, Hoboken, where young Stevens built a house for his bride.

The Phoenix built by Stevens was the first steamboat to go to sea. This ship was the result of a lifetime of work.

61

The Elysian Fields was a public park in Hoboken for excursionists from New York. Stevens owned a fleet of ferries, which was what aroused his interest in steam. His steam ferries carried the picnickers.

3. THE GREAT AMERICAN FAMILY FEUD

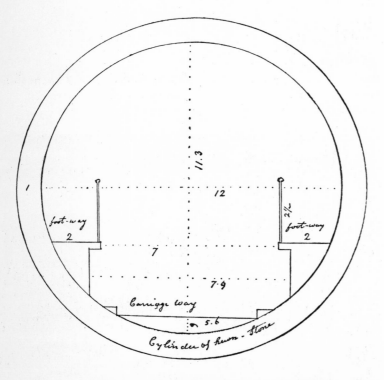

A tunnel under the Hudson was another of Stevens' projects. The stone tube was to contain two sidewalks and a roadbed.

During the years Livingston was abroad, Stevens solved the boiler problem. To make steam rapidly and to hold it at high pressure, he improved an old idea by replacing a single enclosed cylinder with a number of long, narrow pipes whose ends were fitted into the faces of two hollow, broad, flat cylinders. The water flowed from one flat cylinder to the other through the pipes, and since the fire played directly on the pipes, the water was very quickly heated to steam. Stevens had not only experimented with side paddles and stern wheels, he had also built and run a small twin-screw launch called the *Little Juliana*. The New York waterside loungers were by now used to the sight of Stevens' small steamboats, but this was something different. An eye-witness wrote: "As we entered the gate from Broadway, we saw what we, in those days, considered a crowd, running towards the river. On inquiring the cause, we were informed that 'Jack' Stevens was going over to Hoboken in a queer sort of boat. On reaching the bulkhead by which the Battery was then bounded, we saw lying against it a vessel about the size of a Whitehall rowboat, in which there was a small engine, *but no visible means of propulsion*. The vessel was speedily under way."

After several years in France, Livingston returned with Robert Fulton and announced to Stevens that Fulton was to build a steamship for him to satisfy the charter, that Fulton's experiments had gone further than Stevens' had; and he offered Stevens a partnership in the projected boat. Stevens did not agree that Fulton was ahead of him, and he felt that his brother-in-law was already bound to him under

Railroad locomotion was projected by Stevens all his life. In the 1820's, he built his own locomotive to run on a circular track around his estate. His sons became the most successful pioneers in American railroading.

an earlier agreement. Between the two men there now began that correspondence that was to go on for years —a legal argument back and forth that was to touch on every phase of patent law and moral rights. On the surface, the tone of the letters was amiable, frequently interspersed with references to Polly (Stevens' sister), to dear Rachel, the children, and decisions on certain properties held in common by the two brothers-in-law. But if the recriminations were more implied than stated, the hurt was there. Stevens felt that Livingston had broken his word; Livingston felt that Stevens was being stubborn and more concerned with having his own way than fulfilling the New York State charter which would give them all a monopoly on American steamboating with every opportunity for Stevens to work out whatever designs he pleased. Both men were right.

The year before Fulton finally made his run with the *Clermont,* Stevens put his first steam ferry into service across the Hudson, running at three miles an hour. Within a few days, Livingston offered him a third interest in the *Clermont* for only a few hundred dollars. Stevens refused. He was ready to build his own large-scale steamer, to be called the *Phoenix.* He intended to run it up the Hudson in spite of Livingston's monopoly. As the haggling between the two men went on, Fulton made the sensational run up to Albany and back, and the Hudson monopoly was now firmly in Livingston's hands.

Rather than risk a fight with the strongest political power in New York, Stevens sent his boat, the *Phoenix,* out into the Atlantic around Cape May and up the Chesapeake for service on the Delaware, the first ocean passage of any steamboat. A schooner, sent along to stand by in case of trouble, was blown out to sea for three weeks while the sturdy little steamer paddled straight through the gale and finally into Philadelphia. The Stevens line on the Delaware soon established itself as firmly as the Livingston-Fulton line on the Hudson.

Ideas of John Stevens in 1812 for a railroad included stone pillars for the track, with the cars hanging between.

In England, young Fulton became a canal engineer. His iron aqueduct, with parts cast at the site, was acclaimed by the *Edinburgh Encyclopedia*.

ROBERT FULTON

1. SUBMARINES AND SALONS

Long before Fulton married into the Livingston-Stevens aristocracy, he had outgrown his Pennsylvania farm background as the son of an Irish immigrant. When Livingston met him in Paris in 1800, Robert Fulton was a strikingly handsome man of thirty-five with an engaging friendliness. In sophisticated Parisian circles, he was affectionately called "Toot." He had a reputation as an artist, the protégé of Benjamin West; and he was also known as an inventor of remarkable mathematical abilities. In a drawing room, he was amusing and witty; in business conversations he was almost disconcertingly direct. He was a man who knew his own worth and he was at home in the world.

As a boy, he had discovered his hands. He could use tools, and he could draw. Post-Revolutionary America offered him the choice of two professions—itinerant mechanic or itinerant painter. There was nothing in his environment to cause him to think that he could combine both his gifts—inventive draughtsmanship and design—into one profession: engineering. Around Philadelphia, he made easy money as an artist and was told that if he went to England he would be received by Benjamin West.

In London, Fulton lived with West and learned to paint; but his mechanical interests led him to the company of a group of men whom England was learning to call engineers in the modern sense. In England, at that time, the major engineering interest was canal building, and Fulton in 1794 invented and patented a method to raise boats from one level to another without the use of locks. He described the use of a double set of tracks which led from the lower canal up a slope to a higher level. Canal boats, according to his specifications, would have flanged wheels attached to the bottoms so that they could fit the track. The weight of a descending boat would counterbalance the weight of a boat to be raised. Some years later, these designs were to be adopted on the Morris and Essex Canal.

In 1794 he also got a patent on a form of iron aqueduct whose parts could be cast in the open sand near the construction site and then be erected and assembled in place. Many such structures were installed in England, particularly one over the River Dee at Pont-y-Cysyllte, with 52-

Inclined railway for raising canal boats to another level was another Fulton design. Such a railway was actually built later in America.

Excavating machine was one of the first on record. These are Fulton's patent drawings.

foot spans standing on pillars as high as 126 feet.

The first power shovel, or excavator for canals, was patented by him in 1795. Its initial form as sketched in the patent drawing was faulty and would have flown to pieces, but improved versions were put to work satisfactorily.

In 1796 he published his *Treatise on the Improvement of Canal Navigation* in which he described a completely new system of canal design.

As an inventor, Fulton had the faculty of being able to visualize any new project in minute detail. His skill as a draughtsman then allowed him to make a drawing in scale from which he could calculate mathematically the practicability of his idea. His mathematical insight was extremely sound; and although his formal training had been no more than that of any other Pennsylvania country boy, he taught himself the theory and practice of engineering calculation so that he was able to use its inner meaning as deftly as a brush.

When he went to Paris in 1797 to take out French patents, he had professional standing. He was in his early thirties, he had the polish of having lived and worked for several years in the great metropolis of London; and he was introduced to Paris by Joel Barlow, the American Ambassador. After a first attempt at a torpedo experiment, he gave it up to plan for a submarine. For the submarine, he used the money he obtained from the sale of a painting called "The Burning of Moscow," a curiously prophetic picture to have done in 1800, and generally considered to be the first panorama ever painted.

When he ran out of funds, he applied as an American friend of the French Revolution to the Directoire for aid. Not until war broke out with the English and Napoleon became First Consul, however, did the French Admiralty give him any notice; and then he began work in earnest on the submarine *Nautilus*. The money allotted to him was an advance against the following agreement: he was to receive 60,000 francs for destroying a warship of ten guns, and other rewards on a sliding scale up to 400,000 francs for a vessel of thirty guns.

Allegorical picture by Fulton was called *Cruelty Presiding over the Prison Ship.* While in Paris he painted a picture called *The Burning of Moscow,* which sold for $1,000.

Torpedo test on a Danish brig in 1805 was proof to the British Admiralty that Fulton's weapons were workable.

2. FULTON—SHIPS OF WAR AND SHIPS OF PEACE

The *Nautilus* was the second submarine to be built, the first having been the invention of David Bushnell of Saybrook, Connecticut, and used in the American Revolution. Fulton's vessel was an enormous advance over the one-man turtle of Bushnell. It contained all the basic features of a modern submersible. Its superstructure gave it the look of an ordinary boat when surfacing, and it had a mast that folded away into a deck groove when underwater. There was a conning tower, ballast tanks that could be filled and emptied, and, in the first model, room for four men to crank an endless belt that turned a propeller shaft.

In his note on progress Fulton wrote, "On the third of Thermidor, I commenced my experiments by plunging to a depth of five feet, then to ten feet, then fifteen feet, and so on to twenty-five. I went no further as the machine could bear no greater pressure of superincumbent water. My boat had 212 cubic feet of capacity, containing enough oxygen to support four men and two small candles for three hours." Later he designed a brass globe to contain compressed air as a reservoir. He used underwater bombs of his own design. His last test before actual operation took place in August, 1801, in the harbor of Brest, when he submerged and affixed a twenty-pound clockwork bomb to a sloop. The sloop was smashed to bits, and with a full crew Fulton now set to sea in pursuit of the blockading vessels of the British fleet.

The British, however, were forewarned. Their experience with Bushnell's submarines and torpedoes in the American Revolution had made them very wary

of American submersible tactics; moreover they knew Fulton and respected his ability to carry out whatever project he started. Every vessel had orders not to try to fight him; and for an entire summer he pursued one British ship after another without getting close enough to make a contact. He came within a hair of hanging a bomb onto the hull of a seventy-four gun frigate, but she too got away. The French Navy considered the experiment a failure. Fulton, however, was well aware that although he hadn't destroyed any British shipping, he had certainly been able to make them move away from where they had been.

It was during this submarine period that Livingston had come to Paris to negotiate for the Louisiana territory. The steamboat project was very much in his mind, and he discussed it at length with Fulton. In America, Stevens' advances over Fitch might have seemed enormous. However, Stevens, when compared to the brilliant professional Fulton, seemed singularly unimpressive. Livingston felt that Fulton was the one man to do the job that had to be done. Fulton might never have done any steamboat work before; but his background of seven years of invention and engineering in Europe had provided him with such techniques that he would never need as much time as Stevens.

Fulton listened to Livingston and became convinced of the future of commercial steamboating on American rivers. During the submarine building, he executed a model steamer on the Seine, with a flat bottom sixty-six feet long, and eight-foot beam, and a three-foot draught. He had calculated the stresses on the hull carelessly and when the machinery was

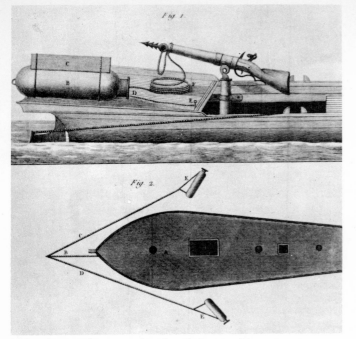

Fulton's torpedo was a time-bomb fastened to an enemy ship by a harpoon fired from the deck of a fast little launch. The British Admiralty suppressed the invention.

The Nautilus was Fulton's first submarine, built for the French in 1801. This painting, by Fulton himself, shows the submarine both on the surface and submerged.

put aboard, the vessel broke. From that one error, Fulton learned a lesson that enabled him to design the *Clermont* without having to go through the interminable steps of trial and error which were taking so much of Stevens' time. The second steamboat for the Seine worked beautifully, and made a steady speed of four and a half miles an hour. The Parisians, like the New Yorkers of the same time, were unimpressed by the sight of a small vessel moving under the power of a steam engine. "What good is it?" was the universal question.

Instead of returning to America with Livingston as soon as the French withdrew interest in the submarine, Fulton was reluctant to leave Europe, the most active stage in the world of engineering. He made a deal to continue his torpedo and submarine experiments for the British Admiralty. He was to get one thousand dollars a month, and one-half the value of all the vessels he destroyed within fourteen years of the signing of the articles.

However, the British were far more interested in suppressing Fulton's plans than in their use. When the war with the French ended, they summarily dropped their contract with Fulton. Once more Livingston pressed him to come to America and offered to back him with all the resources Fulton might need. Fulton accepted. Like a professional, he decided that there was no need to invent new engines when the existing product would do all that was required. He placed an order with Boulton and Watt. He inspected all the experimental little steamboats that were being tried in England, the best of which was William

Symington's *Charlotte Dundas*. This ship, in 1802, had traveled over nineteen and a half miles in six hours, and displaced more than seventy tons.

Fulton, still in England, and without any intermediate step after the trial boat which had run on the Seine, drew new plans for a ship which would be able to fulfill all of Livingston's demands. For an amateur, it would have been a gesture of outright ignorance; in Fulton it showed the daring of a man who felt himself in perfect control of a prodigious talent.

He placed an order with Boulton and Watt for an engine with a cylinder of 24-inch diameter and 4-foot stroke. This would require a boiler 20 feet long, 7 feet high, and 8 feet wide. The price of the engine was $2,670. His drawings showed a hull with a length of 150 feet, a 12-foot beam (later remodeled to 18 feet), and 7-foot–deep hold.

England at that time had placed a strict embargo on the export of any machinery, in an effort to keep other countries from benefiting by her own inventions. In addition, no trained workman or artisan was allowed to emigrate for fear that he would be taking with him plans of an English machine to be built abroad. Only two Boulton and Watt engines had been allowed to leave the country—one to the French government for the Paris Waterworks, and one to Aaron Burr for a water company. Fulton did not specify the use for which he wanted the engine; but the Boulton and Watt people were sufficiently astute to interpret Fulton's design. It was more than ever a mark of Fulton's diplomacy and prestige that he managed to get the engines built and shipped.

3. THE BUILDING OF THE CLERMONT

In the meantime, Livingston got a two-year extension on his charter. The year 1807 was his final deadline. Fulton sailed from Falmouth in October, 1806, with little less than a year to fulfill the contract. In New York, he came face to face with the facts of Livingston's prior commitment with Stevens. Also he himself married into the family that winter. With a time limit to beat, with new family responsibilities, aware that the heads of two powerful families related to him and to each other were at swords' points and that he himself was the focus of contention, he asked only for peace. Livingston too wanted to compromise, and it was at this point that Stevens was offered his third interest for $600, and that Stevens refused.

Livingston was uneasily aware that he had misjudged Stevens. Six years earlier when he had left America, the Stevens he knew was still a self-taught amateur slowly feeling his way one step at a time. Compared with that Stevens, Fulton had been a giant. But in those six years, while Fulton had turned his energies to submarines and torpedoes, Stevens had progressed steadily along the one line he had selected for himself. In steam engines and steamboats, he was now capable of fulfilling the agreement he had made with his brother-in-law ten years earlier. He was actually at work on such a vessel—there was no rea-son that Stevens could find why the *Phoenix* should not be the one to make the critical run.

Yet while Fulton was willing, as a new member of the family, to make peace, he was still a creative man with absolute faith in his own plans. He had not built by rule of thumb or from simple copying of the *Charlotte Dundas*. By this time, he too had both his pride and talent invested in the *Katherine of Clermont;* and he would not agree that Stevens' designs were preferable to his own.

By August, 1807, the installation was completed, and under her own power the ship rounded New York and reached the Jersey shore. More adjustments were made, and within a week, Fulton was ready to make his trial run for the public. In spite of his prestige and the backing of the Livingston power, he was still a "steamboat" man in the days when it was the synonym for impracticality. Here is his own account of the first steamboat passage from New York to Albany and back:

"When I was building my first steamboat at New York the project was viewed by the public with contempt as a visionary scheme. My friends were civil. They listened with patience but with incredulity.

"As I had occasion to pass daily to and from the building yard, I often loitered unknown near the idle groups of strangers and heard the loud laugh at my expense, the dry jest, the wise calculation of losses and expenditures; the dull and endless repetition of the *Fulton Folly*. At length, the day arrived for the

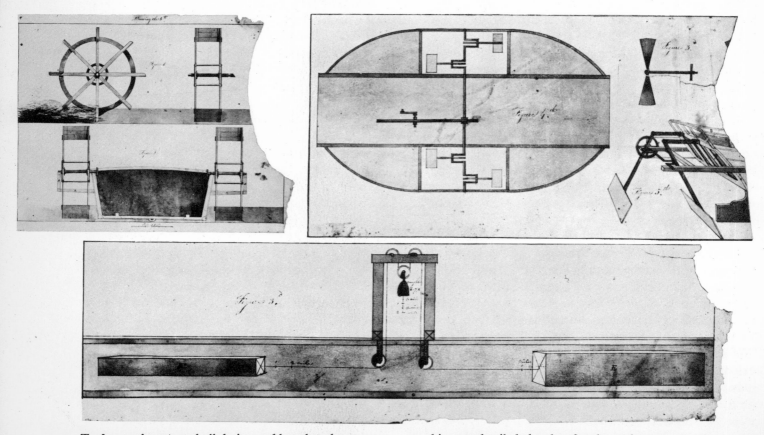

Tank experiments on hull design and length-to-beam ratio preceded his design of the *Clermont*. He drew his own detailed sketches for the various means of locomotion claimed in his patent.

experiment. I invited many friends to go on board and witness the first successful trip. I was well aware that there were many reasons to doubt of my success. The machinery (like Fitch's before) was new and ill made, and unexpected difficulties might reasonably present themselves from other causes. My friends were in groups about the deck. They were silent. The signal was given, and the boat moved a short distance, then stopped. I could distinctly hear repeated, 'I told you it was so; it was a foolish scheme; I wish we were well out of it.'

"I stated that if they would indulge me for half an hour, I would either go on or abandon the voyage for that time. I went below and discovered that the cause was a slight maladjustment of some of the work.

"In a short period, the boat was again put in motion. She continued to move on. We left New York, we passed through the romantic and ever-varying scenery of the Highlands; we descried the clustering houses of Albany; we reached its shores; and then, when all seemed achieved, it was then doubted if it could be done again; or if done, it was doubted if it could be of any great value."

The Clermont was 150 feet long, had an 18-foot beam, and 7-foot depth of hold. She displaced 100 tons. Speed: five miles an hour. Of many pictures, this is probably the most accurate. Below is Fulton's own drawing of the Boulton and Watt engine drive system. The piston was 24 inches in diameter, and had a 4-foot stroke. Boiler was rectangular, 20 feet long, 8 feet wide.

The Chancellor Livingston, built in 1815, was one of sixteen steamboats designed by Fulton before his death.

4. ROBERT FULTON'S
BITTER, TARDY VICTORY

The run to Albany took thirty-two hours, and the boat lay over several days for repairs. To prove the upward passage was no accident, the time to steam down river to New York was only thirty hours. The elapsed time, including the layover, was five days. Pine wood was the fuel used.

There was so little interest in the passage that both Fulton and Livingston had to write to the papers and furnish them with an account. Livingston then proved his worth as a backer. He had his twenty-year monopoly and he determined to make it pay off. With all his power, he called steamboat travel and its possibilities to the attention of the public, and very shortly the line began to pay. They made $16,000 the first year. The *Clermont* was enlarged and the engine improved. The legislature passed an amendment to the monopoly act, adding five years for each new vessel built and put into service. The *Raritan* and the *Car of Neptune* were then added to the service, along with several others.

From the very beginning, the monopoly ran into trouble. Other builders simply disregarded it. Fulton's designs were pirated from under his nose. In those days when business competition had a far more muscular meaning than later, attempts were made to wreck his boats; physical violence was the rule rather than the exception. The law courts saw more of Fulton than did the shipyards.

He died less than a decade later, in 1815. In the intervening years he had built fifteen more steamers for various other lines and other countries. He also fulfilled his earliest interest in naval armaments by designing and building the first steamship of war, the *Demologos* or the *Fulton the First* for service against the British in the War of 1812. A federal government was no more anxious to pay claims against them than rival steamship men; and not until 1846 did the government pay Fulton's grandchildren for the inventor's services and expenses the sum of $76,300.

Fulton's last official act as an engineer before he died was to examine, amend and approve the plans for the world's longest canal, one that would connect the West through the Great Lakes with New York harbor; the greatest feat of engineering a new country could possibly undertake.

After Fulton's death, the steamboat monopoly was attacked more vigorously and was finally broken. The Hudson and all other rivers were open to anyone, and the thesis that the federal government had control over the nation's waterways, a right superior to that of the states, was pronounced by Chief Justice Marshall.

By 1825, steamship travel was so widely accepted that few people remembered the time when they had scoffed at the idea. Fulton, dead, was almost an object of reverence. That he was the engineer who had given reality to the preceding work of countless others was simplified to the statement that he was *the* inventor, as if every detail of the idea of steam locomotion had originated completely with him in a moment of genius. As naïve as the myth was, it served a purpose. The first two decades of the century had made America nakedly aware of all its lacks in the mechanical arts. A new profession was appearing in the American social life; and just as George Washington had been made the inspiration of generations of boys who wanted to become lawyers and politicians, so Robert Fulton was being held up as proof that Americans could make anything they turned their hands to, and make it better than anyone else in the world.

The brief passage of the *Phoenix* over the ocean had gone almost unnoticed because of the fixed idea that steamboating was designed for the flat calm water of rivers and canals. The English, being outstripped by the brilliant sailing records of the American clipper ships, were the first to attempt regular ocean travel. America paid little attention. The great rivers had at last become navigable; and Robert Fulton, who had worked for three different governments, had unwittingly turned America's eyes inward to the inland waterways.

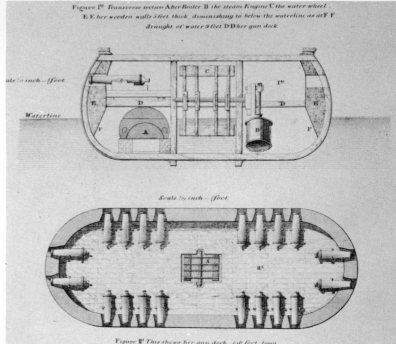

The **Demologos** was a floating fort, the first naval steamship. Its paddle was between double hulls. The purchase of this ship was another blow to Stevens, who had designed a steam-driven ram.

The **Demologos** was launched at New York on October 29, 1814, and was formally christened *Fulton the First*.

DeWitt Clinton

Canvass White

Benjamin Wright

James Geddes

Miserable roads, like the Cumberland, made canals attractive because of unlimited load-carrying capacity and smoothness.

THE ERIE CANAL

1. THE BACKGROUND

There could be no Union without commerce among the several states. As long as the settlements clustered about the river mouths, small sloops and coasters were able to handle what traffic there was. With the slow infiltration into the Wilderness, the navigable streams were left behind, and goods could be moved only by pack train. The turnpikes were few and so bad that people traveled only on matters of life and death, and goods doubled in cost for every few miles on the way to market.

A century earlier, England and France had solved the transportation problem by means of canals that threaded the interior of each country. After the Revolution, America too began to make the same effort.

The first true canal in the country was built in South Carolina—the Santee Canal connecting the Santee River with the headwater of Cooper River which in turn emptied into Charleston harbor. A Swedish engineer, Christian Senf, was brought over; and with one hundred and ten slaves and freemen, one-third of whom were women, working for fifteen pounds a year, he singlehandedly engineered twenty-two miles of canal that rose and fell one hundred and three feet through ten locks. Work began in 1793 and was finished in 1800, at a cost of one million, one hundred dollars. Eventually the canal failed because it was fed by insufficient water at the summit level.

The second attempt was the famous Middlesex Canal in Massachusetts, begun in 1793 and completed ten years later, connecting the Merrimac River to the Concord River and Boston harbor. It was twenty-seven and a quarter miles long, with seven aqueducts, fifty bridges, and twenty locks. The total cost was $613,000 and labor was paid ten dollars a month and board.

William Weston, an English engineer brought over to Philadelphia for the Schuylkill Canal was called upon to engineer the Middlesex project; ten years later, when New York State finally undertook its great project, so little was known of engineering or engineers in America that New York again called on Weston and offered him a fee of $10,000. By this time, Weston felt himself too old to return to America.

There were no American engineers. The Canal Commission established by the New York Legislature, bolstered by the forceful leadership of DeWitt Clinton, had to improvise and invent; and so by the grace of the Canal Commission of the State of New York, their own native intelligence, and some experience as land surveyors, James Geddes, Benjamin Wright, and Charles Brodhead became officially the first American engineers.

Geddes was fifty-four years old, Wright was forty-six. They had both been county judges, and they became judges in the same way they became engineers: they had been frontier surveyors. The man who could settle vital boundary disputes was a man of prestige.

Construction on the canal was divided into three departments: the western section was put in charge of Geddes, the middle section was given to Wright, and Brodhead engineered the east. The first estimate of costs ran to $4,926,738.

The canal was the first American school of engineering; and after its completion, civil engineering truly became a recognized profession. The most famous names in early American science and engineering were all those of men who had served their apprenticeship on the building of the canal: John B. Jervis, Horatio Allen, David S. Bates, Joseph Henry, Canvass White, Nathan S. Roberts, and Ezra Cornell.

The life-long feud between Robert Livingston and John Stevens, surely the most pregnant two-man argument in American history, having shaped the federal constitution, the 1793 patent law, and steamboat design, also raged over the question of whether or not the canal ought to be built. Stevens, now an elderly man by ordinary standards, was merely reaching his prime as an engineer. In the years before the canal was built, he sent long memoranda to DeWitt Clinton and the members of the Canal Commission, pointing out that the cost of the canal would never be paid back, that a steam-powered railroad could be built across the entire state for less than the cost of the canal, and that freight could be carried for one-third the projected rate on the canal.

Livingston took the opposite side. At this point, no railroad of any kind had ever been built anywhere except in mines and quarries, however much talk there might be about such projects. While such a canal would be a stupendous undertaking, at least the major points of the engineering had been worked out. An infinite number of such details, most of them not even foreseeable at the time, would have to be solved for a railroad. Clinton made the canal project an issue in 1817 and, immediately after his inauguration, he broke ground at Rome, New York—on July Fourth.

As always, both men were partially in the right. As Stevens predicted, the canal was a financial loss on a dollar and cents basis. Once railroading came, the day of the canal was doomed. As Livingston maintained, on the other hand, twenty years passed before the day finally came; in those twenty years the canal had turned New York City into the first harbor in America, and the wealth developed in the West so far exceeded the $7,143,789 cost of the canal that the state as a whole never felt the trivial loss.

At Lockport a deep cut was made through rock, with the aid of blasting and makeshift derricks to hoist the rubble.

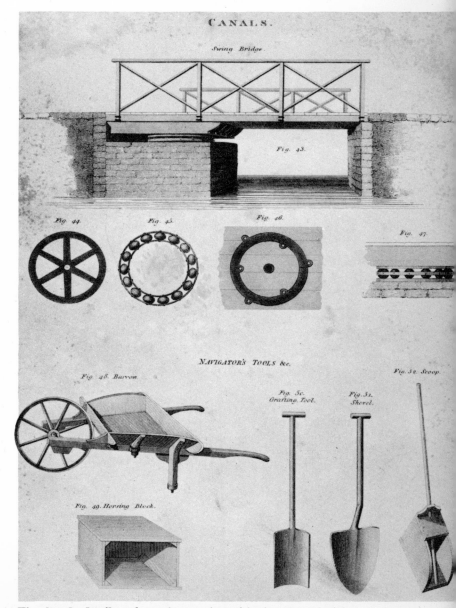

Five hundred miles of canal were dug with shovels and picks. There was much suffering among laborers from malaria.

Lockport, as it looked in all its glory to the eye of an American artist. Lockport became one of New York State's most important towns during the canal's lifetime. The cascade of locks was one of the spectacles of America.

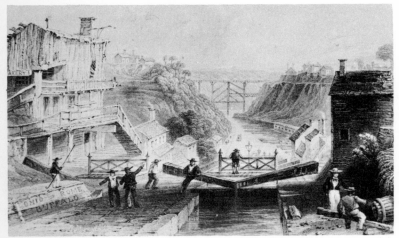

The locks from above; an English artist's view. Foreigners saw all the rough work that Americans were blind to.

Keep to the left was the rule when going through the locks. Barges were towed at a walk by one, two, or three horses.

2. LOCKS AND AQUEDUCTS

A canal is a level highway that has the unique property of continually smoothing its own surface. Canals are not laid along the bottoms of creeks and streams, but are cut into fresh ground which is reinforced beneath. Most American canals are shallow. The Erie was four feet deep, forty-two feet wide at the top, twenty-eight feet wide at the bottom. To keep the canal level, eighteen aqueducts had to be built over streams, rivers, and valleys. A sight as famous to tourists as Niagara was the aqueduct across the Genesee River which was eight hundred and four feet long and was supported by eleven arches.

Where the level of the ground rose or fell, locks which raised or lowered the barges about ten feet at a time, had to be built. On the main line of the Erie, there were twenty-four locks, each fifteen feet wide and ninety feet long. Lockport was the place of sharpest descent, with seven double locks.

Canvass White, who began as Judge Wright's assistant in surveying, was the only man on the job who had any previous knowledge of canals as built abroad. When he was twenty-seven, he went to England for a year, walking more than two thousand miles along the canal routes, inspecting every detail and making drawings. He returned in the spring of 1818 at a time when the engineers were trying to standardize the method of lock construction. The final decision was to use stone blocks, the joints to be pointed with hydraulic cement which had to be im-

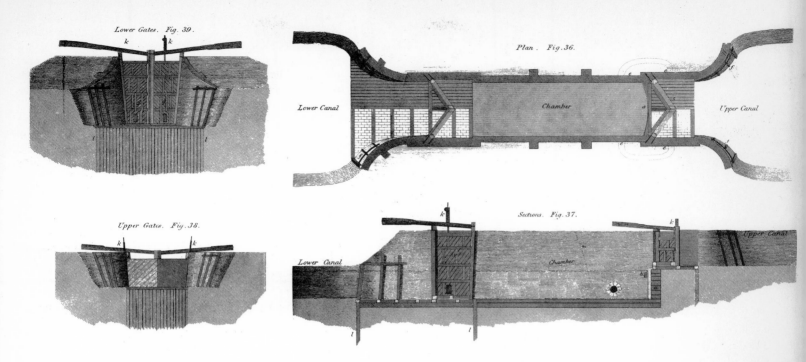

Lower Gates. Fig. 39.
Plan. Fig. 36.
Lower Canal
Chamber
Upper Canal
Upper Gates. Fig. 38.
Sections. Fig. 37.
Lower Canal
Chamber
Upper Canal

Lock details in the 1815 *Edinburgh Encyclopedia* were about all the amateur canal builders had for construction

reference. The first American engineering textbook appeared in the 1820's, written by Captain Mahan, of West Point.

ported at great expense from England.

However, while White was prospecting along the route in Madison County, he came across a lime rock which he was able to convert into a hydraulic cement as good as the imported material. He applied for a patent, permitting its use however to the Canal Commission for a just compensation, which of course he never got. The name hydraulic cement soon passed out of use, and the substance was called concrete.

White, a man who started as a frontier country boy in Oneida County, became a man of delicate and elegant appearance, famous for the quiet manner with which he promised near-impossibilities. On the very day of the opening of the canal, as the official barge began the first passage, the water level between Little Falls and Canajoharie was very low due to the porous bed. White said casually that a river near Port Plain would have to be raised nine feet with a nine-hundred-foot dam, and a feeder ditch run over the canal. When he was asked how long all this would take, he said, "Oh, a few weeks."

He had on hand only the native timber and stones. The whole job was finished in less than sixty days. The canal cut the time of travel between Buffalo and Albany from twenty to ten days; freight charges fell from twenty-two dollars per ton in 1825 to four dollars per ton in 1835 because of the astronomical increase in traffic between East and West; and passengers were able to travel a mile and a half an hour for a cent and a half a mile. A flood of emigrants to the West began their journey by canal.

Rivers and valleys presented a real problem. Aqueducts must be level, watertight, and strong enough to support the water.

Genesee Aqueduct, 800 feet long, was a marvel for European visitors, along with Niagara Falls and the slave markets.

Said a contemporary newspaper: "The canal connecting the Great Lakes of North America with the Atlantic Ocean is finished. On Wednesday, at 10 A.M., October 25, 1825, the waters of Lake Erie were admitted at Buffalo, and the first boat from the lake commenced its voyage to New York. This joyful event was announced to the citizens of the state by the roar of cannon planted in a continuous line

Governor Clinton was on the first barge to travel the Erie.

The opening of the canal was the most exciting event since the end of the war. From Buffalo across the entire state and down the Hudson River there was one long crescendo of celebration. New York harbor was so jammed with ships, ferries, and steamers that one could almost walk from boat to boat. The fireworks lasted all night. New York was hysterical with pride; the entire nation overnight transformed the much-ridiculed Clinton's Ditch into the Great Canal. The transformation in mood was under way— Americans could do anything they turned their hand to, and do it a dam site better than anyone else!

3. CANAL TRAVEL—QUIET, SMOOTH, COMFORTABLE, BUT SLOW

The junction of the Erie and Northern Canals, as painted in 1834 by John Hall, illustrates the busy canal life.

Buffalo was a town of only a few buildings when the canal opened. Within a few years, it grew a hundredfold.

The leisurely pace allowed plenty of time for reading, or talking, or just sitting quietly and thinking.

along the banks of the canal and of the Hudson at intervals of about eight miles, and extending from Buffalo to Sandy Hook, a distance of about 544 miles. The cannon were fired in succession, commencing at Buffalo at the moment of the entrance of the boat into the canal, and the intelligence thus communicated reached this city precisely at twenty minutes past eleven o'clock, at which time a national salute was fired from the Battery, and this acknowledgment that we had received the intelligence was then immediately returned by the same line of cannon to Buffalo. Thus the work is finished; the longest canal in the world is completed in the short space of eight years, by the single state of New York, a state which seventy years ago was a wilderness, thinly peopled by a little more than one hundred thousand souls."

By 1840, forty-five hundred miles of canals were built, forming the highway over which Eastern manufactures moved west in exchange for raw materials.

Wedding of the waters: Clinton pours Lake Erie water into New York Bay.

4. THE ENGINEERING SCHOOL OF THE ERIE CANAL

For almost half a century, the only formal course in engineering was given at West Point by Captain Mahan, the father of the famous naval historian. Mahan was given leave from the Army to study engineering abroad, and his text, *Mechanical Philosophy,* was the standard until after the Civil War. He introduced the idea of banked curves for railways, which had been developed by the French, to America, even though American railroading was to precede French efforts.

Apart from West Point, Americans had to learn the hard way. Those who worked on the Erie Canal went on, in the next decade, to build the American railroads. Along the canals and waterways, Cleveland, Cincinnati, Buffalo, Chi-

cago, and St. Louis became prosperous towns while New York, Philadelphia, Boston, and Baltimore thrived as the seaport termini.

Other engineering feats performed by the graduates of the Erie Canal were the dredging of New York harbor to accommodate the greatly increased traffic, bridge building, and the laying of telegraph lines.

The men who were to build America in the first half of the nineteenth century lived the same colorful easy life as did the boatmen and adventurers of the canal who moved back and forth across the state, all of them figures of romance to the country people to whom the "Canawl" had brought the wondrous outside world.

Even after the railroads opened, people liked the smoothness of canal travel. Night and day, the barges kept moving.

Green seed cotton was easy to grow and harvest, but the crop was useless until Whitney arrived and built a machine to separate the tenacious seeds from the lint.

ELI WHITNEY

1. "HE CAN MAKE ANYTHING"

Of all the post-Revolutionary Americans who grew up without knowing the name for what they felt within themselves, Eli Whitney had the most tortuous career. Yet more than any other one man, he shaped the opposing faces of both the North and South for a half-century to come.

By 1790 slavery was a declining institution in America. Apart from tobacco, rice, and a special strain of cotton that could be grown only in very few places, the South really had no money crop to export. Sea Island cotton, so named because it grew only in

Eli Whitney, by Samuel F. B. Morse. Endless patent troubles had made him uncharacteristically morose.

very sandy soil along the coast, was a recent crop and within a short time was being cultivated wherever it found favorable conditions. Tobacco was a land waster, depleting the soil within very few years. Land was so cheap that tobacco planters never bothered to reclaim the soil by crop rotation—they simply found new land farther west. The other crops—rice, indigo, corn, and some wheat—made for no great wealth. Slaves cost something, not only to buy but to maintain; and some Southern planters thought that conditions had reached a point where a slave's labor no longer paid for his maintenance.

Jefferson and Washington were not untypical of their times in their attitude towards slavery; it was a cruel system, and the sooner the South was free of it, the better everyone would be. Some slaves were freed; and many masters, including the more humane, planned on manumission at their own deaths.

Whitney came south in 1793, when the Southern planters were in their most desperate plight. In ten days he worked the most fateful revolution in a regional economy that had ever occurred. Floods and earthquakes are cataclysmic; but their effects are forgotten and the scarred earth heals. Whitney's cataclysmic invention was the start of an avalanche. In the South, nothing was ever to be the same again.

Whitney's boyhood was precocious in a way that his neighbors could not comprehend. He had an instinctive understanding of mechanisms. It was a medium in which he could improvise and create in exactly the same way that a poet handles words or a painter uses color.

During his youth, the tall, heavy-shouldered boy with large hands and a gentle manner was a blacksmith, a nail maker on a machine he made at home; and at one time, he was the country's sole maker of ladies' hatpins.

In his early twenties, Whitney determined to attend Yale College, so unusual a step for anyone not preparing for either the law or theology that his parents

More time was consumed in making the wire than in stringing it because the proper kind of wire was nonexistent.

To do the work of the fingers which pulled out the lint, Whitney had a drum rotate past the sieve, almost touching it. On the surface of the drum, fine, hook-shaped wires projected which caught at the lint from the seed. The restraining wires of the sieve held the seeds back while the lint was pulled away. A rotating brush which turned four times as fast as the hook-covered drum cleaned the lint off the hooks. Originally Whitney planned to use small circular saws instead of the hooks, but the saws were unobtainable. That was all there was to Whitney's cotton gin; and it never became any more complicated.

Whitney gave a demonstration of his first model before a few friends. In one hour, he turned out the full day's work of several workers. With no more than the promise that Whitney would patent the machine and make a few more, the men who had witnessed the demonstration immediately ordered whole fields to be planted with green seed cotton. Word got around the district so rapidly that Whitney's workshop was broken open and his machine examined. Within a few weeks, more cotton was planted than Whitney could possibly have ginned in a year of making new machines.

objected. He was twenty-three before he got away from home and twenty-seven when he received his degree, almost middle-aged in the eyes of his classmates. Again the most serious drawback facing him was that no profession existed suited to a man of his talents. Whitney settled for teaching (he had taught while attending Yale), and accepted a position as a tutor in South Carolina that promised a salary of one hundred guineas a year.

He sailed on a coasting packet that took a few passengers, among whom was the widow of the Revolutionary general, Nathanael Greene. The Greenes had settled in Savannah after the war. When Whitney arrived, he found to his disgust that the promised salary was going to be halved. He not only refused to take the post, but decided to give up teaching as well. Mrs. Greene invited him to accompany her to her plantation and read law. In the meantime, he could make himself useful in one way or another helping the plantation manager, Phineas Miller, whom she intended to marry. Miller was a Yale alumnus, a few years older than Whitney. Whitney accepted the offer.

Shortly after he settled down, some neighbors visited the plantation and, as usual, fell to discussing the bad times. There was no money crop; the only variety of cotton that would grow in that neighborhood was the practically useless green seed variety. Ten hours of hand work was needed to separate one pound of lint from three pounds of the small tough seeds. Until some kind of machine could be devised to do the work, the green seed cotton was little better than a weed.

"Gentlemen," said Mrs. Greene, "apply to my young friend, Mr. Whitney. He can make anything."

At the urging of Mrs. Greene and Phineas Miller, Whitney watched the cotton cleaning and studied the hand movements. One hand held the seed while the other hand teased out the short strands of lint. The machine he designed simply duplicated this.

To take the place of a hand holding the seed, he made a sort of sieve of wires stretched lengthwise.

Embroidery frame, built by Whitney for Nathanael Greene's widow, impressed her with his exceptional mechanical ability.

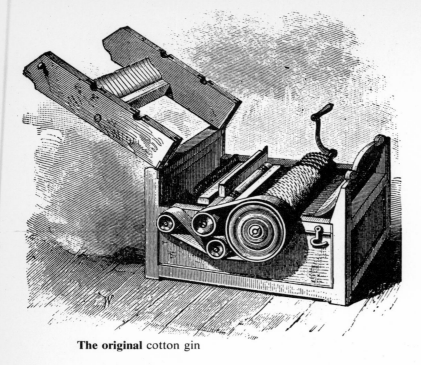

The original cotton gin

2. THE COTTON AVALANCHE

The usual complaint of an inventor was that people were reluctant to give his machine a chance. Whitney's complaint was just the opposite. Before he had a chance to complete his patent model, or to secure protection, the prematurely planted cotton came to growth. With harvests pressing on them, the planters had no time for fine points of law or ethics. Whitney's machine was pirated without a qualm.

Whitney had gone into partnership with Miller. The agreement was that Whitney was to go north to New Haven, secure his patent, and begin manufacturing machines, while Miller was to remain in the South and see that the machines were placed. Having no precedent of royalty arrangement to go on, the partners' first plan was that no machine was to be

Whitney watching the cotton gin—a retrospective wood engraving by an unknown but highly imaginative artist.

sold, but simply to be installed for a percentage of the profit earned. Since they had no idea that cotton planting would take place in epidemic proportions, they did not know they were asking for an agreement that would have earned them millions of dollars a year. It had been Miller's idea to take one pound of every three of cotton, and the planters were furious. Cotton, one of the easiest growing crops, was coming up out of the ground in white floods that threatened to drown everyone.

By the time Whitney and Miller were willing to settle for outright sale or even a modest royalty on every machine made by someone else, the amount of money due them was astronomical. He and Miller were now deeply in debt and their only recourse was to go to court; but every court they entered was in cotton country. At length in 1801, eight years after the holocaust started, Miller and Whitney were willing to settle for outright grants from cotton-growing states in return for which the cotton gin would be public property within the boundaries. Even at that, only one state made a counter offer of half the asking price. Whitney accepted the price of $50,000 for which he received a down payment of $20,000 and no more.

The following year, North Carolina followed along in a slightly different fashion, levying a tax on every gin in the state. This sum, less 6 per cent for collection, went to Whitney and Miller; it came to another $20,000. Tennessee paid about $10,000, and there was another $10,000 from other states. The gross income was $90,000, most of which was owed for legal costs and other expenses. In 1803, the states repudiated their agreements and sued Whitney for all the money paid to him and his partner. That year alone the cotton crop earned close to ten million dollars for the planters. The price of slaves had doubled, and men's consciences no longer troubled them. Manumission was a forgotten word.

The following year, 1804, Whitney applied to the federal Congress for relief and, by one vote, was saved from total ruin. He was penniless, his patent was worthless, he was thirty-nine years old, and most of the past ten years had been wasted either in courtrooms or in traveling from one court to another.

He turned his back on cotton, the cotton gin, and the South forever.

Returning to New Haven, he resolved to start over. He did not know at first in which direction to go, but he was about to enter the less celebrated but most fruitful time of his life; and just as he had changed the face of the South, he was now about to mold the face of the North into a form it has kept ever since. He was to lay the foundation and invent the techniques for what has become known as the "American System of Manufacture."

THE REBIRTH OF SLAVERY

Because of the lack of a money crop, slavery was a declining institution in the South. The invention of the cotton gin for the first time made slavery really profitable, and within two years the price of slaves doubled. Although the importation of slaves was forbidden by law in 1808, smugglers continued the trade on an increasing scale. By mid-century a man purchased for $15 in Africa might bring as much as $1,500, retail. Below is the cargo stowage plan of the 90-foot French brig *Vigilante*.

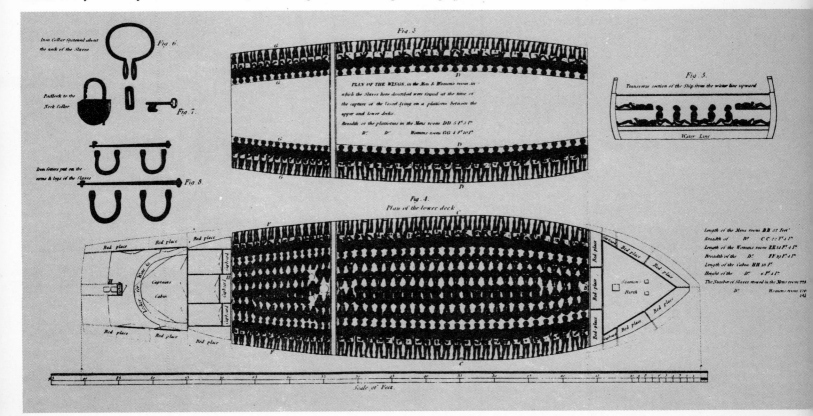

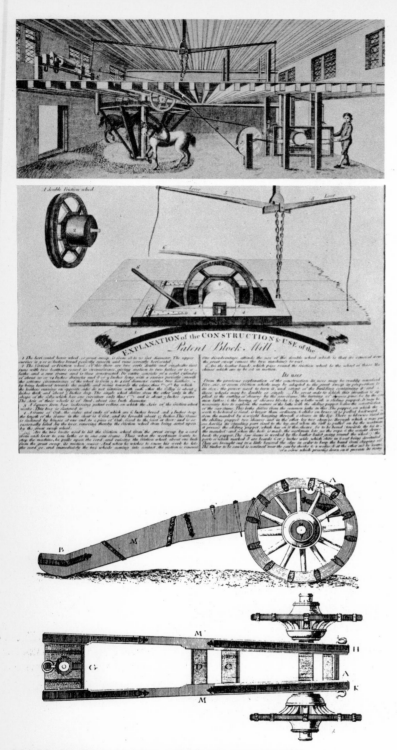

MASS PRODUCTION BEFORE WHITNEY

Whitney did not invent the idea of making an article using inter-changeable parts; he perfected a plan that was already in men's minds. The first man on record with the idea of manufacturing an article with interchangeable parts was a French artillery general, Gribeauval, who in 1765 suggested that cannon carriages be stand-ardized. The limits of tolerance for the heavy pieces were not very great, and he was able to carry out his plan on a small scale.

In England, the first application of mass production to an article with interchangeable parts was made by Joseph Bramah, the great machine designer. His "Patent Block Mill" was set up in a naval war shop to turn out blocks for naval rigging.

The man who first suggested the idea for use in America was Thomas Jefferson, who picked it up in France.

3. WHITNEY CHANGED THE FACE OF THE NORTH

In the early American republic, there was only a handful of skilled machinists. Better than anyone, Whitney knew how small that number was. He then proceeded to invent something far more important than a machine; he invented a system of manufacture which would permit an unskilled man to turn out a product that would be just as good as one made by the most highly trained machinist. He put this system to work on the manufacture of rifles. Without a fac-tory, without even a machine, he persuaded the U. S. government to give him an order for ten thou-sand muskets at $13.40 each, to be delivered within two years. Only Whitney's prestige as the inventor of the cotton gin could have swayed the government to make such a commitment. From anyone other than Whitney, the claim would have sounded insane.

Until then, every rifle had been made by hand from stock to barrel; but the parts of one gun did not fit any other gun, nor did anyone expect them to. It was Whitney's idea to make all the parts of his rifles so nearly identical that the machined parts could be interchangeable from one gun to another. He did this by designing a rifle. For each part of the gun, a template was made. This was identical in prin-ciple to the dress pattern. A man would follow this pattern in cutting a piece of metal. Whitney then had to invent a machine that would allow a man to cut metal according to a pattern. The metal plate to be

WHITNEY INTRODUCED THE FIRST MODERN MACHINE TOOLS

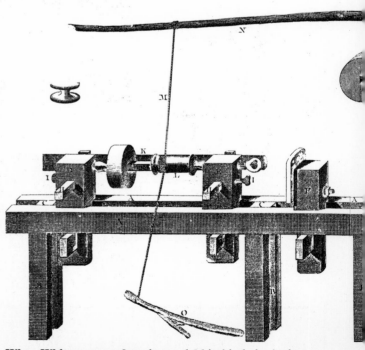

When Whitney was a boy, he worked in his father's shop and became a master mechanic. This spring-pole lathe, driven by foot power, was typical of the tools he used.

cut was clamped to a table, the template to be followed would be clamped on top of the metal, and a cutting tool would follow the outlines of the template. Ordinarily, a chisel would be such a tool. A chisel, however, required skill. Whitney took an iron wheel and cut teeth into the circumference so that it looked like a gear. However, the edge of each tooth was curved slightly, sharpened to a cutting edge and then hardened. As the wheel rotated, one tooth after another came into play. Each tooth was then a separate chisel, but each chisel stroke was exactly the same, and the rotation of the wheel gave a steady cutting stroke. This wheel with its cutting teeth was then driven around the edge of the template. No great mechanical skill was needed.

This invention, subordinate to the entire system, was itself a major innovation. It was called the milling machine, and remained unchanged in principle for a century and a half. For the various duties, Whitney designed many different varieties of millers. Before a single workman walked into his factory, Whitney worked out and built all the machinery he would need for his method of production.

Whitney's New Haven friends had put up bonds amounting to thirty thousand dollars. He himself borrowed from the New Haven bank the sum of ten thousand dollars. The money involved in the order, $134,000, made it the biggest single financial transaction in the country. At the end of the first year, he was just getting into production, a marvelous feat by any standards; but instead of the four thousand

muskets he had promised, there were only five hundred to show. A commission from Washington handed in an unfavorable report and Whitney's backers looked drawn and thoughtful.

Almost eight years was required for Whitney to fill the order, because practice still showed many gaps in his system. The number of details seemed endless. However, most of the ten thousand were turned out in the last two years. In 1811, Whitney took an order for fifteen thousand, and these were turned out within only two years.

Whitney was a man on a large scale. There would have been every reason for him to have been embittered by his experience with the cotton gin, but he was too full of the essence of true creativeness. His letters to Fulton describing his experiences are full of remembered anger, but it was the anger of a man who was fighting. His friendships were warm and they lasted. He gambled on his talent, but in the way an artist does.

Like Hamilton, he believed that the factory was to be a benefit to America. Unlike Benjamin Thompson, he did not despise the people who worked in his factories. He also invented a pattern for the relationship between factory owner and the working hands; but of all his inventions this was the shortest-lived. Within a decade after his death, the American factory began to turn into something quite different from Whitney's design.

The same forces that overwhelmed him in the days of the cotton gin were to engulf the American factory.

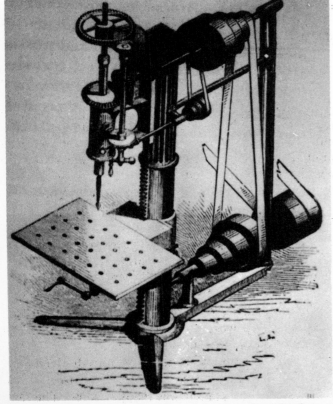

Whitney's factory was the first to use mass-production techniques. He used power-driven precision tools, such as this drill press, to make interchangeable gun parts.

The first milling machine worthy of the name was developed by Whitney. It had a multiple-edged cutting wheel, and a movable work bed, driven by worm gear and screw thread.

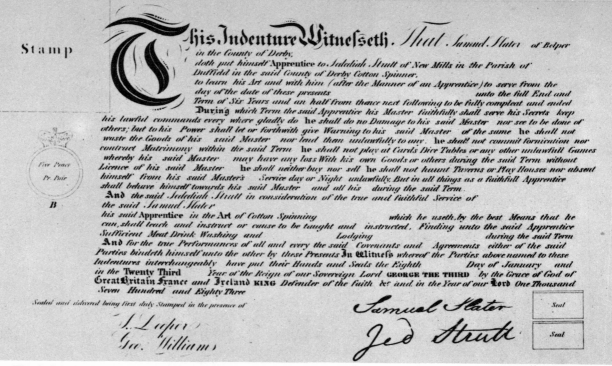

The indentured servant in 18th-century England was bound to his master who boarded him from 4 to 7 years.

THE FIRST SUCCESSFUL FACTORY

1. SAMUEL SLATER

Washington visited the first cotton mill, but it failed, as did most of the early factories.

The first true factory in America was not a native product. Before Samuel Slater opened his mill in Pawtucket, there were many shops which employed a number of hands; but a factory is more than many people working together under the same roof. The American factory, as Eli Whitney designed it, was the third step taken in a changing attitude towards the manufacture of goods.

Until the late eighteenth century, the form of the factory, or manufactory, was simply an enlargement of the way in which a single artisan made every part himself. When he received more orders than he himself could fill, he took in a helper who learned first by doing the simplest tasks, and then in turn reached the stage where he too was able to make the entire article by himself. In some cases, where very many men were employed, it was natural that certain workers would be given only those tasks at which they excelled, and the finished product would then be the result of several men's handiwork.

This was the method of work in shops from the times of antiquity, and it was not changed until late in the eighteenth century, when the division of labor became a conscious process. There could be no machinery developed to make the separate parts of a product until the artisan himself was aware that there *were* separate steps to be performed. Whitney's "American System of Manufacture" therefore could not be applied until this division of labor had taken place.

The English factory system, popularly identified with the cotton mills, was based on this rationalization of labor. The separate steps of carding, roving, spinning, and weaving were assigned to different groups of individuals all working under the same roof, and Arkwright was the first man to drive the primitive spinning wheels and looms by drive belts from a water wheel. Even this simple step was so revolutionary that the "water loom"—and a powered loom—became a magical phrase.

After the Revolution, many attempts were made to introduce factory methods in the new republic. The first cotton mill in Massachusetts was built in Beverly in 1787, but in three years it was ready to close. The fac-

Pawtucket, and for that matter all of New England, was never the same after Slater arrived and set up the first successful factory system.

tories generally failed because the machinery was inadequate, and because Americans preferred English importations. Various states offered bounties and rewards to encourage manufacture, but every effort failed. To import machinery from England was impossible because the British government refused to allow any of its new inventions to leave the country. The American states advertised their bounties in English newspapers to entice English workmen to emigrate; but that too was against the law. England was determined to keep its technological knowledge to itself.

One such advertisement by the Pennsylvania Legislature appeared in Derbyshire. It was read by young Samuel Slater, just finishing his apprenticeship. He had worked for Jedediah Strutt, a partner of Arkwright, and Slater had learned how to use and repair every machine in the factory. He asked Strutt to tell him what his future might be if he remained where he was. Strutt told him to work hard and save his money and he would get his just rewards.

He knew exactly what risks he was running by trying to leave the country. He was careful to avoid taking any sketches of machinery and he did not even tell his mother and brothers of his plans. He went to London, got his passage, and just as the vessel was preparing to leave, he wrote to his family, telling them where he was going.

In 1789 he landed in Philadelphia where he made inquiries about the true situation in the republic. He was told that a mill had recently been completed in Providence by Moses Brown, the famous Quaker merchant, and that Brown was desperately looking for a manager. Slater wrote to Brown, telling him his background and applying for the position.

Moses Brown replied at once and made this handsome offer to Slater: if he could work the machinery they had on hand, all the profits of the business less the cost and interest on the machinery were to go to Slater along with the credit as well as the advantages of perfecting the first water mill in America. In other words, Brown was willing to give the factory to Slater. There is no other record of a man applying for a job by letter and getting the entire plant by return mail.

Samuel Slater

Moses Brown

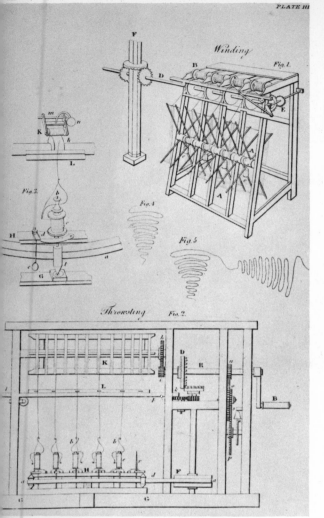

PLATE III

Winding Fig. 1.

Throwsting Fig. 2.

Intricate machinery of the English cotton mills was built by Slater from memory.

Slater mill in Webster, Mass. Slater's own house is in the center of the picture.

Treadmill ran Slater's first mill. Later, like Arkwright, he used a water wheel.

2. BRITISH KNOW-HOW IN PAWTUCKET

When Slater went to Pawtucket with Brown to inspect the machines, his rosy dreams wilted. "These will not do," he protested. "They are good for nothing in their present condition. Nor could they be made to answer."

He proposed to make a clean start and build the series of machines which were known as the "Arkwright Patent." He had brought no drawings but he had memorized the designs of the machines invented by Crompton and Hargreaves as well as Arkwright.

Most American machinists were inadequate; the only metal articles being made were scythes, anchors, horse-shoes, nails, and cannon shot. Fortunately, a Nantucket Quaker named Oziel Wilkinson then lived with his family in Pawtucket. Wilkinson was a blacksmith who had made spades and shovels in quantity for turnpike building. He had been the first to make cold-rolled nails. Slater boarded with them, and Wilkinson was willing to help. Without him, Slater would have been helpless.

Then another difficulty arose. Slater fell in love with Wilkinson's daughter Hannah. While the parents were fond of him, they disapproved of Hannah marrying outside of the Society of Friends, and they planned to send her away to school.

Slater balked, and for a while the entire future of the firm of Almy, Brown and Slater, the future of the American cotton industry, the very future of American business—all hung in the balance. Then, in the words of a contemporary biographer, Slater said: "You may send her where you please, but I will follow her to the ends of the earth!" The Wilkinsons gave in, and the wheels of the world began to move again.

On December 21, 1790, the little factory began to produce, but business was feeble. When seventy-two spindles were working and the plant had been operating for twenty months, the preference for English yarn left them with several thousand pounds that could not be moved at any price. Not until a loom was added did American cotton begin to find a market.

Ten years after Slater landed in America, Almy, Brown and Slater were doing sufficiently well to open a second factory. Scores of imitators followed, but Slater kept well in the lead, and eventually the firm established mills in New Hampshire and Massachusetts, despite the growing competition from innovators.

Drawing on his English training, Slater staffed his factory with children from four to ten years old. The machines were simple, and the parents were delighted to have their children doing something useful in pleasant surroundings. He measured his break with the English tradition by the good food and humane treatment given his hands. In England, the working children were ill-fed, beaten, driven to early drunkenness and degradation. In a time when American children were put to work around the farm as soon as they could walk, the Slater factory system was very highly rated.

Slater neither invented anything, nor improved what he brought here; but he was the first in this country to set up a system of manufacture in which the successive steps of the skilled artisan were broken down into such simple components that a group of children could outproduce the finest craftsman. It was the one system ideally suited to a country that was to be plagued by a shortage of skilled manpower for another seventy-five years. No one saw any discrepancy between such a system and the American goal of enhancing the dignity and human value of the individual. The American factory fed, clothed, and equipped men for the fight against the hostile universe; and the factory system was actually considered to be a victory for the American creed of freedom.

Mule spinning

Power loom weaving

Calico printing

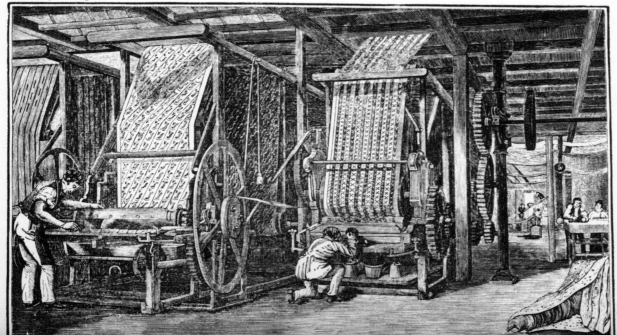

These pictures are from a book written about Slater after his death. The people are dressed in mid-century costume, even though his factories operated forty years earlier. Mule spinning was done by gaslight, an innovation. The overhead shafts were all driven by one water wheel (the largest, at the time, developed fifty horsepower). American calicos had a good home market by the time this picture was drawn, but fifty years earlier, Americans refused to buy any but English "Calcutta" cloth. Although Slater employed women, as these pictures show, most of his workers were children. He offended the community only when he started the American Sunday School for them. He was profaning the Sabbath!

THE LOWELL MILLS

Abbot Lawrence

Amos Lawrence

William Lawrence

Patrick T. Jackson

In 1814 the world's first factory to convert raw cotton into cloth by power machinery within the walls of one building was erected in Waltham, Massachusetts, by the Boston Manufacturing Company. This company had been organized the year before by Francis Cabot Lowell, a Boston importer, whose business had been ruined by the Napoleonic wars and the Embargo Act of 1807. In 1811, when he was thirty-six, he had gone traveling for his health. In England, the textile factories at Manchester made a deep impression on him, but it was still a criminal offense for an Englishman to export machinery or plans. Lowell studied all the details of power looms, and he smuggled secretly made sketches out of the country at considerable danger to himself.

On his return to Boston in 1813, he talked his enterprising brother-in-law, Patrick Tracy Jackson, into pledging part of a fortune made from the India trade for the founding of an American factory. With this promise of backing, Lowell took his smuggled sketches to a machinist, Paul Moody, and together they made revolutionary plans for a completely mechanized textile mill. In that same year, 1813, the Boston Manufacturing Company was chartered as a corporation with the huge capitalization of $300,000; and the Lowell-Moody machinery, by now so different from the original English design as to constitute a new invention, was installed in the Boston Manufacturing Company's first factory in Waltham, Massachusetts. The Lowell-Moody design called for every machine in the plant to be driven by water power.

The company's cottons successfully overcame the popular American prejudice against American-made goods, and by 1820 the company had grown so large that all the water power in Waltham was insufficient for the company's plans to expand into the manufacture and the printing of calicos—the popular name for light, colored cottons, originally imported from Calcutta.

The quest for water power brought them to the Merrimack River, where an abandoned canal lock by-passed a thirty-foot waterfall. Through agents, the Boston Manufacturing Company secretly bought the title to the canal and a huge tract of real estate along the river below the falls. The price paid for the land and the canal was about $100,000. A new company, called the Merrimack Manufacturing Company, was formed in 1822 and capitalized at $600,000. Principal stockholders were Jackson, Moody, Nathan Appleton, and several members of the Boott family. A town was organized and given the name of Lowell in honor of Francis Cabot Lowell, who had died five years earlier. Kirk Boott, who had English engineering training, was made managing director of the plant.

Production began on a large scale in 1823. By 1826, the Merrimack Company was making two million yards of cotton cloth per year. As soon as the factory was operating smoothly, the directors formed another company called "The Proprietors of the Locks and Canals" and bought from themselves—as directors of the Merrimack Company—the canal and all the land of the original purchase.

The "Proprietors" built new factories, dug canals, and sold land. What had been bought for one hundred dollars an acre, now went at one dollar per square foot. Within a short time, the city of Lowell was the textile manufacturing center of the country.

The "Proprietors" sold to each new mill the right to draw enough water in twenty-four hours to give a power of twenty-five cubic feet per second,

Lowell, Massachusetts, at Pawtucket Falls of the Merrimack River, was the first American mill city.

dropping through the thirty feet of the fall. This was equivalent to about sixty horsepower—a huge amount at the time.

In 1825, this sixty horsepower was sufficient to operate all the 3,600 spindles of an entire factory, each spindle consuming the power required a century later to light a ten-watt Christmas tree bulb. At a time when a ponderous steam engine, weighing several tons, developed the same horsepower that would later be used to drive an ordinary lawnmower, the power yield of the thirty-foot Merrimack Falls was an all-important factor in the industrialization of New England.

In 1830, a woolen factory was founded in Lowell by the Middlesex Company, of which Samuel Lawrence and William W. Stone were the principal stockholders. Other members of the Lawrence family who became prominent in textiles were Amos and Abbot, whose philanthropies in the educational field were so well known that a generation of pre-Civil War mothers named their boys Lawrence after them.

Lawrence's Middlesex Mills introduced the power loom for weaving fancy-figured woolens developed by William Crompton. Another American loom inventor was Lucius James Knowles, who had worked in the revolutionary fields of photography and electroplating before becoming interested in textiles.

By 1850, the population of the city of Lowell had grown to 32,000 people tending 300,000 spindles and 9,000 looms. In terms of productivity, Lowell's spindles and looms were superior to those of any other factory any place in the world.

Lowell was famous in its day because of its remarkable working population. Most of the workers were young girls from good farm families. The first generation of Lowell girls looked on factory work as equal in social prestige to school teaching. A few years spent in Lowell's well-paying factories was considered an education. The finest foreign authors, scientists, and educators were brought there on lecturing tours. The girls lived in dormitories that were comfortable and spacious. They learned the style of city living from the shops that sprang up on the Lowell streets, and they were made aware of high religious and ethical standards.

For a while Lowell seemed to promise America that the degrading factory system of Europe would never come here; that America was transmuting the Industrial Age into its own idealistic image. However, the depression of the 1830's drove the mill owners to the wall; and in their desperation, the relationship between the company owners and the girls deteriorated so sharply that the dream of an American factory as visualized by Eli Whitney came to an end after only a brief quarter of a century.

The early mills were model places in which to work. It was a privilege to be an employee.

Girls from the surrounding country formed the bulk of the employees.

Employee benefits included some instruction in the domestic arts and cultural lectures.

President Andrew Jackson, the representative of the common people, refused to spend government money on the kind of internal improvements which would have developed American engineering. American invention was directly affected by the depression that grew out of Jackson's war with the Bank (below). Inventions already under way were postponed for half a decade by the resulting curtailment of capital. On the other hand, sudden poverty drove McCormick and others like him to develop machines and tools they might otherwise have ignored.

PART THREE

Bright Dream— Dark Fulfillment

Hurrah! Gineral! if this don't beat skunkin I'm a nigger, only see that varmint Nick how spry he is, he runs along like a Weatherfield Hog with an onion in his mouth.

The story of America is a story of change. In the three decades from 1830 to 1860 the United States transformed itself from a backward agricultural country into one of the world's exporters of steel and wheat.

Power and wealth trebled in thirty years, but the bitter struggle for sectional control over that power and wealth caused the national mood to plummet from optimism to despair. In 1830, Americans boasted: "The Yankee Nation Can Beat All Creation!" In 1860, they asked: "Can This Nation Endure?"

The high hopefulness of the 1830's was due to the resurgence of the democratic spirit fifty years after the Revolution. The republic had finally settled down with sure confidence that it would go on forever. All the dreams embodied in the Declaration of Independence were resurrected; but while the rise of the democratic spirit in America went along with the rise of the same feelings abroad, the American system of four-year elections allowed for drastic changes in government without the violence or force expressed in the European revolutions of 1830. The 1820's had been a time of depression for many Americans. They had been frightened by the treatment they had been given by the rich. By 1830, their fear had become anger. They made Jackson president; and then made Jackson change into the kind of man they wanted.

The taste of victory sharpened the appetite for more victory; and an American dream began to emerge, although it assumed different shapes and colors depending on the individual dreamers.

The dream was called "American Perfectibility"; and it was the belief that America, of all nations in the world, was destined for the highest fulfillment that the human race could achieve. The roads to salvation were many: through politics, economics, religion, and science.

There were those who believed that America could achieve the perfect political state: the essence of democracy. The heirs of the Federalists always claimed that the common people were incapable of governing themselves. Jackson gave the nation universal male suffrage; and with that suffrage, the nation voted itself free education. Farmers, small businessmen, and mechanics had been in debt. Jackson created banks to see that they could get loans on easy terms.

Continual migration to the West opened new regions. By the 1830's, there were three distinct geographic divisions in the United States: the North, the South, the West; and while their economic demands were very different and very often in conflict, there seemed to be general agreement on one thing: "the manifest destiny of the American republic" to grow, as extremists proclaimed, from the Atlantic coast to the Pacific coast—to stretch from the North Pole to the South Pole. The western hemisphere was destined to be the perfect American republic.

When Canada's demand for more freedom from England broke out into violence, some Americans fully expected that United States troops would be welcomed by the Canadians, but the Canadians violently repulsed the Americans as invaders. The Canadians were strangely content to remain outside the republic. The puzzled Americans felt, however, that sooner or later the Canadians would come to their senses.

The situation in the South was similar. There were Southern planters who wanted Cuba annexed. Political adventurers during the 1840's, inferring the secret approval of American presidents, went to South and Central America, fomented revolution, and hoped for eventual absorption into the American republic. Most of these dreams, begun in violence, ended in failure, and the adventurers had to be publicly repudiated.

AMERICAN PERFECTIBILITY

Nevertheless, Manifest Destiny sprang from the sincere belief of the American people that they had finally found the secret of God's will. Since the American republic was the one form of government which God had ordained for all men, Americans were carrying out God's will by spreading the gospel over their half of the earth.

Still another road to perfection was social reform. America would become perfect when every man was sure of a means of livelihood, when every child was assured of education, when every American was free of debt and the economic oppression of the wealthy. This was a hangover of the early Jeffersonian dream that America was to be a country of small farms and artisans.

Mistrust of large companies was transformed into animosity against new inventions which promised to displace laborers. The 1820's had left horrible memories of unemployment. Walter Hunt invented the first true sewing machine in the middle 1830's. Because he and his daughter sincerely believed that his machine would put many seamstresses out of work, he refused to take out a patent. Some years later, Hunt—who also invented the safety pin and the paper collar—invented a breech-loading rifle and a cartridge for it, which contained its own powder charge. Hunt believed in Manifest Destiny, and so a gun that would more quickly exterminate Indians and the wild animals in the West was an invention that was useful and honorable.

Another trend at the time was the formation of the antislavery societies. The invention of the cotton gin had revived slavery which had been a declining institution at the time of the Revolution. By the 1830's, Southerners were enthusiastically defending slavery as an institution ordained by God. The North, by this time free of slaves, had begun to take a strongly humane attitude against it.

A third road to salvation was through religion. American ministers of the nineteenth century preached eighteenth-century rationalism with the emotional fervor of the great Methodist revival of 1800. Between 1800 and 1830 this religious surge had spread throughout the nation, permeating the writings of the scientists, sustaining the struggling inventors of the thirties like Goodyear, Morse, and Howe with the belief that an all-seeing Providence would guide them to success.

Perfectibility through religion had many prophets. John Humphrey Noyes of Vermont gathered a group about himself in 1848 and established a communal society in Oneida, New York. The religious perfectionist who had the most enduring influence was Joseph Smith of Palmyra, who wrote a book called *The Book of Mormon.* His followers organized the Church of Jesus Christ of Latter Day Saints, and were finally driven to the outermost wilderness on the shores of Great Salt Lake.

The fourth road to perfection was through science. Americans believed the great natural truths of the world were being revealed to men through God's goodness. When all the secrets had been revealed, then men would live in perfect peace and perfect happiness. Interest in science on a popular level was widespread. English lecturers came and were amazed at the response they received. The girls at Lowell were told about gravitation, about astronomy, about electricity. Yet for all the general interest, there were few scientists being trained and no money for research. Nevertheless, there were individuals who were so driven by curiosity and creativeness that they formed a small army that was the vanguard of American science. Their names were Henry, Audubon, Agassiz, Torrey, Draper, and Morton.

ORDINARY AMERICANS WHO WORKE

Carpenter

Cabinetmaker

The imposing Custom House on Wall Street was a symbol of America's status as an importing nation. Though Jackson's tariff policies favored the Northern manufacturers, the moneyed classes were dead against him.

ITH THEIR HANDS ELECTED JACKSON

Cobbler

Hatmaker

Mason

Farmer

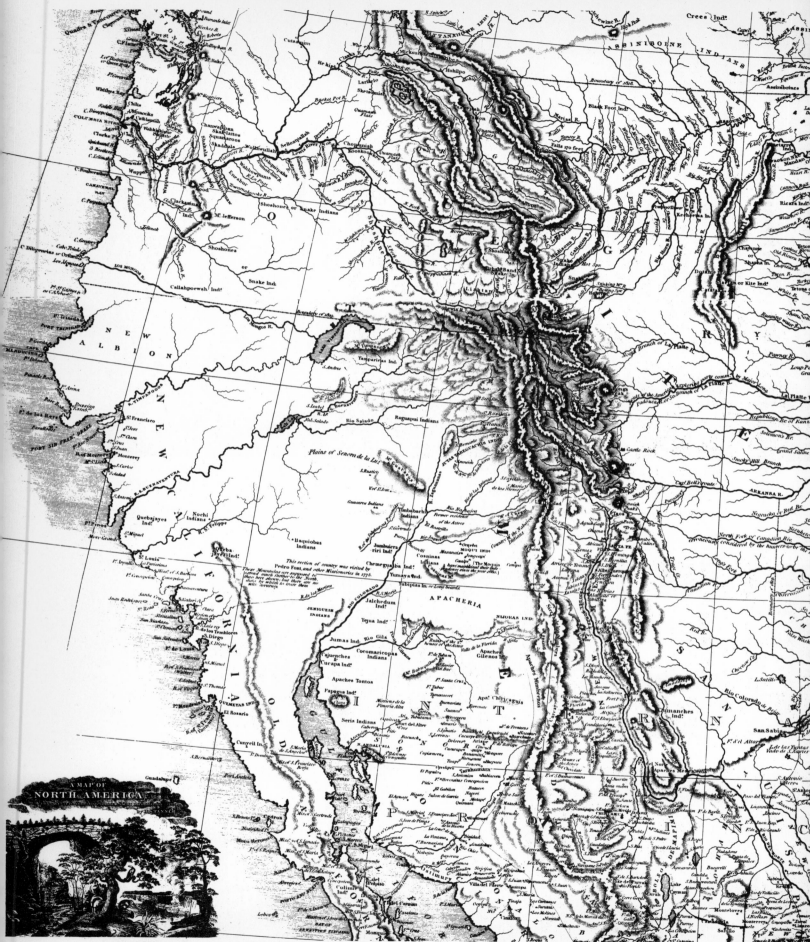

The West was an empty and incomprehensibly vast region. Although the general outlines of the Pacific coast had been charted by the China traders, and Lewis and Clark had marked the Columbia River, almost no one had more than an inkling of the endless mountain ranges and deserts that cover about one-third of the area now occupied by the United States. The easternmost ranges of the Rockies were fixed; beyond that the map makers invented rivers to their taste. The huge mineral wealth of the West was not even dreamed of by the primarily agrarian young nation.

The East looked pretty much as it does today. The plains of the Mississippi watershed were known mostly to hunters and trappers, and to the naturalists who went out to marvel at the new plants and animals. Lack of a transportation system and of a plow that would work in the sticky loam prevented any mass settlement as yet. But the constant pressure to the west soon forced the inventions that made farming possible. The rivers of the middle region suggest a road map—and with good reason, for the rivers *were* the highways, and the streams, the byroads.

95

John James Audubon

THE NATURALISTS

1. JOHN AUDUBON

Lucy Bakewell Audubon kept a store and then a school so that Audubon could paint freely.

Trapper's dress, as sketched in 1826 by himself, soon replaced ruffled satin he wore at first.

"I left home at ten o'clock in the morning, on Saturday the 11th of March, 1843, accompanied by my son Victor. I left all well, and I trust in God for the privilege and happiness of rejoining them all sometime next autumn, when I hope to return from the Yellowstone River, an expedition undertaken solely for the sake of our work on the quadrupeds of North America. The day was cold, the sun was shining, and after having visited a few friends in the city of New York, we departed for Philadelphia in the cars, and reached that place at eleven o'clock at night."

And so begins the fourth great work of the naturalist John James Audubon. He was fifty-eight years old at the time, and his masterwork, *Birds of America,* had already made him world famous.

John James Audubon was born on April 26, 1785, in Les Cayes, Santo Domingo, the natural son of a French admiral whose French wife had borne him no children. Nothing is known of the boy's true mother, for when the admiral returned to France he brought his new son home to a grateful wife who jealously raised the boy as if he were her own. The father, who was wealthy, hoped that the boy would go into the Navy, but young Audubon showed no such desire, and he was sent to Paris to study under the great painter, David. Except for some sketches of birds, Audubon's early art work showed no promise at all. When he was eighteen, his father gave him a farm at Mill Grove, Pennsylvania, hoping that a few years in savage America would teach the boy to be more responsible.

Young Audubon sailed from France and enjoyed himself hugely at far-from-savage Mill Grove with parties, visiting, and hunting whenever the mood was on him. In those days he roamed the woods dressed as a complete dandy. One of his pleasures then, as it always had been, was the joy he found in watching birds. Audubon became a naturalist, not because of any great scientific curiosity, but because of his intense love of nature and his acute sense of detail. Sketching birds began with him as a hobby:

"One day, while watching the habits of a pair of peewees at Mill Grove, I looked so intently at their graceful attitudes that a thought struck my mind like a flash of light, that nothing, after all, could ever answer my enthusiastic desires to represent nature, except to copy her in her own way, alive and moving!! . . . I continued for months together, simply outlining birds as I observed them, either alighted or on the wing, but could finish none of my sketches. I procured many individuals of different species, and laying them on the table or on the ground, tried to place them in such attitudes as I had sketched. But, alas! They were dead . . . and neither wing, leg, nor tail could I place according to my wishes. A second thought came to my assistance; by means of threads, I raised or lowered a head, wing or tail, and by fastening the threads securely, I had something like life before me; yet much was wanting. When I saw the living birds, I felt the blood rush to my temples, and almost in despair spent about a month without drawing, but in deep thought, and daily in the company of the feathered inhabitants of dear Mill Grove."

Audubon fell in love with Miss Lucy Bakewell, the daughter of a Pennsylvania neighbor. To prove to her parents and his that he was a practical businessman, he sold the farm and started a trading partnership with Ferdinand Rosier in 1808. The two young men set up a shop in Louisville, Kentucky. For years, Audubon and his partner had to keep raising new capital to keep the struggling store going, but in vain, because Audubon's main interest could not be denied. In 1809, for example, he made the first experimental banding on an American wild bird. He continually disappeared into the forest to make sketches, leaving the shop to Rosier. One bankruptcy followed another. The partnership was finally dissolved in 1812, and Rosier went into business for himself, very successfully.

Audubon tried to run another shop by himself at Henderson on the banks of the Ohio. His friends criticized him, but his wife understood the creativeness that made him go off into the woods for days at a time to sketch and make observations.

Finally, he gave up the store completely and supported himself by painting portraits as an itinerant artist along the Mississippi. During this time his wife ran a school at Bayou Sara. In 1824, Prince Canino, the son of Prince Lucien Bonaparte, was shown some of Audubon's bird paintings. He encouraged Audubon to publish his pictures as Alexander Wilson had done several years earlier. Audubon's artistry was far superior to Wilson's. Audubon planned to publish several volumes of colored lithographs of birds drawn life size, along with printed descriptions. One thousand dollars was to be the cost of the subscription. Over several years he received one hundred and seventy subscriptions both in the United States and Europe, but in the financial disaster of 1837, half of his subscribers were wiped out.

Nevertheless, Audubon struggled through with the publication of his detailed studies and received international recognition. Only a few years later, he continued the massive work with his *Viviparous Quadrupeds of North America*.

Here are some typical entries: "May 10, Wednesday—Morning was fine. A party of dragoons, headed by a lieutenant, reached the shore before we had proceeded afar; . . . I decided to go to see the commanding officer. My guide asked me if I 'could ride at a gallop,' to which, not answering him, but starting at once at a round run, I neatly passed him ere his horse was well at the pace; . . . in a few minutes we entered a beautiful dell or valley and were . . . at the encampment. I dismounted, and met Captain Burgwin, a young man brought up at West Point. I showed him my credentials, at which he smiled and politely assured me that I was too well known throughout our country to need any letters. While seated in front of his tent, I heard the note of a bird new to me, and as it proceeded from a tree above our heads, I looked up and saw the first yellow-headed troupial alive that ever came across my own migrations. The captain thought me probably crazy, for I suddenly started, shot at the bird, and killed it. Afterwards I shot three more at one shot, but only one female amid hundreds of these yellow-headed blackbirds. They are quite abundant here. When they rose, they generally flew to the very tops of the tallest trees, and there, swelling their throats, partially swelling their wings and tails, they issued their croaking note.

"June 19, Monday—Harris and Bell have returned, and to my delight and utter astonishment, have brought two new birds; one, a lark, small and beautiful, the other like our common golden-winged woodpecker, but with a red mark instead of a black one along the lower mandible running backwards."

Over the years, his excursions into American forests took him from the Great Lakes to the farthest point of Florida, from the Atlantic seacoast to far beyond the Mississippi. He followed the path of Lewis and Clark up the Missouri River.

"It was no desire of glory which led me into this exile," he wrote. "I wished only to enjoy nature."

Whatever his motives, Audubon's life was a legacy to science and art.

Natchez, Mississippi, in 1822. This rare Audubon landscape was painted only two years before Prince Lucien Bonaparte encouraged him to publish his pictures of wild life.

2. LOUIS AGASSIZ

Another foreign-born naturalist who enriched American science was Jean Louis Agassiz, born in Switzerland in 1807. He came to the United States in 1846, after he had already achieved fame, and became a citizen in 1861.

Agassiz's work was important for two reasons: one, because he gathered the data which was later used by Darwin in developing a theory of evolution; and secondly, because of his enormous influence in spreading interest in the exact biological sciences in this country. He founded the Museum of Comparative Zoology at Harvard in 1848 and established a pioneer marine station at Buzzard's Bay in 1873, the year he died.

As a young man, Agassiz studied medicine as his father wished, but his interests kept pulling him elsewhere, although he received degrees in medicine and philosophy. His first scientific work was published when he was a little over twenty-one. It was a description of Brazilian fishes, based on material that had been sent to Humboldt, the famous zoologist. The book attracted so much attention that he was encouraged to start on a major work called *Fossil Fish*. Later, when it was published, it gave him a reputation as one of the foremost zoologists in Europe.

Agassiz pointed out the factors which led him to find relationships between the various species of fish. Although he himself did not believe

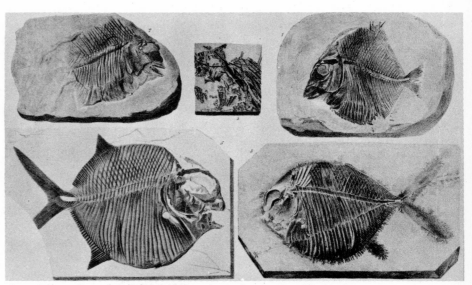

Agassiz's work on fossil fish led Darwin to the theory of evolution.

Darwin's letter to Agassiz shows his gratitude for Agassiz's refusal to carry their scientific differences over evolution into their friendship.

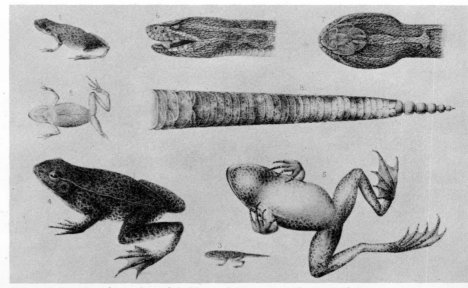

Frogs and snakes from Agassiz's *Natural History of the United States.*

in Darwin's theories, his reasoning was so clear as far as he went that Darwin was continually to refer to Agassiz's work. Agassiz also studied glacial formations in the Alps, and his research led him to publish his *System of Glaciers* in 1836. Agassiz was among the first to point out that the polar glacial cap had once come down and covered most of Europe. Later he found evidence to believe that the same thing had happened in the western world. Years passed before scientists were willing to accept this theory; then they agreed that this was his most dramatic contribution.

On a special pension from the King of Prussia, he came to the United States in 1846 to give a series of lectures and to gather material for a book on the study of fossils in North America. In 1848 he asked for release from his scientific obligations to the Prussian government and took the chair of zoology and geology at Harvard, created for him by Abbot Lawrence.

Agassiz worked with intense energy and perseverance. Volume after volume came from his pen, some popular in tone and some extremely erudite. The frogs and turtles below are from his monumental, four-volume *Contributions to the Natural History of the United States*. He was no armchair naturalist and traveled all over the western hemisphere, including an extended stay in Brazil.

Swiss glacier studies suggested to Agassiz the revolutionary theory that an ice cap had once extended as far south as the Mediterranean.

Island of St. Ignace in Michigan was headquarters for a field trip.

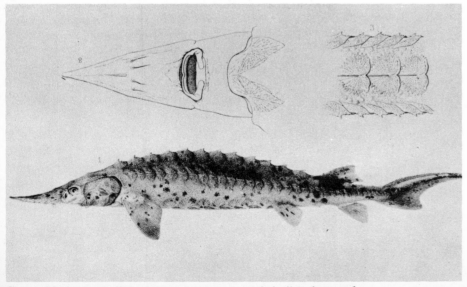

Gar and baby turtle illustrations are only two of similar thousands.

AGASSIZ'S CONTRIBUTION TO NATURAL HISTORY

Agassiz advanced man's understanding of the world with two great statements. The advance and recession of glaciers in the form of "Ice Ages" was one. His second was the generalization which was, so inspiring to Darwin: The life history of the individual repeats the history of the type. He said, "Changes which animals undergo during their embryonic growth coincide with order of succession of the fossils of the same type in past geological ages."

3. JOHN FREMONT
HIS EXPLORING EXPEDITION
THROUGH
THE ROCKY MOUNTAINS
IN 1842

Pyramid Lake, seven hundred feet higher than Great Salt Lake.

588

ENCAMPMENT AT CHOUTEAU'S LOWER TRADING HOUSE, RIGHT BANK OF THE KANZAS RIVER, 700 FEET ABOVE THE LEVEL OF THE GULF OF MEXICO

Determination of latitude, June 9, 1842—altitude of Polaris.

OBSERVATIONS.

Double altitude of Polaris.			Time of chronometer.		
Deg.	*min.*	*sec.*	*h.*	*min.*	*sec.*
75	24	50	3	29	59
75	25	05	3	31	50
75	26	00	3	33	35
75	26	20	3	35	22
75	27	00	3	37	00
75	28	40	3	38	44
75	28	50	3	40	42
75	28	10	3	42	05
75	30	40	3	44	14
75	30	50	3	46	07

Thermometer 55°.

RESULT OF CALCULATION.

True altitude.			Mean time.			Latitude.		
Deg.	*min.*	*sec.*	*h.*	*min.*	*sec.*	*Deg.*	*min.*	*sec.*
37	42	26	9	31	43	39	05	53

June 9, 1842—altitude of Antares in the meridian.

Double altitude of Antares.			True altitude.			Latitude.		
Deg.	*min.*	*sec.*	*Deg.*	*min.*	*sec.*	*Deg.*	*min.*	*sec.*
49	42	50	24	49	17	39	06	00

Astronomical data was kept from the first day of Lieutenant Fremont's expedition to chart a precise map of the West.

Fort Laramie was reached in one month, on July 13, 1843. The group included Kit Carson and Thomas H. Benton.

562

Table of meteorological observations.

Date.	Time.	Barom.	Thermometer.		Altitudes.	Remarks.
			Attached.	Free.		
		Millim.	*Cent.*	*Fahr.*	*Feet.*	
1843. June 10	Sunrise -	733.74	5.0	39.3	900	Clear sky; fog; wind N.
	1h. 41m. p. m.	735.43	22.0	69.0	938	NE. wind; clear, and fine cumuli.
	Sunset -	733.95	14.8	55.4	933	Slight breeze from NW.; clear.
11	Sunrise -	734.00	8.8	48.6	933	Clear; cumuli; slight breeze from SW.
12	Sunrise -	728.95	12.9	55.0	1,036	Wind S.; clear; clouds in E. horizon
	Noon -	726.02	24.9	75.4	1,331	Wind S.; clear; few cumuli.
13	Sunrise -	726.15	15.6	59.5	1,267	Wind N.
	1h. p. m. -	726.19	25.1	76.0	1,329	Wind N.; clear; cumuli.
	Sunset -	724.96	22.0	67.0	1,406	Sky covered with scattered clouds; calm; bright sunset.
14	Sunrise -	723.79	16.3	60.0	1,406	Thunder and rain; rainbow in the W.
15	5h. 55m. a. m.	721.67	17.8	61.6	1,486	At sunset last night a very vio-

Meteorological data was also kept. The expedition's nature was both scientific and political. The U.S. wanted California.

Sierra Nevada Range, reached February 14, 1844. Beyond lay the valley where Mr. Sutter lived at New Helvetia.

d on a bleak day in January in 1844.

lt columns, on the Columbia River. Fremont's men
rock and mineral samples all along the route.

r's Fort, under Mexico, four years before the gold
By chance, no mineral samples were taken here.

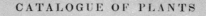

CATALOGUE OF PLANTS

COLLECTED

BY LIEUTENANT FRÉMONT,

IN HIS

EXPEDITION TO THE ROCKY MOUNTAINS.

BY JOHN TORREY.

Botanical samples were collected and turned over to
John Torrey, an outstanding American naturalist.

Fremontia Vermicularis was named after Fremont. Torrey
also examined the findings of the Wilkes polar voyage.

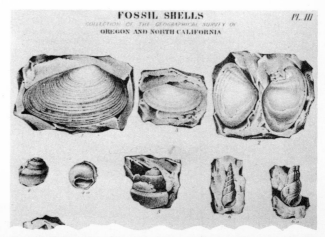

Fossil shells were found on mountain tops. Later Agassiz
pointed out the significance of these baffling finds.

WILLIAM BEAUMONT

PIONEER AMERICAN PHYSIOLOGIST

Dr. William Beaumont and his family

Beaumont's book, entitled *Experiments and Observations on the Gastric Juice,* carried an introduction stating that though he expected to have his opinions questioned, his observations of fact must not be denied. Beaumont had one thousand copies of his book printed at his own expense in 1833.

crepancies, which he may find it difficult to reconcile; but he will recollect that the human machine is endowed with a vitality which modifies its movements in different states of the system, and probably produces some diversity of effects from the same causes.

I had opportunities for the examination of the interior of the stomach, and its secretions, which has never before been so fully offered to any one. This most important organ, its secretions and its operations, have been submitted to my observation in a very extraordinary manner, in a state of perfect health, and for years in succession. I have availed myself of the opportunity afforded by a concurrence of circumstances which probably can never again occur, with a zeal and perseverance proceeding from motives which my conscience approves; and I now submit the result of my experiments to an enlightened public, who I doubt not will duly appreciate the truths discovered, and the confirmation of opinions which before rested on conjecture.

I submit a body of facts which cannot be invalidated. My opinions may be doubted, denied, or approved, according as they conflict or agree with the opinions of each individual who may read them; but

On the sixth of June, 1822, a young French-Canadian voyageur, Alexis St. Martin, was accidentally shot in the chest while in the Mackinac store of the American Fur Company. Fortunately, the garrison of the U. S. Army in the village had assigned to it a thirty-seven-year-old physician named William Beaumont, who had given up private practice only two years before.

Beaumont was called at once to attend to St. Martin and found that the left side of the lower chest and the abdomen walls were shot away. Beaumont dressed the wound and treated the boy with great care, but privately he was sure that the patient would die.

For four days the young voyageur tossed in pain and high fever, then miraculously, his temperature returned to normal. A section of lung which had protruded through the wound sloughed off, leaving a hole in the body wall through which the surgeon could put his index finger clear into the stomach. Beaumont dressed the wound daily for a year; but the lips of the hole in the stomach would not close. Because of the position of the wound, Beaumont was able to bandage the Canadian boy's body so that his stomach could still function as a normal organ.

About one year after the accident, it became necessary to give St. Martin a cathartic, rhubarb and sulphur, which Beaumont administered through the hole in the stomach. He noted that it worked as well as if it had been administered orally, and so he conceived one of the most remarkable series of experiments in the history of medical science.

For the next few years, Alexis St. Martin made himself a living test tube for the study of digestive chemistry. Dr. Beaumont took small samples of food tied to strings, inserted these samples through the hole in St. Martin's body and, several hours later, withdrew from the stomach what was left.

Beaumont proved that the digestive juices of the stomach were formed by the walls of the stomach. He actually watched their action through a hand lens, just as he saw with his own eyes the digestive and shredding action of the stomach muscles. He established that the gastric juice was formed through the contact of the food particles with the walls of the stomach in the same way that any foreign body stimulates a mucous membrane to self-protection. He disproved the theory that the action of digestion was due to the secretions of hypothetical "gastric glands."

He also established that the process of digestion in man was purely chemical, requiring no "vital force." He showed further that the emotions could affect the rate of digestion—even halt it completely if the emotion was fear, rage, or anger.

Beaumont's experiments on the action of gastric juices appeared in book form in 1833 after he had returned from the army to take up private practice in the city of St. Louis, where for a time he and his family shared a house with Robert E. Lee.

Beaumont's discoveries were reprinted in Germany and elsewhere very shortly after publication in America. Although his entire research career was compressed into the few years spent as an army surgeon, his work on the chemistry of digestion entitled him to the role of one of America's great pioneer medical researchers.

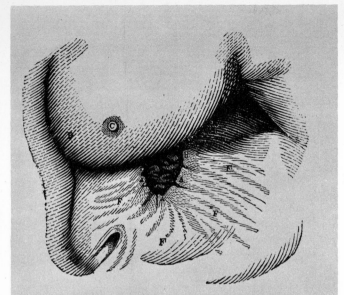

This engraving represents the ordinary appearance of the left breast and side, the aperture filled with the valve; the subject in an erect position.

A A A The circumference and edge of the aperture, within which is seen the valve.

B The attachment of the valvular portion of the stomach to the superior part of the aperture.

C The nipple.

D The anterior portion of the breast.

E The scar where the opening was made with the scalpel, and the cartilages taken out.

F F₂F F Cicatrice of the original wound, around the aperture.   D

A page from Beaumont's classic account of digestive processes shows the position of the hole in St. Martin's stomach. Because the hole was so high, an ordinary bandage over the wound acted as a plug, permitting normal function.

---

142   EXPERIMENTS AND

ving been eaten, would not contain a sufficient quantity of gastric juice to digest it perfectly. It is possible that the portion presented at the perforation may be in a more advanced stage of digestion, than the rest of the mass, and consequently lighter, and float on the surface of the more solid portions of the food. In ordinary cases, such would be found to be the case; but when much fat meat or oily food has been used, the oil always maintains an ascendency in the gastric cavity.

Experiment 26.

Jan. 11, 1830.   At 3 o'clock, P. M., dined on *bread* and *eight ounces* of *recently salted, lean beef, four ounces* of *potatoes,* and *four ounces* of *turnips,* boiled.   In *fifteen minutes,* took out a portion of the contents of the stomach.   The *meat* made its appearance, in an incipient stage of digestion.

At 3 o'clock, 45 minutes, took out another portion. The meat and bread only appeared, in a still more advanced stage of digestion.

The texture of the meat was, at this time, broken into small shreds, soft and pulpy, and the fluid containing it had become more opaque, and quite gruel-like, or rather, glutinous, in appearance.

I put this second parcel in a vial, and placed it in water, on the sand bath, at the temperature of the stomach, (100° Fahrenheit,) as indicated by the thermometer immediately preceding its extraction, and continued it there.

At 5 o'clock, took out another quantity.   Digestion had advanced in about the same ratio as from the first to the second time of extracting; and when compared with the second parcel, contained in the vial on the bath, little or no difference could be perceived in them; both were nearly in the same stage

A careful diary was kept of all the experiments, which were carried on constantly for seven years. St. Martin occasionally rebelled and went off on prolonged drinking sprees, and came back only when he needed more money.

St. Martin outlived Beaumont by many years and made a good income from medical schools. Here he agrees to a fee of $400 for three months at Rush Medical College, but only if his son, who needed employment, were to be hired too.

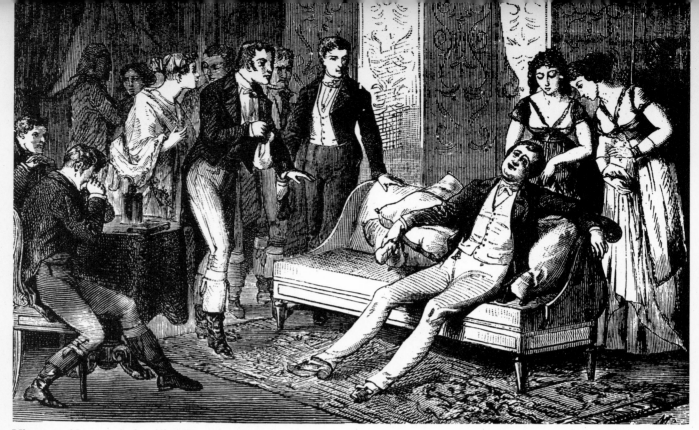

Nitrous oxide, popularly called "laughing gas," was first used in experiments by Sir Humphry Davy of the Royal Institute. A later demonstration in America suggested its use as an anesthetic to Dr. Horace Wells, a dentist.

Sulphuric ether, commonly called simply "ether," was known in the early 1800's to be able to produce unconsciousness. One of the experimenters was Dr. Charles T. Jackson, of Boston. After anesthesia was publicly acclaimed, Jackson claimed that his ideas were pirated, became the center of long and furious turmoil, and finally went insane.

Hypnotism, as practiced by the Austrian doctor, Mesmer, had impressed the world, because it could mask a person's sensibilities, but it was not practical for serious surgery.

Dr. Crawford Long was first to use ether for surgery (1842). His work went unnoticed for ten years, and he was the only principal in the "ether controversy" whom it didn't ruin.

ANESTHESIA

1. THE DISCOVERY

Mid-nineteenth-century readers of Harriet Beecher Stowe's *Uncle Tom's Cabin* were moved to tears by the scenes of the death of the child Eva St. Clair. Later generations of readers found the scenes far too mawkish for their taste. Between the two bodies of readers there was more than just a change in literary fashion; it was a difference in their common experience. Mid-nineteenth-century Americans knew death and pain much more intimately than did their children and grandchildren. Every family had experienced the heartache and anguish of sitting by a bedside, watching a beloved, helpless child sink lower into death. Just as later generations of Americans found themselves alien to the naïve Christian idealism of Mrs. Stowe, so they were another civilization as far as their intimate experiences with death and pain were concerned. The difference in American outlook can be traced to the remoteness of death in American life, and along with this remoteness from death is a similar remoteness from pain. The great emancipation of Americans from sickness and pain began in the 1840's with the discovery that the inhalation of ether or nitrous oxide could be a preventative of pain.

From the earliest times, surgery was an excruciating experience. Men who were willing to risk their lives in battle would shrink with dread from the pain that came from the deliberate cutting of the living flesh by a surgical instrument. Men and women preferred to conceal a malady from their family and friends, knowing that they would eventually die of unchecked disease, rather than submit themselves to the agony of surgical operation.

Through the history of surgery runs the story of the unsuccessful attempts to destroy pain with opium, Indian hemp, alcohol, and hypnotism. The nineteenth century opened with Sir Humphry Davy's work at the Royal Institute. He was the first to experiment with nitrous oxide, "laughing gas." The stupefaction and intoxication that it produced were so marked that public demonstrations of laughing gas became very popular. In Boston on December 10, 1844, such a demonstration was made by a traveling lecturer named Colton. In the audience was a thirty-one-year-old dentist named Horace Wells, who noticed that one of the volunteer subjects who was severely hurt while under the gas reported that he had felt no pain at all. The following day Wells asked Colton to accompany him to the operating parlor of another dentist in Hartford, Connecticut,

named J. M. Riggs. Wells sat himself down in the chair, had Colton administer the gas to him, and then permitted Riggs to extract a tooth. On coming to his senses, Wells said, "It did not hurt me more than the prick of a pin. It is the greatest discovery ever made."

Two years before this, a surgical operation had actually been performed while the patient was anesthetized by sulphuric ether. Sulphuric ether had been known for almost a hundred years. "Ether parties" had been fairly common in the eighteenth century. A group of celebrants would gather in a room, close the door and the windows, stop up the keyhole, and, on a table in the middle of the room, place an open bowl of ether. Within a short time the ether fumes would permeate the room and create an effect identical with the intoxication from drinking alcohol. An excessive exposure to the ether fumes would result in stupefaction. The idea of using the stupefaction resulting from sulphuric ether to make a patient unconscious during a surgical operation suggested itself to a number of people.

The surgeon who performed the first operation with ether was a young resident of Georgia, Dr. Crawford Long. He tells his own story:

"The first patient to whom I administered ether in a surgical operation was Mr. James M. Venables, who then resided within two miles of Jefferson. Mr. Venables consulted me on several occasions in regard to the propriety of removing two small tumors situated on the back part of his neck, but would postpone from time to time having the operation performed from dread of pain. At length I mentioned to him the fact of my receiving bruises while under the influence of the vapor of ether without suffering, and as I knew him to be fond of and accustomed to inhale ether, I suggested to him the probability that the operation might be performed without pain, and proposed operating on him while under its influence. He consented to have one tumor removed, and the operation was performed the same evening. The ether was given to Mr. Venables on a towel, and when fully under its influence I extirpated the tumor. It was encysted and about half an inch in diameter. The patient continued to inhale ether during the time of the operation, and when informed it was over seemed incredulous until the tumor was shown him.

"He gave no evidence of suffering during the operation, and assured me, after it was over, that he did not experience the least degree of pain during its performance. This operation was performed on the 30th March, 1842."

Crawford Long did not publish his results, and so it was necessary for others to rediscover his techniques independently.

Dr. Horace Wells, after experimenting on himself in December, 1844, used nitrous oxide on his dental patients, until a failure of the method (above) forced him to stop.

2. "THIS IS NO HUMBUG!"

The man who was the first to demonstrate to the world the practicability of ether as an anesthetic was William Thomas Green Morton. He was born in 1819 in Charlton, Massachusetts, entered the Baltimore College of Dental Surgery in 1840, and after two years' study began to practice in Boston. His pioneer work on dentures and plates led him to the necessity for the extraction of roots, an excruciating operation, and he was forced to interest himself in means of killing sensation. He tried alcohol, laudanum, opium, and hypnotism, and made a series of experiments on animals to establish the narcotic properties of sulphuric ether over the entire system. On September 30, 1846, he extracted a tooth from a patient made unconscious by ether.

Morton was anxious to test his results further, and the naturalist, A. A. Gould, suggested that he try to convince Boston's outstanding surgeon, Dr. J. C. Warren, to perform an operation on an anesthetized patient. Present at that first trial, on October 16, 1846, was Dr. Washington Ayer who later wrote:

"The day arrived; the time appointed was noted on the dial, when the patient was led into the operating room, and Dr. Warren and a board of the most eminent surgeons in the state were gathered around the sufferer. 'All is ready—the stillness op-

pressive.' It had been announced 'that a test of some preparation was to be made for which the *astonishing* claim had been made that it would render the person operated upon free from pain.'

"Those present were incredulous, and, as Dr. Morton had not arrived at the time appointed and fifteen minutes had passed, Dr. Warren said with significant meaning, 'I presume he is otherwise engaged.' This was followed with a 'derisive laugh,' and Dr. Warren grasped his knife and was about to proceed with the operation. At that moment Dr. Morton entered a side door, when Dr. Warren turned to him and in a strong voice said, 'Well, sir, your patient is ready.' In a few minutes he was ready for the surgeon's knife, when Dr. Morton said, '*Your* patient is ready, sir.'"

The hospital records of the Massachusetts General Hospital state: "Gilbert Abbott, age twenty, painter, single; tumor on face . . .

"This case is remarkable in the annals of surgery. It was the first surgical operation performed under the influence of ether. Dr. Warren had been applied to by Dr. Morton, a dentist, with the request that he would try the inhalation of a fluid which, he said, he had found to be effectual in preventing pain during operations upon the teeth . . . After four or five minutes of breathing through a tube connected to a glass globe, the patient appeared to be asleep, and the operation was performed as herein described. To the surprise of Dr. Warren and the other gentlemen present, the patient did not shrink, nor cry out, but during the insulation of the veins he began to move his limbs and utter extraordinary expressions, and these movements seemed to indicate the existence of pain; but after he had recovered his faculties he said that he had experienced none, but only a sensation like that of scraping the part with a blunt instrument. . . ."

At the end of the operation, Warren said to all those present: "Gentlemen, this is no humbug!"

The operation created a sensation in the medical world and Oliver Wendell Holmes, the famous physician, wrote to Morton: "My Dear Sir:—Everybody wants to have a hand in a great discovery. All I will do is to give you a hint or two, as to names, or the name, to be applied to the state produced and the agent. The state should I think be called 'Anaesthesia.' This signifies insensibility, more particularly (as used by Linnaeus and Cullen) to objects of touch. (See Good—Nosology, p. 259.) The adjective will be 'Anaesthetic.' Thus we might say, the state of anaesthesia, or the anaesthetic state. The means employed would properly be called the anti-aesthetic agent. Perhaps it might be allowable to say anaesthetic agent, but this admits question.

"The words, antineuritic, aneuric, neuro-leptic,

neuro-lepsia, neuro-etasis, etc., seem too anatomical; whereas the change is a physiological one. I throw them out for consideration . . .

Yours respectfully,

O. W. Holmes."

Morton applied for a patent on the process, allowing the free use to charitable institutions throughout the country, but his action stirred endless trouble for him because he ran afoul of one of the most contentious figures of his time—Dr. Charles Thomas Jackson of Boston, one of the first to set up a laboratory to teach chemistry to students by having them perform their own experiments. Jackson, born in Plymouth, Massachusetts, in 1805, was graduated from Harvard Medical School in 1829. He studied abroad for several years and returned in 1832 on the same ship with Samuel Morse, with whom he discussed telegraphy; it is barely possible, as Jackson claimed, that he was the first to tell Morse of the electromagnetic experiments performed by Faraday and Sturgeon, but Jackson went on to say that Morse stole all his ideas.

Jackson opened his chemistry laboratory in Boston in 1836, introducing the teaching methods of Liebig and Berzelius. Jackson's interest in sulphuric ether came from efforts to relieve the effects of chlorine gas. Jackson also found that fairly light inhalations of ether relieved the chest pressure due to severe colds, and at first thought that ether was a specific for pulmonary infections. More intense doses, however, made him realize that the effect was quite different. To see what would happen, he performed an experiment on himself, deliberately inhaling sulphuric ether until he lost consciousness. Until then sulphuric ether had had a very bad reputation because of the number of serious accidents that had occurred during ether parties, but Jackson now claimed that the gas could safely be inhaled with atmospheric air if the proper precautions were taken.

After Morton had already used ether for dental extractions, he had some conversations with Jackson which later led Jackson to claim that Morton had pirated his ideas. Jackson had many supporters.

Morton's patent was generally infringed. He applied to Congress for aid, and a bill proposing a grant of one hundred thousand dollars was submitted in 1852. Payments began the following year. This grant was bitterly fought by the partisans of both Jackson and Wells, who felt that Morton was appropriating the credit for the work of other men. Wells had committed suicide in disappointment, and Jackson was in a rage. He submitted the entire case to the French Academy as a neutral body. They divided the credit three ways. Morton refused the grant, but there was enough credit for everyone.

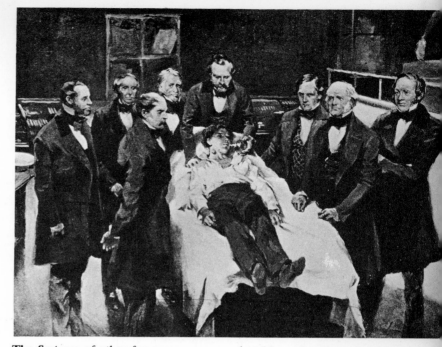

The first use of ether for surgery occurred at Massachusetts General Hospital, on October 16, 1846. Dr. Morton applied the anesthetic, and Dr. J. C. Warren performed the operation.

Dr. W. T. G. Morton, a dentist, was the first man to demonstrate to the world the properties of ether as an anesthetic. After years of controversy, persecution by his rivals finally drove him out of his mind.

Dr. J. C. Warren, one of Boston's most distinguished surgeons, helped assure the acceptance of the use of ether as an anesthetic because his endorsement carried great weight in the medical profession.

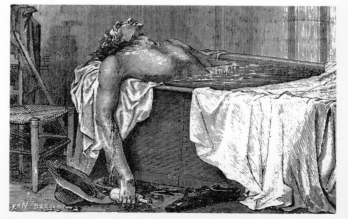

Horace Wells committed suicide in bitter obscurity. Europeans sympathized with all Morton's rivals. In their tradition, he would not have patented his discovery.

JOSEPH HENRY

1. A STRANGER IN HIS OWN TIME

ELECTROMAGNETISM

BEFORE HENRY

Volta demonstrated before Napoleon that it was possible to produce a steady current of electricity (top). The next important step was made by Georg Simon Ohm, who found that the amount of current flowing through a wire was directly proportional to the strength of the voltaic battery supplying the current. The most germinal experiments in electromagnetism itself were made by Oersted (above), who discovered that a steady current of electricity produced a magnetic field which surrounded the wire.

In the spring of 1837, scientists in an English laboratory attempted a casual experiment: to see if electric sparks could be drawn from a thermocouple. One end of the thermocouple was imbedded in a piece of ice—the other end lay on a red-hot stove. Charles Wheatstone touched together the two pieces of wire that completed the circuit. He drew no spark. Michael Faraday said that Wheatstone was going about it in the wrong way, made a few adjustments, and tried his hand. Still no spark.

Then a third man, a visiting American, coiled a length of wire about his finger in a tight corkscrew curl. After a few minutes, he remarked that whenever the two gentlemen were ready, he would gladly show them how to draw the spark. He then went ahead and simply added the little coil he had made, now wrapped around a piece of iron rod, to one of the thermocouple leads. This time, when he brushed the ends of the two wires together, he drew sparks that were clearly visible.

Faraday clapped with delight and said, "Hurrah for the Yankee experiment! What in the world did you do?"

And so Joseph Henry had to explain self-induction to the man whom the world had already credited with the discovery of induction.

There was a century and a quarter of time and a world of knowledge between Franklin's electrostatics and Clerk Maxwell's electrodynamics. Most of that knowledge was gathered by one man, Joseph Henry; in only fifteen years—1829 to 1844. By most of Henry's contemporaries, the magnitude of his work was largely unappreciated; yet his research ranks as one of the great experimental achievements.

By his own choice, Henry was a stranger in his own time. His friends mistook his scientific idealism for lack of the American spirit; international science ignored him because he was an American. Not until after he was gone, and the contemporaries of his youth long since dead, did strangers realize that a giant had lived, worked, and died with far too little notice; and that the considerable public fame achieved during the latter half of his life had been for the least of his works.

In the end, however, science paid him its greatest tribute—raising him on the pedestal of the lower case: Henry became *henry*, along with *ampere, volt, ohm, and farad.*

In the 1820's, most people assumed that the way electricity and magnetism were related could best be shown by the following demonstration: A tiny paper boat about an inch long floated on a dish of water. The boat carried a magnetized needle. Dipping down into the center of the pan was the lower end of a straight wire, suspended from above. When electric current was passed down through the wire, the paper boat containing the magnet would slowly sail around the wire in a perfectly circular path. When the electric current was increased, the "magnet-boat" moved faster. The inference was drawn that a steady current created about itself a circular magnetic field. The magnetic field was said to be *induced*. The greater the current, the more intense was the induced magnetic field.

Joseph Henry, a mathematics teacher in a country school in a provincial town in an undeveloped nation, asked himself this question: If electricity could create magnetism, then why shouldn't magnetism in turn create electricity? He not only came up with the answer, but went far beyond his predecessors in the profundity of his research.

In Henry's background there was nothing to indicate either the extent of his ability or the direction his interest would take. He grew up in poverty near Albany, a rich little backwater town that never felt the surge of the westward movement. Farm hand, storekeeper's apprentice, the dreamy boy barely knew how to read. When he was thirteen his pet rabbit ran away and Henry tunneled under a church in pursuit. He came up inside a locked room which contained a library of romantic novels. He forgot the rabbit and read the books, one after another.

He was so enraptured by the high sentiments of melodrama that next year when sent to Albany to earn a living, the fourteen-year-old boy made a beeline for the Green Street Theater where the great John Bernard was directing his famous company. For two years, Joseph Henry, strikingly handsome, too tall for his age, was a hard-working talented apprentice to the "periwig-pated fellows who tear a passion to tatters."

In his sixteenth year, he made his second great discovery when he was too ill to go to the theater. Restless and bored, he happened to pick up a book left by a boarder. Even late in life, he could still recall the opening paragraph of the first page: "You throw a stone or shoot an arrow into the air, why does it not go forward in a line with the direction you gave it? On the contrary, why does flame or smoke always mount upwards although no force is used to send them in that direction?" Joseph Henry had found the world of science.

Henry was never to be able to make minor decisions. Once he ordered a pair of shoes and from day to day changed his mind about whether he wanted square or round toes. The exasperated cobbler let him have one shoe round-toed, the other square. Important decisions, however, Henry made on the moment. With no background or training, Henry had decided to go on the stage. Now with even less preparation, he abruptly made up his mind to become a natural philosopher.

Henry walked to the Albany Academy, presenting himself as a student. Fortunately he had so much talent that the real world changed itself into the shape of his private dream. In seven months of night classes and special tutoring, he devoured enough learning to get himself an appointment as a country schoolmaster so that he could afford to go on with his studies. Teaching and attending classes at the Academy took more than sixteen hours a day, but Henry was in love with his life.

Later, he gave up teaching and talked Dr. Beck, the professor of chemistry, into making him the demonstration assistant who set up the experiments for public lectures. Henry's theatrical training had taught him that every demonstration must be absolutely foolproof, convincing, and as dramatic as possible. This experience gave him the techniques of speed and simplicity which characterized his own experiments.

When he completed his course at the Academy, he took a job as surveyor and engineer on the Erie Canal. The days of his poverty seemed ended, and the future was wide open. From the seaports of the East out to the distant hills of Wisconsin, there wasn't a place where a man with Henry's training couldn't make a fortune. After a few months, however, he was offered the professorship of mathematics and natural philosophy back at Albany. He felt the country needed advanced teachers even more desperately than engineers. Reluctantly, he accepted the post.

For his few months of work, the State of New York paid him $2,083. What he saved out of that, and a life insurance policy of $4,000, was all that he would leave on his death in 1878, even though he was eventually to have a public trust of millions of dollars at his disposal.

CONVERSATIONS

ON

CHYMISTRY,

IN WHICH

THE ELEMENTS OF THAT SCIENCE

ARE FAMILIARLY

100

Emily. It is as white, and dazzling as the sun!— Now a piece of the melted wire drops to the bottom: I fear it is extinguished; but no, it burns again as bright as ever.

Mrs. B: It will burn till the wire is entirely consumed, provided the oxygen be not first expended; for you know it can burn only while there is oxygen to combine with it.

Caroline. I never saw a more beautiful light. My eyes can hardly bear it! How astonishing to think that all this caloric was contained in the small quantity of gas that was enclosed in the receiver; and that, without producing any sensible heat!

Mrs. B. The caloric of the oxygen gas could not produce any sensible heat before the combustion took place, because it was not in a free state. You can tell me I hope to what modification of heat this caloric is to be referred?

Caroline. Since it is *combined* with the basis of the gas, it must be *chemical* heat.

Emily. Chemical heat is then extricated in all combustions?

Mrs. B. Certainly. By the decomposition of the gas, the caloric returns to its free state, and thus produces a quantity of sensible heat, proportional to the rapidity of that decomposition.

Caroline. How wonderfully quick combustion goes on in pure oxygen gas! But pray are these drops of burnt iron as heavy as the wire was before?

Mrs. B. They are even heavier; for the iron in burning, has acquired exactly the weight of the oxygen which has disappeared, and is now combined with it. It has become an oxyd of iron.

Caroline. I do not know what you mean by saying that the oxygen has *disappeared*, Mrs. B. for it was always invisible.

Mrs. B. True, my dear; the expression was incorrect. But though you could not see the oxygen

As a young actor, Henry had no knowledge of science until he stumbled on one of the currently popular books which gushingly dramatized current scientific concepts.

An electromagnet that would lift a ton was built by Henry. The horse-shoe magnet (*a*) was made of soft iron and had a great number of turns of insulated wire about it. Current from the galvanic battery (*bc*) made the horse-shoe magnetic, so that it exerted force on the flat slab of iron, called the armature, which fit across the pole faces. From this armature hung a platform pan upon which known weights could be loaded.

2. HENRY PRODUCES ELECTRICITY FROM MAGNETISM

In 1826 Joseph Henry rode back to Albany, carrying the basic gift of the greatest researchers—instinctively he could reduce an idea to simplicity: logic worked with the speed of intuition.

His teaching schedule was heavy, and the only time he could steal for research was the summer vacation when he was permitted to convert one of the classrooms into a laboratory. His first work was to build electromagnets along the lines described by Sturgeon and based on the principles of Arago and Oersted. A length of bare wire was loosely wrapped around a bar of soft iron coated with shellac. When electric current was passed through the wire, magnetism was induced in the iron. Sturgeon bent his bar into the form of a horse-shoe, and seven pounds of metal could be lifted into the air when he turned his current on; and just as dramatically dropped when the current was turned off.

In the Albany schoolroom, one summer, Henry built a magnet that could lift one ton—three hundred times more powerful than Sturgeon's. Instead of insulating the iron as Sturgeon had done, Henry carefully insulated the wire. This allowed him to wrap an enormous number of turns of wire within a very small space. Henry described it in the *American Journal of Science,* published by Silliman of Yale. No one abroad read the paper.

In building his extraordinarily powerful magnets, Henry was led to the problem of generating electricity from magnetism. He discovered that all the previous investigators were misled by the fact that a *steady* electric current induced a *steady* magnetic field. They, therefore, had been seeking some arrangement whereby a steady magnetic field would induce an electric current. The usual test was to wind a length of wire around a piece of magnetized iron, and rub the free ends of the wire together, hoping to see some sparks.

He discovered that the right answer lay in *not* using a steady magnetic field, but a magnetic field that was *changing.* Current could be caused to flow through a closed loop of wire by the simple method of moving a magnet near the wire.

He went a step further. First he passed an electric current through a wire and thereby generated a magnetic field around the wire. Then, by making the electric current unsteady, he made the magnetic field fluctuate along with the current. A second wire placed near the first was therefore *in a changing magnetic field,* and electric current was induced to flow in the second wire even though it was not fed by any battery. By simply varying the current in one wire, he was able to induce current in another wire *to which it was not connected.*

All this work and still more was done in consecutive summers before 1831; but Henry was reluctant to publish until he could achieve an overwhelming mass of data. For the rest of his life he was to regret not publicizing his results. "I ought to have published earlier," he said sadly, but only to his most intimate friends, "But I had so little time! I wanted to get out my results in good form, and how could I know that another on the other side of the Atlantic was busy with the same thing?"

The blow fell on Henry in May, 1832. Still filled with the confidence that he was years ahead

Induced current could be made to flow through a closed loop of wire, Henry discovered, simply by moving a magnet near the loop. When the magnet was brought to a halt, the magnetic field became stationary, and the electric current ceased. Henry reasoned that if a moving magnet could induce a current in a wire, then one coil of wire could induce a current on a second one. This was the discovery of the principle of the transformer which made electric power a reality. In the picture, a galvanic cell at the right supplies current to the upper coil. Current induced on the big lower coil deflects the galvanometer at left.

of the world of science on a great work, he casually picked up a magazine and read two devastating paragraphs; he was years ahead of nobody. His great work had been done independently by another man. The two paragraphs came under the heading "Proceedings of the Royal Institution." They began:

"Feb. 17—Mr. Faraday gave an account of the first two parts of his researches in electricity; namely Volta-electric induction and magneto-electric induction."

And the article ended: "If a single wire be passed by a magnetic pole, a current of electricity is induced through it which can be rendered sensible."

Faraday's 1832 paper was based on results achieved as recently as the previous autumn, and although Henry actually had been ahead of him, he now felt that there was no point at all in publishing his own results. He was sick with despair. However, Professor Silliman of Yale continually pressed him to contribute to Silliman's journal. Henry finally sat down and began the series of papers that was to achieve for him everything he had ever hoped—but the full achievement was to be recognized only after his death.

The first paper appeared that July. It began with the statement that in spite of the discoveries of Oersted, Arago, and Ampere, no one had been able to make magnetism produce an electric current.

"With this view, I commenced experiments," he wrote, and hid all his own deep disappointment behind the blunt impersonality. "In the meantime, the result so much sought after has . . . been found by Mr. Faraday of the Royal Institution."

He then reported Faraday's work, and introduced his own experiments with only the briefest and most indirect allusion to his own originality.

His apparatus consisted of two separate coils completely independent of each other. The coil around the horse-shoe made a closed circuit through a battery. The coil around the armature was connected neither to a battery nor to any other visible source of current, but only to a galvanometer.

"I stationed myself near the galvanometer and directed an assistant at a given word to . . . connect the . . . battery attached to the magnet . . . . The north end of the galvanometer needle was deflected 30°, indicating a current of electricity in the wire surrounding the armature. . . ."

In other words, current had been made to flow through a wire that was not connected to any source of electromotive force. An instant later, however, Henry must have been disappointed because the galvanometer needle returned to its zero position even though current was still flowing through the wire coiled around the horse-shoe. Henry signaled his assistant to turn off the horse-shoe current. To his amazement, the moment that the current was stopped, the galvanometer needle jumped again, but in the other direction.

What was happening is very simple in retrospect—when the current was turned on in the horse-shoe coil, the magnetism in the armature *changed* from nothing at all to its full value. This momentary change in magnetization induced an electric current in the surrounding wire. When the current in the horse-shoe coil was abruptly stopped, the magnetic field in the armature *changed* back to zero; and so once again there was an impulse of current in the wire which surrounded it.

Henry summed up the effect: "An instantaneous current in one or the other direction accompanies every change in the magnetic intensity of the iron. . . ."

The "Peacemaker," a huge gun aboard the steam frigate, *Princeton*, exploded in 1844. Henry was asked to head the investigation which followed. This excursion into solid state physics marked the end of his electrical research.

3. HENRY'S TELEGRAPH, TRANSFORMER, AND ELECTRIC MOTOR

Henry had now established that at the instant voltage is applied to wire, the surging current creates a momentarily increasing magnetic field. Any wire in this changing field will have a current induced in it—and Henry was to discover that the words "any wire" included *the very wire that created the field in the first place.*

As early as 1829, Henry had observed the magnetic effect which a current had on itself—now called "self-induction."

In his 1832 paper, Henry described the phenomenon for the first time. Henry's friends were dismayed that the enormous prestige of these discoveries had gone to Faraday rather than to Henry. Not since Benjamin Franklin's work had there been such a chance for American science to achieve

world distinction. The young republic was particularly sensitive to the European attitude that America had nothing cultural to offer. Instead of sympathizing with Henry, it blamed him. He was so depressed that he thought seriously of giving up science but his friends sought to increase his opportunities for research by getting him an appointment to the Princeton faculty. While still at Albany, Henry invented the electrical relay which he used to create the first electromagnetic telegraph system.

At Princeton, he continued his researches, describing mutual induction so clearly that the following experiment may be considered the paper which embodied the design of the electric transformer:

"The principal articles of apparatus used in the experiment consist of a number of flat coils of copper ribbon. . . . Coil No. 1 was arranged to receive the current from a small battery, and coil No. 2 (of very few turns) placed on this, with a glass interposed to insure perfect insulation; as often as the circuit of No. 1 was interrupted, a powerful secondary current was induced in No. 2. . . . The shock, however, from this coil is very feeble, and can scarcely be felt above the fingers."

In other words, the current had been increased, but the voltage had been stepped down. This arrangement of coils was the first step-down transformer. "Coil No. 1 remaining as before, a longer coil (with a great many turns) was substituted for coil No. 2. With this arrangement, the magnetizing power was much less . . . but the shocks were more powerful." He had cut down the current, but stepped up the voltage—the prototype of the first step-up transformer. Henry's experimental technique was so ingenious and his insight so clear that he was able to prove that the discharge of a condenser was of an oscillatory nature; the most important experiment in capacitance since Franklin's analysis of the Leyden jar.

Henry's last great contribution to electricity was the experiment in which he anticipated Hertz. In 1842, he discovered that needles in the basement of a building could be magnetized by the effects of an electric spark two floors above.

"It would appear that the transfer of a single

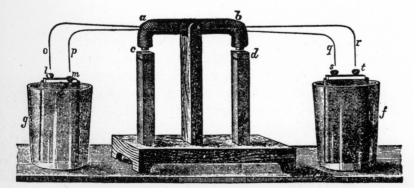

The first electric motor was made by Henry in 1831. An iron rod wrapped with wire rocked on a pivot, making alternate contacts with galvanic cells through wires (*op* and *qr*). It was just a toy, but a neighboring blacksmith, Davenport, built a real motor with a spinning armature.

An electrical relay and the first electromagnetic telegraph were built by Henry in 1831, anticipating Morse by six years. Henry's receiver was a bell. At Princeton he sent signals through a mile of wire, and stated that relays could extend his circuit indefinitely.

spark is sufficient to disturb perceptibly the electricity of space throughout at least a cube of 400,000 feet of capacity; and when it is considered that . . . (the spark is oscillatory) it may be further inferred that the diffusion of motion in this case is almost comparable with that of a spark from a flint and steel in the case of light."

He clearly understood that this was a wave phenomenon, identical with that of the propagation of light. Twenty-five years later, Maxwell stated all of Henry's discoveries in the four equations of electrodynamics.

The United States government was seeking a director for the newly founded Smithsonian Institution. Henry was offered the post. He felt that here for the first time was an opportunity to give American science a cohesive form. Twenty years earlier, a sense of duty to science had made him give up the opportunities for wealth in engineering. In the same way, he now gave up research to act as the first national administrator of science.

It was in this capacity as director of the Smithsonian that Henry was best known to his contemporaries, as the advisor on science to Abraham Lincoln during the war, as the man to whom young inventors like Morse, Bell, and others went for encouragement. Several times he was offered positions that would pay him a much larger salary, but he always refused.

As head of the Smithsonian, Henry made several notable applications of science to American living, including weather charting and research on fog signals. He helped organize the American Association for the Advancement of Science and was its president in 1849. He was president of the National Academy of Science from 1868 to 1878. He was the first to measure the relative temperatures across the surface of the sun; and his sun-spot analysis inspired Secchi, the Vatican astronomer, to undertake his classic work.

In the last decades of his life, he emerged as a determined and dominating figure of rocklike integrity, but except for his daughter no one knew until long after his death that the shy, outwardly cold old man had always ached for the credit due him in his early years.

Formal portrait of Henry in his later years, by Mathew Brady

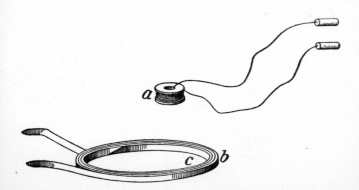

The transformer grew out of experiments with this coiled copper ribbon and wire spool. Voltage was measured by the intensity of shocks received through the handles. Feeble currents were detected by the acid taste detected when a current was applied to the experimenter's tongue.

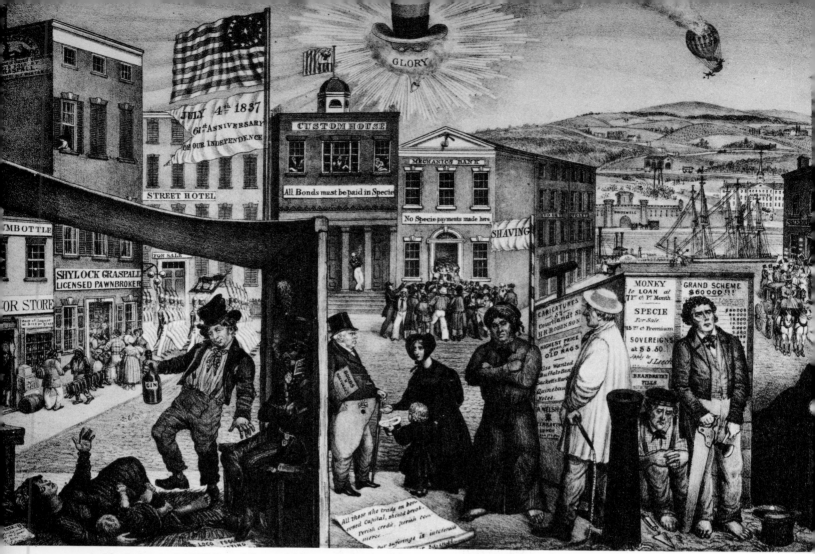

Hard times of 1837 found Samuel Morse desperate for money to eat while working on telegraphy; bankrupted McCormick's iron foundry. In the same year, Goodyear's family was starving, and young Elias Howe was developing consumption.

YANKEE INVENTION AND THE AMERICAN MYTH

By 1830, thirty-two years had passed since the death of John Fitch; thirty years since the early experiments of Fulton; and Eli Whitney was five years dead. Fulton was remembered as a great hero and a great inventor; Whitney as a successful manufacturer (everyone blithely ignoring that in his lifetime he had been driven frantic by the unrestrained infringement on his cotton gin patent); and Fitch was completely forgotten. John Stevens was still alive, an old man now, actively forwarding the cause of American steam railroading. By 1830, Americans had not only grown used to the idea of their inventors; they were beginning to enshrine them. The career of an inventor had become an honorable one that could lead to glory and riches.

Until 1830, the popular heroes of America were statesmen and military figures. Forty years later, when biographies of famous men were written, the category of inventors was equally important.

Americans had conveniently forgotten the difficulties placed in the way of these early pioneers of American inventiveness. All that remained was the memory of their glorious success. A new legend was taking form: an American who really applied himself could make anything better than anyone else. Inventiveness was beginning to seem a Yankee trait. Americans who grew up in the first three decades of the nineteenth century came to maturity deeply immersed in the American myth. It is only this profound belief that can explain the harrowing careers of Charles Goodyear, Samuel Morse, and Elias Howe. They were absolutely sustained from within by the belief that Americans who worked hard enough in whatever field must eventually succeed.

The new attitude towards invention created the necessity for a new patent law, passed in 1838. Up until that point the government had granted a patent to anyone who claimed one. Two inventors claiming exactly the same invention could receive patents, and they would have to fight out their differences in the civil courts.

The patent law of 1838 set up for the first time the principles of search, requiring the patent office to withhold a patent until all prior patents and other pending claims had been examined, to be sure that the claims made in the application were original. Until 1838, no more than five hundred government patents had been granted; but the quest of American perfectibility through invention proved so stimulating that within the next few years, over ten thousand patents were granted, and in succeeding decades the number of patents accelerated to enormous proportions. Actually, the number of inventions multiplied so fast that the government facilities for prior search and examination have never caught up with the volume of applications. Nevertheless, the principle of search was a great step forward in encouraging inventors.

The most decisive economic fact in the thirty-year period from 1830 to the outbreak of the Civil War was the depression of 1837 and the financial failures of the banks in that same decade. Backers of promising inventions suddenly found themselves penniless. The telegraph, the reaper, the development of rubber, and a host of other inventions were retarded in their development by at least five years. Economic recovery did not set in until the close of that decade, and in the forties prosperity was once again general throughout the country.

Both the North and the West developed and grew wealthy as mechanical inventions multiplied. Only the South failed to benefit by the new devices. Southern economy reached its peak about 1850 and thereafter fell into a decline in comparison to the accelerating growth of both the North and the West.

A gallery of American inventors, painted in the years of success,
shows Goodyear seated at left of table, Morse at right.
Leaning against the left of the pillar is Joseph Henry, at the right is John Ericsson. Seated at the far right is Elias Howe.
Standing left of Goodyear is McCormick.
On the wall is Franklin, the godfather of them all.

The Louvre was painted by Morse to show great paintings to untraveled Americans. In 1832, Morse was one of America's best painters.

SAMUEL
F. B. MORSE

AND HIS
ELECTROMAGNETIC
TELEGRAPH: 1

Men have always found the means to communicate with others at a distance. Bonfires flickered on hill after hill in the darkness of prehistory to signal distant tribes that an enemy was on the way, or that herds of game had moved into new areas. In the seventeenth century, the word *telegraph* came into use when Englishmen began experimenting with semaphore devices. An observer would decipher the signal on a distant hill and then send it on to the next watcher.

In the late eighteenth century, the Chappé system was perfected. The telegrapher on top of a tower with a spyglass decoded the message signaled from another tower fifteen miles away. He would then go below, crank the semaphore arms of his own instrument, and laboriously relay the message to another tower some fifteen miles farther on. In the United States, lower Cape Cod is still studded with a number of telegraph hills: remnants of the first commercial semaphore system installed and worked by Jonathan Grout in 1800, to transmit from Martha's Vineyard to Boston merchants the news of incoming vessels, their cargo, and their condition.

The young republic wanted a network along the entire Atlantic coast and a prize of thirty thousand dollars was offered for a telegraph system that would be workable for a thousand miles.

An accident of history determined that the offer did not qualify the word "telegraph" with the word "semaphore." After several years of silence from the general public, the government in the late 1830's was surprised to find that its half-forgotten offer had been taken up by a man who proposed to use the word "telegraph" in a very novel way.

The man's name was Samuel Finley Breese Morse.

Both Morse and America had come a long way since the turn of the century. Morse had been born in 1791 in Charlestown, Massachusetts, the son of Jedediah Morse, a famous New England minister. He was a boy at Andover in the same decade in which John Fitch died in despair, when Oliver Evans was being ridiculed by skeptics who refused to believe what he made plain before their eyes. Morse entered Yale in 1807, a few months after Fulton made his first voyage to Albany in the *Clermont;* in effect, Morse was growing up with the American myth.

In 1811, he went to England to study art with Washington Allston. As a painter, he showed great promise, but he was trapped by his unquestioning acceptance of the intellectual fashion, then current, that the art which represented scenes of history and antiquity was higher than the art which portrayed living people. On his return to America in 1815, he found himself in a country too raw, too busy, and too poor to recognize or care about an art so far removed from reality. On the other hand, America of 1815 was deeply interested in portraits. By 1817, he was being paid sixty dollars for a picture, and he could complete four a week. He made a tour of the South and in 1818 returned with three thousand dollars, enabling him to marry Lucretia Walker of Concord.

With this capital, he moved to Charleston, South Carolina, gave up portrait work and devoted himself for the next eighteen months to the painting of an enormous historical picture for the House of Representatives at Washington. He failed to sell it. His money was gone, and he moved to New York for a new try. There he was commissioned by the city to go back to Washington to do a full-length portrait of Lafayette who was visiting the country. He did two portraits. All of Morse's portraits show power; but his "Lafayette" was the work of a mature and controlled talent. Still Morse was dissatisfied, even though in the next few years he was to be the acknowledged leader of young American artists. In 1829 he returned to Europe to continue his studies.

In America, artists who insisted on their *genres* either starved quietly, or else, like the Peales, opened private museums to display their wares along with other curiosities of the day. Taking his cue from the Peales, Morse decided to paint the sort of picture which would interest an America that had never seen either the original or copies of the "Mona Lisa," "The Last Supper," or any of the other masterpieces of the world of art. He painted "The Louvre" which showed for background as many of the masterpieces hanging in that museum as he could cram in. Full of hope, in 1832, he packed his canvases and returned to America on the packet *Sully.* He boarded the ship a painter, and disembarked an inventor.

Aboard the *Sully,* Morse got into a conversation about European experiments on electromagnetism. The work of Faraday had been published only a few months earlier and had at once been duplicated in most European laboratories. "Drawing sparks from a magnet" was one of the scientific marvels of the moment. Morse immediately suggested that a combination of sparks could be used as a code to send messages over a wire. The idea took fire within him, although he was almost totally ignorant of the most basic principles of electricity. Morse, by this time, was also ridden by the witch of belief that Americans could do anything they set their minds to. Lack of background meant nothing—God would provide. He had spent twenty years studying the art of painting; yet it never occurred to him that a career of electrical invention might also demand preparation.

Self Portrait of S. F. B. Morse, son of the famous theologian, Jedediah Morse.
As an itinerant painter, Morse was quite successful, and made several thousand dollars a season.

THE SIGNAL TELEGRAPH.

The word "telegraph" referred originally to semaphore signals. Such telegraph systems had been in use for a century before Morse.

2. SAMUEL MORSE'S
FALTERING FIRST EFFORTS

During the month-long voyage, Morse made some preliminary sketches. The next three years he spent unsuccessfully trying to realize them in the attic of his brother Richard's home. However, in addition to his complete lack of electrical information, he had neither time nor a free mind. His wife had died, and he was responsible for three small children.

In 1834, he formulated an ambitious plan for historical paintings to fill the four remaining blank panels of the Rotunda of the National Capitol. He petitioned various members of Congress, but John Quincy Adams refused to believe that any American painter was capable of work in the style required. Morse's rejection was such a bitter disappointment that for all practical purposes he gave up painting even though he was forty-three and at the height of his power.

In the following year he got an appointment as Professor of Arts and Design at the newly established University of the City of New York, the project of culturally-minded New Yorkers like James Fenimore Cooper, Washington Irving and others. His salary was small, but he was able to live on it. He returned to his plan for an electromagnetic telegraph.

He gathered together some galvanic batteries, iron bars, and wire. He made the connections he had outlined for himself and closed the circuit. Nothing happened. He made a few more adjustments. Still nothing. For days he continued his fruitless tinkering. Finally, in desperation, he turned for help to a colleague in the chemistry department—Leonard Gale. Gale looked at Morse's pathetic contrivance and took pity on him. Morse had been told that to make an electromagnet one wound wires around a horse-shoe bar of iron.

Gale, who had read Henry's papers, found the windings made haphazardly, without any insulation. He showed Morse how to wind a magnet properly, and how to arrange a battery for such a circuit. By the time Gale was finished, Morse's apparatus was showing some response.

The details of Morse's early plans for a telegraph were both naïve and unnecessarily complicated.

The principle was the same as Henry's: an operator opened and closed an electric circuit so that a series of current pulses were sent through a pair of wires to a receiving instrument. Later forms of the telegraph were to use a signal key, manually operated, to open and close the circuit.

Morse used only a single battery in his circuit and so he was severely limited to the length of wire over which he could send a detectable message. The longer the wire, the greater the electrical resistance. Morse, with Gale's help, progressed from twenty feet, to a hundred feet, and then to a thousand, but no further.

In September, 1837, he put on a demonstration at New York University in which he sent a message over seventeen hundred feet of wire. One of the witnesses was a prosperous ironworks owner in New Jersey, Stephen Vail, who agreed to put up $2,000 and work space if his son Alfred could become Morse's assistant. Morse agreed, making the luckiest decision of his life. Alfred Vail had not only true inventiveness but a keen eye for practicality. Over the years that followed, Vail was largely responsible for working out the final form of Morse's code, for introducing the key, discarding the composing stick, and reducing the entire machine to the compact form that was adopted eventually. He also invented a printing telegraph that was patented in Morse's name according to the terms of Vail's contract.

Shortly after meeting Vail, Morse came across the government's offer of aid to an inventor for coastwise telegraphy. In December of 1837, he appealed to

Morse's first ideas came while he was sailing home from France. He told the *Sully's* captain, "When you hear of the magnetic telegraph, remember it was invented on your ship."

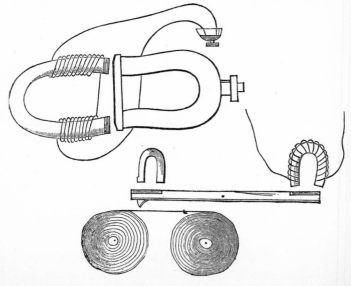

Sketches made by Morse on the *Sully* show his plan to use an interrupted electric current to move a stylus. They also show he did not know how a battery made current.

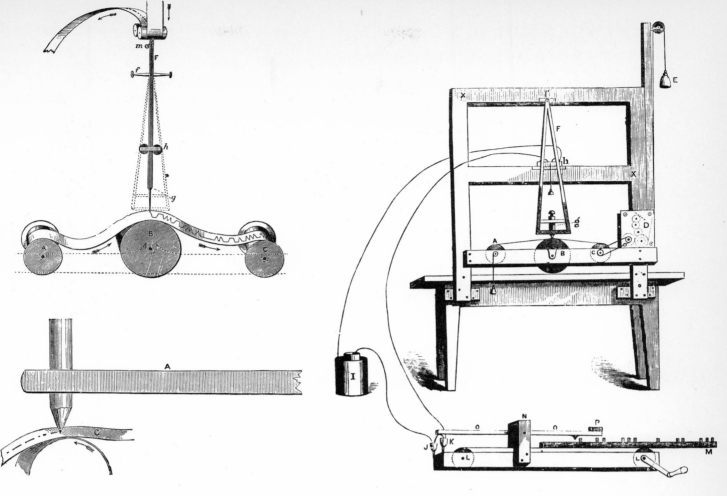

THE CUMBERSOME FIRST MACHINE

Morse's original plan did not include a key. Instead, he copied the early printer's use of a composing stick. Slugs of metal were ridged along one face—the number of ridges and the distances between them varied—and each slug represented a letter. The entire message was mounted in a line of slugs and pushed along beneath a wooden finger that made and broke the circuit. Morse's code at the time was too complicated to be memorized by an operator.

The machine's receiving end was equally involved. Later, operators were to be able to decipher the dots and dashes by ear. The original receiver was an electromagnet which actuated a pencil pressing down on a moving strip of tape. Each pulse from the sender made the pendulum swing. The paper tape then showed a series of sawtooth marks that corresponded with the ridges of the original slug—and the message could be deciphered from the paper strip.

Congress for help. The Chairman of the House Committee on Commerce, Francis O. J. Smith, was so impressed by Morse's demonstration that he resigned his seat and became Morse's partner. Smith was a cantankerous sharpshooter whose gift for public rhetoric and penchant for private double-dealing brought Morse trouble for the rest of his life.

The panic of 1837 put an end to any government appropriation plans. Smith rushed Morse off to Europe to secure foreign patent protection. In England, Morse was told that Wheatstone had already invented an electromagnetic telegraph as he could see for himself if he went to the nearest Post Office. On the continent, Morse was told that Steinheil had already invented an electromagnetic telegraph. Let him go to the nearest railroad station and see it.

While in France, Morse made friends with another disappointed inventor, Daguerre, who was having as

much trouble trying to place his photographic process as Morse was having with telegraphy. Companions in misfortune, each agreed to act as the other's agent in his own country.

In Russia, Morse learned that Baron Schilling, the Russian Minister to Austria, had invented an electromagnetic telegraph as far back as 1825, but that the present czar considered the possibility of instantaneous communication between people at distant ends of Russia so subversive that he had banned any mention of such a thing in the press. Morse hurried back to America, broke; Mr. Smith went to Washington. None of the foreign systems were as simple as Morse's; he would not give up hope, although his situation was more desperate than ever. To augment his small income from painting he opened a small studio for taking pictures according to Daguerre's formula. This too proved a failure.

The telegraph receiver was a printing instrument for a long time. Even after Vail simplified the system, the paper was marked with dots and dashes by a stylus operated by an armature which covered the poles of an inverted horse-shoe magnet.

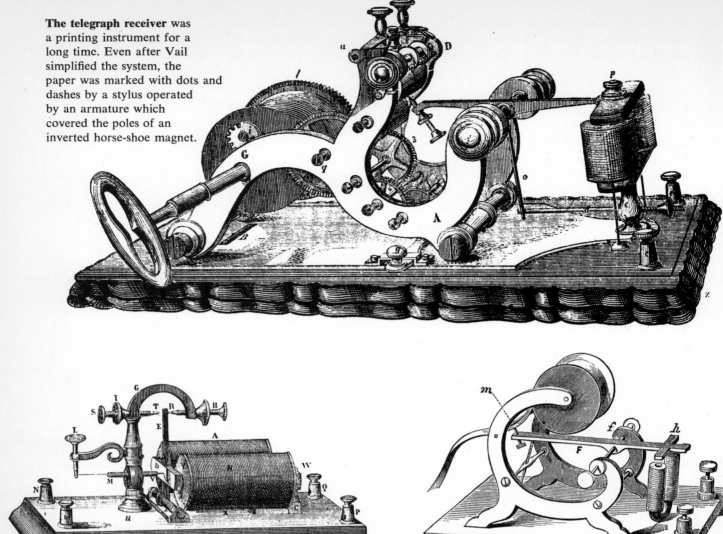

The heart of the system was the relay.

Another stylus and paper strip model.

3. "WHAT HATH GOD WROUGHT?"

Morse's poverty during the hard years was absolute. A former painting pupil tells this story:

"Well, Strother," Morse asked one day, "how are we off for money?"

"Why, Professor, I'm sorry to say that I've been disappointed, but I expect a remittance next week."

"Next week," said Morse sadly. "I shall be dead by then."

"Dead, sir?"

"Yes, dead by starvation."

"Would ten dollars be of any service?"

"Ten dollars would save my life. That's all it would do."

I took Morse to dinner, paid the bill and gave Morse ten dollars. Morse said: "This is my first meal in twenty-four hours. Strother, don't be an artist. It means beggary. Your life depends on people who know nothing of your art and care nothing for you. A house dog lives better."

Apparently Strother took the advice. He gave up art, entered the Army and rose to the rank of general. He led a far happier life than his teacher, but he was to be remembered only as the man who once gave ten dollars to Samuel Finley Breese Morse.

Gale had left New York to teach in the South. Morse finally took a trip to Princeton to ask Joseph Henry for advice.

Henry had no particular interest in working out the details of electromagnetic telegraphy himself. He had solved the basic problem by inventing the relay and had then gone on to far more provocative and interesting work on his own. Sooner or later, he knew, a man would come along who was sufficiently single-minded to do the job. Morse impressed him as that man.

Morse had sincerity and Henry was willing to help him. Patiently he explained the errors in Morse's system and pointed out that a single battery, no matter how strong, could send a signal of electrical pulses only a limited distance. The relay which Henry had developed some six years earlier was the device which would solve Morse's problem.

The sender's circuit was not connected directly to the receiver. In place of the receiver was a horseshoe of soft iron wrapped around with wire. Across the pole pieces of the iron was a movable armature. As the operator's signals opened and closed the circuit, sending pulses of current through the magnet coil, the armature, too, opened and closed. The armature, however, was actually a switch which activated a second circuit containing its own battery, its own coil, its own magnet, and operated exactly the same way as the first. In turn, this second circuit controlled a third independent circuit. In this way, an endless chain of circuits was possible. Each circuit contained its own battery and its own relay.

Henry explained to Morse that such a chain system could transmit a message of electrical pulses for thousands of miles and the signal at the end would be just as powerful as the signal originally transmitted.

Morse returned to New York and improved his system according to Henry's advice.

The government appropriation for which Morse had applied in 1837 was not finally granted until 1843, although ex-Congressman Smith's promise to him had been renewed month after month.

When the bill was finally introduced, the House thought it a huge joke, magnetism sounding something like mesmerism to the members. Morse, now a man of fifty-two, listened to the stupid humor from the gallery and then left in despair. The session was to end in the morning. There would be no time for President Tyler to sign the bill even if it were to be passed. Morse paid his boarding-house bill and bought a ticket on the steam cars for New York, leaving him only thirty-seven cents. Next morning at breakfast, the daughter of his friend, the Commissioner of Patents, came with the fantastic news that Smith's friends had succeeded in getting through the bill shorn of all the silly amendments, and Tyler had signed it at midnight. Morse was so overjoyed that he promised her that she could send the very first message over the very first system. Her choice was to be the text, "What Hath God Wrought?"

The terms of the government grant of thirty thousand dollars called for a test line to run between Washington and Baltimore, a distance of forty miles. Smith awarded himself the contract for construction. Morse and Vail had decided on an underground line of complicated construction within a tubular lead shield. The construction engineer, Ezra Cornell, invented a special plow that would dig a trench, unroll prepared cable, and then roll the earth back into the trench. Smith charged almost twenty thousand dollars on the first few miles. Morse was beside himself with worry. Cornell, on his own initiative, tested the line already laid and found it riddled with short circuits. Smith, it turned out, had decided not to waste valuable money on nonsense like insulation.

Cornell suggested stringing bare wires overhead as the cheapest, fastest way to get to Baltimore without precipitating a public scandal; but Morse was in a panic. Once again he ran off to Joseph Henry for advice. Henry backed Cornell, and the entire line was strung from trees and poles using broken bottle necks as insulators. The line was completed just as the Whig convention gathered in Baltimore to nominate a president. Vail was the operator in Baltimore with instructions to send to Morse in Washington the news as it broke on the floor.

Politicians coming from Baltimore with express dispatches found that their news had preceded the steam cars. A man named Morse was talking over a wire to Baltimore.

Morse was asked to move his wires to the Supreme Court room of the Capitol; he drew a crowd of government officials, judges and congressmen. At the high point of the Whig convention, came this exchange between Morse and Vail:

From Morse: "Have you any news?"

"No."

"Mr. Seaton's respects to you."

"My respects to him."

"What is your time?"

"Nine o'clock, twenty-eight minutes."

"What weather have you?"

"Cloudy."

"Separate your words more."

"Buchanan stock said to be rising."

"I have a great crowd here."

"Van Buren cannon in front, with foxtail on it."

Political news was interrupted occasionally with personal messages such as this one:

"As a rumor is prevalent here this morning that Mr. Eugene Boyle was shot at Baltimore last evening, Professor Morse will confer a great favor upon the family by making inquiry by means of his electromagnetic telegraph if such is the fact."

A few weeks later the Democrats also held their convention in Baltimore, and Morse sent his telegraphic dispatches to newspapers. But after that, public interest cooled. The government set aside eight thousand dollars a year to maintain the telegraph as part of the Post Office, but in 1845 the rising trouble with Mexico deflected official interest. This again was a major disappointment to Morse. Like many of his contemporaries, he was afraid of the power which the telegraph would give to a private owner to alter or withhold news and messages.

4. THE TELEGRAPH IN EVERY COMMUNITY BY 1850

With the telegraph back in his own hands, Morse and his partners organized the Magnetic Telegraph Company for a line between New York and Philadelphia. It was to be a private stock company. At this point, Morse shut out Vail and most of his early helpers.

The real organizer of lines from the seaboard to the Mississippi was an Irish-born promoter who changed his name from O'Reilly to O'Rielly. He knew nothing about telegraphy or engineering, but he could sell stock. Each town-to-town line was a separate promotion; and like a master showman, he sent out advance scouts with the news that the Lightning Wire was coming. He raised money as fast as he could string wire. In less than two years, he hung thousands of miles of wire wherever he could find poles, creating more stock companies than the patent owners back East could count.

Newspapers quickly found ways to use the telegraph, and the Associated Press set up its own wire service. By 1848 small communities were reading the latest dispatches from the Mexican War hot off the Lightning Wire. Before long the railroads were using the telegraph for signaling, dispatching, and traffic. Freight trains entering New York with cattle for export would wire ahead to a ship's captain, telling him how many head were coming. He then was able to arrange his deck space accordingly so that he could sail within thirty minutes of loading. For a long time all messages along the line began with "DEAR SIR," and ended, "RESPECTFULLY YOURS."

Morse in his later years

STRINGING THE "LIGHTNING WIRE"

A lineman of the 1850's

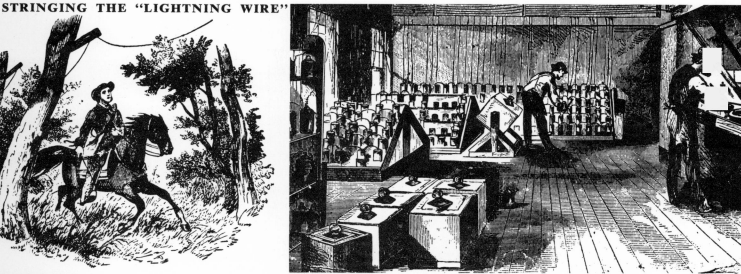

Western Union battery room before the days of generators

High masts at a river crossing

Cable for a river crossing was spun on the spot. Submarine cables were used later when gutta percha proved to be a good underwater insulator.

122

The early lines were constantly breaking in bad weather. In one instance, there were one hundred and seventy breaks in thirty miles of wire. First copper wire was tried and discarded for iron. Then iron was in turn dropped in favor of twisted cable. The linemen who were responsible for repairs led busy lives. Not only did they have nature to contend with, but they had to patch up after angry farmers who cut the wires because of the humming sound made by the wind.

Even worse, there was no traffic system for the various independent companies or even for individual operators. Twenty operators might be trying to send messages at once, all on the same wire.

Not until 1856, when Hiram Sibley organized the Western Union, did there begin to be any order. Then more and more lines came into existence, paying a royalty. Morse's days of poverty were over, and he spent his old age as a rich, handsomely decorated celebrity. He had fought innumerable patent suits and won them all, even though at one point he had to deny that he received much help from Joseph Henry.

The first half of the nineteenth century was hospitable only to driving, aggressive men and then only if they were driving in the direction of the material expansion of the country. When Morse gave up his early career and became an inventor, he became transformed into a man of his time. Under the same pressures, Henry steadfastly remained the kind of man he wanted most to be. Morse was satisfied with what he became.

Mexican War news was featured in papers throughout the country under the impressive flash headline: "News by Lightning Wire."

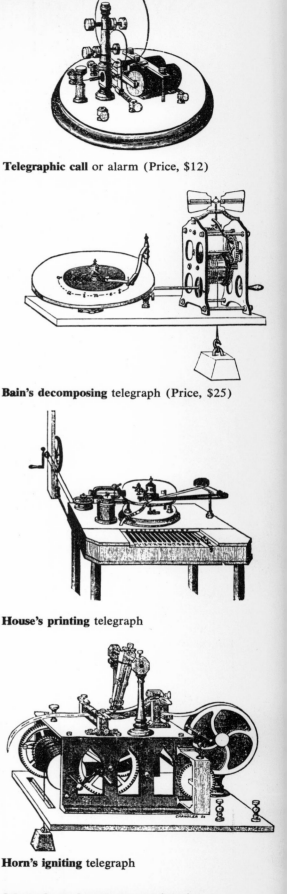

Telegraphic call or alarm (Price, $12)

Bain's decomposing telegraph (Price, $25)

House's printing telegraph

Horn's igniting telegraph

Other telegraph systems were in existence, but Western Union eventually gathered all patents, and combined the best features of each. The basic patent was Morse's.

123

CHARLES GOODYEAR

1. SALT, CREAM CHEESE, SOUP, INK—NOTHING WORKED

UNITED STATES PATENT OFFICE.

CHARLES GOODYEAR, OF NEW YORK, N. Y.

IMPROVEMENT IN INDIA-RUBBER FABRICS.

Specification forming part of Letters Patent No. **3,633**, dated June 15, 1844.

To all whom it may concern:

Be it known that I, CHARLES GOODYEAR, of the city of New York, in the State of New York, have invented certain new and useful Improvements in the Manner of Preparing Fabrics of Caoutchouc or India-Rubber; and I do hereby declare that the following is a full and exact description thereof.

My principal improvement consists in the combining of sulphur and white lead with the india-rubber, and in the submitting of the compound thus formed to the action of heat at a regulated temperature, by which combination and exposure to heat it will be so far altered in its qualities as not to become softened by the action of the solar ray or of artificial heat at a temperature below that to which it was submitted in its preparation—say to a heat of 270° of Fahrenheit's scale—nor will it be injuriously affected by exposure to cold. It will also resist the action of the expressed oils, and that likewise of spirits of turpentine, or of the other essential oils at common temperatures, which oils are its usual solvents.

The articles which I combine with the india-rubber in forming my improved fabric are sulphur and white lead, which materials may be employed in varying proportions; but that which I have found to answer best, and to which it is desirable to approximate in forming the compound, is the following: I take twenty-five parts of india-rubber, five parts of sulphur, and seven parts of white lead. The india-rubber I usually dissolve in spirits of turpentine or other essential oil, and the white lead and sulphur also I grind in spirits of turpentine in the ordinary way of grinding paint. These three articles thus prepared may, when it is intended to form a sheet by itself, be evenly spread upon any smooth surface or upon glazed cloth, from which it may be readily separated; but I prefer to use for this purpose the cloth made according to the present specification, as the compound spread upon this article separates therefrom more cleanly than from any other.

Instead of dissolving the india-rubber in the manner above set forth, the sulphur and white lead, prepared by grinding as above directed, may be incorporated with the substance of the india-rubber by the aid of heated cylinders or calender-rollers, by which it may be brought into sheets of any required thickness; or it may be applied so as to adhere to the surface of cloth or of leather of various kinds. This mode of producing and of applying the sheet caoutchouc by means of rollers is well known to manufacturers. To destroy the odor of the sulphur in fabrics thus prepared, I wash the surface with a solution of potash, or with vinegar, or with a small portion of essential oil or other solvent of sulphur.

When the india-rubber is spread upon the firmer kinds of cloth or of leather it is subject to peel therefrom by a moderate degree of force, the gum letting go the fiber by which the two are held together. I have therefore devised another improvement in this manufacture by which this tendency is in a great measure corrected, and by which, also, the sheet-gum, when not attached to cloth or leather, is better adapted to a variety of purposes than when not prepared by this improved mode, which is as follows: After laying a coat of the gum, compounded as above set forth, on any suitable fabric I cover it with a bat of cotton-wool as it is delivered from the doffer of a carding-machine, and this bat I cover with another coat of the gum—a process which may be repeated two or three times, according to the required thickness of the goods. A very thin and strong fabric may be thus produced, which may be used in lieu of paper for the covering of boxes, books, or other articles.

When this compound of india-rubber, sulphur, and white lead, whether to be used alone in the state of sheets or applied to the surface of any other fabric, has been fully dried, either in a heated room or by exposure to the sun and air, the goods are to be subjected to the action of a high degree of temperature, which will admit of considerable variation—say from 212° to 350° of Fahrenheit's thermometer, but for the best effect approaching as nearly as may be to 270°. This heating may be effected by running the fabrics over a heated cylinder; but I prefer to expose them to an atmosphere of the proper temperature, which may be best done by the aid of an oven properly constructed with openings through which the sheet or web may be passed by means of suitable rollers. When this process is performed upon a

Goodyear's patent application for the sulphur-and-heat curing process

---

Charles Goodyear's discovery of the vulcanization of rubber makes one of the most perplexing and exasperating tales in American history. The man had no right to achieve success. His background was all wrong. He came up against obstacles that should rightly have defeated any man. Most of the time he didn't know what he was doing.

The only possible explanation for Goodyear's persistence was his thorough belief in the American myth and the sustenance he received from it. He himself said, "I was encouraged in my efforts by the reflection that what is hidden and unknown and cannot be discovered by scientific research, will most likely be discovered by accident, if at all, by the man who applies himself most perseveringly to the subject, and is most observing of everything related thereto."

Goodyear's work took him into the deepest thickets of organic chemistry and he went as blithely wide-eyed as Hänsel and Gretel on their way to the witch. Organic chemistry was then in its infancy. No one knew any more about rubber or the chemistry of rubber than he did, and he knew nothing. Goodyear simply believed his way to success.

In 1735 a party of French astronomers, on an expedition to Peru, discovered a tree that yielded a peculiar sap or gum which was colorless in its native state and had the property of becoming hard and tough when exposed to the sun or the heat of fire. The natives used the gum to make simple articles: a boot and a bottle. The French brought the substance back with them and gum elastic was introduced in Europe where it was regarded merely as a curiosity. Joseph Priestley, in a letter to a friend, remarked that he had used it to rub out mistakes in a manuscript, and the word "rubber" came into use. The pure substance had these properties: under heat it became very soft and gummy, while at low temperatures it became as hard as rock.

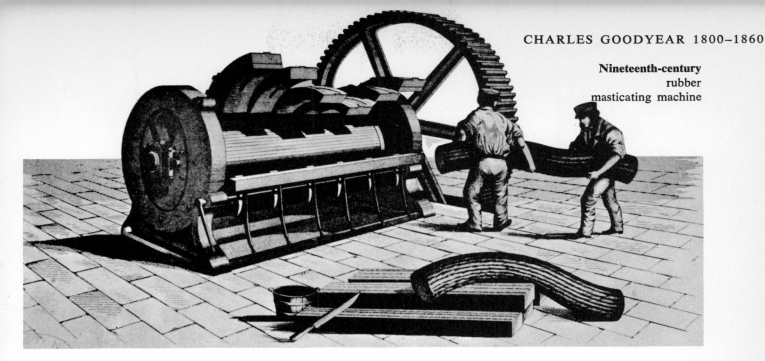

Nineteenth-century rubber masticating machine

The first rubber factory was established in Vienna in 1811. About 1820 the French used rubber threads mixed with cotton to make suspenders and garters. In England, Mackintosh used it as a very thin layer between two pieces of cloth to make waterproof coats that stiffened to armor in the winter rain and had to be kept in cool cellars during the summer. About the same time a ship captain brought five hundred pairs of the crude Indian boots to the United States. They were worn as waterproof overshoes. They were incredibly clumsy but Americans began to buy a half million pairs a year at five dollars a pair, even though they were extremely perishable.

The sudden popularity of India rubber in the United States started a boom in the 1830's. E. M. Chaffee of Boston was seeking a substance that would be an improvement in his patent leather business. He settled on a mixture of one pound of raw gum to three quarts of turpentine, and added lampblack to give him color and gloss. A calendering machine of his own design spread a thin film of the mixture on cloth. In 1833, with several other men, he founded the Roxbury India Rubber Company, capitalized at thirty thousand dollars, and in 1835 he patented his mixing mill and calender.

Business was phenomenal. Capitalization was increased to almost half a million dollars in two years, and Chaffee made cabin covers, wagon covers, caps, shoes, and coats. Other companies started in business in Boston, Framingham, Salem, Lynn, Chelsea, Staten Island, and Troy. The furor was called "the India-rubber fever."

Two summers reduced the coats, caps, and wagon covers down to the molten state and they gave off so offensive an odor that they had to be buried in the ground. By the end of 1836 the impending doom of the rubber industry was known very clearly to the insiders; the public was still unaware that the loss to

stockholders already amounted to two million dollars. It was shortly before this that Charles Goodyear walked into the New York shop of the Roxbury company and made a purchase. He walked out, unaware that he was being trailed by the shadow of his future.

Goodyear had bought a rubber life-preserver because he felt that he could improve the valve that was used for inflation, completely unaware that the very substance of the life-preserver was far more defective than any mechanical part. Within three weeks, he invented a valve far superior to the one used in the life-preserver. When he returned to the office of the Roxbury Rubber Company, the agent told him that he would have been far better off to find a way of improving rubber. Instead of running for his life, he took the advice seriously.

Charles Goodyear was born in New Haven, Connecticut, in December, 1800. When he was twenty-one, he became a partner in the successful hardware firm of A. Goodyear and Sons. The firm existed until 1836, when the crash of the banks drove them out of business. Before this, however, Charles Goodyear decided to withdraw from a doomed business and devote himself to a career of invention. He picked for his field the one industry that was itself approaching bankruptcy as fast as A. Goodyear and Sons.

He approached rubber as if it were leather, and he frequently spoke of "curing" rubber, thereby reducing an insuperable problem to something that sounded familiar. In all innocence, he believed that he could solve the problem within the next few months. He wrote, "I was blessed with ignorance of the obstacles I had subsequently to encounter, but I soon learned that the difficulties attending the experiment in gum elastic obliged me to wait the return of both warm and cold weather, at least twelve months, and often much longer before I could know with certainty that my manufactures would not decompose...."

2. GOODYEAR RIDICULED AND CALLED CRAZY

Goodyear began experiments with Brazilian gum elastic, making thin films at home with his wife's rolling pin. He mixed crude gum with every possible substance that came to his hand: salt, pepper, sugar, sand, castor oil, soup—on the exquisite logic that sooner or later he would have tried everything on the face of the earth and come upon the one successful combination. Ralph Steele of New Haven advanced some capital, and Goodyear opened a shop with hundreds of pairs of rubber shoes. On the first hot day that came along, the shoes melted into a stinking mass.

Until then, Goodyear had used the basic mixture devised by Mackintosh: gum elastic in turpentine. Goodyear began to believe that the stickiness was due to the turpentine. He bought some crude gum and outlined for himself a long series of experiments. Before he could begin, a handy man around the plant used some of the gum elastic to improve the appearance of his trousers. While waiting for the gum elastic to dry, he sat down. When Goodyear returned, the man had to be cut out of his clothes.

Goodyear gave up his shop and intensified his mixing experiments. Witch hazel, cream cheese, black ink—all proved total failures, with one exception: magnesia. He mixed half a pound of magnesia with a pound of the gum and produced a compound that was whiter than the gum and as firm and flexible as leather. He made book covers, piano covers, showed them, got encouragement, laughed with joy—and within a month, found the product to be a failure. At this point, he gave up his house and moved his wife and children to the country, while he set out alone for New York and new support. In the city he found two friends, one of whom gave him the use of a room in Gold Street as a laboratory; the other, a druggist, agreed to advance him on credit whatever chemicals he might want.

At this time he believed that his magnesia formula could be improved. He boiled the gum mixed with magnesia in a solution of quicklime and water and got sheets firmer and smoother than anything before. The newspapers praised him as the man who had saved the India rubber industry. Three weeks later he discovered that a single drop of the weakest acid—even apple juice—was enough to neutralize the quicklime and destroy the product.

His next step was to throw out the magnesia. Pure quicklime must be the answer. Pure quicklime was *not* the answer—it destroyed the gum completely.

Goodyear liked to decorate his samples with painted patterns, and on one occasion he used bronze paint. The bronze did not please him and so he removed it with *aqua fortis*. One drop of the acid on the rubber discolored the cloth so badly that Goodyear threw it away. The appearance of the spot stuck in his mind, and a few days later he dug up the discarded shoe; where the acid had fallen, the troublesome stickiness had gone.

The *aqua fortis* Goodyear used was nitric acid with a residual trace of sulphuric acid. Goodyear knew so little about chemistry that he thought he was dealing with pure nitric acid. He exposed a few sheets of rubber material to the fumes of the acid mixture. The result was superior to anything he had got before, and he applied for a patent. He hired an old India

Goodyear accidentally dropped a piece of sulphur-treated rubber on a stove and saw that it toughened.

rubber works on Staten Island, opened a salesroom on Broadway, and prepared to manufacture on a large scale—when the second great crisis of bank failures hit his backers. Within two months he was once again reduced to absolute beggary.

At this point Goodyear actually did have a process which, for thin films of rubber, was commercially feasible. But the financial failure threw him into such dejection that he did not realize exactly what he had. His family had joined him in New York, and to support them, he pawned everything in his possession. Most of the time he was weak with hunger. At this time, as a means of demonstration, he made himself a complete outfit of India rubber clothing and wore these wherever he went. Someone at this point, who asked how Goodyear could be recognized, was told, "If you see a man in an India rubber coat, India rubber shoes, an India rubber hat, and in his pocket an India rubber purse, and in that India rubber purse not one cent, then that is Goodyear."

In September of that year, 1837, Goodyear went back to Roxbury, where the original rubber company was operating on a skeleton basis. Chaffee, the first promoter of the India rubber process in the country, still believed in the substance. He took in Goodyear and allowed him the use of his plant for experiment. Using his "acid cure" process, Goodyear made shoes

Daniel Webster, aged Secretary of State, successfully defended Goodyear's patent with less than one hour's preparation. Webster took the case because he needed the $15,000. This was more money than Goodyear had earned up to that time in the years of dogged work he had devoted to his experiments.

and cloth good enough to be bought by a population that ordinarily flinched at the very sound of the word. He was immediately flooded by offers for licenses, and Goodyear made close to five thousand dollars. He was able to bring his family to Roxbury with him. Once more success was at hand.

To crown his success, he received an order from the United States government for one hundred and fifty mailbags, to be made of India rubber. Goodyear filled the order and hung the finished bags in the shop for public demonstration.

Having worked so hard, Goodyear decided to take his family on a vacation. He returned after two weeks of hot weather to find that success, far from being at hand, was as distant as ever, for the hundred and fifty mailbags had run in the heat. The surfaces of the bags were still intact, proving that they actually had been cured, but the interior of the fabric where the acid vapor had not penetrated was as sticky as ever. The contract was canceled; other goods began to be returned; by the end of the summer, Goodyear was once again reduced to poverty.

Just before the failure, Goodyear had taken in Nathaniel M. Hayward, the foreman of the Roxbury works. Hayward had his own process for curing rubber: mixing the gum elastic with powdered sulphur and drying the substance in the sun, a process he called "solarization." The process had come to Hayward in a dream. To Goodyear's surprise, Hayward's product was just as good as his own. He was completely unaware that it was exactly the same, both of them depending on the use of sulphur. Goodyear's position was now so desperate that it was a question of finding a roof and bread for his family.

"For four years I had attempted in vain to improve a manufacture that entailed ruin on all concerned. It was generally agreed that a man who could proceed further in such a course fairly deserved all the distress brought upon himself, and was justly debarred from sympathy."

Nevertheless, he kept on working.

His developed acuteness of observation told him that the fine line around the char was "cured" rubber.

3. GOODYEAR FINALLY STUMBLES INTO SUCCESS

Goodyear's brother-in-law lived in Woburn, and the Goodyears moved there, living on the brother's charity. It was during this winter that Goodyear finally got the lead towards the process now known as vulcanization:

"I was surprised to find that a specimen, being carelessly brought into contact with a hot stove, charred like leather. I endeavored to call the attention of others who were present . . . to this remarkable effect . . . since gum elastic always melted when exposed to a high degree of heat. Nobody but myself thought the charring worthy of notice. . . . However, I . . . inferred that if the charring process could be stopped at the right moment, it might divest the compound of its stickiness throughout. . . . Upon further trials with high temperatures, I was convinced that my inference was sound. . . . What was of supreme importance was that upon the border of the charred fabric, there was a line which had escaped charring and was perfectly cured."

Goodyear was able to detect that tiny line, perhaps no more than a few millimeters wide, and recognize it for what it was. For that reason he was perfectly justified in saying later:

"While I admit that these discoveries of mine were not the result of scientific chemical investigation, I am not willing to admit that they were the result of what is commonly called accident. I claim them to be the result of the closest application and observation."

Of that first test, Goodyear's daughter said later:

"I casually observed the little piece of gum Father was holding near the fire, and I noticed that he was unusually animated by some discovery. He nailed the gum outside in the intense cold. Next morning he brought it in and held it up exultingly. It was perfectly flexible, as when he'd nailed it up. This was proof enough of the value of his discovery."

Goodyear was only at the beginning of a series of experiments with stoves, fires, and brick kilns to determine exactly how much heat was required. By all his neighbors he was considered a pleasant but helpless madman.

Goodyear now received a very generous offer for the exclusive use in France of his acid gas process. But now, even though he was deeply in debt, and his family living on potatoes and wild roots, he wrote back to the French firm that he could not accept their offer because he was now at work on a far superior process. His friends thought him absolutely mad.

"During the winter of 1839–40, during a long and severe snowstorm," he wrote, "I found that my family was left without food or fuel. . . . The recollection of a kind greeting received some time previous from Mr. O. B. Coolidge of Woburn, suggested a visit to him, although he was almost a stranger. He resided at a distance of some miles, yet, enfeebled by illness as I was, I resolved to reach his house through the storm. At last I reached the dwelling of Mr. Coolidge and stated to him my condition and my hopes for success from my discovery. He received me cordially and not only supplied me with a sum adequate to my immediate wants, but also with facilities to continue the experiments on a small scale."

The money was soon gone, and in desperation he took some samples of his material and walked to Boston, because a former employee had promised that if he would call on him, there would be a loan of fifty dollars.

"When I arrived in Boston, he disappointed me. . . . I strayed into East Boston and stayed at the house of a friend who made me comfortable for the night. Early next morning I walked home . . . ten miles, to learn on the threshold that my youngest boy, two years of age, who was in perfect health when I left home, was then dying."

In addition, a local dealer who had promised to take care of the family on credit backed down.

"I next addressed myself to my brother-in-law, Mr. William de Forest, from whom I obtained fifty dollars. This enabled me to go to New York, and lay my project before Mr. William Ryder, who agreed to furnish capital for manufacture on joint account. To the firmness and perseverance of this friend, and to the skill and assiduity of his brother, Mr. Emery Ryder, even more than to their pecuniary aid, am I indebted for practical success. This success had barely time to see fair public demonstration when Mr. William Ryder failed, leaving me once more without resources."

In the winter of 1841, though, money began to come to Goodyear. His new product was markedly successful, and there was a flood of applications for licenses. His debts amounted to thirty-five thousand dollars and he was able to pay them all off to the last penny. Goodyear never realized all the earnings due him, because he miscalculated his royalty and set too low a figure.

The vulcanization of rubber was a great impetus to the electrical industry because rubber was used for various forms of insulators. He lived to see his invention give rise to enormous factories in the United States, England, France, and Germany, employing over sixty thousand workers, producing over five hundred different kinds of articles worth more than eight million dollars a year. He splurged on promotion, spent more than he earned. He died in 1860, owing two hundred thousand dollars. His friends no longer thought him a madman.

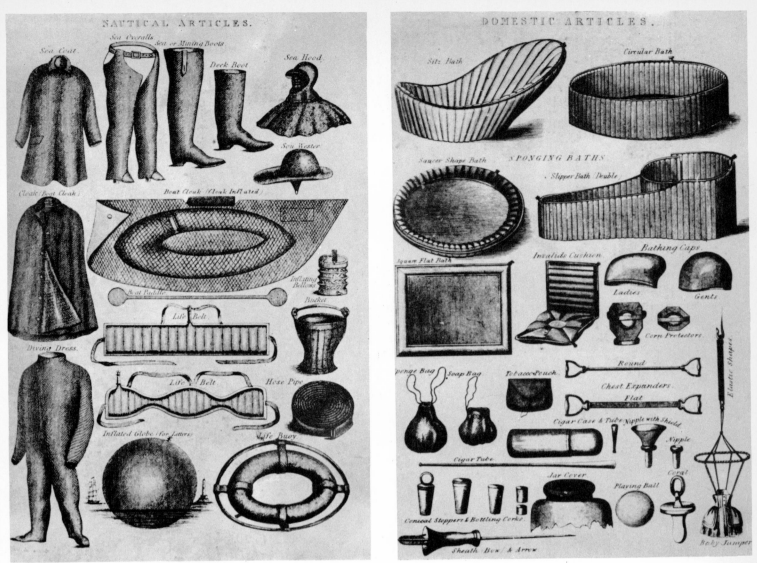

Goodyear's faith in his product was unbounded. He wanted to make everything out of rubber.

Goodyear's Vulcanite Court at the great exhibition in London, 1851

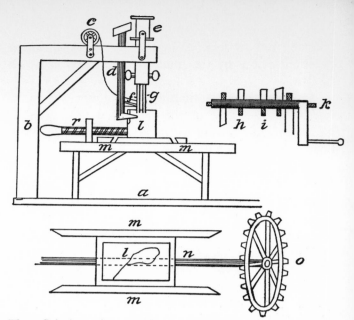

Thos. Saint's sewing machine of 1790, to sew leather with a chain stitch, was never more than a plan on paper.

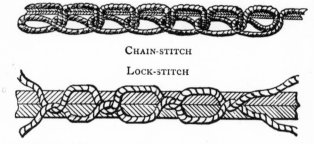

CHAIN-STITCH

LOCK-STITCH

A seam sewn with a chain stitch would unravel if one stitch tore. The lock stitch was far stronger.

Isaac Singer's first machine

THE SEWING MACHINE

1. INVENTED THREE TIMES OVER

By the 1830's the republic was half a century old, and half a continent wide. The time was beginning to pass when every farm household produced all its own necessities. The cities were growing rapidly and city dwellers earned cash wages to buy the articles their parents and grandparents had made at home.

To supply the wants of the town, factories had to turn out large quantities of goods. In 1831, although most women still made their own dresses and their husbands went to tailors, George Opdyke started the first ready-to-wear clothing factory in America. All the work was done by hand. Other such factories sprang up and seamstresses and tailors were kept busy because the demand was enormous. The American market was ready for a machine that could sew.

The first sewing machine on record was the 1790 conception of Thomas Saint, an Englishman. His machine was designed to sew leather. Although his plans were completed, no machine was ever built.

It was forgotten and the records lost for almost a hundred years. However, the economic need for such a device was increasingly obvious, and so the sewing machine was reinvented over and over, independently, by a number of other men.

In the late 1820's a French tailor named Barthelemy Thimonnier invented a sewing machine which produced a chain stitch by means of a crochet type of needle. The chain stitch had the disadvantage that when the thread was broken in any one place the entire seam unraveled. Nevertheless, Thimonnier's machine was so much faster than handwork that once he received his patent, in 1830, he had no trouble finding buyers. Eighty sewing machines were employed in making uniforms for the French Army in 1831, and Thimonnier immediately prospered. In France, however, the early 1830's produced the same revolutionary spirit which, in the United States, had elected Jackson. Mistakenly, political repression was identified with the introduction of labor saving devices, and a mob of tailors raided Thimonnier's shop, smashed every machine and threatened the inventor's life. He fled and made a living by selling handmade wooden machines at ten dollars apiece. In 1848 he had an improved machine that was in factory work once more, but the Revolution destroyed everything he had. Thimonnier was defeated not by lack of ingenuity, inventiveness or persistence, but by the time and the place in which he lived.

At about the same time as Thimonnier was working in France, one of the most brilliant, versatile and unworldly inventors in American history was developing the same idea in New York.

Walter Hunt, between the years of 1832 and 1859, invented and developed a greater number and variety of original ideas than anyone else. Among them were: machinery for making nails and rivets, ice plows, a sea camel (a small floating drydock), velocipedes, the paper collar, a revolver, a repeating rifle, a bullet with a metal cartridge containing its own explosive charge, and the safety pin.

The safety pin was invented in three hours one afternoon to discharge a debt of fifteen dollars which Hunt owed to J. R. Chapin, a draftsman. Chapin paid four hundred dollars for all rights to the various forms in which Hunt twisted an old piece of wire. Hunt's ideas came so fast that he had no time to make more than a passing show of getting himself legal protection.

After carrying the idea for a sewing machine around in his head for several years, in 1832 he set to work in a shop on Amos Street in New York and built a machine "for sewing, stitching, and seaming cloth." Hunt's machine could sew only a straight seam; the work could not be turned and the seam was only a few inches long.

The basic needs of a sewing machine are: a needle that will carry the thread through the material and out again, forming a complete stitch; a means of advancing the work after each stitch; and a source of power to drive the needle and advance the work. Hunt's machine had an inadequate feed. His basic invention was a needle with an eye in its point. The needle moved in a straight line like a piston's rise and fall. It was driven through the two pieces of cloth, momentarily leaving a loop of thread underneath the work. Through this loop, a small shuttle carried another thread. On the needle's upward stroke, the two locked threads were pulled taut forming a "lock stitch" which would not unravel when the thread was broken in any one place.

Hunt urged his daughter Caroline to employ the new invention and go into the business of manufacturing corsets. This was 1838 and one of the new trends of American thought, as in France, was the belief that machinery displaced the laboring classes and was therefore immoral. Both felt that too many seamstresses would be thrown out of work. Rather than injure society, Hunt withdrew his machine. He never applied for the patent.

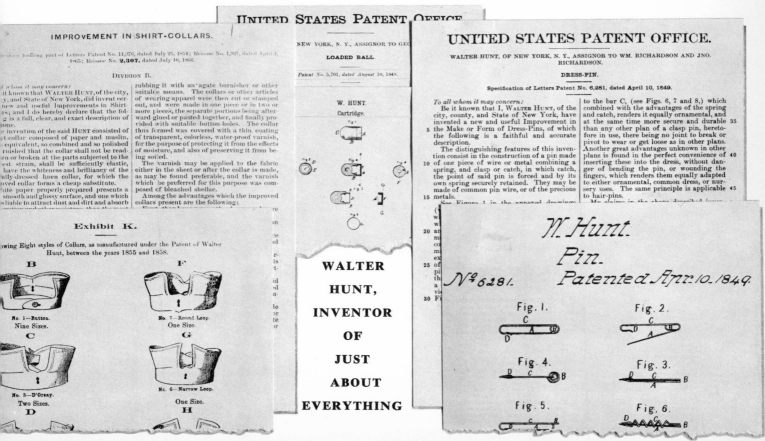

Walter Hunt, one of America's most prolific inventors, invented the safety pin, paper collars, and a metal cartridge. A fantastic success was a special pair of shoes enabling a circus performer to walk up walls.

2. ELIAS HOWE
THE BITTER TRIALS
AND EVENTUAL TRIUMPH

The first Howe sewing machine

In the very same year that Hunt in New York shelved his machine, an undersized, twenty-one-year-old apprentice in Boston overheard an argument between his employer, Ari Davis, a model builder, and a customer who had come to ask about a knitting machine.

"What are you bothering with a knitting machine for?" Davis screamed. "Why don't you make a sewing machine?"

"Can't be done," said the customer.

"*I* can make a sewing machine," Davis said.

"Well, you do it, Davis, and I'll assure you an independent fortune."

1—The argument ended there and Davis forgot his boast. The apprentice, who was in desperate need of any kind of fortune, independent or otherwise, paid attention to what he had heard.

Elias Howe had fled from his father's farm in Cambridge to the factories at Lowell, from Lowell to a Boston machine shop, and from the machine shop to Ari Davis. When he was twenty-one he was earning nine dollars a week on which he was feeding his wife and three children. By 1843, Howe was so desperately poor he decided to work on the idea of a sewing machine in his spare time and perhaps earn a few dollars more.

" I am Poor, but will not Kneel to one who Treads your Soil."

"Loan me a few Shillings, that I may pay the Washing and send my sick wife and children to America."

4—On September 10, 1846, Howe received his patent. At this point, Fisher, who had laid out some two thousand dollars, lost interest. Elias Howe's brother, Amasa, took one of the machines to England where he finally interested William Thomas, manufacturer of corsets, umbrellas, valises and shoes. He paid fifteen hundred dollars for the English rights to the machine and agreed to give Howe a royalty on every machine that was sold except those he used himself. Moreover, he insisted that Howe come to England to perfect a leather-sewing machine in his factory. On February 5, 1847, the Howe brothers set sail. Elias Howe's wife and three children followed. The arrangement did not work out at all. Thomas treated Howe as an employee and conveniently forgot the royalty arrangement.

5—Howe left him and found himself destitute in London. He borrowed money to send his family home; then pawned his machine and patent papers to pay for his own passage. To feed himself, he acted as cook for his fellow steerage passengers. He arrived in New York in April, 1849, penniless, and looked for work in the machine shops. Word reached him that his wife was dying of consumption in Cambridge and he had to borrow ten dollars from his father to get to her bedside before she died. Howe's whole outlook changed. Until now, he had been gay and indomitably hopeful. After his wife's death he became quiet and bitter—full of a sense of outrage.

"May there not be ANOTHER Stitch?"

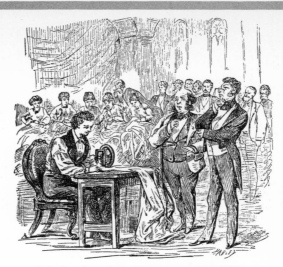

The first Contest between Hand and Machine Sewing at Quincy Hall, Boston.

2—At first he tried to imitate his wife's motions and gave it up as hopeless. In that same year he conceived the idea of using two needles exactly as Hunt had done, one moving up and down into the work, the other moving back and forth beneath the work like a shuttle through the looped stitch. Hunt's machine, discarded and gathering dust, had solved most of these problems, yet Howe had to go through every step of the way once more all by himself. He lacked Hunt's brilliance and versatility. Perhaps for that very reason, Howe was able to devote himself with more single-mindedness to this one project than Hunt had ever given anything in his life.

3—Howe found a partner in a former schoolmate named Fisher who agreed to take in and feed Howe's family, provide his attic as a workshop and advance up to five hundred dollars for tools. In return, Fisher was to receive a half interest in the invention. Within a few months, Howe had a machine that could sew a seam. Two months later, in July, 1845, he sewed all the seams on two woolen suits. That summer, too, he arranged with the Quincy Hall Clothing Manufacturing Company in Boston for a demonstration in which he would sew in competition with five of the best seamstresses. Howe's machine finished his five seams a little sooner than the five girls finished theirs and his work was declared to be superior. The owners, though, bought no machines.

Mr. Howe again in America, Encounters the Infringers of his Patent.

Elias Howe the complete victor.

6—While he was in England, his sewing machine had begun to be adopted in the United States. The money due him from royalties would certainly have saved his wife's life. Also, Thomas had been manufacturing his machine in England without royalties. Howe was determined to fight the infringers not only to protect himself, but out of anger that his wife had been so needlessly deprived. His old partner, Fisher, had sold his interest to George W. Bliss, who advanced the money needed to carry on the suit. As security, Bliss demanded and got a mortgage on the farm of Howe's father. Howe went to court and relentlessly fought all infringers with a determination born of his bitterness. He was sustained in every court, though his opposition was powerful.

7—After Howe's victory, he was approached by a combination of manufacturers who agreed to all his terms, and the sewing machine pool headed by Isaac Singer was on its way to fantastic wealth. On royalties alone, Howe earned over four thousand dollars a year. The sewing machine was one of the first inventions, typical of America, to make living easier and more comfortable. The sewing machine not only appeared in every home, but found innumerable uses in American factories. The American shoe industry grew out of adaptations of the sewing machine. Civil War uniforms were machine made on a large scale with Howe's invention. He received honors from every country and died an extremely rich man.

Isaac M. Singer

Singer's sewing machine factory

Palatial Singer sales room

Singer used promotional songs.

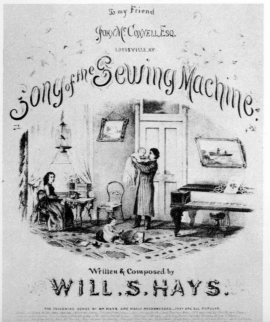

3. ISAAC M. SINGER
MACHINIST, PROMOTIONAL GENIUS

Howe's most powerful adversary was Isaac Merritt Singer. Singer was an excellent machinist. In the Boston shop of Orson C. Phelps, he watched a crude sewing machine. He immediately saw what was wrong with it, and unaware that Howe had already discovered the same principles which had previously been discovered by Hunt, Singer became the third man within a space of twelve years to invent the identical sewing machine. The next day he showed sketches of improvements to Phelps and an assistant named Zieber.

"Phelps and Zieber were satisfied that it would work. I had no money. Zieber offered forty dollars to build a model machine. Phelps offered his best endeavors to carry out my plan and make the model in his shop; if successful we were to share equally. I worked at it day and night.

"The machine was completed in eleven days. About nine o'clock in the evening we tried it; it did not sew. Sick at heart, about midnight, we started for our hotel. On the way Zieber mentioned that the loose loops of thread were on the under side of the cloth. It flashed upon me that we had forgotten to adjust the tension on the needle thread. We went back, adjusted the tension, sewed five stitches perfectly, and the thread snapped, but that was enough. I took it to New York to patent it."

The patent was granted in 1851. The power for Howe's machine had been a hand crank; Singer used a foot treadle which left the operator's hands free. Howe's needle moved horizontally; Singer's moved up and down so that the work could be advanced more easily, and turned to sew a curving seam. Singer, however, used an eye-pointed needle like Howe's, and the courts decided that Singer was infringing on him.

Singer's real genius was in promotion. Before he came into collision with Howe, he started a factory and set up palatial sales offices.

Howe's suit lasted from 1849 to 1854 and the court ordered Singer to pay Howe $25,000, based on a royalty for every machine that had infringed his rights. Singer suggested a pooling of all the best sewing machine patents, the first patent pool in American industry. Howe agreed. Seven companies were involved in the pool, and they were to pay Howe twenty-five dollars for every machine sold. Later the royalty was reduced to five dollars. Within ten years from the time that Elias Howe returned from England to America and his wife's death, his total earnings came to almost four thousand dollars a week. He died in 1867.

Singer, besides creating the patent pool, was the first man to spend a million dollars a year on advertising. He left the company in 1863 and retired to England. When he died he left thirteen million dollars. Thomas, the man who had bought the English rights for fifteen hundred dollars, earned well over a million dollars on his purchase. Howe's brother started the Howe factory and made a million dollars.

The only people connected with the invention of the sewing machine who did not make a million dollars were Thimonnier, who lived apart from the current of industry, and Walter Hunt, who was too sensitive to see seamstresses forced out of work. But Hunt made his own fortune out of the metal cartridges. His daughter Caroline lived in mid-century splendor, and rode her fine carriage unhaunted by visions of starving seamstresses. Probably she thought the bullets were used only on rabbits and birds.

Scientific American.

THE ADVOCATE OF INDUSTRY, AND JOURNAL OF SCIENTIFIC, MECHANICAL AND OTHER IMPROVEMENTS.

VOLUME VII.]   NEW-YORK, NOVEMBER 1, 1851.   **[NUMBER 7.**

THE
Scientific American,
CIRCULATION 16,000.
PUBLISHED WEEKLY
At 128 Fulton street, N. Y., (Sun Buildings),
BY MUNN & COMPANY.
Hotchkiss & Co., Boston.
Dexter & Bro., New York City.
Stokes & Bro., Philadelphia.
Jno. Thomson, Cincinnati, O.
Cooke & LeCount, San Francisco, Cal.
Courtenay & Wienges, Charleston, S. C.
John Carruthers, Savannah, Ga.
M. Boullemet, Mobile, Ala.
Barlow, Payne & Parken, London.
M. M. Gardissal & Co., Paris.
Responsible Agents may also be found in all the
principal cities and towns in the United States.
Terms—$2 a-year—$1 in advance and the remain-
der in 6 months.

RAIL-ROAD NEWS.

Railroads in Europe.

We have rather been consoling ourselves with the idea that our recent railroad enterprise was greater than that of all other nations together. This seems to be a mistake, for the Continent of Europe, mixed up with despotic governments, appears to be as truly alive to the importance of railroad communication, as the most go ahead of all our States. The London Times has recently been publishing statistics of the progress of the different countries, which exhibit these results:—Belgium has 532 miles of railways, 353 of which have been constructed and worked by the State, the remainder by different private companies. The expense of constructing the whole has been £9,576,000, or £18,000 per mile. The annual expenses are 63 per cent. of the receipts, and the profits three and a half per. cent. on the capital. In France there are 1,818 miles of railway under traffic, 1,178 miles in progress, and 577 miles projected. The cost of construction per mile has been £26,832, and the whole expenditure requisite for the completion of the 3,573 miles is estimated at £95,870,735. The average annual net profit on the capital employed does not exceed two and seven-tenths per cent.

In Germany there are 5,342 miles of railway in actual operation, 700 in progress, and 2,414 miles projected. Of the railways in operation, 1,812 miles were within the Prussian territories, and 771 miles in the Dutch Netherlands, the Danish Duchies, and the ex-German Austrian provinces, and therefore only 4,571 miles can be considered as strictly within the Germanic confederation. Two-fifths of these 4,571 miles were constructed and worked by the State, the remainder by private companies. Those in Prussia, however, are all the result of private enterprise. The expense of construction of the 5,342 miles is estimated at £12,500 per mile, being single track only. The working expenses are about fifty per cent. of the receipts, and the net profits are nearly three per cent. In Russia a railway from Warsaw to Cracow, 168 miles in length, is in operation; one connecting Warsaw with St. Petersburg, 683 miles in length; and one of about 400 miles, from St. Petersburg to Moscow, is in progress. A railway for goods from the Wolga to the Don, 105 miles in length, is also contemplated. In Southern Russia a line of railway between Kief and Odessa has been surveyed. In Italy no extensive system of railway has yet been executed. A few lines, diverging from the principal cities, such as Naples, Milan, Venice, Leghorn, and Florence, are alone in operation. In the kingdoms of Sardinia, Spain, and Portugal, railways are only in prospective.

By multiplying £1 by $4,85 we can arrive at the cost per mile of some of these roads. It will be observed that the French lines—the highest—cost $130,135,20 per mile, or nearly three times as much as those of Massachusetts, the cost of which averages $43,781.00, or about £9,000. If the European lines pay at such an enormous cost, need we be afraid?

SINGER'S SEWING MACHINE.---Fig. 1.

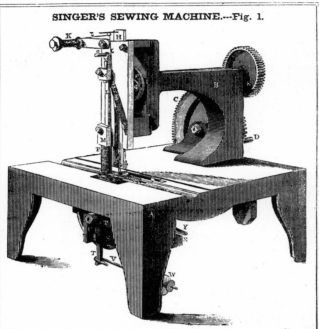

The accompanying engravings represent a perspective view, figure 1, and a side elevation, figure 2, of Isaac M. Singer's Sewing Machine, which was patented on the 12th of last August. A is the frame, made of cast-iron, and B is a cast-iron standard to support part of the working machinery. C is a large driving wheel, worked by the handle, D. E is a small second wheel, driven by C, and works the shaft that vibrates the needle; E' is another wheel to work the shuttle shaft, a, hung in the bearing straps, b b, fig. 2. F is a round plate on the revolving shaft of E; it has a small roller stud on its inner face fitting into a plate, G, slotted of a heart-shape, to answer the purpose of a cam. This plate, G, is secured to the vibrating arm, H, to which the needle, I, is fastened. The needle performs three strokes up and down during one revolution of the large wheel, C. The thread, J, of the needle is supplied by a bobbin, K, and goes through an eye in the needle, near its point. The cloth is laid flat on the table on the top of a small rough-faced roller S, with the edge to be sewn under the needle. The cloth is held down by a pad, R, acted upon by a coiled spring, P;

Figure 2.

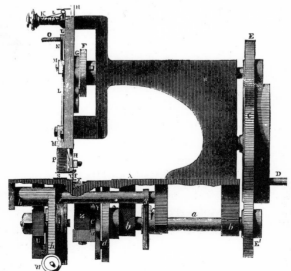

this pad is raised by a pin, O, and kept fixed by a catch bar, N, which presses against a shoulder piece, M. There is another shoulder piece, M, to secure the arm, L, of the pad, R in its place. When the cloth is laid on the table, on the wheel, S, the catch, N, is thrown out, and the pad, R, is pressed on the cloth by the spring, P, and is retained firmly in its place but still allowed to be carried forward as it is stitched. The way in which the stitch is performed is by two threads, one supplied with a shuttle, X, the other by the needle, I. With-

out two threads, no good stitch has yet been made by any sewing machine. X is the shuttle carrying a thread which passes from a pirn inside through a small eye on the side next the needle. Now, to form the stitch, which is just like the lock or link of a chain, the thread in the needle, after having passed through the cloth, opens, and the shuttle passes through this loop, therefore, when the needle is drawn back, and the shuttle also to the end of its raceway, the two threads are drawn tight, forming a link drawn on the cloth, and thus link after link of these threads form the seam. The drawing of the threads tight, and the forming of the loop on the end of the needle for the shuttle is an essential feature to the successful working of these sewing machines. For this purpose the shuttle, X, has a motion to coincide with that of the needle, I, and it is imparted by the same devices, d, fig. 2, being like plate, F, and Y like cam G, only the shuttle runs horizontally at right angles to the needle; e, fig. 2, is the shuttle arm, and Z is the guide or raceway, in which it runs. Thus the motions of the needle and shuttle are explained. The other lettered devices not explained are those belonging to the cloth-feeding motion. The roller, S, that moves the cloth has a rough face, and rotates, but moves round slowly, only making its movements forward the length of a stitch for every stitch taken; this is done by catches or pallets, a well known way to do so. These pallets are vibrated by a rocking shaft, f, having a bar, g, on it, which is moved by a cam, c, on the shaft, a. To the small rocking shaft, f, there is secured a suspended lever, h, having a collar, h surrounding said shaft, near its bearing end, i. This lever has a hook, V, on its lower end, to which is affixed a setting screw, W. The hook, V, catches on the hand of an arm, T, which has pallets or catches in a box, that catch into notches on the shaft of the feed wheel, S; every time, therefore, the lever, h, is vibrated, the feed wheel, S, moves the cloth the exact length of a stitch forward; the set screw, W, is for regulating the length of feeding the cloth forward to make short or long stitches.

This machine does good work. The patent claim will be found on page 390, Vol. 6. Sci. Am. The agent of this machine is W. H. Shepard, No. 256 Broadway this city.

Things to be Invented.

Among the things that are wanted by every body is a substitute for pen and ink. It seems that a single instrument ought to perform the function, and that fluid ink may be dispensed with. Cannot some substance be found, simple or compound, that will make an indelible mark upon paper, being hard enough also to hold a fine point? Or cannot paper be so prepared, without great addition of expense, as to aid the purpose?

THE CHRISTIAN HAT.—The improvements of the age have reached almost every thing except the abominable flower-pot hat, that so much needs the kindly attention of reformers. We are glad to notice that attention is being directed by some of our public journals to the unreasonableness of a stiff and perspiration-proof covering for the head. The flower-pot hat cannot pretend to beauty; it is certainly uncomfortable and unhealthy. Why then shall we not seek a substitute? The hat should be very light and porous, and by all means soft or elastic; and if any article of our dress calls for especial ornament, the covering of the head speaks most loudly for something to set off the front that slightly distinguishes one man from another. The Turban is probably most susceptible of such modifications as would be most easily adjusted to the purposes required; and we think some such change of the head-dress would require little urgency to get into general favor.

Singer's machine was given a front page spread by the *Scientific American* for November 1, 1851, which detailed its operation. Other articles on the same page told mid-century readers of America's position in railroading, suggested the invention of a ball point pen, and criticized the prevailing "abominable flower-pot hat."

THE REAPER
AND THE SINGING PLOW

1

Daniel Webster, Henry Clay and John Calhoun dominated American political life in their time because of their passionate adherence to the credo: "The Union must be preserved," even though they all had sharply divergent ideas of what the Union ought to be. Calhoun was the leader of the Sectionalists, and Webster, his bitter opponent, passionately proclaimed the necessity of a centralized federal government. Yet, no matter how violently they fought each other, they knew how to temper their convictions when factionalism became so intense that disruption threatened to result. They believed that the Union would endure if only, as various problems arose, intelligent men would compromise.

In 1830 the irrevocable rupture between North and South was still in the future. Differences between the two regions had continually been resolved as they preserved a rough balance of power by dividing the expanding West between them.

In the thirty years that followed, this artifice of patch and compromise

was to fail. As the West grew, it took on an identity of its own. The West had its own interests, its own power, its own internal struggles. Very often the West was at odds with both the North and the South.

The growth of the West was an agricultural expansion. Settlers found new soils that demanded new crops. Old ways of farming were no longer suitable; the raw land was fertile, but the labor needed to make a livelihood for even a single family was almost man-killing. The heavy loam was sticky. Prairie roots were too tough to cut easily. Yet the West had to be opened, and the tool to do the job was the plow.

The first plows were simply pointed sticks that gashed a groove in the ground deeper than the roots of the turf and weeds. The stick threw up earth equally on both sides. Then one face of the stick was smoothed so that only one ridge of earth was cast up in the form of a furrow. Eventually the stick developed into a wedge formed by two planks. The plank that threw up the furrow was called the *moldboard;* the other, which ran along the trench shoring up the earth, was called the *landside*.

The plow used in the Massachusetts colony was made of wood—two heavy beams joined in a "V." Almost a dozen oxen were required to pull it, and massive as it was, the design was so poor that a man had to add his weight to keep the plow from bucking out of the ground. There were only thirty-seven in the colony seventeen years after the landing.

Vastness beckoned to America—the great plains, fertile valleys, the towering mountains, and the far Pacific. From the stony eastern cities and the rocky hillside farms a stream of American families moved westward a few miles a day on a thousand-mile front. To make their settlements possible, Americans had to invent tools that would seed the earth and reap the harvests on a scale commensurate with the grandeur of the land.

Pat Lyon, famous smith, had his prototype in John Deere, of Grand Detour, Ill., who made the first steel plow.

Steel was self-scouring in the sticky, black soil, but the only steel in Grand Detour was in circular saw blades.

Thomas Jefferson designed the classic American plow, but never patented it. After him, during the next fifty years, plow patent applications poured into the Patent Office.

2. JOHN DEERE'S PLOW OF SAW-STEEL

Thomas Jefferson, the first American to make a study of the plow, discovered the importance of making the plow's cutting edge a straight line. He sought no patent. The first patent on a plow was granted in 1793 to Charles Newbold of New Jersey, who spent his entire fortune of thirty thousand dollars developing an efficient plow of cast iron; but the neighboring farmers decided against it. Iron would poison the ground, they said.

Twenty years after Newbold lost his money experimenting with plows no one would buy, Jethro Wood invented another iron plow, the nineteenth to be patented in America, based on Jefferson's theories. Wood sold every plow he could make, but he was hounded by infringers.

Jethro Wood's plow worked well enough in the sandy earth of the East, but the soil of the West—of Illinois, Indiana, and Wisconsin—was far different. Farmers complained that they seemed to be trying to plow a mixture of tar, mud, and molasses. To plow a clean, fast furrow, the earth must fall away in a smooth curl from the moldboard. This was called *scouring*. The sticky mud of Illinois soil refused to scour, and clung in great gobs to iron plows. Men thought the problem could be solved by making slight changes in the shape of one part or another of the plow; and every variety of design was patented out of as many different combinations of wood and iron.

In 1833, a young blacksmith, John Deere of Grand Detour, Illinois, came to the conclusion that the fault lay in the iron itself, not in the iron's shape. One day, on a visit to a sawmill, Deere noticed how a discarded steel blade shone where it had been polished by friction. He wondered whether steel would also clean itself when cutting earth. He made a plow out of a discarded circular blade, using a wooden mallet to avoid denting the surface. With this new steel plow, he cut a dozen smooth straight furrows in Lewis Crandall's field without having to stop once. His neighbors took the plow and kept going down the field just to be sure they weren't seeing things. He sold his first plows for ten dollars each.

John Deere moved to Moline where he started a factory. Twenty years after he made his first steel plow, the great push of settlers to Oregon and California was under way, and a John Deere plow could be found in almost every wagon train.

When the furrows of soil slid smoothly past the steel, the plowshare vibrated with a humming sound, and John Deere became famous for his "singing plow."

Abraham Lincoln had enough money to engage in historic debates with Stephen Douglas largely because of a $1,000 fee paid him by the Manny reaper interests in their patent war against their powerful competitor, Cyrus McCormick.

3. McCORMICK'S REAPER

By far the most important single step towards the American mechanization of agriculture was Cyrus McCormick's reaper. In the late thirties, grain had to be imported from Europe to make up for the shortages in the American crop. The shipment of wheat from Chicago amounted to only seventy-eight bushels in 1838. Ten years later, Chicago alone was shipping two million, with every promise that the yield would continue to increase. The economic future of the North was becoming clear, and the defeat of the Confederacy was foreseen by far-sighted Southerners eight years before secession. Except for the political tradition that allowed the South a disproportionately powerful voice in the selection of presidential candidates, the South was on its way to becoming the least important of the nation's three great regions.

Wheat was one of the factors that killed the old South. In western soil, wheat was easy to sow and to grow. Reaping was another matter. A man had to cut with a scythe and slowly move down the field, swinging as he went. An acre a day for a strong man was a good average yield. Farmers helped each other to harvest crops, but everyone's wheat came to full

growth at about the same time, and there were only about ten days, given good weather, in which the crop could be gathered in. At reaping time, hired hands came high. Until McCormick invented his mechanical reaper, a man grew only as much wheat as he himself could reap by hand. If more grain stood in his field, it was left for the cattle to graze.

McCormick's reaper has no great rank as a feat of creative imagination, but it was introduced at the precise time when it helped to change history in the West where it was needed, where great expanses of land could be put to use if men had the means of gathering all the wheat they could grow. Without the West, McCormick's reaper would have met the same fate as the earlier model of Bell in England. Even in the eastern United States, reapers were only slowly adopted. The uneven rocky land of New England required a far more refined machine than McCormick's early models which were ideally suited to flat prairie. The reaper made the West pay.

In a sense, the Civil War was created by two American machines—the North rolling its frontier westward thirty miles a year behind the McCormick reaper; the South rich and solid on the cotton gin. For a touch of irony, McCormick was born in Virginia; Whitney came from New England.

Cyrus H. McCormick

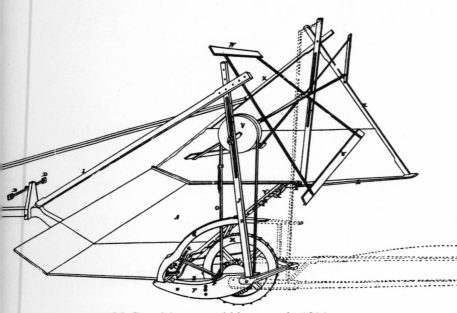

McCormick patented his reaper in 1834.
Over 20 other reapers had been patented
in the U. S. before. McCormick's was the best.

McCormick's reaper of 1847 showed many
improvements. McCormick's production genius
enabled him to make 4,000 reapers in 1856.

4. McCORMICK AND
HIS RIVALS

Cyrus McCormick was born in 1809 three days after the birth of Lincoln. The McCormick family were prosperous farmers. The father, Robert, was himself an inventor with his own smithy. His son, Cyrus, grew up familiar with the tools of his time, at home in the blacksmith shop on his father's farm.

Robert McCormick's great failure was a mechanical reaper which he finally gave up as hopeless. Cyrus McCormick, who had always identified himself with his father, was impelled to prove that in this respect, at least, he was more a man than his father. He took over the reaper as his responsibility.

He was a young man with narrow interests and few friends. He held himself aloof from almost everyone, but not because he courted anonymity; a man who dresses with almost dandyish elegance is a man who wants to be noticed.

His younger brothers and sisters used to tease him for being so straitlaced, but secretly they were in awe of him. When he became a millionaire before he was forty, they made no secret of their awe, and he, in return, was very generous.

In 1831, when he was twenty-two, he gave the first public demonstration of his reaper and cut six acres of oats at Steele's Tavern in one day. Four horses pulled the machine which was doing the work of six men. Two of the McCormick slaves, "Old Joe" Anderson and Anthony, had to hold the horses because the clatter of the machine was frightening. Neighbors who had seen earlier performances of the father's reaper admitted that it was "a right curious sort of thing" but "nobody ever believed it would come to much."

The fact that went unappreciated was that horsepower was being substituted for human labor. From that point of view, a reaper is a device which converts the pulling power of a horse into the intelligence, judgment, experience, and strength necessary to harvest a field of standing grain.

The first reaper did not cut too evenly, and some of the grain was damaged. McCormick continually improved his machine and in 1834 secured a patent, but made no attempt to market a machine with which he was still dissatisfied.

Essentially the reaper substituted a number of cutting shears for the swinging blade of the scythe. A horse walked down a field pulling a two-wheeled chariot which had an axle about six feet long. Connected to the chariot was a flat iron bar parallel to the axle, a few inches above the ground. Protruding from the front of the bar were a number of broad, flat steel fingers which separated the grain stalks into bunches as the reaper moved forward. At the base of the fingers was a saw-toothed cutting bar that moved back and forth in a sideways motion so that as the steel fingers gathered the grain, the moving knife cut the stalks. A device called the reel pressed the grain into the fingers. The power to drive the reel and the cutting blade came from one of the wheels: as the machine was pulled forward, the turning wheel drove all the interlocking mechanisms.

Shortly after the reaper trial, Robert McCormick gave Cyrus a farm of two hundred acres and took him in as partner in a small iron foundry. In the mid-thirties the price of iron was soaring sky-high. Cyrus McCormick had neither the need nor the incentive to bother with the reaper he had developed. The financial crash of 1837 reached its full effect in Virginia two years later, and the McCormicks were thrown into poverty, losing farm and foundry. For the next five years the father and all the sons worked on the father's farm to pay off pressing creditors.

The financial pressure made McCormick turn once again to his reaper; however, he was driven to perfect it just at the time when other farmers lacked the cash to buy a machine costing over a hundred dollars. The farmers' bankruptcy had similarly smashed the hardware firm of Goodyear and Sons. Both Goodyear and McCormick were driven to invention at the same time and by the same crisis.

In 1841 McCormick finally sold two machines. In the next year he sold seven more. In the next two years he sold eighty. Then McCormick, at the age of thirty-six, with sixty dollars in his pocket, rode out to see the West of Illinois, Ohio, and Indiana. He saw the rolling fields and at once understood where his machine was really needed. For several years, he had machines built and assembled in other men's shops, but in 1847 he selected the small town of Chicago as the site of his own manufactory and talked William Ogden, the mayor, into becoming his partner. He also talked Ogden into putting up fifty thousand dollars. In the next two years the business was so prosperous that McCormick was able to buy him out.

McCormick built and sold a thousand reapers in 1851. He won a first prize in the London exposition and became a world figure, a member of the Legion of Honor, and a knight of several minor orders. In 1857, twenty-three thousand machines made him a profit in that one year alone of a million and a quarter dollars.

McCormick had many rivals and competitors. When he wasn't suing them for infringement, they were suing him. In that highly eloquent day, lawsuits were carried on with a ferocity that was merciless. Opposing sides pelted each other to stupefaction with claims and counter-claims, attachments and counter-attachments, writs and restraints.

McCormick was widely infringed by other manufacturers, who got behind the Mannys in a patent suit defended by Abraham Lincoln and Edward Stanton. McCormick lost.

5. McCORMICK'S HOLY WAR WITH THE NEW YORK CENTRAL

McCormick fought his rivals to a standstill, and they came back for more. His most serious rival for a time was Obed Hussey, and then later John H. Manny. When the legal battle with Manny came up in 1854, all of McCormick's competitors got together to finance Manny's legal costs; for if McCormick could ruin Manny, he would ruin them all. The Manny backers retained George Harding against McCormick's Edward N. Dickinson, one of the ablest patent lawyers of his day.

The case was to be tried in Springfield, Illinois, before Judge Drummond. The Manny backers thought it would be a shrewd move to associate with Harding a popular local lawyer. They found a man in Springfield who was a close friend of Drummond's, named Abraham Lincoln. Enormous war funds were available for both sides. McCormick was demanding four hundred thousand dollars from Manny as damages.

Before the case came to trial, both parties consented to a transfer to Cincinnati. Since this was Lincoln's first big case, he came prepared with a long technical brief; but since the trial was not in Springfield, Lincoln was no longer needed. Without consulting Lincoln, the Manny backers had obtained Edward M. Stanton. The polished, elegant eastern lawyers unceremoniously pushed Lincoln aside into the role of spectator. It was Lincoln's deepest humiliation and disappointment. He stayed, however, to earn his fee; and his hurt was overbalanced by his admiration for Stanton's peerless performance during the trial. Although Lincoln stood silent in the courtroom, his one-thousand-dollar fee enabled him to devote more time to politics and to go to the stump soon after for the famous series of debates with Stephen Douglas.

Lincoln never forgot Stanton's brilliance at the trial, and although he and Stanton had never met again, Lincoln swallowed his humiliation and insisted on having Stanton serve in his cabinet.

Until 1858 McCormick lived as always, aloof from people, immersed in the detail of his work and the endless litigation which he apparently enjoyed with gusto. He lived in hotels and on the trains that took him from city to city for endless conferences. The tall, slim, serious-minded dandy of twenty-two had grown into a "massive Thor of Industry." In the mid-1850's his mother died, and in 1858 the most eligible bachelor of Golden Chicago, now forty-nine, portly, and with several millions, finally "succumbed to Cupid's glances" and Miss Nettie Fowler of New York—many years his junior.

The *Chicago Daily Press* said:

The burning of the McCormick Reaper Works in 1871 threw McCormick into momentary panic until his wife urged him to rebuild. In the process, he rebuilt most of Chicago.

"If our townsman . . . has delayed the ceremonies for a few more years than is customary . . . we risk nothing in pronouncing the prize well worth his waiting, and in *reaping* one of the fairest flowers our city can boast, he has but added the orange blossoms to the laurels of his world-famous title of nobility."

McCormick traveled like a mid-nineteenth-century millionaire—like American royalty. He was an indefatigable fighter on any issue, on any scale. In 1862, when his children were very small, he had been in Washington on business with his family. His wife, children, nurses, and servants, and voluminous portmanteaus, valises, and trunks were sent ahead to board the train. At the last moment, McCormick arrived at the station. When he checked his tickets he discovered there was an overcharge of $8.70 on his wife's baggage. To McCormick this was an outrage. He refused to pay. The conductor refused to revise the freight rates. McCormick refused to ride on the train. He called off his family and retinue just as

the train began to move. The conductor refused to hold back the train long enough to get off McCormick's luggage. This was *lèse-majesté*. McCormick wired his indignation to the president of the New York Central. The president of the New York Central wired Philadelphia to put off McCormick's luggage when the Washington train came in. The wire was late, the luggage went on to Chicago, was stored in a warehouse; the warehouse was hit by lightning and burned down. It couldn't have happened to a wilder man.

McCormick sued the New York Central for twenty thousand dollars, but withheld the suit until after the war was over; he knew he was unpopular on account of his Southern sympathies. Immediately after the war, he hired Roscoe Conkling and won twelve thousand dollars. The New York Central appealed. The case of the $8.70 baggage charge marched from court to court up to the exalted heights of the Supreme Court, which ordered a new trial. More lawyers were retained. On the second trial, McCormick was awarded fifteen thousand dollars. The New York Central appealed all the way back up to the Supreme Court again. Constitutional issues were temporarily set aside as the Court again looked at the volumes of papers referring to McCormick and the brutal train conductor.

Five times the case was tried, each time being battled up to the Supreme Court of the United States. Major political parties and presidential aspirants became involved. After more than twenty years the New York Central gave up, deciding that its main business was not in the law courts. McCormick had died in 1884, but his estate was awarded his twenty thousand dollars. Even though the costs far exceeded that figure, McCormick's adored and adoring wife, Nettie, knew that her husband had won the victory that was dearest to his heart. She wrote to her son, "You see, your dear father's course from first to last is . . . vindicated!"

The Crystal Palace Exhibition of the Industry of All Nations in New York was America's answer to Prince Albert's successful exhibition in London. The purpose was to show the state of American invention and mechanical development. The year was significant because it marked the beginning of American awareness of engineering. Yale College established the Sheffield Scientific School about that time, and the first generation of college-trained engineers was soon to appear on the scene in the United States. 1850 was a crucial year politically because it marked (see below) the historic debates in the Senate which led to the Compromise of 1850. Henry Clay's impassioned speech was to preserve the Union for another ten years, during which time the ties between the North and the West were made indissoluble by the railroads.

AMERICAN
ENGINEERING

The graduates of the Erie Canal went out into the world and the word *engineer* came into common use as men like Ezra Cornell and Horatio Allen made names for themselves and new industries for America. The engineering colleges of America did not begin until after the Civil War. They were founded to train the men needed to handle problems that had been made routine by self-educated engineers in the decades before the war.

Self-trained American engineers built the first railroads, designed and built the great clipper ships, mined the coal at Mauch Chunk, followed the Forty-niners to California, and substituted machinery for the pan and sieve.

During the fifties, engineering rapidly changed the character of the North and the West. The railroad brought western grain into competition with

the produce of New England farms and New England began to lose its rural character. The short lines radiating out of Boston spread its industrialization to all the surrounding area. The lines running west carried the machine tools from the northern cities, and new factories sprang up beyond the Appalachians. The east-west lines tied the North and West together so that their economic differences became more and more reconciled. In 1850, both in the North and South, most rail lines ran east and west. The two networks were tied tenuously by the only north-south line in the country, running from Wilmington, North Carolina, to Washington.

The clipper ships brought in vast cargoes of immigrants who settled in northern cities and on western homesteads. In the North, the population grew steadily—the South stood still.

The fifties saw the end of the generation of politicians like Webster, Calhoun, and Clay, because problems were arising that had to be solved in ways that were alien to the tradition of these old giants. As the South declined in economic power, it grew more desperate and would not give up a power that now far exceeded its proportional strength. The North and West were becoming impatient with political compromises that no longer seemed necessary.

The increasingly efficient North had only contempt for an economy that wasted its land by primitive methods, and saddled itself with human livestock it could neither afford to feed nor give up.

The machines of the North were turning faster and with far more power than the strongest arguments of the abolitionists; and it was the machinery that carried the day.

The B. & O.'s Tom Thumb weighed 1 ton, had 1 cylinder, and developed 1 to 1½ horsepower—but it passed a horsecar.

THE STEAM ENGINE RAIL-ROAD

1. THE IDEA

The great family feud between the Livingstons and the Stevenses had begun with steamboats, and had then ranged through the Constitution, the federal patent law, and the building of the Erie Canal. By 1830, Chancellor Robert Livingston was dead; and he had died, as he thought, in victory because he had succeeded with the Erie Canal over John Stevens' objections. Robert Fulton was dead of overwork and harassment. The only one left who had been on the scene at the beginning of the opera was John Stevens of Hoboken, now an old man of eighty-one,

and, through his sons and grandsons, he was to have the last word.

To Stevens, it had always been clear that the only way to open America was through "the steam engine rail-road." Even when he lost the battle over the Erie Canal, he continued his prolific letter writing, seeking recruits to the cause of rail-roading. He had to be very explicit. To his contemporaries, the word *rail-road* did not have its later meaning. Because highways were so bad everywhere, early engineers had worked on the idea of laying a double track of wooden rails so that a horse walking between them could pull a stagecoach with what seemed like inconceivable smoothness. Sometimes, plates of iron were laid on top of the wooden rails to make them last longer.

The high-pressure steam engine developed by both Stevens and Evans in America was light enough and small enough to pull many times its own

Parades and speeches marked the opening of each new line. The railroad was plenty of cause for excitement, for to many towns it meant the only real connection with the outside. Above: Boston's grand celebration in 1833.

The Best Friend of Charleston, built for South Carolina, blew up, was rebuilt and renamed the *Phoenix*.

weight, and so a steam carriage became a real possibility. In 1815 he received from New Jersey the first rail-road charter in the United States; in 1825 he built a locomotive. By 1830 Stevens was no longer alone with steam engines on wheels. Even before 1820 he had secured several licenses for building steam engine rail-roads, but he had been unable to raise the capital to go ahead. With interest rising all about him, he was able to project the Camden and Amboy Rail-Road and Transportation Company. Even so, his was not the first rail-road in America. A year or two before, his disciples had gone their own way, and some had formed the South Carolina Canal and Rail-Road Company, another group organized the Mohawk and Hudson, still another was behind the Baltimore and Ohio, and there was a fourth called the Delaware and Hudson.

Steam engine rail-roading had burst on America with a roar.

$$W\left(\frac{fr}{R} - \sin. i\right) = n\,W\left(\frac{fr}{R} + \sin. i\right);$$
$$\text{or, } \frac{fr}{R} - \sin. i = \frac{nfr}{R} + n\sin. i;$$
$$\text{whence, } \frac{fr(1-n)}{R(1+n)} = \sin. i.$$

If the carriages are not to be returned, then we

Engineering of the time was far from quaint or naïve, regardless of how quaint the first engines looked.

A PRACTICAL TREATISE

ON

RAIL-ROADS AND CARRIAGES,

SHOWING THE

PRINCIPLES OF ESTIMATING

THEIR

STRENGTH, PROPORTIONS, EXPENSE,

AND

ANNUAL PRODUCE,

AND

THE CONDITIONS WHICH RENDER THEM

EFFECTIVE, ECONOMICAL, AND DURABLE;

WITH THE

THEORY, EFFECT, AND EXPENSE OF STEAM CARRIAGES,
STATIONARY ENGINES, AND GAS MACHINES.

ILLUSTRATED BY FOUR ENGRAVINGS AND NUMEROUS USEFUL TABLES.

By THOMAS TREDGOLD, CIVIL ENGINEER,

MEMBER OF THE INSTITUTION OF CIVIL ENGINEERS, &c.

"Our present modes of conveyance, excellent as they are, both require and admit of great improvements."—QUARTERLY REVIEW.

NEW-YORK:
E. BLISS AND E. WHITE, 128 BROADWAY.

M.DCCC.XXV.

Tredgold's Treatise, published in 1825, was one of the first books on railroad engineering in America or Europe.

Tredgold's 1825 project, published only four years before steam railroading became a reality, sounded as radical to his contemporaries as plans for interplanetary travel would seem a century later.

EVOLUTION OF THE EIGHT-WHEEL, SWIVEL-TRUCK "AMERICAN TYPE" ENGINE

1—The first engines were simply boilers mounted on wheels, with any sort of piston and crank mechanism that would turn the wheels.

2—A rotatable truck, invented by John Jervis in 1831, allowed engines of ever-increasing length to follow sharply curved track.

3—Two pairs of driving wheels, connected by rods, came next, but boilers were still sheathed in wood, and the driver had no cab.

By the late fifties, the mature American Type engine was all

2. THE LOCO-MOTIVE

In 1804, Oliver Evans had built his *Orukter Amphibolos,* which was the first steam traction engine in the world. In 1825, Stevens built his own model of a self-propelling steam engine to run on a circular track on the lawn of his Hoboken estate simply to prove a point.

Three years later, the Delaware and Hudson Canal Company sent Horatio Allen to England to examine the possibility of using a mobile steam engine to replace the horses on the rail-road of the company's coal mine at Carbondale.

In 1829 the Darlington and Stockton Rail-Road Company in England had to decide whether horse locomotion or steam power would be better for their wooden rail stage lines. Performance is what counts, and the company advertised for the best steam engine locomotives to compete at Rainhill

decorated with gilt and oil paintings and brass—and sometimes even a cast-iron slave boy holding a flag staff.

for a fifteen-hundred-pound prize. The specifications were widely published, and there were four entries. Stephenson's *Rocket* won handily, the other three not even starting because of mechanical difficulties. One of the losers was the *Novelty* entered by Ericsson, who was later to become famous as the builder of the warship, *Monitor*. Ericsson's *Novelty* showed great speed in the pre-trial runs, but the *Rocket* developed impressive pulling power.

After Stevens' 1825 demonstration, the next locomotive to run in this country was one that had been made in England and brought back by Horatio Allen for the Delaware and Hudson Canal Company. The seven-ton engine was called the *Stourbridge Lion*. On August 8, 1829, Allen stepped aboard the engine he had brought home and made the preliminary adjustments for a trial run along the short stretch of track used to haul cars of coal to the canal from the mine in northeast Pennsylvania.

"When the time came, and the steam was of the right pressure, I took my position on the platform of the Locomotive alone, and with my hand on the throttle valve handle said, 'If there is any danger in this ride it is not necessary that the life and limbs of more than one should be subjected to that danger.'

"The Locomotive, having no train behind it, answered at once to the movement of the hand. . . . Soon the straight line was run over, the curve was reached and passed before there was time to think as to its not being passed safely. . . . Soon I was out of sight in the three-mile ride alone in the woods of Pennsylvania. I had never run a Locomotive nor any other machine before," said Mr. Allen, fifty years later, "and I have never run one since."

The *Stourbridge Lion* did not see many more runs because it proved too heavy for American roads. America had to develop its own engines to fit its own conditions.

Railway Locomotives.

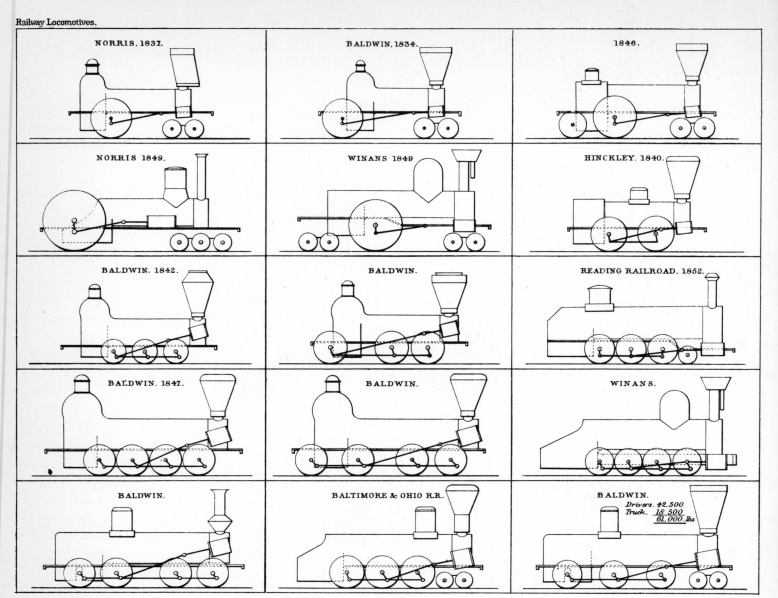

American locomotives had gone through a remarkable series of developments by 1850. All sorts of drives were tried to meet the terrain extremes. All were distinctive, and English engineering texts treated them as a special category.

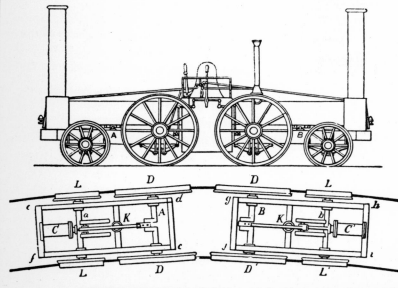

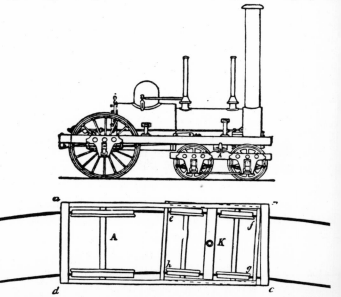

The first step in the evolution of the "American locomotive" was the double-ended, flexible *South Carolina*, built in 1831.

A swivel truck to negotiate the tight curves of American lines was first used on John B. Jervis' locomotive, in 1831.

THE TRAIN! THE TRAIN!

A lithograph of the American Sunday School Union showed the excitement caused by the appearance of the first trains.

American locomotives were sold over the world. Brochures of Baldwin, Vail and Hufty were printed in three languages.

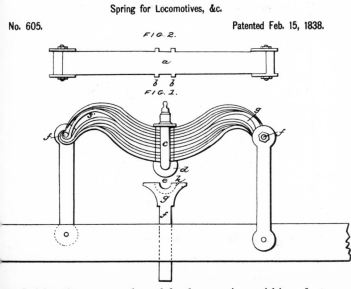

Leaf springs were adapted for locomotives within a few years of the time the first trains appeared in America.

2. THE LOCO-MOTIVE (Continued)

At about the same time that the *Stourbridge Lion* was being prepared for its trial, Peter Cooper built and tried a little locomotive on the Baltimore and Ohio, named *Tom Thumb*. It weighed one ton, had one cylinder, and developed between one and one and a half horsepower. The fire tubes were made of musket barrels, because iron pipe was unavailable in this country. It was the first engine to pull a load of passengers in America. One of Cooper's trips was famous because he raced against and pulled ahead of a horse drawing the same load on a parallel track. However, minor mechanical failure slowed Cooper down at the last minute and the horse won.

Horatio Allen left the Delaware and Hudson and joined the newly formed South Carolina Canal and Railway Company. He designed his own engine and had it built by the cannon works at the West Point Foundry. It was called *The Best Friend of Charleston.* The little locomotive pulled forty passengers in four cars at twenty-one miles an hour. *The Best Friend* has the distinction of being the first locomotive in America to explode. The fireman had become irritated by the hiss of steam from the safety valve. He held down the valve. Since the valve couldn't pop, the engine did.

Horatio Allen then designed another engine called the *South Carolina* which embodied an important American invention. English engines were heavy and rigid, and had four wheels mounted on two fixed-position axles. Such inflexible construction demanded track with extremely shallow curves. English landscape and engineering made such roads possible; American landscape was more rugged and English locomotives were often derailed on the curving American roads. Allen solved that problem by mounting the locomotive on two pivoted trucks which allowed the wheels to follow a sharply curved track. This idea, or a variation of it, became standard on all subsequent locomotive and railroad car design. The English did not begin to copy it until many years later.

The same problem was solved in 1831 by John B. Jervis who built a rotatable truck which he called "a bearing carriage" for the Mohawk and Hudson Railroad. A few years later, Ross Winans secured a patent on a method very similar to Allen's. The issue went to trial and up to the Supreme Court in a case that cost both sides a quarter of a million dollars—an enormous sum of money for the 1830's.

In 1836, Henry Campbell of Philadelphia patented a locomotive that came to be known universally as the "American type." His engine had two pairs of driving wheels and a rotatable truck.

By 1860, American locomotives were bigger, more powerful than any others. They had steamed as far west as the Mississippi in force, and were ready to cross.

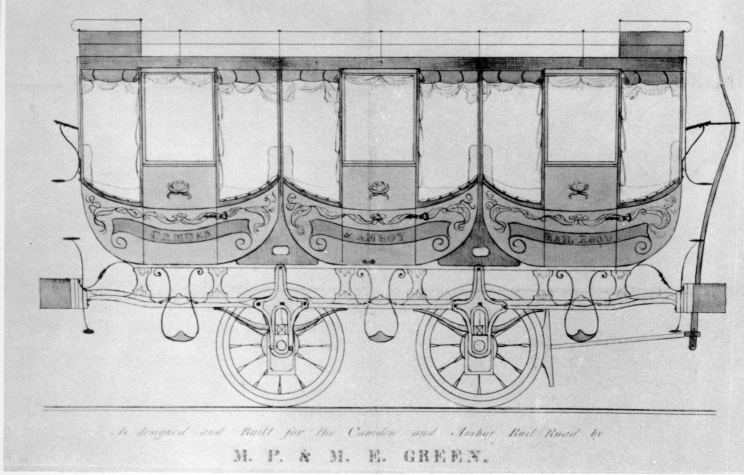

As designed and Built for the Camden and Amboy Rail Road by
M. P. & M. E. GREEN,

Before 1840, coaches imitated styles set by the only precedent that was known—stagecoaches and carriages of the time.

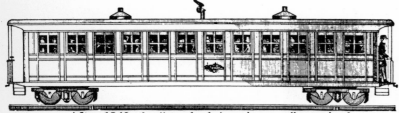

After 1840, the "standard American car" remained in use until Pullman's innovations in the '70's.

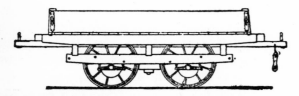

The first freight cars in the United States were simple platforms mounted on four wheels.

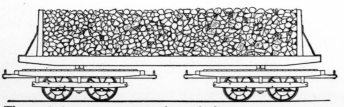

The next stage was to mount long platforms on two primitive cars used as swivel trucks.

3. CARRIAGES AND COACHES

The earliest American carriage was of the stage-coach type, just as in England, but once again American design began to depart radically to suit its own needs. With the invention of the double truck, longer cars were possible. As the first step away from the stagecoach on tracks, three carriages were mounted in tandem on a single bed to insure greater stability from the trebled weight. This design was an intermediate step to the typical long American coach. Here was an idealistic description of an American coach in the forties.

"In cold weather, a small stove is placed near the center of the carriage, the smoke pipe of which passes out through the roof; and a good lamp is placed at each end for illumination through the night. The vehicle is thus perfectly lighted and warmed. The seats are cushioned, and their backs, consisting of a simple padded board about six inches broad, are so supported that the passenger may at his pleasure turn them either way, so as to turn his face or back to the engine. For the convenience of ladies who desire to be apart, a small room is some-

INTERIOR OF AN AMERICAN RAILWAY-CAR.

The interior of an early B. & O. car was dirty, smoky, crowded, noisy, and half as wide as this picture indicates.

times attached at the end of the carriage, admission to which is forbidden to gentlemen."

But in actual practice:

"This morning, at nine o'clock, I took passage on a railroad from Boston for Providence. Five or six other cars were attached to the locomotive, and uglier boxes I do not wish to travel in. They were made to stow away some thirty human beings who sit cheek by jowl, the best they can. Two poor fellows who were not in the habit of making their toilet squeezed me into a corner, while the hot sun drew from their garments a villainous compound of smells made up of salt fish, tar, and molasses. By and by, just twelve—only twelve—bouncing factory girls were introduced who were going on a party of pleasure to Newport. 'Make room for the ladies,' bawled the superintendent. 'Come, gentlemen, jump on the top, plenty of room there!' 'I'm afraid of the bridge knocking my brains out,' said a passenger. For my part, I flatly told him that since I had belonged to the corps of the Silver Greys, I had lost my gallantry and did not intend to move. The whole twelve were introduced and made themselves at home sucking lemons and eating green apples. . . ."

Boiler explosions were frequent on the early railroads. Here the passengers are protected by bales of cotton.

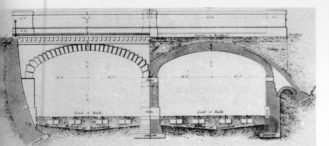

The English adhered to the most refined practices of bridge and road engineering.

The Americans built trestles and bridges from whatever materials were handy.

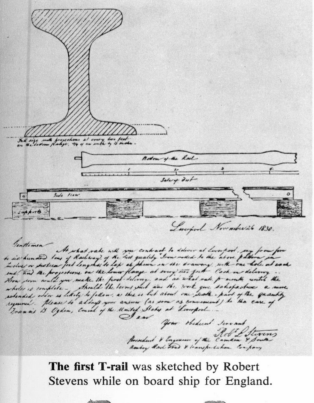

The first T-rail was sketched by Robert Stevens while on board ship for England.

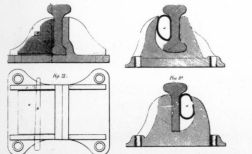

English track was complicated and expensive. Stevens simply spiked his T-rails to ties.

4. THE ROAD AND ROBERT STEVENS

Some of the most basic inventions in American railroading were never patented. The T-rail, now in universal use, was invented by John Stevens' son, Robert, in 1830 while on his way to England for the South Amboy and Camden Railroad to order locomotives and track. To pass the time on the *Hibernia,* he began to whittle models of rail that would be practical, strong, and easy to build in America.

The original rails, as delivered to Robert Stevens, ran to sixteen-foot lengths, and were three and a half inches high. The head, on which the wheel bore, was two and one-eighth inches broad. The base of the track was three and a half inches wide. Standard practice abroad and here was to lay the wooden rails on square granite blocks sunk into the earth. However, once he began to lay track, he found himself moving ahead faster than Sing Sing could furnish him with granite. Unwilling to wait, he had his men square off logs and lay them crosswise on an improvised roadbed of broken rock. These were the original wooden ties. When Robert Stevens gingerly piloted the locomotive himself over the new section, he found the road far more elastic and comfortable than anything he had ridden before. The T-rail, the hook-headed spike, the balance valve, and the fishtail for rail joints were all inventions of Robert Stevens, and none of them were ever patented. He was too busy thinking of the details of the next job.

Within ten years, Stevens' method of laying track became standard the world over.

American and English engineering practices diverged very sharply from the beginning. The English built double lines, while the Americans built single lines with sidings for passing. The English built beautifully designed, substantial stone bridges, viaducts and tunnels. The Americans simply laid track—up hill, down dale, through virgin forests. If a stream or river had to be bridged, wooden trusses were used, hewn from the nearest spot. Furthermore, because of the invention of the swivel truck, American lines were able to make curves twice as sharp as the English would tolerate. In America, a 500-foot radius curve was not at all uncommon. This saved expensive track. Thus the Americans were able to lay twice as much mileage as the English for a far smaller capital investment per mile. The difference, of course, was paid by the passengers in terms of swaying, jolting, and queasiness.

John Stevens' sons, Robert, Edwin, and John Cox, all lived and worked in their robust father's tradition. The English railroad pioneer inventor, Stephenson, was very much like Stevens, and he, too, had a worthy son as colleague and successor. The two railroading families met in 1850 in friendly rivalry in another field. Several of the Stevens sons, with some other young bloods, founded the New York Yacht Club, and as a syndicate built the racing schooner, *America.* They sailed the *America* across the Atlantic where Yacht Club Commodore Stevens issued a sporting challenge to all England to a race for any trophy or a wager up to ten thousand guineas.

At first there were no takers because the *America* was obviously unbeatable, and the *London Times* cried: "Fie! For shame on England!" Then Stephenson stepped up with his yacht *Titania,* game to lose but willing to race. Seven other schooners and eight cutters followed Stephenson's example. During the race, Queen Victoria's quartermaster watched the finish line. Her Majesty asked him who was first, who was second and what was the order. He snapped shut his spyglass, saying, "*America* first—no second!"

The flamboyance of the 1840 poster-timetables was inversely proportional to the comfort offered by the railroads.

Fig.1

Floats of all shapes were towed in a tank by Mark Beaufoy in the first scientific study of hull design. An Englishman, he performed these experiments at the time of the American Revolution.

A huge tripod, sixty feet high, supported a pulley arrangement which pulled the floats through the water. Resistance of the towed body was measured on the scale at the lower left.

obliterated from the public mind the sensation produced by this achievement, without bombastic eruptions.

The fact is too palpably plain to be for a moment questioned, that Americans have much more to gain by ocean steam navigation than other nations. Hence the reason why all Europe manifested so much surprise at the torpidity of Americans in embarking into this great commercial scheme. The American character seems to be but partially known abroad. It is only necessary for him to receive an affirmative answer to the question, *will it pay?* when he gathers up his scattered thoughts, and concentrates them into a single idea, or into the compass of a telegraphic despatch; and then, as on wings of lightning, he is ready to circumnavigate the globe, or to embark in any enterprise within the grasp of thought, or the conception of the human mind.

What, may we not inquire, is the

John W. Griffiths, first clipper designer, took a deeply nationalistic pride in an American trait which Americans, a century later, would deny possessing.

CLIPPER SHIPS

1. JOHN W. GRIFFITHS

When the yacht *America* walked away from the British regatta in 1851, it was only doing what American ships were doing on every ocean. By the middle of the nineteenth century, the American sailing ship—the clipper—was setting a new standard for the entire world. American clippers held most of the world's speed records, and in the Chinese treaty ports crack British East-Indiamen would lie at anchor day after day, waiting to be loaded, while American clippers would blow into port, take aboard the tea of British shippers, and then dash off again for a ten-thousand-mile cruise to London, maintaining an hour-after-hour average of ten or more knots.

In 1850 the clipper was less than a decade old. It was distinctly an American type although, like most of the best nineteenth-century ideas, it stemmed from a French development of the preceding century.

At the time of the American Revolution, many English commanders confessed themselves outrun by "a strange foreign-looking little vessel, sharply raked, which proved to be a French lugger." French naval designers of the eighteenth century had done extensive work on hydrodynamic hull design, and their findings were embodied in a class of small vessel, one to two hundred tons burden, with long, low, slender lines. Stem, stern, and masts were all sharply raked. Many of these vessels were turned over to the Americans, who used them as privateers and later as slavers, often rigged as schooners. They were faster and more able than anything else afloat.

Many were built in this country, in the Baltimore shipyards at first, and came to be known as "Baltimore Clippers." Using the ideas with which these vessels were designed, a completely new class of ship was evolved: the American clipper.

The basic principles of the new approach were worked out in detail by John W. Griffiths, marine architect of New York, who in February, 1841, displayed a model made according to his design at the American Institute. He later wrote a book called *Marine and Naval Architecture,* which explained all his methods. At just about the same time, another young American ship designer named Donald McKay was working along exactly

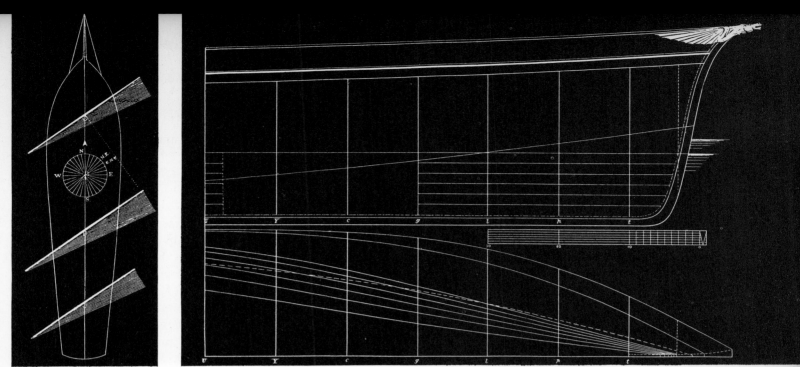

the same lines. These two names—Griffiths and McKay—are coupled with America's greatest era in shipbuilding.

Until the 1840's all large American ships were built with the greatest breadth of beam well forward, which made the bow fairly blunt, while the sides of the vessel tapered toward a rather narrow stern. This design had been based, Griffiths said, on the erroneous belief that "because most of the various species of fish are largest near the head, and have their greatest transverse section forward of the center of their length, it must necessarily follow that the ship must be so constructed. . . . The author can discover no analogy between the ship and fish in their evolutions through the trackless deep. . . . The ship must contend with the buffetings of two elements, while the fish knows but one, and that one always tranquil. . . ."

While working for the firm of Smith and Dimon, the famous shipbuilders of New York, Griffiths carefully worked out the shapes which would present the least resistance to movement through water. The laws of hydrodynamics stated that the maximum velocity of a solid body moving through a fluid was determined by the radius of the smallest curve along the line of flow. A ship with a bluff bow, therefore, had a curvature of fairly small radius. Griffiths advocated that the sides of the vessel that moved through the water should be long, shallow arcs. "Let the fullness be taken off the bow and quarter and added to the breadth midships, and the ship will steer easier, sail faster, and carry the same amount of cargo." This meant a very sharply pointed stern and bow. To preserve ample deck space for the working crew, Griffiths advocated an overhanging deck, which meant that the lines of the bow were given a negative curvature.

Griffith's lectures in 1841 met sharp objections at first. Then, two years later, the shipping firm of Howland and Aspinwall commissioned Smith and Dimon to build a 750-ton vessel to Griffiths' specifications. The naval historian Arthur H. Clark said, "Her bow, with its concave waterlines and the greatest breadth at a point considerably further aft than had hitherto been regarded as practicable, was a radical departure, differing not merely in degree but in kind from any ship that preceded her." Old salts who watched the building of this first clipper—the famous *Rainbow*—said, "Her bows are turned inside out!"

The *Rainbow* was launched in January, 1845, for the China trade. She sailed to China in ninety-two days and flew home in eighty-eight days.

Before Griffiths, hulls were blunt at the front, with the widest point one-third of the distance back from the bow. The plan view at the left, drawn to illustrate how a ship sails to windward, shows a typical hull shape of pre-clipper times. Griffiths revolutionized ship design. His bows (above) had a slender, long-curved entry like a canoe. The forward topsides were concave. The broadest point of the hull was amidships.

. . . the ship . . . s . . . . . . , ... , . . . p . . . of the and carry the same amount of cargo. truth One of the principal objections to this turbar increase of breadth, is, that it makes a vessel ship roll. This opinion is without a ates t foundation in practical stability or fluid. sound philosophy, and we think it never point, would have been entertained by prac- forme tical men, but for the invitation to draw evade the tonnage laws, by building a dist narrow ships. It is a great mistake to It fol identify the rolling of a ship wholly water with the principal dimensions, (as we turbar shall show in its appropriate place.) rudde Another reason assigned for a full and l quarter, and a straight transom, is the the th appearance of the ship, or that it is an has q addition to her beauty, we do not so un- ing th derstand the import of the term *beauty*. bottor We can give no other definition than adapt the following: *fitness for the purpose,* the st *and proportion to effect the object de-* becau *signed.* The eye becomes familiarized the s with a certain shape, and habit causes the s us to think *that* the best we know the sharp most about. The good steering quali- the e

The clipper ships, an American symbol of beauty, looked strange to Griffith's contemporaries. He defended their appearance on utilitarian grounds.

157

At the age of twenty, Donald McKay, a shipwright's apprentice, had his picture taken by daguerreotype.

At the peak of his career, McKay was world-famous for his clippers. During the Civil War, he built monitors for the Union Navy.

AMERICAN SHIPWRIGHTS OF THE 1830'S.

Boring "trenail" holes.

Caulking the seams with oakum.

Making "trenails," or oak pegs.

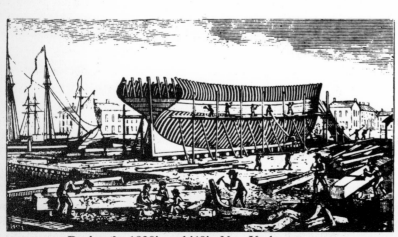

During the 1830's and '40's, New York was the center of the shipbuilding industry.

2. DONALD McKAY

The following year Smith and Dimon were commissioned to build a vessel of 890 tons; this became the storied *Sea Witch*. The *Witch* sped South from New York around the Horn and northwest across the Pacific to Hong Kong in one hundred and four days and shot back to New York from Canton in eighty-one days. She was the fastest ship on the seas.

Donald McKay and his brother Lauchlan came down from Shelburne in Nova Scotia and learned the building of ships in the great New York yards of Brown and Bell, Christian Bergh, Smith and Dimon, and Isaac Webb. The two young brothers learned their trade brilliantly and were already master craftsmen in the decade from 1830 to 1840, when more experimentation with sailing vessels was going on in the United States than at any other time.

Lauchlan McKay left the New York shipyards in 1836 and was appointed carpenter in the United States Navy, serving aboard the *Constellation,* on which Farragut was then a lieutenant. During these same years Donald McKay left the New York yards and went to Newburyport, where he built for John Currier the ship *Delia Walker*. While the *Delia Walker* was building, Lauchlan McKay left the navy and joined his brother at Newburyport, where in 1839 he wrote the first American treatise on shipbuilding, called *The Practical Shipbuilder*. Donald McKay and his wife both gave him invaluable help. For the first time, the American method of building complete ship models was described.

Ship models had been made in Europe as early as the eighteenth century, but they were skeletons made up of pieces representing the half frames. The Americans were the first to use models which showed the lines of flotation. Griffiths said, "The invention of waterline models, like many others, was the result of mere accident. In the eastern states and in the British provinces, men . . . made from a block the form of the vessel they intended to build. . . . In making one of those block models, the block was found to be too small to make the required depth, to which a piece was added, and when finished it was discovered that the longitudinal form of the vessel was shown by the line uniting the two pieces together. The question at once arose, if one seam was an advantage, two would be still greater; and as early as 1790, waterline models were made for building purposes."

Lauchlan described how such models were to be built, and his book was a complete exposition of the art of "taking off" from models to the finished ship. The clipper design was foreseen in Lauchlan McKay's 1839 book when he wrote, "The weight and burthen of a vessel with raking bows are sustained further aft

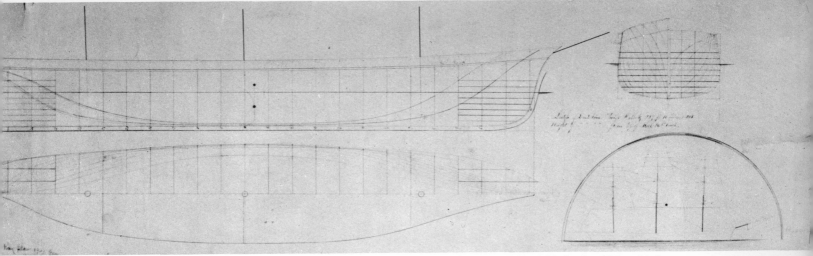

Original pencil drawing of the clipper ship *Lightning* by McKay. More extreme than the California clippers, this ship was 2,084 tons. Length—244 ft., breadth—44 ft. This was the fastest sailing ship ever built.

than in full nose. The center of gravity is consequently further aft."

Like Griffiths, the McKay brothers were aware that there was an easier entrance line than the old spoon-shaped bow. The *Delia Walker* was finished in 1840, and while the ship was impressive because of its speed and ease of handling, it was still not a full clipper. McKay built several other vessels as a partner of John Currier: the *Mary Broughton,* 323 tons; the *Courier,* 380 tons; and the *Ashburton,* 449 tons. At that point the firm dissolved. Writes one historian: "The models and molds being equally divided—with a saw." In 1843, Donald McKay formed a new partnership—the firm of McKay and Pickett—which built two packet ships for New York, the center of the packet activity. In 1843, Enoch Train of Boston, a wealthy ship-owner, came across McKay and commissioned him to build the *Joshua Bates.* The *Joshua Bates* so pleased its owner that Train said to McKay, "You must come to Boston; we need you; and if you need financial assistance to establish a shipyard, let we know the amount, and you shall have it."

For Enoch Train, McKay built the *Washington Irving,* the *Anglo-Saxon,* the *Ocean Monarch,* the *Anglo-American,* and the *Daniel Webster,* all of which carried the black "T" of Train's newly formed Liverpool Line. All of these were fast and able ships. They established McKay's reputation, but they were still not real clippers.

Heavy passenger traffic from the east coast to the California gold fields promised immediate returns for fast vessels, and the year 1850 saw Donald McKay's first true clipper ship, the *Stag-Hound,* the first of a new 1,500-ton class of vessel. Early the next year the New York firm of Grinnell, Minturn and Company visited McKay and fell in love with a ship being built for Enoch Train. They offered Train double the contract price. Train made the deal, and Grinnell and Minturn

bought the *Flying Cloud,* a ship that was never surpassed in beauty of design, weatherliness, and consistent speed under all conditions. Her dimensions were 229 feet on deck, 40 feet 8 inches in breadth, 21 feet 6 inches depth, and a registered tonnage of 1,783. The *Flying Cloud* set fantastic records: on her maiden voyage she made a day's run of 374 miles; in four consecutive days logged 1,256 miles; and made a landfall at San Francisco eighty-nine days out of New York.

In the class of vessels called the California clippers, McKay built the 1,505-ton *Flying Fish* in 1851, the 1,817-ton *Staffordshire,* the 1,790-ton *Bald Eagle;* and in 1852 he built the magnificent 2,421-ton *Sovereign of the Seas,* and completed the 1,600-ton *Westward Ho.* In the following year, he built the 2,200-ton *Empress of the Seas,* and the 3,357-ton *Great Republic.*

McKay was not the only great clipper builder. Ships of entrancing loveliness were the *Mandarin,* 776 tons, built by Smith and Dimon, and the 1,361-ton *Surprise,* owned by A. A. Low and Brother. There were also the 1,392-ton *Game Cock,* the *Race Horse,* the *Witchcraft,* and the *John Bertram.* These were built in various yards by James M. Hood and George Rains, J. Williams and Son, Jacob A. Westervelt, and Isaac Taylor.

The Lightning made a record run to Liverpool in 13 days, 19½ hours; made a day's run at average of 18½ knots.

The biggest clipper ever built was the *Great Republic,* launched at Boston in 1853. Her 3,357 tons were twice that of the average clipper. Her foremast was four feet in diameter and 130 feet tall. She burned before she sailed.

3. THE CLIPPER ERA

Lauchlan McKay, in addition to building ships, was one of the supreme shipmasters of his time. He was in command of the *Sovereign of the Seas,* the longest and sharpest-ended vessel then built, and went out to San Francisco making a record voyage. Off the coast of Chile the vessel was dismasted in a storm, but Lauchlan McKay rerigged her at sea and kept her going. Having delivered a cargo of gold miners, Lauchlan McKay put in at Honolulu, took aboard a cargo of 8,000 barrels of whale oil and some bone, and sailed for home again. On this passage, too, the ship sprang a fore-topmast, which McKay repaired at sea, and she eventually arrived at Sandy Hook in eighty-two days out from Honolulu.

On this trip the *Sovereign* sailed 5,391 nautical miles in twenty-two days. In 1853 the *Sovereign* sailed from New York to Liverpool, crossing from pier to anchorage in thirteen days, twenty-two hours. The next ship under Lauchlan McKay's command was his brother's greatest vessel, the *Great Republic,* which never went to sea. The ship burned and sank in the harbor when they were making ready to sail to Liverpool.

Captain Lauchlan McKay went as builder's representative aboard the *Lightning* on her maiden voyage from Boston to Liverpool in 1854, when she made a day's run of 436 nautical miles. Lauchlan McKay was also the skipper of the English clippers sent on the Australia run. At the end of the clipper era, he returned to shipbuilding in Canada, where his firm launched twenty-nine vessels of all classes.

The clipper era passed, but Americans had finally learned to build ships according to scientific principles, and this was the era's great achievement.

A former master of a clipper ship, when asked if the clippers were really superior to other vessels, replied that a clipper was never still. The ships "ghosted" along in the lightest airs. Certainly a great part of the clipper's performance was due to the masterly handling by skippers out to make records by driving their crews to the limit. Very few Americans sailed before the mast on the clippers, because by that time the wages paid by American shippers were so low and life at sea so hard that the American seaman, who had been such a source of pride to America in the early years of the century, would no longer have any part of the sea. The clipper crews were generally tough derelicts, packet-rats, or shanghaied foreigners who were made to work for the pitifully small salaries offered by American shippers. As lovely as the ships were, Americans knew that the

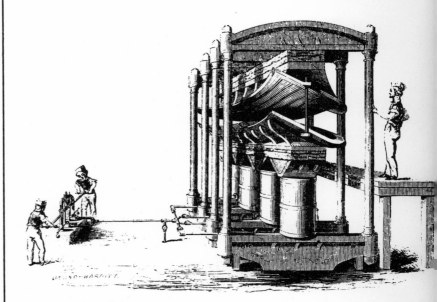

Shipwrecks were common in the era of sail. The U. S. maintained a chain of life saving stations along the coast.

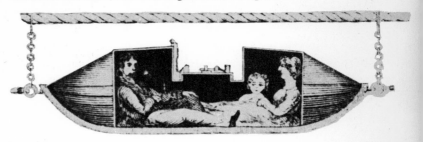

The Life-car invented by Joseph Francis of New York slid along a ship-to-shore cable. These cars were iron.

conditions of the crews were a national disgrace. In addition, shipwrecks were common in the era of sail.

The officers of the clippers were Americans, mostly from New England, and constituted a special aristocracy. Occasionally captains' wives accompanied them, and the most remarkable of these women was Mary Patten, wife of the captain of the *Neptune's Car*.

The *Neptune's Car* sailed from New York to San Francisco in June, 1856. Before reaching Cape Horn, Captain Joshua Patten had to put his first mate under arrest for incompetence and neglect of duty. In the wintry seas off the Cape, Captain Patten was taken sick with a brain fever and went blind. His second mate could not navigate. Mrs. Patten, only nineteen years old, had learned the science of navigation on a previous voyage, and she took command of the 1,800-ton vessel. For fifty-two days Mrs. Patten, "a beautiful woman of the finest New England type, with a refined, gentle voice and manner," nursed her husband, navigated, ran a crew of desperate men, and brought the ship safely into San Francisco harbor. She became one of the darlings of the feminist movement.

To the list of Things Which Women Could Do As Well As Men, the believers in American perfectibility—through giving women equal rights—added the profession of captain of a great ocean clipper.

THE LIFE CAR

The first hydraulic press to stamp complicated shapes from metal sheet was invented by Joseph Francis to make iron surf boats. These boats had corrugated sides to stiffen them. The surf boats were later superseded by his Life-car which was in use until the 1880's. Francis had greater success with his iron boats in Europe than he did in America, where they were considered too radical.

161

An 18th-century iron forge, by the English artist, Richard Earlom

Coal mining was begun in earnest during the 1840's to feed America's burgeoning smelters and steel mills.

Before then, charcoal was preferred as fuel for the manufacture of iron and steel, but coke made better steel.

The Nashua (N. H.) Iron Company produced forged iron for machine shops, ships, and railroads. Their "perfect machinery enables them to produce Locomotive Tyres so accurately as not to require any turning or boring."

FORGE, PAN, AND DERRICK

1. IRON

On September 15, 1844, William A. Burt, in charge of a party of government surveyors working its way among the hills near Lake Superior, noticed that his compass was behaving erratically, swinging 87° from normal. The party spread out to search for outcrops of iron ore which might account for the wild deviations. Traces of deposits were found just beneath the sod. Burt took samples of the ore, noted the district on his map as Iron Hills, and continued on his way. That was all he ever did about the Mesabi range, the greatest iron mining region ever discovered.

In the forties, railroad builders like Robert Stevens had to import rails from England. American methods of making iron were a century behind those of Europe.

Iron's affinity for oxygen means that it is usually found in nature as the red or black oxide—common rust. Iron became usable as soon as men learned to separate the oxygen with heat and some form of pure carbon—originally charcoal. The oxygen was removed as carbon dioxide; but some of the carbon remained in the iron. When the carbon content is from two to four per cent, the iron is brittle. It can be cast in molds, but it cannot be forged. When the carbon content is less than two per cent, the iron is called steel, a form which is tough and elastic. Iron without any carbon is very soft and malleable.

Kelly's converter, like Bessemer's, made steel by burning carbon out of molten iron with blasts of air.

From Tubal Cain on down for thousands of years, the iron-master's universe ranged within that four per cent of carbon. A skilled iron-master knew by experience when the carbon content of molten iron was exactly right for the product he wanted: cast iron, hard steel, mild steel, or wrought iron.

In the early 1850's, two men on different continents, with different backgrounds, at opposite poles of society, looked at a defective piece of iron and both had the same revolutionary insight.

Henry Bessemer was a successful English inventor, factory owner, and member of several learned scientific societies. William Kelly made sugar-boiling kettles for Southern planters in a shanty shop on a country crossroads in Kentucky. Bessemer had thousands of pounds with which to experiment; Kelly had a doubting wife, hungry small children, and an irascible father-in-law. Yet to both men the only reality in life was the question of how to control the less than four per cent of carbon in iron.

In molten iron, the carbon is dissolved just as sugar dissolves in water. Both Kelly and Bessemer discovered that when pig iron, with four per cent of carbon in it, is heated to a molten state, and air is bubbled through the white-hot liquid, the oxygen of the air and the dissolved carbon combine to raise the temperature still further. The carbon that goes into this combustion leaves the metal in a white-hot blast of carbon dioxide, and the molten iron is left with only a fraction of the original carbon—and on cooling becomes high grade steel.

Once the chemistry is clear, the question is asked: what is so odd? It was simply that men were asked to believe that one could heat up molten iron by blowing cold air through it without any outside source of heat—or as humorists said, one could turn iron into steel by sneezing into a crucible. Kelly's neighbors actually thought him insane, and his father-in-law wanted him to be examined by a doctor. However, the steel that resulted told its own story. Kelly perfected his process in 1851, six years before Bessemer received his United States patent.

Queen Victoria knighted Henry Bessemer. Kelly's father-in-law, to whom Kelly had assigned his patent as security for a loan, left the patent on his death to his daughters. His son-in-law might have invented a new way to make steel, the old man admitted grudgingly, but he was sure as hell crazy, too.

The American steel industry, pushed by the frenzy of railroad building, began when Kelly met Alexander Holley. In the late 1850's, Holley, an engineer, secured the American license to Bessemer's process. Only then did he discover that Kelly's patent anticipated him; but Kelly did not ride out to do battle with him. Kelly preferred the dynamic, steel-loving Holley as an ally rather than his wife and sisters-in-law, who continued to withhold his patent—for his own good, of course; and so the two men came to terms. Within fifteen years America began to rival England as steel supplier to the world.

For the rest of their lives, one or another of the sisters could be found staring off into space for a few minutes—wondering, that's all. Just wondering.

2. GOLD

All the gold that was produced in the United States before 1828 amounted to only $110,000 and came from North Carolina. In the following year, gold was discovered in Virginia, but the real rush was to Georgia. In 1833 and 1834, the gold from Virginia, the Carolinas, and Georgia came to $2,000,000. The total gold mined in the United States between 1792 and 1847 was 1,187,170 fine ounces. Gold mining in the South would have been of only minor importance except that it developed the miners who would be the first to appreciate and develop the California discovery—which was no new discovery at all.

For many years, gold had been known to exist in California, and no one did anything about it. In 1816, Robert Jameson published *A System of Mineralogy* in Edinburgh, stating: "On the coast of California, there is a plain fourteen leagues in extent, covered with alluvial deposits, in which lumps of gold are dispersed."

No attempt was made to keep the news a secret, for in 1842 the representative from California to the Mexican Congress reported the existence of gold in his district, and two years later repeated his story: "On my departure from Los Angeles in May, 1843, there was in circulation about two thousand ounces of gold which had been extracted from the previously mentioned placer."

Even the Americans knew about it. The U. S.

Consul at Monterey reported to Commander Montgomery in 1846: "At San Fernando, near San Pedro, by washing the sand in a plate, any person can obtain from one to five dollars per day of gold that brings $17 per ounce in Boston . . . but few have the patience to work for it."

One can only speculate why so little attention was paid to these reports. The American government was probably counting on its plans for a change of national ownership of the area, and the Mexicans, too, were not anxious to attract a flood of miners into California. The wealthy *haciendados* were violently opposed to anything that would make their workers leave the fields. The Franciscan friars were afraid that an influx of Americans would disturb their Indian wards with heresy. Then along came John A. Sutter, a Swiss

merchant, who ran one of the great ranches at New Helvetia.

In 1848 he formed a partnership with James Marshall, who was assigned the task of building a sawmill to be driven by water power on the south fork of the American River. Marshall happened to notice that several bright bits of yellow mineral lay beneath the water. He guessed that they were either pyrite, which he knew to be brittle, or gold, which would be soft and malleable. He took several of the tiny chips and found that they could be flattened beneath a hammer. He said to the men working with him, "Boys, by God, I believe I have found a gold mine."

When Sutter tested the samples, according to directions in an old encyclopedia, they assayed twenty-two carat.

San Francisco was a tiny village in 1848. A year later, 20,000 floaters surged through the town. Above: a lithograph of the mail queues at the Post Office.

Gold mining, at first, consisted simply of washing gravel in a bowl, or pan, or shovel. The average jack-booter did all right with these processes.

3. GOLD! GOLD! GOLD!

Henry Bigler, a Mormon worker, made this entry in his diary: "This day some kind of mettle was found in the tail race that looks like goald . . . discovered by James Martial, the boss. . . ."

Sutter asked all the mill hands to say nothing for six weeks because he correctly feared that all his workmen would leave him. One of them, however, a carpenter named Charles Bennett, went to San Francisco, where he told his story and showed some flakes to Isaac Humphrey, who had been a miner in Georgia. Humphrey was the one man with the background to sense what was going on. In March he went to New Helvetia and took a laborer's job with Sutter. As soon as he had time to himself, he built the same kind of rocker that he had used in the Georgia diggings. From the moment he started to wash gravel, he began obtaining several ounces of gold a day. Humphrey's excitement was caught by the other men on the ranch, and they all left Sutter at once, stealing his cattle and his horses. Hysteria finally overcame Californian phlegm. A week later the first news of the strike appeared in the newspaper, the *Californian,* published in San Francisco.

"GOLD MINE FOUND—In the newly made raceway of the sawmill recently erected by Capt. Sutter . . . gold has been found. One person brought $30 worth to New Helvetia, gathered there in a short time . . . gold has been found in almost every part of the country."

The fever finally struck and men went crazy overnight. Two weeks after its first announcement, the *Californian* lost its staff and went out of business with this comment:

"The whole country, from San Francisco to Los Angeles, and from the seashore to the base of the Sierra Nevada, resounds with the sordid cry of *Gold! Gold! Gold!* while the field is left half-planted, the house half-built, and everything neglected but

THE HOPE GOLD COMPANY'S MACHINES

The ore breaking room

The furnace

the manufacture of picks and shovels, and the means of transportation to the spot where one man obtained $128 worth of the real stuff in one day's washing; and the average is $20 per diem!"

The excitement was so tremendous and the influx from around Cape Horn and across the Isthmus of Panama was so great that in the remaining nine months of that year ten million dollars' worth of gold was found. The daily average was about an ounce per man. "It was no uncommon event for a man alone to take out $500 a day, or for two or three working together to divide the dust at the end of the week by measuring it in tin cups. But we were never satisfied," wrote one of the early miners.

The gold was mostly in the form of veins along the fissures left from ancient volcanic action when the earth was still cooling. Gold from the molten core was vaporized and before it could escape as a gas to the atmosphere, it condensed on the walls of the opening at the cooler surface layer. These volcanic openings became sealed up as scars. As mountain erosion took place, water tended to seep into these fissures turning them into streams and creeks. That is why the first gold found lay at the foot of gulches and stream beds.

The transformation of the miner's apparatus marks a continual stream of the sort of invention which is man's adaptation to necessity. In the beginning, a shovel, a frying pan, or any kind of shallow container was used to shake up the gravel so that the heavier flakes of gold would, by gravity, settle to the bottom. The overlying gravel washed away and the residue was picked over for gold. Soon the washing vessel became a basin with sloping sides about a foot and a half in diameter and about four inches in depth. Later, the miner used a wooden box with sloping sides about three feet long and mounted on rockers. Above the upper end of the box he placed a small sieve into which the fresh gravel and water was thrown. As the "cradle" was

rocked with water pouring over the sieve, only the finest sand and the gold fell through the openings to the floor of the "cradle" where the rocking continued the process of separation. Eventually miners lengthened the cradle into a trough ten feet long, and the sloping bottom was riffled like a laundry board where the finer particles of gold tended to collect. This was called the "long Tom." Finally, the miner put mercury into the riffles because the mercury became amalgamated with the gold, trapping it, while the sand and the gravel floated on top of the mercury. In this form, each step of the process was elaborated on a much larger scale to become the enormous gold extracting mill.

The United States had paid Mexico fifteen million dollars for the whole area that included California, New Mexico, Nevada, Utah, Arizona, and parts of Colorado and Wyoming. One year after the purchase, 1849, California produced enough gold to have bought the region three times over.

For the first two years the self-government of the diggings was on a fairly high order of democratic comradeship. The population was about 100,000, but all the men were working hard and there seemed to be plenty of gold for everyone. In the third year, trouble came when the gamblers, saloon keepers, and prostitutes began to appear. Another cause for violence was the exaggerated American dislike of foreigners, expressed politically in the "Know Nothing" party. Out of conviction and self-interest, the diggers were antislavery. They set up and enforced their own rules forbidding slave-owners from the Southern states to stake claims in the name of their "black bondsmen." In the same way, Peruvians and Chileans could not make claims for their peons.

By 1858, California had yielded half a billion dollars.

The decision of California in 1850 to be a free territory affected the outcome of the war that began ten years later.

DUPLICATED HAND OPERATIONS ON A LARGE SCALE.

The ore pit or drying room

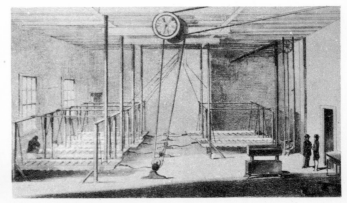

The amalgamating room

Samuel Kier sold lamps to burn oil that came up from his salt wells.

Col. E. L. Drake supervised the first well drilled for oil.

William A. (Uncle Billy) Smith did the actual drilling of Drake's well.

4. OIL

It was no accident that in the late forties and early fifties men were looking for a cheap illuminant as a substitute for whale oil.

New Bedford had become the center of the whale oil industry. Agents like J. B. and S. Wing not only outfitted a ship for the owners, but hired the crew and sold the oil at the end of the voyage, turning over the profits to the shareholders. Since only a few agencies controlled almost eighty per cent of the fleet, it was inevitable that they would force the retail price higher and higher. The public was now accustomed to a standard of household lighting unknown at the beginning of the century, and while people were not eager to return to darkness, neither were they eager to pay New Bedford prices.

The first substitute for whale oil was an oil distilled from coal. Abraham Gesner, a Canadian geologist, in 1854 took out a patent on such a product, calling it "kerosene." The sale of Gesner's "kerosene" was steady but not phenomenal because of the oil's rank odor.

All this time, the natural mineral oil—petroleum —was being sold in drug stores and in tent shows under the name of "Seneca oil" or "snake oil"; a foul-smelling medicine which was supposed to cure every ailment from cancer to cramps. The oil could be found in Pennsylvania, in shallow surface pools. The Indians collected it by soaking a blanket in the pool and then wringing out the blanket in their storage pits. The oil occasionally overflowed into the rivers and creeks, and on certain religious festivals, the Indians would set the rivers afire. Oil was a divine substance.

To the whites it was a nuisance. The earliest migrations from the coast were limited by the distance men were willing to travel from sources of salt. There were no settlements beyond the first mountain range until men discovered in Pennsylvania and Virginia that it was possible to dig wells for natural brine. But most of the wells had to be abandoned because they were contaminated by the foul-smelling mineral oil which lay over the brine.

In 1857, A. C. Ferris noticed a small tin lamp burning smoky petroleum as a display for a wholesale drug company. He realized at once that if he could find a way to refine the oil and remove its stench, he would have an excellent illuminant. He had enough capital to employ a chemist and a corps of salesmen to go around New York demonstrating a lamp expressly designed for this new fuel. Before long his problem was to find enough "Seneca oil" to satisfy the demands of his customers. He imported oil from abroad and finally bought some land in

Pennsylvania. Unfortunately he was a few miles away from the region that was later to be known as "Oil County" and lost twenty thousand dollars digging worthless holes.

What Ferris was doing in New York, Samuel M. Kier was doing in Pittsburgh. He had discovered oil coming up from one of his salt wells on the Allegheny River in 1849. He sent a sample to Professor Booth of the University of Pennsylvania, who told him that the oil seemed to be largely composed of naphtha which ought to make a good solvent for gutta percha. The gutta percha manufacturers were not interested, so Professor Booth then advised Kier to refine his oil and get a suitable lamp designed. Having paid for advice, Kier had the good sense to follow it. From 1850 on, he was able to sell all the oil he could get from his own salt works.

Ferris' example suggested to George H. Bissell and Jonathan G. Eveleth of New York the novel idea of drilling directly for oil instead of using the by-product from salt wells. The same derrick that stood over every salt well could be used for oil. Even the drilling process ought to be the same. They took in as partner and field superintendent, Colonel E. L. Drake.

In May, 1858, Drake went to Titusville on Oil Creek, selected a site, and began to drill. He struck water in such volume that his workers were flooded. Drake's ingenuity saved the situation. On the spot he invented the modern method of driving iron pipe, one length after another, down into the hole, keeping out the water, the quicksand, and the clay. He struck oil in small quantities, but the ferocious mountain winter set in and stopped operations. The following year Drake started over again and went to Kier for advice.

Kier suggested Uncle Billy Smith as the man to drill deep salt wells. Uncle Billy and his sons began work towards the end of May, 1859. Using Drake's method of sinking pipe, they continued drilling and by August had gone almost seventy feet through rock. On the twenty-eighth, they were about to stop for the night, when the pipe began to fill.

"Look at this," Uncle Billy said to Colonel Drake.

"What is it?" Drake asked.

"It's your fortune coming!" said Uncle Billy.

The next day, Drake installed a spring pump and eight barrels were pumped into old fish cans and any other receptacles that were at hand. Within two months the well was yielding twenty-two barrels a day.

The news of the strike spread as rapidly as the word of gold had spread from California. The word *kerosene* which had been a trade name for a different substance, was popularly applied to petroleum. Everyone began drilling everyplace, and most of them found oil. Within two years strikes ran to two thousand barrels a day.

Drake started drilling for oil in May, 1858. His men struck water in such volume that they were flooded.

The derrick used in the drilling of oil wells, such as Drake's, was exactly the same as had previously been used for brine.

5. OIL, THE NEW WEALTH

This is what the region looked like to Mr. T. S. Scoville two years after Smith and Drake struck oil:

"Everything muddy and dirty. Hotels crammed full, two in a bed everywhere, and three if they can get them in, not to mention the number of small-stock travelers that pile in with the rest. . . . Buildings rough outside and in, set on stilts, all new, all hurried; great preparations for drilling, pumping, buying, selling, building—all excitement, life, and activity. At Tidioute there are some 200 wells in progress, and all the way from there here, 30 miles by raft, one is not out of sight of derricks and wells, hundreds and hundreds of them. . . ."

A contemporary account by another, cooler, observer describes the drilling:

"The apparatus for boring is very simple. A derrick is erected, consisting of four timbers from thirty to forty feet, connected with framing ten feet square at the base, and about four or five at the top . . . At the top is a pulley over which a stout rope runs, one end of which is attached to the drill and the other to a windlass. The drill consists of a steel edge . . . attached to a long iron bar . . . three inches in diameter . . .

"The rope attached to the drill is then fastened firmly to the end of a long spring pole. This pole is secured at the outer end, some distance from the derrick. A springing motion is . . . given to the smaller end of the pole from which the drill hangs, by . . . having a strap or rope suspended from it, with a step-piece at the bottom, in which two men each place a foot. By kicking outward and downward a little, the pole comes down, and the natural spring throws it back to its original position, thus moving the drill up and down a short distance. A man stands by the drill, constantly turning it, to vary the side on which it strikes, and to produce a round hole . . . The depth at which oil is found varies from 30 feet to 400, the average at McLintock's being 150 feet.

"Steam power is rapidly being introduced . . . engines of about five horsepower . . . but at present

Early wells were pumped directly into open vats, and from there the oil went into wooden barrels for shipment.

Forests of derricks covered Pennsylvania hillsides. Pit Hole's population jumped from 100 to 14,000 in six

it appears that almost every man wants to put his own foot into it, and *jump himself* rich. . . ."

A contemporary description of how the first oil was refined would not vary very sharply in principle from one written at a time of more highly advanced technology. Here is one such report written during the Civil War:

"All the oil as it comes from the well is impure, and is known as crude oil. This must be refined before it is suitable for use. These refineries are very numerous in a small way . . . but there is an extensive one at Corry . . . This establishment, known as the Downer Refinery, is owned by parties in Boston, who manufactured oil from coal previous to the discovery of oil wells, and is probably the most perfect refinery ever constructed. The crude oil, as it is received from the wells, is stored in immense vats underground, from which it is . . . conveyed in pipes to different parts of the works. The first operation is distilling, in which the oil is placed in receivers over a coal fire, and the vapor carried off . . . and condensed . . .

"That which first comes off is the light oil, and is called naphtha. There is no dividing line between naphtha and oil, but when the operator thinks it is heavy enough he shuts off the naphtha and calls it oil. The oil thus obtained by distilling is further purified by a course of treatment that also, to some extent, deodorizes it. The oil is conveyed from one operation to another by pumps, the conveying pipes being provided with suitable valves . . . thus avoiding, to a great degree, the danger from fire. Lastly, it is carried to iron tanks in the barreling room, where it is barreled and shipped."

The scenes of California were being repeated all over again as new wealth gushed strength into the North's economy.

A local paper wrote:

"Less than ten years ago it is doubtful if a hundred thousand dollars were at any time in circulation in the country contiguous to Oil Creek. Now, it is not an uncommon thing in the same neighborhood for a million of dollars to change hands in a single week. . . ."

months. Signs on the offices of the Foster Farm Oil Co. and the Shoe and Leather Petroleum Co. show the origins of some of the early wild-catters. Petroleum displaced whale oil just as electricity was to displace kerosene.

Close check was kept as the cable was paid out. Dudley's "Awaiting the Reply" shows tenseness at a suspected flaw

THE ATLANTIC CABLE

1

Cyrus W. Field

In the decade following Morse's first public demonstration in Washington, telegraphic networks spread across America and Europe. An inevitable step was the connection of the two continental systems by a cable on the ocean floor, even though the difficulties seemed insuperable.

The first problem was insulation. One early suggestion for insulating submarine wire was to wrap the wire tightly with layers of flannel and cotton covered with a mixture of rosin, beeswax and rubber. Other suggestions included tar and asphaltum. Submarine insulation had been solved by the use of gutta percha, a sap somewhat similar to rubber, obtained from Malaya. Gutta percha is a nonconductor which deteriorates in the sun, but retains its electrical insulating properties under water.

The first underwater cable insulated with gutta percha was laid successfully in 1845 between England and the Continent. In the United States, the first successful sea cable was Morse's cable between Governor's Island and Castle Garden, in 1842. Later there was a thirteen-mile line between the islands of Martha's Vineyard and Nantucket.

With the insulation problem apparently solved, three questions had to be answered:

Where was the cable to be laid?

How could messages be sent over a thousand miles of wire without relays such as Henry's?

Who would have sufficient strength of personality to organize and oversee the infinite variety of details involved in such an undertaking?

The three questions were answered by three different men. Their joint talents were equally responsible for the greatest engineering feat of the century up to that time.

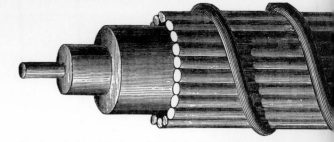

Sectional view of the cable shows the wire surrounded by layers of insulation, reinforced to withstand any possible strain or erosion.

Matthew Maury was the most distinguished scientist of the American South. He had entered the United States Navy as a midshipman in 1825 and had seen active service for several years. In 1836, Maury published *A New Theoretical and Practical Treatise on Navigation for Junior Naval Officers,* and under the pen names of Henry Bluff and Will Watch, wrote blistering articles attacking the methods of educating young naval officers. As a result of the rumpus he raised, a naval academy was founded at Annapolis in 1845, similar to the Army's West Point; but Maury had made so many enemies among the senior officers that he was forced to leave active service. He was made Superintendent of the Depot of Charts and Instruments at Washington in 1842, which became the United States Naval Observatory and Hydrographical Office.

It was here that Maury began his great work of charting the ocean currents. On every sea voyage, American sailing masters were given blank charts which were to be filled in with daily descriptions of wind direction and velocity, compass variation, air and sea temperature, and currents.

After five years, he published *The Wind and Current Charts of the North Atlantic* which suggested lanes for sea travel insuring the fastest and safest passages. As a result of Maury's work, the average sailing time from New York to San Francisco around the Horn was cut from 180 to 133 days—a saving of almost seven weeks.

Two twenty-mile-wide ocean lanes across the Atlantic were mapped by Maury in 1855, and all American vessels were ordered to follow them. Maury had also been compiling data on the sea bottom. In 1852 he completed his topographic map of the Atlantic floor, showing for the first time the submarine mountain ranges and deeps. The map showed an underwater plateau, which Maury called the "telegraphic plateau," between Ireland and Newfoundland.

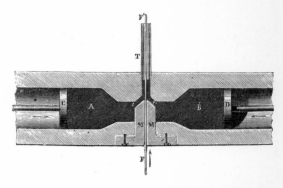

Gutta percha was applied with this apparatus. Wire (F) passes through a bath of the molten mix (A, B), while pistons (C, D) maintain pressure.

The second question—telegraphy without relay—was answered by William Thomson, an Englishman, later famous as Lord Kelvin. His solution of the problem of dielectric loss formed the direct link between Henry's work on the oscillatory discharge of the Leyden jar and Clerk Maxwell's fourth equation of electrodynamics.

The third need—an organizing genius—was supplied by an American, Cyrus W. Field—a retired paper merchant who, at thirty-five, looked forward to a life of ease, entirely unaware that he was to be swept up into an enterprise that would make him risk his fortune, his sanity, and his integrity in a test that was to go on for twelve years.

The project of a cable from the United States to Newfoundland was broached to Field in 1854. The colossal scale of the undertaking appealed to him. He consulted Morse, who had no idea of the difficulties involved; and Morse gave him easy approval. Field then sounded out several New York businessmen. They agreed to go along.

The final step in the protection of the cable was to wrap the whole structure with many strands of jute and cover it with a layer of tar.

The New York, Newfoundland and London Electric Telegraph Company was organized in May, 1854, with a capital of $1,500,000. Cyrus Field went to England to buy cable. His brother, the company's engineer, went to Newfoundland to start land construction. The cable for the first leg of fifty-five miles to Newfoundland arrived from England in the summer of 1855, and the laying of the line began immediately.

The steamer, *James Adger,* was to tow the cable-carrying bark, *Sarah Bryant.* Bad weather delayed a start for several days, then strong winds arose and the towline parted. Next morning a new start was made. The cable was spliced; and after a run of a few miles, the *Adger* was sent off course by currents. Another gale made up, leaving both vessels wallowing helplessly. To save themselves, they had to cut loose forty miles of underwater cable.

The first submarine cable was laid by Samuel Morse under New York harbor. The French artist who drew the event had his own ideas of terrain.

HOW THE CABLE WAS STOWED AND LAID

The cable lay in great coils in the holds of the ships *Niagara*, furnished by the United States, and *Agamemnon*, of Britain. Below is a view of the *Agamemnon's* hold as the cable was being stowed in England. The owner of the silk hat and gold-headed cane is not identified. Complicated machinery (upper left) paid out the cable as the ship sailed along, with the tension being carefully adjusted by sensitive brakes to support the enormous weight hanging thousands of feet down to the bottom of the ocean. The cable went over a huge wheel at the stern of the ship, where it passed by a guard constructed to prevent fouling of the rudder as the ship tossed in rough and stormy seas.

2. THE FIRST ATLANTIC CABLE—A FAILURE

The first step—the attempt to lay a short line to Newfoundland—was a failure. The following summer, more capital was raised and the connection from the mainland to Newfoundland was successfully made. The cost to date was over a million dollars and only the smallest step had been taken.

Field went to England again and organized the Atlantic Telegraph Company of Great Britain, which absorbed the original American company and raised close to two million dollars. The British government promised vessels to help lay the cable and asked for favored use of the cable on its completion. Field fought a bill through Congress getting him similar support. For cable laying, the United States Navy detached its largest vessel, the *Niagara,* and sent along the *Susquehanna* as its tender. The Royal Navy assigned the *Agamemnon* and the *Leopard* to the same task. The four vessels met on the coast of Ireland in Valentia Bay on August 14.

The shore end of the cable was fixed, speeches were made, and the flotilla sailed, paying cable as it went. Constant communication was maintained between the ships and Thomson at the shore end.

Four days out, 360 miles had been laid to a depth of two miles, and the cable was transmitting. At nine o'clock that evening, signal strength flickered, vanished, and then returned. At 3:45 in the morning, miles below the surface, a fraction of an inch of copper failed, and the great cable was parted. With flags at half-mast, the flotilla steamed back to Valentia Bay. The cost was a half million dollars.

The following summer Field had a new plan of action. In June, 1858, the flotilla made a rendezvous in midocean, each carrying half the cable. The *Niagara* and the *Agamemnon* spliced ends and then sailed off in opposite directions, the *Niagara* towards America, the *Agamemnon* east to Ireland. After three miles, the *Niagara's* end was fouled. A new splice was made, and this time forty miles were laid before signals stopped. After a third start, two hundred miles of cable were paid out. A break then occurred on the *Agamemnon.*

The ships' captains returned to Ireland and advised the Board of Directors that the whole thing was impractical. Only Field's impassioned optimism convinced the board to make another try. On June 17, the cable fleet left Ireland with Field aboard the *Niagara.* Two weeks later, the ships arrived at midocean, spliced cable ends and began again. The weather was good. Both vessels continually reported to each other with absolute clarity. One week later, at seven o'clock in the morning, the lookout on the *Niagara* called "Land Ho!" At 2:30 P.M. the American vessels entered Trinity Bay, Newfoundland, just as the receiver was bringing the news that the *Agamemnon* had raised the Irish shore. At eight o'clock that night, August 8, 1858, Cyrus Field went ashore, walked fifteen miles to the nearest telegraph station, reaching it at two-thirty in the morning. He sent wires to Mrs. Field, the Associated Press, and to President Buchanan, telling him that Queen Victoria would greet him just as soon as the two ends of the cable were connected with land networks.

Before the cable was laid, the company's stock was selling at three hundred dollars. It rose immediately to a thousand. The public reaction after years of skepticism was one of hysterical jubilation. Spontaneous celebrations broke out all over the country. Poems were written, songs composed, and Longfellow's diary says: "August 6th—Go to town with the boys. Flags flying and bells ringing to celebrate the laying of the telegraph." In New York, celebrations awaited the Queen's message.

All through America, there was the conviction that a glorious new era had arrived for men, that instant communication between the old world and the new would put an end to all strife and misunderstanding. There would be peace—*peace—peace!*

In the meantime, the two operators at opposite ends of the cable were the only ones who were aware that something was dying even before it was born. Eleven days of night and day adjustment passed and finally the Queen's message began to arrive at four-fifteen in the afternoon. Two hours of constant repetition were required to get through the following sentence: "The Queen desires to congratulate the President upon the successful completion of the great international work, in which the Queen has taken the greatest interest."

The rest of the message was not completed for another twelve hours, but impatient celebrants did not bother to wait. In New York a pandemonium of church bells, factory whistles, fireworks, gun reports tore the town apart. The city was festooned with banners, and banquets were held. As a final touch of joy, the City Hall was set afire.

Disappointment was so bitter when the cable finally went dead that most people began to doubt that the cable had ever worked at all. It had been too good to be true.

For weeks, both operators worked sleeplessly trying to re-establish communication, but the silence was unbroken. Months later it was reported that the fault was due to insulation. When the wire was being made, careless workmen had left coil after coil of the gutta-percha–covered cable exposed in the sun, against all instructions.

3. THE GREAT EASTERN AND THE ATLANTIC CABLE

All during the war, Field kept pushing away at his project. In July, 1865, with the *Great Eastern,* the largest steamboat afloat and now adapted for cable-laying, another attempt was made. The great vessel and three tenders left Valentia harbor with ceremonies as joyous as on the first occasion. Communication with the shore was kept up all the time. There were failures; but on each occurrence the huge steamer retraced its path, hauling in cable until the faulty section was found and mended. When the *Great Eastern* was only 660 miles from Newfoundland, after maintaining perfect communication with Ireland, the cable parted. For almost two weeks the *Great Eastern* cruised back and forth over the ocean, finding and losing the cable, trying to raise it with inadequate hoisting tackle. Finally a buoy was thrown over to mark the spot. It was a time of the greatest despair, and even the indomitable Field broke down and wept like a child.

Still Field refused to give up. The following year, 1866, a new corporation was formed, the Anglo-American Company, which absorbed all the previous companies. Once again, the *Great Eastern* sailed from Ireland with almost 2,500 miles of cable in her hold. But this time every flaw of past technique was known. Within ten days, the *Great Eastern* was steaming past the spot where the '65 cable was lost, and cable was still being paid out. Field cabled to London, "We are within 400 miles of Heart's Content. Expect to be there Friday. When shall Atlantic cable be opened for public business?" London replied, "If you land Friday, open Saturday."

At seven o'clock Friday morning, July 27, Heart's Content came into sight and at 8:55 Cyrus Field went ashore. He personally telegraphed the news of the safe landing. Then without any delay, but to everyone's surprise, he returned aboard the *Great Eastern* and steamed back out to sea.

At that moment of triumph, his disappearance seemed inexplicable, but Field was fulfilling a promise to himself. The *Great Eastern* was returning to the spot where the cable had been lost the previous year. Back and forth over the empty ocean she cruised, feeling the bottom with new grappling apparatus. The lost end of the '65 cable was actually found and raised, and on being tested, proved to be in perfect condition. With new wire spliced to the old cable, the *Great Eastern* then returned to Newfoundland and the second wire was landed, working flawlessly. The recapture of the old cable caught the world's imagination far more than the first successful completion and Field was vindicated.

The cable broke when the *Great Eastern* was almost to Newfoundland. All attempts to retrieve it failed.

AFTER TWELVE YEARS OF EFFORT, THE TEL

The Great Eastern dropped a buoy where the cable parted.
The next year, she returned and picked up the broken end.

Parades and jubilant celebrations marked the opening
of the third and finally successful cable.

PHIC CABLE FROM ENGLAND WAS BROUGHT ASHORE AT HEART'S CONTENT ON JULY 27, 1866.

PART FOUR
The Tools
of War

easured in the bloody units of men, death and destruction, the American Civil War was fought on a scale that dwarfed any preceding war in human history. Within four years, more than two thousand combats were waged, and a hundred and fifty of these were major battles. The theater of operations was half a continent wide. On one occasion, a single flanking movement swept around an arc of eight hundred miles. Six hundred thousand men—more than one-quarter of

those who fought—were killed. A great number of these died of infection; antiseptics were unknown at the time. The war cost the North almost five billion, and the price to the South was total economic ruin.

As in most wars, the tools of peace which had been developed in the previous thirty years were encased in armor and mounted for battle. The Civil War introduced the tactical use of the railway and telegraph. The war also marked the first use of the railway gun, the electrically exploded torpedo, the repeating rifle, and the machine gun.

White Point Battery—Charleston, S. C., 1863—painted by C. W. Chapman, shows the deceptive tranquillity between moments when the biggest guns of both sides roared. Here were tried the famous Parrott guns, the Confederate experiments with mines, and the ill-fated submarine. Fort Sumter lies dimly in the distance, and Castle Pinckney is at the extreme left.

A telegraph wagon of the Union Army contained batteries, chemicals, wire, and replacement parts. The telegrapher in the wagon is dressed in civilian clothes because the Military Telegraph was not part of the military service.

The telegraph office at military headquarters was often the scene of operation for the commanding officer. The teen-age boy operators transmitted and received the most vital military intelligence with unblemished discretion.

Telegraphers resting after Gettysburg. The exhausted boy in the striped shirt was probably no more than twelve years old. In the Civil War, telegraphers were invested with the same glamour that later surrounded war pilots.

THE WAR TELEGRAPH

1. THE BOYS

At the outbreak of the war, there had been no plan to use telegraphy. A signal corps, as such, existed only in the most rudimentary form; however, the electromagnetic telegraph had already become an integral part of American life. The news of the outbreak of the war was sent to the nation over the telegraph. Orations were made, pledges were given, men began to march, and the voice of their description was the stutter of telegraph keys.

There was war, and yet there was no front, and so there was panic and suspicion. One week after the war started, the government closed down the Washington office of the American Telegraph Company, fearing that the operators might be in telegraphic communication with the Confederate forces at Richmond over the line that had not yet been torn down. Secretary of War Cameron, in desperation, besought Thomas A. Scott, general manager of the Pennsylvania Railroad, to form a corps of telegraphers on whom the Union could rely. Scott called in four of the best operators on the Pennsylvania Railroad: David Strouse, Homer Bates, Samuel Brown, and Richard O'Brien. From this nucleus of four, a corps of telegraph operators was enlarged until it reached twelve hundred. The telegraphers of the North were mostly boys in their teens, some as young as twelve. They were civilians attached to the Signal Corps, not members of the regular army. The service was so dangerous that by the end of the war there were only two hundred survivors. The telegraph boys advanced with the front lines. When retreat became necessary, the boys had to remain behind as long as possible, to announce that the rear guard was out of the danger line. Then, if captured, they had to destroy the instruments. These boys knew all the movements of the army and had the confidence of all the senior staff officers. There was not one case on record where this confidence was betrayed.

2. MILITARY ORGANIZATION OF THE TELEGRAPH

The first field use of the telegraph in war occurred on June 3, 1861, under McClellan, in the western hills of Virginia. When McClellan advanced, a field telegraph kept pace with him. Confederate prisoners were astounded to find wire strung and transmitters operating in positions which they had evacuated only a few hours earlier.

The question of jurisdiction over the telegraphers was ambiguous from the start. The Signal Corps expected their service to include telegraphy, and A. J. Myer, Chief Signal Officer, wrote the following letter to the Secretary of War:

"Sir: I have the honor to submit the following statement. By the terms of the Act under which I hold my commission, it is the law of the United States, that the 'Signal Officer of the Army shall have charge, under the direction of the Secretary of War, of all signal duty, and of books, papers, and apparatus connected therewith.'

"Under this law I am entitled to the general charge of the telegraphic duty of the Army, whether such duty is performed by means of signals transmitted by electricity or by aerial signals.

"A practical knowledge of electric telegraphy, and a conviction of its utility in military operations, was the leading inducement to my acceptance of my position.

"I would respectfully suggest that such orders may issue as will place me in control of this duty, and secure to me the facilities for its proper discharge.

"Respectfully, etc."

The reply from the Assistant Secretary of War, Scott, was evasive. There was a strong civilian bias that telegraphy was too complicated for the military mind, just as there was a strong military feeling that telegraphy was too important to leave in the hands of private companies. Nevertheless, Myer went ahead and ordered his Signal Corps to design a standard portable apparatus for a temporary telegraph line twenty miles long. The apparatus included reels of insulated wire that could be unreeled just as fast as a man could walk. For field operations, the wire could be laid along the ground.

When the line was to have some permanence, the Signal Corps designed a standard ashen staff twelve feet long, two inches in diameter, and fitted with insulators. There were to be forty such staffs to a mile. Each telegraph wagon was to carry four hundred lances, batteries, and ten miles of wire, and was to be accompanied by three operators. Line was to be strung at the rate of ten miles in four hours.

Wire stringing and much of the guard and maintenance work was done by soldiers, and sometimes local civilians,

The conflict between civilians and the military for jurisdiction over the telegraph never ceased. The telegraph companies finally defeated the Signal Corps, and a separate semi-military department was created, subject only to the Secretary of War. The active managers of the private companies were given commissions, the operators remained as civilians, very badly underpaid. Actually, a telegrapher who accompanied a general was not subject to his direct orders, and in many cases there was sharp friction between the officers and the men on whom they relied for communication with the rest of the army. Anson Stager, General Superintendent of the Western Telegraph Company, was the first Telegraph Officer.

Fortunately Stager began the military management of the telegraphs under McClellan, one of the few generals who appreciated the use of the telegraph as a tactical weapon in spite of initial opposition by his subordinate officers. McClellan was also to be the only Union general to see the advantages in the use of balloons for military observation. When McClellan's star began to fade, Stager retired to civilian life. The next Telegraph Officer was

commandeered by Signal Corps officers. Some friction was caused by the ambiguous position of the civilian

operators. But things worked out very well on the whole, and some 6,000,000 messages were transmitted during the war.

Stager's friend and assistant, Eckert. In spite of all friction, a magnificent job of engineering was performed by the Corps. During the war years they strung 15,389 miles of wire and transmitted more than 6,000,000 military telegrams.

The Southern forces had no such system. They used the existing commercial lines whenever possible. Certain Southern generals had telegraphers on their staffs, but most Confederate generals did not.

Lincoln made the telegraph office in the White House his second headquarters. He called the telegraphers by their first names, or more frequently, when the operator was very young, he would call him "sonny." Watching one of the young assistants making up a battery, Lincoln fixed his glasses and said, "Well, sonny, mixing the juices, eh?"

During the years of the Civil War the telegraph was extended for the first time to the Pacific coast. It was assumed that the feat would take several years; however, the job was completed in the phenomenal time of four months. The East and Far West were in instantaneous communication with each other by telegraph for several years before the Union Pacific even began to lay track.

Standard apparatus was developed, despite the confusion, and each wagon carried equipment to string a 10-mile wire.

The lines followed railroads wherever possible. This station was along the road from Washington to Fairfax.

THE BALLOONISTS

1. THE BACKGROUND

The English Channel was first crossed by air in 1785. John Jeffries and François Blanchard made it in two hours.

Above the Dover cliffs, on a winter day in 1785, the sky was clear, and the breeze, from the north-northwest, was gentle. The two aeronauts were men in their early forties: the American was the Boston-born physician, John Jeffries; the Frenchman was the famous François Blanchard. At one o'clock sharp, the balloon, filled with the newest buoyant substance, hydrogen gas, left England and floated out over the Channel towards the French coast.

Jeffries was making the trip as a member of the Royal Society. He had left Boston at the beginning of the Revolution, and served as an army surgeon with British troops at Halifax. His scientific interests were wide and included meteorology. In the balloon basket, he had several instruments, and his purpose in making the flight was "to throw some light on the theory of winds in general."

By two-thirty, the balloon had covered three-quarters of the crossing, but began to lose altitude in spite of the men's efforts. Everything possible was thrown overboard. Finally, the American said, "We are both lost. If you know of any way to save yourself, I am prepared to sacrifice my life." Blan-

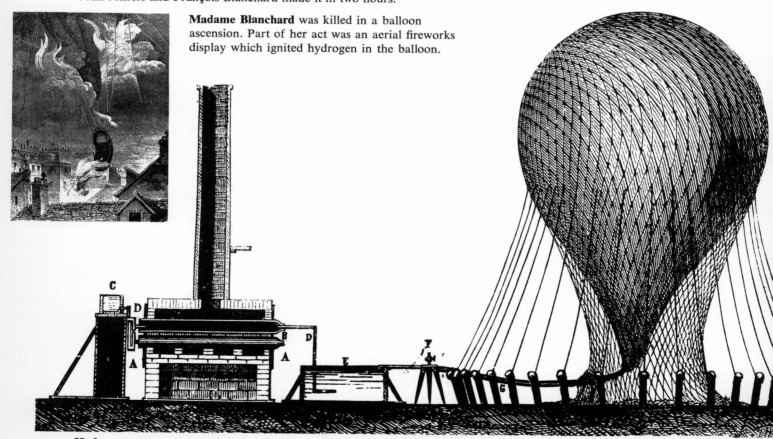

Madame Blanchard was killed in a balloon ascension. Part of her act was an aerial fireworks display which ignited hydrogen in the balloon.

Hydrogen gas generator of the early 19th century. Steam was passed over red-hot iron filings. The water decomposed, releasing hydrogen as the oxygen combined with the iron. The hydrogen bubbled through water (E) and into the balloon.

chard, however, had one further suggestion. They tossed their heavy winter clothing over the side and proceeded in their underwear. The balloon immediately began to rise; they passed over the French beach at three o'clock, and within a short time made a landing in a tree. For the first time, the Channel had been crossed by air.

Until the Civil War, ballooning in the United States never received the scientific interest and attention given to it in Europe. Ascensions were made at country fairs, and George Washington saw one of the earliest flights. American balloonists, like early demonstrators of nitrous oxide, were mostly showmen and projectors of magnificently impossible enterprises, based on the chimerical dream that lighter-than-air carriers could be navigated. What they lacked, of course, was an engine whose ratio of power-to-weight was greater than early steam engine designers could build.

A prominent American balloonist of the mid-century was Thaddeus Lowe. Balloons had been used for military reconnaisance as early as Napoleonic days, but Lowe was the first to take up a telegraphic transmitter to direct gunfire. Also for the first time, cameras were used to make panoramic photographs of enemy ground emplacements. In May, 1862, before Richmond, from a height of one thousand feet, the entire area was taken in sixty-four overlapping photographs.

Thaddeus Lowe designed a huge balloon for transatlantic travel, and carried a side-wheel steamer as lifeboat.

The interior of the basket of Lowe's proposed balloon. The balloon was never built, and was impractical from every point of view. 19th century balloonists dreamed of the day of controlled flight which, in 1860, was still three decades away.

After 1850, hydrogen gas for balloons was generated on a large scale by the action of sulphuric acid on iron. The gas was produced in the rows of barrels and then washed and dried before use.

2. THE REPORT OF
T. S. C. LOWE,
MILITARY BALLOONIST

"It was through the midnight observations with one of my war balloons that I was enabled to discover that the fortifications at Yorktown were being evacuated. The entire great fortress was ablaze with bonfires, and the greatest activity prevailed. The incoming wagons were light and moved rapidly (the wheels being visible as they passed each campfire), while the outgoing wagons were heavily loaded and moved slowly; there was no longer any doubt as to the object of the Confederates. General Heintzelman then put our whole army in motion in the very early hours of the morning, so that we were enabled to overtake the Confederate army at Williamsburg. . . .

"On arriving in sight of Richmond, I took observations to ascertain the best location for crossing the Chickahominy River . . . In the meantime, desperate efforts were made by the Confederates to destroy my balloon . . . Twelve of their best rifle-cannon were simultaneously discharged at short range, some of the shells passing through the rigging of the balloon and nearly all bursting not more than two hundred feet beyond me. . . .

"The great camps about Richmond were ablaze with fires. . . . They were cooking rations preparatory to moving. I knew that this movement must be against that portion of the Union army then across the river. At daylight the next morning, May 31, I took another observation . . . and soon discovered three columns of troops with artillery and ammunition wagons moving toward the position occupied by General Heintzelman's command.

"All this information was conveyed to the commanding general who, on hearing my report that the force at both ends of the bridge was too slim to finish it that morning, immediately sent more men to work on it.

"I then telegraphed my assistants to inflate the large balloon, *Intrepid,* in case anything should happen to either of the other two. I then took a six-mile ride on horseback to my camp on Gaines' Hill, and made another observation from the balloon *Constitution* . . . To carry my telegraph apparatus, wires, and cables to this higher elevation, the lifting force of the *Constitution* proved to be too weak. As I saw the two armies coming nearer and nearer together, there was no time to be lost. It flashed through my mind that if I could only get the gas that was in the smaller balloon, *Constitution,* into the *Intrepid,* which was then half-filled, I would save an hour's time, and to us that hour's time would be worth a million dollars a minute. . . . I ordered the *Intrepid* disconnected from the gas-generating apparatus, and the *Constitution* brought down the hill. In the course of five or six minutes, the gas in the *Constitution* was transferred into the *Intrepid.*

"Then with the telegraph cable and instruments, I ascended to the height desired and remained there almost constantly during the battle, keeping the wires hot with information.

". . . It was one of the greatest strains upon my nerves that I ever have experienced, to observe for many hours a fierce battle, while waiting for the bridge connecting the two armies to be completed. This, fortunately, was accomplished and our first reenforcements, under Sumner, were able to cross at four o'clock in the afternoon.

"The first and only Confederate balloon used during the war, which I afterward captured, was described by General Longstreet as follows:

"'The Federals had been using balloons in examining our positions, in 1862, and we watched with envious eyes their beautiful observations as they floated high up in the air, well out of range of our guns. While we were longing for the balloons that poverty denied us, a genius arose for the occasion and suggested that we send out and gather silk dresses in the Confederacy and make a balloon. It was done, and we soon had a great patchwork ship of many varied hues which was ready for use in the Seven Days' campaign.

"'We had no gas except in Richmond, and it was the custom to inflate the balloon there, tie it securely to an engine, and run it down the York River Railroad to any point at which we desired to send it up. One day it was on a steamer down on the James River, when the tide went out and left the vessel and balloon high and dry on a bar. The Federals gathered it in, and with it the last silk dress in the Confederacy. This capture was the meanest trick of the war and one that I have never yet forgiven.'"

The battle of Fredericksburg lasted for several days. Although Lowe's balloon was up for only a short time, his reports were crucial to the Union action. Richards' vigorous painting shows the balloon at upper left.

Balloon observers, floating at only a few hundred feet, were frequently fired upon, but none were shot down.

Inflating equipment was cumbersome and slow. During the last two years of the war, balloons were not used at all.

ORDNANCE

1. THE WEST POINT FOUNDRY

By the time of the outbreak of the Civil War, the West Point Foundry of Gouverneur Kemble was very different from the small forge first set up in 1818 at Cold Spring, New York, on the Hudson, just opposite West Point. The foundry was the Union's major establishment for the manufacture of heavy cannon and produced over 3,000 big guns and 1,600,000 projectiles.

Kemble had a fairly literary background. Born in 1786 in New York City he was graduated from Columbia College in 1803 at seventeen. He was one of a group of brilliant young men of the arts and letters led by Washington Irving. The Kemble home in Passaic, a favorite gathering place, appeared as Cockloft Hall in Irving's *Salmagundi*.

Kemble served as Consul to Cadiz during Monroe's administration, and made a detailed study of Spanish methods of casting cannon. When the United States fought the Tripolitan Pirates in 1815, he procured supplies for the tiny American fleet from Mediterranean ports. When he returned to the United States, in the words of Washington Irving, "he turned Vulcan and began forging thunderbolts."

Kemble produced the first fairly perfect cannon ever cast in the United States. Twelve years later, because of Kemble's experience in working iron in large masses, the first railroad builders turned to him to build their locomotives. He built Peter Cooper's famous "Tom Thumb," using musket barrels for boiler tubes.

The first famous American type of cannon was the smoothbore, low-trajectory "Columbiad." This was succeeded by a design worked out by the famous American artillerist, Dahlgren; and the Dahlgrens were followed by giant rifles designed by Robert Parker Parrott, who had heard of the rifled cannon then being built by Krupp in Germany.

At the time this picture was painted by John Ferguson Weir, Kemble was almost eighty. The foundry was under Parrott's management. Kemble appears as a visitor in the lower right-hand corner seated with some ladies. In the left-hand corner can be seen the breech of a Parrott rifle.

Most of the Union's heavy ordnance was produced at the West Point Foundry. Here a heavy Parrott rifle is being cast, end up. After casting, the gun will be cooled from the inside by a device similar to that at the right foreground. Then it will be machined inside and out, the rifling grooves will be cut, and a heavy wrought-iron hoop will be placed over the breech for reinforcement.

Typical naval guns in use during the Civil War included (left) Cochran's breech-loading gun, (center) a Dahlgren muzzle-loa

2. THE DAHLGREN GUN

American cannon design had been improving constantly over the first half of the nineteenth century, but American artillerists claimed that the thickness of metal was incorrectly distributed along the length of the barrel. Lieutenant Dahlgren finally found a formula for a cast-iron cannon design that made the armament of the U. S. Navy superior to any other navy in the world, until Krupp began to build cannon of steel. Dahlgren's principle was this: make the barrel wall no thicker than necessary to contain the pressure of the expanding gases within the barrel. That meant that the thickness of iron near the muzzle could be much less than that at the breech, where the explosion took place. Dahlgren demanded that all surface projections had to be discarded so that the cannon had the smooth shape of a bottle.

This new perfect simplicity of outer shape had a surprising effect on the internal structure of the crystals. When a casting is cooled, the crystals tend to align themselves along the lines of the heat flow.

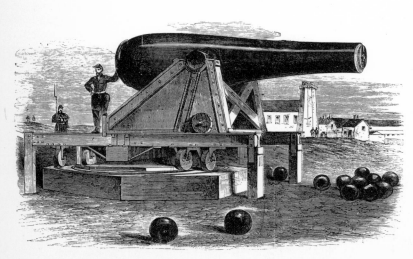

The "Constitution," a 15-inch muzzle-loader, used Dahlgren's bottle design and Rodman's casting methods.

190

nd (right) a Dahlgren rifled muzzle-loading gun.

The smooth shape of the Dahlgren gun meant that the lines of heat flow were uniformly radial, so that the crystalline structure was free of all the weaknesses and strain that make fracture probable.

The West Point Foundry took the Dahlgren gun and improved it still further by the use of a new cooling process devised by T. J. Rodman. Castings had always been cooled from the outside. This made the outer surface tougher than the inner wall, which was exactly where the greatest strength was needed. Rodman was the first to cast guns on a hollow core and cool the *inner* wall of the cannon, letting the heat flow radially inward. Using Rodman's method, a much higher propelling charge could be withstood by a cannon, which in turn meant that the range was greatly increased. By 1860, Dahlgren guns, Rodman cast, were adopted by the U. S. government for all seacoast cannon and for the heaviest men-of-war. They were mounted in Charleston harbor, just in time for their capture by the Confederate forces.

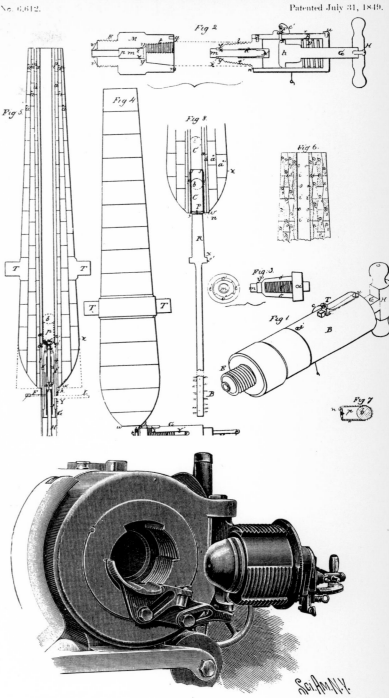

B. CHAMBERS.
Breech-loading Ordnance.
No. 6,612.   Patented July 31, 1849.

Breech-loading guns were first made at about the end of the fourteenth century. These early guns were usually quite small and made to fire through an orifice in a wall. The breech was essentially a plug held in place by a block of wood. Guns of this nature fired stone balls weighing up to 15 pounds. As powder improved, there was much trouble from gases escaping through the rude joints, and from breech explosions, and breech-loaders fell into disuse during the 18th and first half of the 19th centuries. Apparently the first breech-loading mechanism to use screw threads was developed by an American, B. Chambers, whose patent drawings appear at top. The interrupted thread (below) saw some use on small cannon during the war, and variations of this have since become the standard.

Premature explosion of a 300-pound shell blew the muzzle off this 10-inch Parrott rifle while firing on Fort Sumter.

Massive wrought-iron bands, applied hot and shrunk into position, encircled the solid breeches of Parrott guns.

30-pound Parrott rifles. A gun of this type fired over 4,000 rounds in the attack on Charleston before bursting.

3. THE PARROTT GUN

1860 was a transitional year in another phase of artillery. Explosive shells were beginning to replace the solid balls of iron which could be deflected without damage. The transition was slow because contact fuses were far from satisfactory. Too many shells exploded before leaving the barrel of the gun. However, the use of iron armor on ships made it imperative to increase the firing charge of offensive weapons. The Rodman guns were being pushed to their limits. At the West Point Foundry, Rodman's successor, Captain Parrott, found a way to strengthen the breech by encasing it with wrought-iron hoops. In many cases, this additional reinforcement was fantastically successful, and both the power and range of cannon fire were increased. The coiled iron hoop was mounted red-hot onto the breech, and shrank to fit on cooling. In some cases, this unequal

Rossiter's Picnic on the Hudson shows Gouverneur Kemble sitting in the lower right-hand corner. Kemble was the founder of the West Point Foundry which built the early U. S. locomotives and the most famous guns used in the Civil War. Standing behind Kemble is his brother-in-law Robert Parker Parrott, who succeeded Kemble as director of the Foundry. The Parrott rifle was one of the most effective heavy guns used in the war, and was developed from an idea of Krupp.

application of heat and tremendous compression rearranged the crystalline structure within the wall, and there were many Parrott guns that exploded before firing a hundred shots.

Yet, in 1863, General Gillmore reported:

"By far the most remarkable example of endurance furnished by any of our guns, and perhaps the most remarkable on record, was that of a 4.20-inch (30-pounder) Parrott rifle. . . . The gun was cast at the West Point Foundry in 1863; its ordnance number is 193; it was mounted on Cummings Point in December, 1863, for the purpose of throwing shells into the city of Charleston; it was placed on a plain wooden carriage manufactured on Morris Island. Sixty-nine days elapsed between the first and last discharges of the gun. It was being fired the four thousand six hundred and sixth round when it burst."

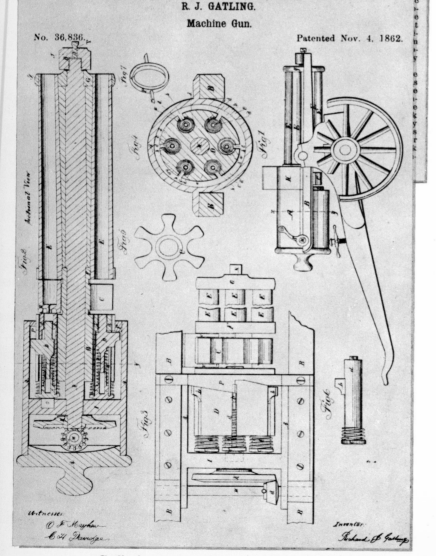

R. J. GATLING.
Machine Gun.

No. 36,836.

Patented Nov. 4, 1862.

Witnesses:

Inventor:

Gatling's gun was only one of many inventions. Others were a screw propeller, a cotton planter, a steam plow.

The improved Gatling gun and drum feed magazine

4. THE GATLING GUN

The most important artillery innovation of the Civil War was the machine gun invented by Dr. Richard Jordan Gatling, a physician with a high degree of mechanical ingenuity. He was born in North Carolina but sided with the Union. Very early in the war he realized that the overwhelming number of casualties on both sides was caused by exposure and disease.

Man's dream has always been to find a machine so destructive that by pressing a button, or turning a crank, a handful of technicians can replace an entire army. Gatling took time from healing the sick to produce more wounded. To reduce the horrors of war by reducing the number of men involved, Gatling planned to increase the fire power of the individual soldier. Starting work on the gun immediately after the outbreak of the war, he was able to put on a public demonstration in the winter of 1862, when his gun fired 350 shots per minute.

The gun consisted of a cluster of breech-loading rifle barrels, all mounted parallel to a central shaft.

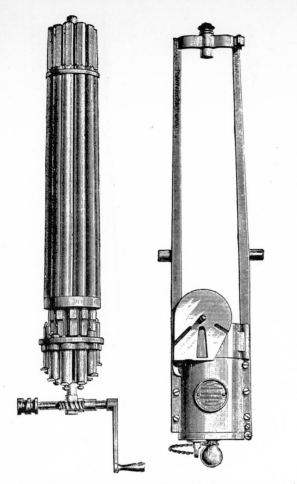

A crank and worm gear operated one of the many models.

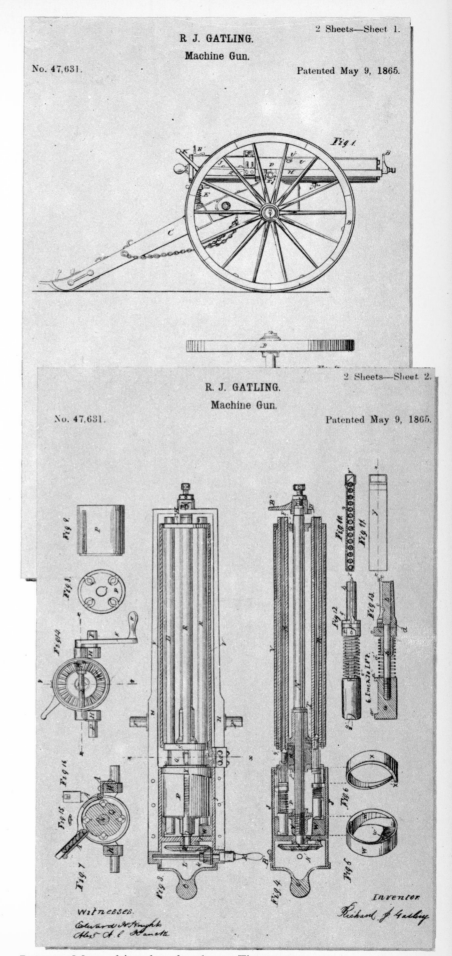

Each individual rifle barrel was loaded and fired while the entire cluster revolved. Each barrel was fired only once in a revolution, but as many shots were fired during that revolution as there were barrels, a ten-barrel Gatling gun firing ten times in one revolution. The cartridges of early models were mounted in a hopper at the top of the gun by one man, while another man turned the crank which rotated the cluster of barrels. Even at a time when the manufacture of metallic cartridges was in its infancy and the ammunition was necessarily imperfect, the Gatling gun performed remarkably.

Gatling ordered six guns to be made at once, but when they were ready for delivery, the factory caught fire and burned down. He started work again and produced several more of his guns, but the Chief of Ordnance took no interest in the invention. General B. F. Butler, on his own responsibility, bought twelve guns to be used in the James River campaign. Their performance was so impressive that the government decided to adopt them, but by that time, the war was over. In 1866, an order from the Chief of Ordnance for one hundred guns was placed. Within twenty years the gun was able to fire at the rate of 1200 shots a minute, at all degrees of elevation and depression.

Later model was driven by a bevel gear. The gun was not automatic, in the sense that recoil was not utilized.

Grant's calcium light being used to reconnoiter the shores of the Potomac

5. THE DEPARTMENT OF GOOD IDEAS

The Winans steam gun, captured by Major-General Butler's men, near the Relay House

Railroad battery, used by the Pennsylvania and Baltimore Railroad to protect workmen while rebuilding burned bridges

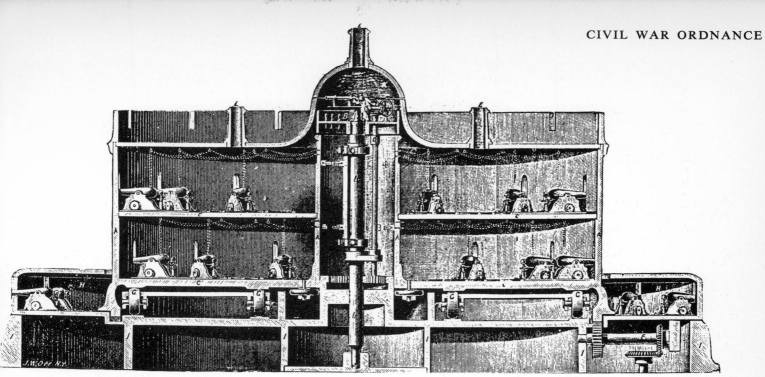

Stationary revolving turret proposed for harbor defense. The gears at the lower right were to cause the whole structure to revolve on huge rollers (*G*). Guns were to be fired electrically by the operator in the cupola by means of switches and a galvanic battery. The operator's platform was to revolve independently, by means of a hand crank and a shaft (*D*). There were additional guns to be mounted in a stationary casemate (*H*).

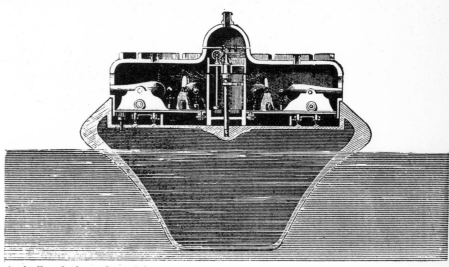

A similar design adapted for naval use on ships. The *Monitor* was quite similar to this.

A cordon of the revolving turrets, connected by chains, was to form an impregnable barrier across the harbor mouth.

The first victim of the *Merrimac* was the sloop-of-war *Cumberland*. The *Merrimac*, impervious to the *Cumberland's* fire, simply pulled alongside and poured broadsides into the wooden ship. Above, a shell explodes in the sick bay.

The Merrimac's design, mistrusted for twenty years, was immediately adopted by both North and South for river and harbor warfare. Many ironclads were just rebuilt paddle-wheel river boats. Above, the battle at Memphis.

IRON SHIPS
OF WAR

1. THE MERRIMAC APPEARS

A telegraph cable along the muddy bottom of Chesapeake Bay connected Fort Monroe on the Potomac with Washington. Early in March, 1862, a message of frantic excitement came sputtering from the operator in Fort Monroe, John O'Brien, who was only fourteen years old. With one hand on the sending key, the boy looked out of his window and watched the Confederate ironclad *Merrimac* steam silently up the river and begin its pitiless action against the wooden Union vessels. Through relays all along the line to Washington came John O'Brien's running account of the slaughter:

"She is steering straight for the *Cumberland* . . . the *Cumberland* gives her a broadside . . . she keels over . . . seems to be sinking . . . she comes in again . . . she has struck the *Cumberland* and poured a broadside into her . . . God! the *Cumberland* is sinking . . ."

The Federal Navy knew that the *Merrimac* was being built, and for weeks had been nervously waiting for the strange ship to appear. The advance descriptions varied from day to day as the Confederates deliberately leaked confusing stories. Nothing, though, had prepared the Union commanders for what was in store for them.

To men accustomed to sailing ships with tall spars and graceful lines, the *Merrimac* was grotesque. She showed scarcely any freeboard or deck. From the water, sheer slabs of iron plate rose to form a boxlike vessel, dark, metallic; with neither conventional bow nor stern. Regularly spaced along the sides were covered ports, whose armored lids could be raised to disclose the batteries of cannon within. No paddle wheels showed. The *Merrimac* was metal, smoke, and cannon fire.

From the day of its first appearance, the *Merrimac* spread terror throughout the North. Singlehandedly, it seemed, the armored gunboat could steam its way up the coast, slide in and out of every Union harbor, pick off every Union vessel one at a time, and then move out absolutely unharmed. Cannon balls merely bounced off her without causing any harm. The *Merrimac* was a creation straight from a nightmare.

To the men on board the *Merrimac,* the experience had also been frightening. She was on her trial run. Her guns and her engines had never been tested. Before leaving for Hampton Roads, the crew had gone through the rites of men fully expecting to die within a few hours. But after the easy victory over the *Cumberland,* the spirit of the crew changed to one of boundless confidence.

For two days the *Merrimac* maneuvered in the Roads, picking her targets at leisure. Then on the third morning, March 9, 1862, she met a craft even more strange than she was herself.

The dreaded *Merrimac* was based on a design which the Federal government had been considering for some twenty years. Colonel John Stevens, at the turn of the century, had suggested and designed a floating battery which had been rejected in favor of the *Demologos,* built by his rival, Robert Fulton. The second generation of the Stevens family improved upon the father's earlier suggestion by adding iron armor thick enough to repel any shot. The Stevens family actually began to build such a ship in the 1840's, but successive Federal administrations alternately gave and canceled appropriations for the ship's completion. The project blew hot and cold for twenty years, and at the outbreak of the war was still undecided. The design was too radical for everybody except Joseph Henry, whose scientific advice was disregarded.

The South, however, was forced to accept radicalism. The Confederacy knew it could never match the North, vessel for vessel. The South's only chance lay in designing vessels of enormous power, to be manned by small crews. Moreover, the ships would have to be practically impervious to cannon fire. Mallory, Secretary of the Confederate States Navy, wrote:

"Not only does economy, but naval success, dictate the wisdom and expediency of fighting with iron against wood, without regard to first cost."

The *Merrimac* that came steaming into Hampton Roads was actually a rebuilt, cut-down, armored version of a United States warship of the same name— a forty-gun frigate of 3,500 tons, which had been sunk by the Union forces while retreating from the Norfolk Navy Yard. When the Confederate Army took over the Yard, they decided to salvage the ship. Confederate Commander Brooke prepared sketches on the basis of the old Stevens model. The entire superstructure was replaced by a rectangular casemate, 170 feet long. The walls of this floating fortress were slanted at an angle of thirty-five degrees and were over two feet thick—twenty inches of pine and four inches of oak, bearing two layers of two-inch iron plating, which had been rolled from rails. A grating formed the roof of the casemate, twenty feet wide and 160 feet long. The pilot deck, forward of the casemate, was protected by four inches of armor. Above the water she was invulnerable. The officers of her 300-man crew were Captain Buchanan and Lieutenant Jones, both trained in the United States Navy.

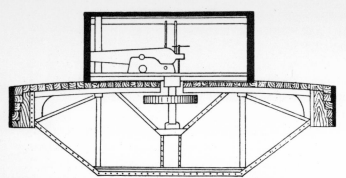

The turret was made of steel plate and revolved on a central shaft. Decks and topsides were heavily reinforced with wood. Turrets of later models turned on tracks.

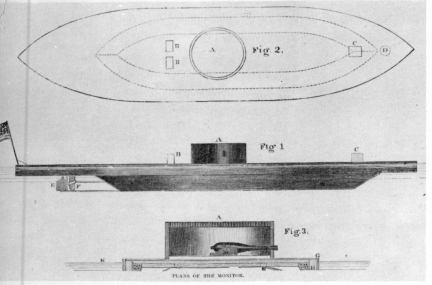

Scale drawings show the *Monitor's* strange underwater lines. The upper hull was armored, and had great overhang to protect the vulnerable hull proper. Like the *Merrimac*, it had a screw propeller. In the drawing, the smokestacks are at (B), the pilot house is at (C), (D) is the anchor well, and (K) represents the water line.

126 days after construction began, the *Monitor* was launched. Her shakedown cruise was a race to meet the *Merrimac*.

2. THE MONITOR
ANSWER IN IRON

The Union became aware that ironclad warships were necessary as soon as word came of what the Confederacy was doing with the *Merrimac*. If the South got command of the sea for even a few weeks, the war might very well be lost. Work was begun in New York on an armored vessel even more radical than the *Merrimac*. The *Monitor* had to fulfill three requirements: she had to be invulnerable to shell; she had to have a shallow draught to navigate the southern shoal waters; she had to be so simple that she could be completed in time to meet the *Merrimac* before the Confederate ship could do too much damage. It was a race between two shipyards.

The keel of the *Monitor* was laid October 12, 1861. She was ready for the sea on February 15, her entire construction taking only one hundred and twenty-six days. She displaced twelve hundred tons; her extreme length was one hundred and seventy-nine feet; her beam, forty-one and a half feet; her draught, only ten and a half feet. Two small square smokestacks rose six feet above the deck and were removable for battle. There were also two blower openings, raised four and a half feet above deck. Like the *Merrimac*, the *Monitor* had practically no freeboard, and it was expected that in any sea at all the decks would be awash most of the time. Below deck, the ventilation was by forced draft. Almost every feature of the *Monitor* was original, and every feature of the *Monitor* was the work of its designer, John Ericsson. The ship's total cost was $275,000.

The most remarkable feature of the *Monitor* was a rotating turret, twenty feet across and nine feet high, which stood just about at the center of the ship and revolved on a central pivot at the bottom of the hull. This comparatively small armored structure protected the two guns and the gunners within it. Since the turret could revolve, her guns could always be brought to bear upon the target, so that the two guns were the equivalent of a very great number. The turret's protection was eight layers of one-inch plate, and the roof was of rolled iron. The guns in the turret were two eleven-inch Dahlgren smooth-bore cannon. The vessel could have carried heavier weapons, but there were none ready at the moment, and the *Monitor* had to get to sea as fast as possible.

The ship was commanded by Lieutenant Worden with Lieutenant Greene as his second in command; Engineer Newton was in charge of the ship's machinery. Her crew were all volunteers, because service on board the *Monitor* was considered so risky that it was deemed above and beyond the call of duty.

The Monitor was no luxury ship, and actually was much more cramped than these idealized drawings indicate.

The guns were 11-inch smooth-bore Dahlgrens. The original plans called for breech-loading, rifled cannons, but the ship had to use what was available. Heavy steel doors covered the ports during reloading.

3. THE BATTLE

Before the *Monitor* could get to the scene, the *Merrimac* had killed two hundred and fifty, wounded a larger number, and sunk two of the most important ships of the Union Navy. There was nothing that stood between the ironclad and New York but the little *Monitor,* which was already steaming south through a brutal gale on the open ocean—weather and water for which she had never been designed. When the *Monitor* arrived in Hampton Roads on March 9, 1862, she was leaking, her ventilating system was out of order, and her crew was sick. Nevertheless, she steamed into action at once, and the famous battle got under way. The guns of the *Merrimac* could be brought to bear only after the ship had been maneuvered into a broadside position. But the *Monitor,* by virtue of her revolving turret, could keep her guns on target and continue to fire as fast as she could load, regardless of her course of travel. In terms of major damage, neither ship was seriously battered, but the agile *Monitor* was definitely the superior of the two vessels.

The U. S. S. Osage was a monitor designed for river warfare. The conoid at the stern is an armored housing for the paddle wheel. Ericsson's rotating gun turret was the most important invention to come from the war.

4. JOHN ERICSSON
DESIGNER OF THE MONITOR

At this time John Ericsson was a man of fifty-nine, already famous as an inventor. Ericsson, indeed, was a genius. As a boy in Sweden, he had constructed models of machines merely from descriptions of them. He made his own drawing materials out of whatever came to hand: a pair of compasses from birchwood; a drawing pen from a pair of steel tweezers. He had never seen a windmill, but he worked out on paper the mechanism which connected the windmill crank with a pump lever. His father was a woodcutter for a canal project and brought his son to the attention of Count Platen, the president of the Gotha ship canal.

When Ericsson was twelve years old, Platen made him a member of a surveying party working on the canal. After a short time, the boy was put in charge of his own section, directing the labor of six hundred soldiers. One dragoon's sole job was to carry about the stool on which Ericsson stood to use the surveying instruments. On coming of age, he became an engineering officer of the Swedish Army and rose to the rank of captain. His main interest was steam engines, and in 1826, he was given permission to go to England and introduce an engine of his own.

In the famous Rainhill locomotive trials in which Stephenson won world fame with his locomotive "Rocket," Ericsson was also one of the contenders. His locomotive was called the "Novelty." Stephenson and Ericsson understood the terms of the trial in very different ways. Ericsson built a light locomotive, intended for speed, and set the remarkable record of thirty miles an hour without load. Stephenson realized that the contest was to show the strength of the locomotive. His engine was geared for power and was many times heavier that Ericsson's. Stephenson's "Rocket" pulled seventeen tons for seventy miles at thirteen miles an hour. Nevertheless, Ericsson created so much interest with his "Novelty" that English railroad builders kept him profitably at work.

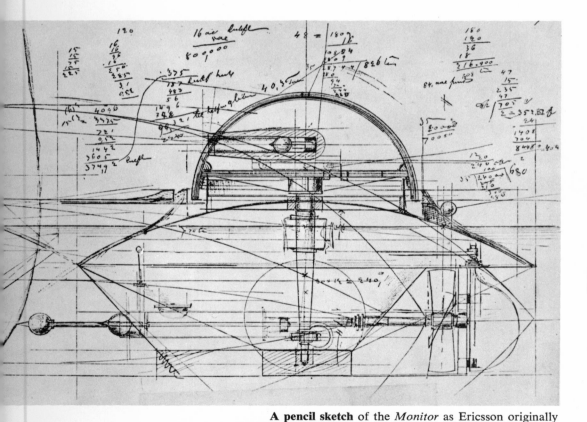

A pencil sketch of the *Monitor* as Ericsson originally conceived it shows a dome-shaped turret. This soon gave way to the more easily constructed cylindrical form.

As a young man, Ericsson was a Lieutenant in the Swedish Army.

During this period in England, he perfected his most lucrative invention, the steam fire-engine, which was wheeled into action at the burning of the Argyle Rooms in 1829. The newspapers said of it: "For the first time, fire was extinguished by the mechanical power of fire."

Ericsson turned his attention to steam navigation in the 1830's and built a very successful twin-screw ship for ocean navigation, but at that time the English were interested only in paddle-wheeled propulsion. The encouragement of an American naval officer brought Ericsson to the United States in 1839, where he spent the rest of his active but lonely life. His first commission was the *U. S. S. Princeton*. It was the gun explosion aboard this same *Princeton* which changed Joseph Henry's career.

After the success of the *Monitor* in the Civil War, a similar class of vessel was adopted by all the major navies of the world. Forty years later, monitors were still seeing action in the Russo-Japanese War, and the revolving gun turret had been incorporated into the design of every class of vessel built for battle.

The U. S. S. Terror was typical of the postwar monitors—double-turreted, ocean-going, and built of wood. Almost a dozen of these were built, and as Ericsson predicted, they soon rotted. The next class, of iron, saw service almost until the First World War. The U. S. Navy, the first to use monitors, was also the last to give them up.

A gale at sea sank the original *Monitor* before the war was over. This excellent wood engraving shows her in her final form, with the bridge mounted on the turret, and the smokestacks combined into one tall pipe.

The barrel torpedo was used against Union ships blockading the river mouths. The barrels supported iron cylinders full of powder. Floating downstream, they were to straddle an anchored vessel and then be exploded by a slow fuse.

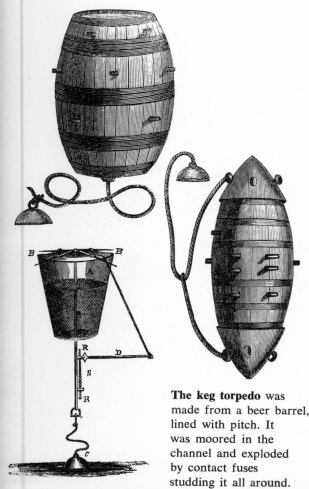

The keg torpedo was made from a beer barrel, lined with pitch. It was moored in the channel and exploded by contact fuses studding it all around.

A pronged wheel set this one off. If wheel (B) was knocked off it pulled down lever (D) and released plunger (S) which sprang upward and detonated a cap.

TORPEDO WARFARE

1. THE INFERNAL MACHINE

Until the American Civil War, the idea of using submarine mines and torpedoes was looked upon as abominable and inhuman. Most members of the Confederacy shared this general attitude, but the realities of the situation made the South adopt a new point of view towards "infernal machines." Northern shipyards were turning out vessels as rapidly as the Federal government could man them with crews. On the other hand, the South had to hold some three thousand miles of seacoast, including their most important harbors, with practically no navy at all. The South, therefore, had no choice but to defend itself with any means at hand, even with hateful torpedoes.

Their ingenuity in devising mines and torpedoes was so great that they successfully withstood the attacks of the Northern raiders and blockaders for years longer than anyone had anticipated. Their tactics of laying mine fields were later studied by all the first class European military powers.

American interest in torpedoes began with the experiments of David Bushnell in the American Revolution. Robert Fulton made great advances in submarine and torpedo design in the early part of the century. Samuel Colt conducted experiments on underwater mine explosions from 1842 to 1845. His submarine mines were detonated by an electrical impulse, sent from shore through an insulated cable. On five different occasions, Colt successfully destroyed the vessels under test. In 1843, he blew up a vessel of five hundred tons which passed over his mine at the rate of five knots. Two years later he successfully exploded an electric submarine mine through a wire forty miles long. With Colt, American experimentation on electrically exploded mines ceased in the mid-forties.

The Confederate mines were of two kinds: self-acting and controlled.

Land mines were first used by the Confederates, then also by the North, though everybody considered them inhumane.

The pronged torpedo exploded when a boat going upstream tripped a spiked lever. Boats going down slid by safely.

A typical land mine was a buried keg of gunpowder, set off by a pressure fuse covered by a board or other camouflage.

Self-acting mines fired on contact with the hull of a vessel. Controlled mines were set off by an electric current transmitted through wires that extended to the shore. A concealed observer on shore watched the approach of enemy ships. When the enemy was in the area of the mine, the observer closed a switch and the mine exploded.

Ninety per cent of the mines laid by the Confederates were of the self-acting type, activated by mechanical means. The mine was some form of waterproof container, a barrel lined with pitch, a metal tube, or even an old boiler. The powder was usually exploded by percussion caps set off by contact with a passing ship. There were also some self-acting electrical mines: in one case, the mine was inactive until contact with a ship broke a glass container of acid within the mine. The acid then flowed into a battery and generated a detonating current. Electrical mines were often faulty because the circuits used were tricky, the batteries were not always reliable, and insulation was not dependable. Even the procurement of wire represented almost insuperable problems to the South.

The man responsible for the Confederates' use of a torpedo defense was the same Matthew Fontaine Maury whose topographical hydrographic chart of the Atlantic Ocean bottom had made the Atlantic cable a possibility.

Maury had grown up in the tradition of service to the Union. He hated slavery as an institution; he did not approve of secession. Yet when the time came to make a choice, as a Virginian he felt it was necessary for him to side with his state. When Virginia seceded, he submitted his resignation to the Naval Observatory in Washington, and the following morning departed for Richmond. He saw the Confederacy facing the same naval problem which had plagued the Russians a few years earlier in the Crimean War, and he recommended a similar approach—mines and torpedoes against overwhelming naval strength. Even though the Russians had had no success against the English fleet, Maury believed that their strategy had been correct.

Matthew Maury left his job at the Naval Observatory to make torpedoes for the South.

A store of torpedoes was captured early in 1865 beneath the "Iron Bluffs" at Columbus, Georgia, a principal munitions manufacturing center for the Confederacy.

A spar torpedo, mounted on this Confederate ironclad, could be lowered and rammed underwater against a ship's hull. Painting by C. W. Chapman. Beyond lies Charleston.

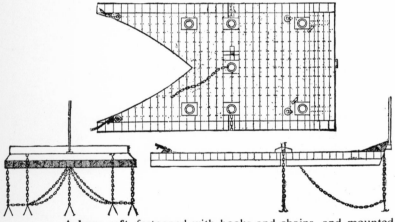

A huge raft, festooned with hooks and chains, and mounted on the bow of the Union monitor, *Devil*, converted the vessel into a makeshift but effective minesweeper.

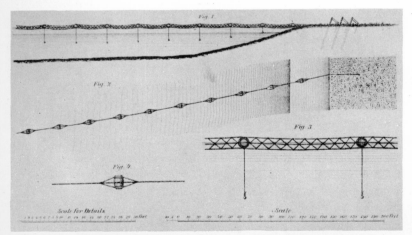

Torpedo nets, supported by barrels, and stretched across the river near Charleston, protected Union ships from mines set adrift at night to float down with the current.

2. "DAMN THE TORPEDOES"

Maury arrived at Richmond with a plan for a broad project of torpedo defense and spent a year trying to convince Confederate authorities that mines, activated by an electric spark and controlled from a distance through wires, were useful in mining the rivers and harbor approaches. He finally succeeded in putting on a demonstration that convinced the chairman of the Committee of Naval Affairs of the Confederate Congress, who saw to it that $50,000 was to be placed at the service of Captain Maury for a Naval Submarine Battery Service. At the same time, a Torpedo Bureau for land mines was established under Brigadier General G. J. Rains.

Maury's main obstacle was a lack of electrical wire. There were no Southern factories for the manufacture of wire. So desperate was his need that a man risked his life on a secret mission to New York to purchase insulating wire through Southern sympathizers. The mission was unsuccessful, and the agent returned alive but empty-handed. Maury's first supply of wire came from an abandoned submarine cable which the Federals had attempted to lay across Chesapeake Bay.

During the year of Maury's work on electric mines, his bluff, outspoken personality won him as many personal enemies in the Confederate Navy as he had made for himself twenty years earlier by his advocacy

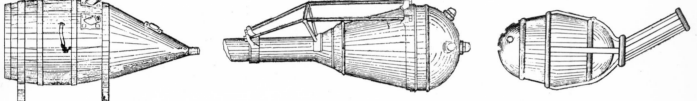

Confederate spar torpedoes carried up to 150 pounds of powder. The one at right was once a copper soda-water tank.

of the Naval Academy. In 1862, he was just beginning to mine the James River. However, he was summarily taken from the project and sent to England as head of a purchasing commission to get torpedo material. It was a job that could have been done by any intelligent civilian without technical knowledge.

Before leaving the Confederacy, Maury turned over his papers and plans to his assistant, Lieutenant Davidson, who carried on the work for the rest of the war.

By 1864, the Union Navy had worked out drag techniques for mine sweeping and torpedo clearing. In their final attempt to force a way into the James River, the main fleet stood miles away, while cutters and launches moved on ahead with anti-torpedo nets which stretched from shore to shore. The mine-sweeping squadron crept up the river at about half a mile a day. Most of the mechanical torpedoes were swept clear, and they caught the few self-acting electric torpedoes that had been strewn in their path. Maury's invention now received its full vindication, for, as his daughter relates:

"Finally, after having swept over and passed with their drags one electric torpedo which had been in the water eighteen months, a fine steam corvette, the 'Commodore Jones,' was sent ahead to feel a coppice on the bank for masked batteries and rifle-pits. Davidson,

concealed in a marsh on the opposite bank, with the two wires of the galvanic pile in his hand, intended to allow her to pass, hoping that larger game would follow. But she stopped right over the torpedo and waited for the rowboats, with their sweeps and grapnels, to go ahead dragging again. Fearing that these boats might now foul his wires, he determined not to let her pass his magic line. He closed the circuit, and up she went! Engine and boilers were blown clean out of the vessel for fifty feet. The hull was shattered, and fragments of the wreck filled the air; out of a crew of one hundred and fifty men only three escaped to tell the tale. It was all the work of a minute. The terror-stricken enemy stood still in his tracks, and fearing that the Confederates might come down upon him at night with their torpedo boats, floating torpedoes, and little ironclads, he proceeded to sink his own ships in the channel, to barricade the river, and to blockade *himself out* of Richmond."

Admiral Porter explained that his wariness of electrical torpedoes hampered his first attack upon Fort Fisher at Wilmington. The Secretary of the United States Navy reported that "the Navy lost more vessels by torpedoes than from all other causes whatever." The number was thirty-one, including seven armorclads.

3. THE CONFEDERATE SUBMARINES

The Confederacy also tried submarines against the Union Navy. The first Confederate submarine was privately built by James McClintock and Baxter Watson at New Orleans in 1861. The design differed very little from Fulton's of fifty years before. The *Pioneer* was twenty feet long, a little over three feet wide, and six feet deep. She displaced four tons, and was manned by three men who worked a hand-cranked propeller.

The *Pioneer* set out against the West Gulf blockading squadron under Farragut, but sank with all hands before action when she became unmaneuverable during a dive.

The two original builders, joined by H. L. Hunley, projected a second submarine, which was considerably longer and was to be powered by electric motors and batteries. However, no satisfactory engine could be designed and the vessel was finally hand-propelled by four men instead of two. This went down in shallow water, and the crew was able to escape.

A third submarine, the *Hunley,* was still larger and had water compartments at either end, which allowed for better trim and ballast—the motor power being the muscles of eight men. The *Hunley* was unstable. Four times in succession, the submarine got out of control and dived to the bottom. On each occasion, a fresh young crew suffocated to death within the small hull, but there was never any lack of volunteers for the dare-devil mission.

The *Hunley* finally engaged an enemy on her fifth trial. The fifth crew, on the night of February 17, 1864, destroyed the *U. S. S. Housatonic* off

The David was a semi-submersible ram-torpedo boat, built of wood and iron. In action nothing showed but the smoke-stack and the hatch coaming. The drawings at top show the boiler forward, and the engine and propeller aft.

Fort Sumter, but the submarine was caught in the hole its torpedo tore apart and sank with its victim.

Still a fourth Confederate experiment was a semi-submersible—operated by a steam engine. The *David* could submerge until its deck was hidden, and all that then protruded above water was the hatchway and a small smokestack. It was really a fast little launch with a long spar like a bowsprit on which was mounted an explosive charge. The tactic was to ram the torpedo against the enemy's hull, then backwater and escape if possible.

The Federal Navy, too, had a torpedo boat which, in 1864, sank the *Albemarle*. The Federal torpedo boat was a steam launch that depended on its speed and maneuverability to evade enemy fire. After the war and for a considerable period longer, it was assumed that submarines were unusable and, in the future, the torpedo bearer would be a light, fast, expendable boat. Fifteen years after the close of the war the *United States Naval Encyclopedia* said, under the section on torpedo boats:

"As submarine boats have apparently been given up, it is probable that for harbor defense there is nothing cheaper and surer than light boats with the spar torpedo. These would also be useful at sea if carried by large vessels and lowered in action.

"For coast defense, torpedo rams . . . would seem to be best. When torpedoes can be discharged from guns or tubes under water, torpedo ships for cruising upon the high seas will doubtless come into favor."

De Villeroi's submarine was being built according to plans made by Fulton. It was seized by the Federal forces in 1861 and was never brought to completion.

Cross section of the *Hunley* (below) was drawn during the war by a Northern artist who was inspired by exaggerated reports of the submarine menace. He correctly showed that the driving mechanism was hand-operated, though there is no connection between the crank and the propeller—a fact which does not seem to bother any of those concerned. The original of this charming drawing is over six feet long and is brilliantly colored. It is in the Submarine Library of the Electric Boat Company, in New London, Connecticut.

The Hunley killed more Confederate volunteers than Union sailors. She sank four times during trials and was destroyed along with the only ship she attacked. She was built of sheet iron and the propeller was hand-driven.

The 1876 U. S. Centennial at Philadelphia contained about 70 acres of floor space, most of which was divided among the five main halls. More than eight million people paid fifty cents apiece to see the exhibitions from every

civilized country in the world. On Pennsylvania Day, above, 274,920 attended the grandest fair the world had seen.

PART FIVE

The New Era

The Republic was one hundred years old in 1876. In celebration of the great event, the nation held a gigantic fair. The site was Philadelphia, the home of the Declaration of Independence and the two Continental Congresses. The date of the opening ceremonies was the tenth day of May.

"The ninth of May, 1876, was dark and cheerless, but all were busy giving the last touch far into the night. The tenth opened at early dawn, still cloudy and uncertain. The rain held off; the crowds began to gather . . . " said a contemporary chronicler.

"The seats . . . are gradually filled; distinguished visitors arrive one after the other, and are received with acclamations. There goes His Excellency, Dom Pedro of Brazil, that man who is every inch a true emperor, with the Empress—the only crowned heads who grace our opening. There comes the British Commission in full uniform, and following are the representatives from all the nations of the earth, to join with us in this our triumphal day. The Emperor and Empress take seats on the central platform. The hour of the opening has arrived, and the grand orchestra strikes up the national airs of all nations. The moment we have dreamed of . . . has come. . . . One feels in his heart, O happy day! that I have lived to see it and had it come in my time! Music is heard in the distance; it draws nearer. It is the President. . . . Acclamations rend the air, and at this moment the clouds break away, and a burst of sunshine illuminates the animated scene. . . .

"The orchestra begins Wagner's *Centennial Inauguration March,* of which so much was expected. . . . To one who is an enthusiastic admirer of Wagner, it must be confessed that it is somewhat disappointing. Still, it *is* Wagner. None can dispute that. . . . Then all is hushed, and Bishop Simpson asks God's blessing on our work. Whittier's hymn follows, with the grand chorus, the orchestra, and a thousand voices swell up on the bright morning air—

"Our fathers' God from out whose hand
The centuries fall like grains of sand,
We meet today, united, free,
And loyal to our land and Thee,
To thank Thee for the era done,
And trust Thee for the opening one."

213

American cities had become so congested that new methods of transportation were needed. New York had built its first elevated railway, and by 1876 forty trains a day were rumbling along behind smoking steam dummy engines.

American engineering was at work on its masterpiece, the Brooklyn Bridge. The center span of 1595 feet was by far the greatest ever attempted. 13,128 wires were strung separately to make the four great supporting cables.

THE NATION'S INDUSTRY, 1876

The American steel industry was breaking records to supply the railroad and machinery builders. The Bessemer process was in complete acceptance, and production in the United States was beginning to rival that of England.

American taste was embodied in the *Minnehaha,* a gorgeous soda-water dispenser. Considered one of the fair's most beautiful exhibits, it proved to a sensitive public that machines did not mean the death of beauty.

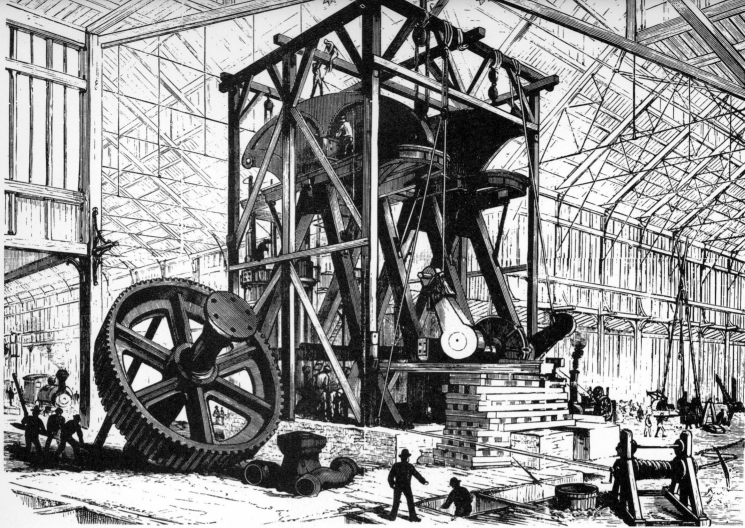

The great Corliss engine was the greatest steam engine ever built. It generated 1600 horsepower and supplied all the power used in Machinery Hall. It was subsequently bought by George Pullman for his railroad car factory.

President Grant and the visiting Emperor of Brazil opened the fair, whose theme was Power, by starting the engine.

THE CENTENNIAL

1. THE PROFITEERS

The era that was opening was to be full of marvels and tragedies far beyond the dreams of the fair-goers. The period from 1865 to 1900 was to see the birth of an America that would have been unrecognizable to Jefferson, to Hamilton, to Washington, and to Franklin. The agrarian democracy of Jefferson lost out completely to the beliefs of Hamilton. On the other hand, Hamilton's predictions came true through methods and procedures that would have shocked him as abominations.

The republic had been founded one hundred years earlier for the express purpose of defining, protecting, and enhancing the rights of the individual. Americans felt that never before in the history of the world had there been an advanced society whose citizens had known such individual freedom as had Americans in their first century of existence. Their mechanical inventions and science had been dedicated to consolidating this freedom. However, these same inventions had created untold wealth, and this wealth, in turn, had

The Statue of Liberty had not been finished by 1876, but the French sculptors completed the hand, sent it on ahead.

The hand arrived safely and on time at Philadelphia, and was set up at the fair where it became a major attraction.

created immeasurable personal power. The men who wielded this power were exercising their individual rights, but an era was opening in which this new strength was to give their personal wishes a leverage that was irresistible.

The new era had begun with the Civil War, which was the violent answer to those who had wanted to dismember the republic. But the war itself created agonizing problems. To obtain the supplies needed to win the war—the railroads, uniforms, guns, money—the Union had to pay an enormous price in hard cash. Vast private fortunes were made. These fortunes wielded enormous economic and political power. For example, Huntington, one of the builders of the Union Pacific Railway, used the money from the railway to buy the California legislature which passed laws to increase his opportunities for earning more wealth. In the end, the Union was paying far more than money for the victory; it paid out political power to be used against itself, and went on paying for half a century more.

Profiteers took for granted that the national wealth was theirs by divine right, and complained in hurt tones when the public rebelled. Drew, the psalm-singing, purse-mouthed financier, stole millions and re-

gretted that the United States was a democracy. His partner, Jim Fisk, was less sensitive and thumbed his nose at America. Boss Tweed went cynically to jail, and came out laughing. They were all exercising their individual rights, they claimed. Wasn't this what the Constitution guaranteed?

In 1865, though, the future could not be discerned; and the war ended in a mood of soaring confidence. Without a pause, this elation took the form of renewed vigor of expansion. The 35,000 miles of steam railroad line of 1865 lengthened to 200,000 by 1900—as much as there was in all of Europe.

The state of Oregon increased its population ten times during the same period. In addition to vast new lands opened to wheat production, new methods of farming by machine increased the yield of each acre by twenty-three per cent between 1880 and 1899. In the few years before 1870, every square inch of farm land west of the Mississippi, with the exception of the state of California, increased in value by at least one hundred per cent. The number of manufacturing cities employing up to 25,000 workers was trebled. In 1860, Chicago was the ninth city in the Union, with a population of 109,000. In 1900, a population swollen to 1,700,000 made her the second largest city in America.

The Main Hall was the largest building in all the world. Young Robert Millikan, who later became one of America's great scientists, remembered the exhibition as a fairyland. He came away with an ambition to become an engineer.

American gothic furniture, stiffly and geometrically ornate, was considered beautiful because it frankly showed the mark of the factory machines which carved and built it.

The rush of the American stand-up lunch was an international legend, and the plain coffee urn was more typical of everyday machines than the elegant soda dispenser on page 215.

Petroleum had assumed national importance, and had already devastated the whaling industry, though it had been only 17 years since oil was first discovered in Pennsylvania. In the foreground is a model of an early wooden tank car.

O THE FAIR

The Pennsylvania Railroad built a huge station right on the grounds to handle the swarming crowds. These visitors are arriving packed in converted peach cars.

Statues of winged horses flanked the gates of Memorial Hall, and helped prove to the world that preoccupation with machinery had not blinded Americans to art and beauty.

The Republicans, under honest but gullible President Grant, were generally corrupt and incompetent. Bribery, conspiracy, and downright pilfering were common after the Civil War. Here Grant bids a gloomy farewell to Secretary of War Belknap who was impeached (though acquitted by the Senate, he resigned) for being caught red-handed taking funds.

The Democrats were no better, though limited to narrower fields. Boss Tweed, of New York, matched the entire Republican machine when it came to "boodling." Tilden, though linked in this Nast cartoon with the stripe-suited Tweed, actually helped break up Tweed's operations. Nast, a loyal Republican, never once attacked Republican graft.

3. BIG BUSINESS, LITTLE POLITICS

The physical change in America that was most easily seen was simply violent growth. The men who were most directly involved with that growth were themselves men of violence—not necessarily because they wanted to be, but because the power at their command was on an imperial scale. The names of the entrepreneurs of the period—Huntington, Fisk, Drew, Gould, McCormick, Vanderbilt, Swift, Armour, Rockefeller, Villard, Morgan—make a roster that is unique. They were a generation who were born during the depression of the thirties, spent their formative years in the expansion of the forties, and were the personification of the American credo so idealistically believed in their boyhoods: any American could get whatever he wanted if he would go after it hard enough. They were all vigorous men of absolute indomitability, offering no apologies, asking no quarter. Darwin's recently propounded thesis of the survival of the fittest was condemned in almost every church in America. But although such doctrine could be scorned on Sunday, on the remaining days of the week it made good sense to a well-meaning man who wanted to feel no qualms about driving a competitor out of business, even if it meant ruin to thousands.

American business had always used rough tactics. In the beginning of the century, Fulton's and Livingston's steamboats were deliberately rammed by competitors. Whitney's cotton gin was pirated under his nose. Lawsuits were fought with vindictive fury. One shop raided another for its customers and laughed in its competitor's face. These tactics, when pursued with the power available after the Civil War, turned business disputes into national crises.

The individualistic giants who were to dominate the American scene for the last third of the century were themselves figures of transition. In their own images, they created vast ramified companies that began a trend toward monopoly that could never again be reversed, for when the men passed at the end of the century, the corporations remained intact and continued on with a vitality of their own. It was as if proud

Cornelius Vanderbilt, president of the New York Central Railroad, was a man whose simple ambition was to own and control all the railroads leading into New York City. He was probably the greatest railroad organizer in American history, and through consolidation, improved travel in the East immeasurably—and he was absolutely ruthless.

Daniel Drew was Vanderbilt's opponent. He controlled the Erie Railroad, along with Jim Fisk, Jay Gould, and Boss Tweed. Using forgery, robbery, and private strong-arm men, Drew looted the Erie so thoroughly that it was unable to pay a dividend for fifty years. Drew complained loudly about the United States. "It's too democratic," he said.

men had erected pedestals for themselves, only to find the pedestals continuing to grow out of an inner magic, dwarfing the figure on the top, then engulfing it, until the man was lost in the great granite shaft that was already mountain high.

As strong as were the individual financiers, just so weak were the politicians serving them in the national and state legislatures. With the possible exception of Cleveland, not one president was really equipped for his high office. A man who was merely incompetent rated highly; more often than not, the presidents were both incompetent and tolerant of corruption. In the Time of the Giants, only shadows dwelt in the White House.

But in 1876 a summer had been taken out of history and set aside for one long Fourth of July, Circus, and County Fair combined. Bands blared, fireworks blazed, orators wept, and crowds cheered. Americans looked around the fairgrounds and saw only the signs of their material progress. For that alone, they had a right to be vastly proud of themselves. It was a wonderful time to be alive, they said, and once again they were right. But then, no time is a time for dying.

Pursued by a court order, issued when Vanderbilt discovered the Erie was unloading watered stock, Erie directors Gould and Fisk took six million dollars in cash and fled to New Jersey. When the boat crossed the middle of the river they faced New York and thumbed their noses. After bribing the legislature they were soon back in business in New York.

Pullman's dining car was familiar to most Americans who visited the Centennial, and the name Pullman meant luxury.

GEORGE MORTIMER PULLMAN

1. HIS CAR

The plans for the Centennial had been worked out in meticulous detail, but errors were bound to happen. In the Main Hall, Section Two was called "Manufactures," with a sub-group called "Carriages, Vehicles, and Accessories." However, by mistake, the gold and silver model of a Pullman Palace Sleeping Car found itself in Section Three, devoted to "Education and Science." To complete the confusion, two of the newest developments of the Pullman Palace Car Company were in still another building, under the category of "Scientific Instruments, Railway Cars, and Appliances." George Mortimer Pullman's new additions to American comfort were the Drawing Room Car and the Hotel Car. The crowds paused to look at both displays and marveled. By 1876, the Pullman Sleeping Car had been twelve years on the American scene, and the name of Pullman was the synonym for aristocratic luxury.

The first sleeping cars had appeared forty years earlier, in the late 1830's, in Baltimore. Their appearance before the public was described in the *Baltimore Chronicle:*

Coach travel at the time was far from luxurious and generated such comments as this picture story about the railroad from New York to Boston. Captions read, left to right, "No sleeping room," "No comfort," "No meals."

"The cars intended for night traveling between this city and Philadelphia, and which afford berths for twenty-four persons in each, have been placed on the road and will be used for the first time tonight . . .

"Nothing now seems to be wanting to make railway travel perfect and complete in every convenience."

However, the millenium had not arrived, because nearly nine years later, Charles Dickens said of the same American sleeping car, "To tell you that these beds are perfectly comfortable would be a lie."

The need for some tolerable accommodations was apparent to many people. Theodore T. Woodruff, an inventor and master car-builder on the Terre Haute and Alton Railroad, formed a company in 1857, when he was forty-six years old. Woodruff's "Seat and Couch Railway Cars," patented in 1856, allowed for three tiers of berths. The lowest tier was made by moving the seats together, each seat enclosing additional sections to piece out a full-length bed. The backs of the seats were then folded over at the top of the chair to form a second tier of berths. From the wall above the window of the car, a third single berth was swung out and down on hinges. Woodruff went into business with two million dollars' capitalization, of which $217.50 had been put up by a young man named Andrew Carnegie. Woodruff was so successful that within two years Carnegie's income from his few shares was five thousand dollars a year. It was just about this time that twenty-five-year-old George M. Pullman began conducting his own experiments in Chicago.

George Pullman was one of ten children in a family that lived in Brocton, New York. The father was a general mechanic, and George, whose schooling was finished at the age of fourteen, in 1845 became the assistant to his older brother in a cabinet-making business. When he was twenty-one, he contracted to move houses off property taken over by the state for the widening of the Erie Canal. Young Americans were on the alert for "a good idea to make money," and after one night of excruciatingly uncomfortable travel Pullman, like Woodruff before him, conceived the idea of a really comfortable sleeping car. He discussed it with a friend, Ben Field, who agreed that it was probably a good idea. Like most such ideas, it was put away. There were other, greener fields.

With six thousand dollars, at the age of twenty-four, Pullman went to Chicago and found work that called for his experience and driving energy. It was 1855 and the city, built too low between the river and the lake, suffered continually from flooded cellars. Pullman got contracts to raise the level of city streets and whole blocks of buildings to a new level. One of his most impressive feats was said to be the raising of an entire hotel without disturbing any of the occupants. From the beginning, Pullman knew the advantage of surrounding himself with a legend.

PATENT APPLICATION DRAWINGS OF THREE SALIENT RAILWAY CAR DEVELOPMENTS

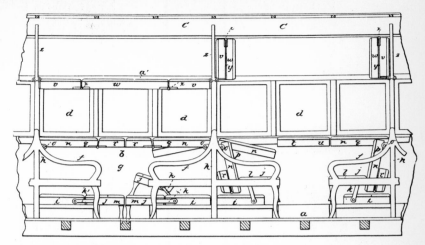

T. T. Woodruff, in 1856, received a patent on a three-tier berth arrangement. Woodruff's company was successful for a few years until Pullman's luxurious car came along.

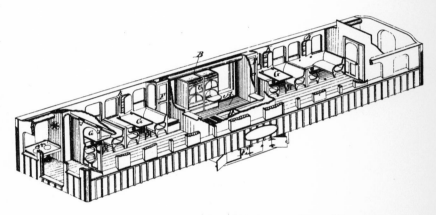

The Pullman dining car, patented in 1869, was an immediate success. The central kitchen insured that half the car would be "free from odors borne by the draught to the rear."

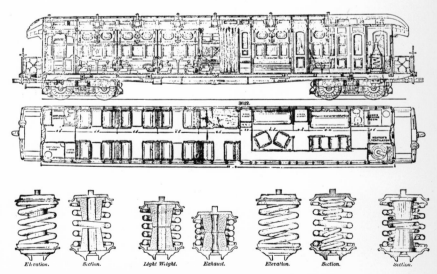

The Pullman sleeping car stressed comfort and lavish decoration; 54 feet long and ten feet wide, it was much bigger than previous cars. It had only two tiers of berths.

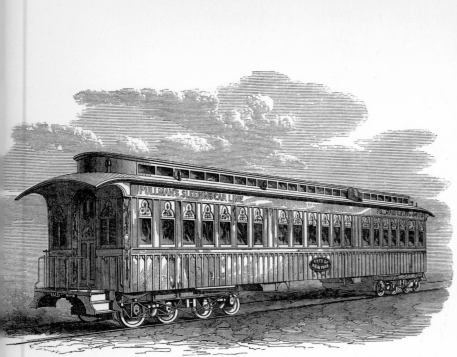

The Pioneer, Pullman's first sleeper, was similar to this 1869 model, except that it rode on four-wheel trucks.

The Pullman car of 1876 was in the best taste of the time, with inlaid woods, plush upholstery, and lots of headroom.

2. THE SLEEPING CAR, AND THE HOTEL AND DINING CAR

In 1858 Pullman had enough capital to go back to his old idea of a comfortable sleeping car. He arranged with the Chicago and Alton Railroad Company to remodel two of their coaches. The cars were forty-four feet long, with flat roofs like boxcars only six feet from the floor, and had single-sash windows, which were not more than a foot square in size. They were the typical American coaches of which Charles Dickens had said dryly, "There is a considerable amount of wall."

The remodeled cars cost Pullman between one and two thousand dollars. They were much less novel in design than Woodruff's. Pullman was not then, and never did become, an ingenious mechanical inventor. The car's first conductor described the interior:

"The first Pullman car was a primitive thing. Besides being lighted with candles, it was heated by a stove at each end of the car. There were no carpets on the floor, and the interior of the car was arranged in this way: There were four upper and four lower berths. The backs of the seats were hinged, and to make up the lower berth, the porter merely dropped the back of the seat until it was level with the seat itself. Upon this he placed a mattress and a blanket. There were no sheets. The upper berth was suspended from the ceiling of the car by ropes and pulleys, attached to each of the four corners of the berth. The upper berths were con-

structed with iron rods running from the floor of the car to the roof, and during the day the berth was pulled up until it hugged the ceiling, there being a catch which held it up. At night it was suspended about halfway between the ceiling of the car and the floor. We used curtains in front and between all the berths. In the daytime one of the sections was used to store all the mattresses in. . . . There was a very small toilet room in each end, only large enough for one person at a time. The wash basin was made of tin. The water for the wash basin came from the drinking can which had a faucet so that people could get a drink. . . ."

Pullman's earliest cars were not successful. Discouraged with his failure, he followed the fifty-niners to Colorado where he shrewdly opened a general store. In four years he ran up a stake of twenty thousand dollars and returned to Chicago, ready to gamble it all on another attempt in the sleeping car field. He was thirty now. His second model, which he called the Pioneer, was lavish. Instead of the upper berth being lowered out of the ceiling, he copied the design of Woodruff for the hinged berth, but dispensed with Woodruff's middle tier. With only two tiers, Pullman's car was roomier than anything that had been dreamt of before. His real invention was railroad comfort.

Pullman's Pioneer had improved trucks with springs reinforced by cushions of rubber. The car was a foot wider, and the new upper berth made the ceiling two and a half feet higher than any car then in use. It was obvious to Pullman from the very beginning that the new dimensions of the car would mean that station

George Pullman was a master of publicity; once he sent a trainload of artists and writers on a trip to the Pacific.

Following the trip, *Leslie's Weekly* published glowing accounts and pictures of the wonders of the Pullman car.

platforms would have to be narrowed, bridges would have to be raised. "My contribution was to build a car from the point of view of passenger comfort; existing practice and standards were secondary."

Some years earlier the French railroad had built a special train of cars for Napoleon which included a sleeping car, a dining car, and a lounge car. Pullman was reproducing the privilege of royalty for the middle-class American.

A macabre kind of good luck played into Pullman's hands. Shortly after his car was completed, Abraham Lincoln was assassinated, and the government commandeered the most palatial car in the country to carry the body of the beloved President from Chicago to Springfield. Every line between the two stations had to alter station platforms, bridges, and all other clearances, so that the outsize car could pass.

On the strength of this publicity, Pullman's *Pioneer* was allowed to run on the Michigan Central, and the price of a berth was two dollars a night.

Along the line which the train passed, newspapers described the "sleeping carriage" in the most glowing terms. All of them stressed the cost, even making the point that the price of painting alone was five hundred dollars. Readers were told of the elegant window curtains, "looped in heavy folds," the "French plate-bearers suspended from the walls," the "several beautiful chandeliers," and the "ceiling painted with chaste and elaborate design on a delicately tinged azure ground."

Five more cars were put into operation in 1866 on the Chicago, Quincy, and Burlington Railroad; and as Pullman was to do constantly from this point on, an excursion was arranged for the important citizens at his expense. He was the early master of the art of public relations, and in many cases his publicity came to be accepted as history. He pyramided every cent into furious expansion; the Pullman Palace Car Company was incorporated in 1867. Only two years after he started, he owned and operated forty-eight cars on the Michigan Central Railroad, the Great Western Railroad of Canada, and the New York Central, and he had one million dollars tied up in rolling stock.

In that same year Pullman applied for patents on two distinctly different types of car. One was the "hotel car," where "passengers, and especially families, may ride, eat, and sleep." Each car carried a small kitchen, several staterooms, and a dining room. The dining car had no sleeping accommodations at all. The hotel car, the *President,* was not too successful, while the second invention, the dining car called the *Delmonico,* caught on.

Within the complex framework of American railroading, Pullman constructed his own empire, which grew more rapidly and was more powerful than any of the individual lines on which his cars ran. When the Union Pacific and the Central Pacific finally joined lines, he already had over fifty-five cars on the road. One of the first trains to make the transcontinental trip carried a Pullman car with his compliments to the directors of the Union Pacific and the Central Pacific as they inspected the new line.

3. THE GREAT RAILWAY STRIKES

The most important contribution to railroad travel associated with Pullman's name was the "vestibule car." Before this, passengers moving from one car to the other while the train was in motion were subject to terrifying hazards. The trains joggled along at high speed, making it difficult to judge the step across the intervening space. Sudden draughts blew across the open platforms. The Pullman Company's vestibule was a bellows that connected the end of one car to the next, so that the passenger stepping through was protected. The invention of the vestibule is usually attributed to Pullman; actually, the patent was granted to an employee named Sessions, whose job was to perfect just such a system.

In the early seventies, the holders of Woodruff's patent brought suit for infringement against Pullman. The courts decided in favor of Woodruff, but Pullman refused to pay, and the Woodruff Company was unable to prosecute further. Several years later, the Pullman Company bought up all the Woodruff patents.

By 1880 Pullman was one of the most powerful men in American railroading. His personal ideas of luxury affected the taste of his generation. When he died in 1897, the *Railroad Gazette* said: "The Pullman construction has undoubtedly affected railroad car building very favorably on the whole, however ... Mr. Pullman has been responsible for a great deal of misapplied money and labor in car decoration, and for years he did much to corrupt the public taste."

Pullman decided to build his own town just outside of Chicago in which would be located all his shops and the homes of his workers. When the town of Pullman was finished, a writer said, "Imagine a perfectly equipped town of twelve thousand inhabitants, built out from one central thought to a beautiful and harmonious whole ... a town where all that is ugly and discordant and demoralizing is eliminated."

The workers who lived in the model town spoke of the company "in an undertone, as a Russian might mention the Czar. Residents believed that they were watched by the company's 'spotters.'" In addition, the workers were bitter about high rents, grocery charges, and gas rates. In 1894, Pullman's city erupted into violence.

Labor unrest had grown since the end of the war. In the "no-holds-barred" wars between the industrial giants, the Fricks, Carnegies, and Vanderbilts were simply carrying to extremes the American belief that the individual had the right to get "all that was coming to him." But the go-getters were now backed by an economic power that had never been known before. The dislocation of social balances showed up in the resentments of farmers and laborers; and the magnates looked at the rebellion with anger, as if their own individual right were being questioned.

The first great industrial rebellion came in 1877 when the directors of the eastern railways in combination declared a ten per cent wage cut. Railway employees went on strike, supported by the huge mass of unemployed, snowballing into an avalanche of violence. The next decade was even more turbulent. The 1890's opened with strikes at Homestead, where strikers were provoked into open war against the invading army of the Pinkertons.

The directors of the major railroad companies had formed themselves into an association, to dictate wages and working conditions all over the country. In 1893 the Pullman Company declared dividends amounting to two and a half million dollars, the customary eight per cent, but at the same time, a wage cut of twenty-five per cent was announced. During the following months, the Pullman workers joined the American Railway Union and elected as their leader, Eugene Victor Debs. A union delegation visited Pullman and threatened a nationwide sympathy strike unless the company agreed to a settlement. Pullman refused. On June 26, 1894, Railway Union members throughout the United States called on every signalman, brakeman, switchman, fireman, and yardman not to handle, move, or in any way assist in running either a Pullman car or any train carrying such a car.

For ten days the strike was carried on in a peaceful and orderly fashion. Then the issue was put to President Cleveland: the unions were interfering with the United States mails. Attorney General Olney, a former railroad attorney, invoked the Sherman Anti-Trust Act, which had originally been passed to limit the strength of just such mammoth companies as Pullman had created. The strikers retorted with violence and promptly derailed a mail train. On July 4, Cleveland, protecting the mail, sent a regiment of the Regular Army into Chicago.

The Governor of Illinois was John P. Altgeld, just as devoted to duty as Cleveland. Altgeld was ready to use the state militia to maintain order, but he felt that the use of federal troops was a violation of states' rights. The entire issue now became hopelessly confused. Olney's action had precipitated the federal troops and the injunction, not because he wanted peace and order maintained, but to set a precedent for the United States government to break the strike. Cleveland wanted to protect the federal mail; Altgeld was interested only in maintaining states' rights and avoiding bloodshed. The strike was broken with fearful violence; and Pullman, who had introduced imperial luxury to ordinary Americans, also ushered in an era of class warfare.

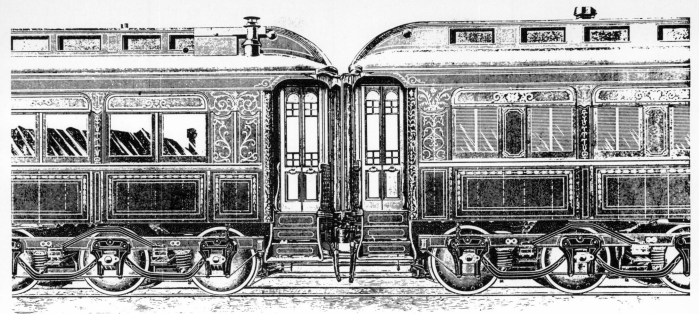

The vestibule car was patented in 1887 and was one of the Pullman Company's greatest contributions to safety.

By the 1890's, Pullman's cars had become so ornate that the *Ladies' Home Journal* protested the violation of taste.

The parlor car was an outgrowth of the unsuccessful hotel car and met with complete public acceptance.

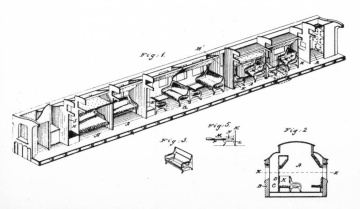

The unsuccessful hotel car, patented in 1869, was to be a "convenient car in which families may ride, sleep and eat."

The Pullman strike in 1894 was bloody and tragic, but it was inevitable in terms of the national forces at work.

The cowboys who tended the steers on the range, and who drove them to the railheads for sale, were a tough and poorly-paid lot. Their bleak existence was glamorized by the writers and artists of the day, but they were minor figures in the great beef industry. Watercolors by Frederic Remington.

THE REFRIGERATOR CAR

1. THE BEEF INDUSTRY

The Pullman Palace Sleeping Car was only one of the two important additions to railroad rolling stock after the Civil War. The glamorous Pullman car affected the taste of the American public (although Edward Bok, the editor of the *Ladies' Home Journal* and the *Saturday Evening Post,* wrote: "a veritable riot of the worst conceived ideas."); the ugly refrigerator car changed its economy. Gaudy adjectives described the Pullman car; the refrigerator car's importance can be described only in staggering numbers.

The most important industry in America is food: its production, preparation, and distribution. Any invention that affects food production assumes monumental proportions. Meat is a staple of American diet and the refrigerator car changed the nature of the American beef industry. As a feat of creativity, the refrigerator car has no rank at all; in the economic history of America it was a jeweled pivot on which massive forces turned.

Before the refrigerator car, beef was grown, slaughtered, dressed, and consumed locally. Chicago, like every other community, fed only itself. Tracing the rise of the meat industry, *Harper's Weekly* of October 28, 1882, says: "In 1827, Mr. Archibald Clybourne established a small slaughterhouse on the north branch of the Chicago River for supplying the garrison of Fort Dearborn and the little settlement nearby with fresh beef. . . . The business of the first year amounted to 150 head of cattle killed and dressed."

Sometimes, however, an enterprising man thought of buying western beef cheap to sell at eastern prices.

"In 1846, Mr. H. R. Smith of New York City, after a journey of twenty-two days reached Chicago and began the collection of the first herd of Illinois cattle intended for the New York market. Having obtained 225 head of cattle, he started with them in May, and after a journey of one hundred days, he landed them in prime condition in New York, where he disposed of them at a profit of $8 per head. During this drive of nearly a thousand miles, every river had been crossed by swimming."

The first locomotive whistle was heard on the prairies near Chicago in 1849. Within only one year, the Chicago slaughterhouses, all of them still comparatively small, were beginning to rival those of Cincinnati, "Porkopolis of the West," which processed about 40,000 hogs a year. Until the coming of the railroad, Cincinnati was the meat center of the nation because it had access to the rivers to the South.

When the railroads crossed the Mississippi, they moved into the vast regions of the West where mammoth herds of cattle grazed over land from which the buffalo had been swept away. Until then, western herds had not been important to the nation. With direct rail access to the cities of the East, the herds became pure gold. In 1867, J. G. McCoy of Chicago looked at the map of the West to find where the cattle trail from Texas would cut the path of the railroad. The pinpoint on the map came close to the unknown name of Abilene in Kansas. Sixty days later McCoy had a yard built for three thousand head, and riders were out on the range with the news that he would buy every steer brought to the railhead. His offer, that year, allowed him to ship thirty-five thousand head of cattle on the hoof. The man who worked out the most famous trail for the cattle from Texas to Abilene was named Jesse Chisholm, and with his name the Chisholm Trail has passed into a western legend.

The hard-working herders who drove the cattle to Abilene became romanticized in fiction and drawings by Frederic Remington under a name that will always be glamorous to America—the *cowboy*. Eastern magazine writers invented a character for them, and the "cowboys" tried hard to live up to the legend. Payday for these drovers who had spent weeks of isolation and danger with the slowly moving herds created a life of violence and dead-drunk hilarity that has also moved into American legend. Payrolls were met in Abilene when the cattle were sold. The gamblers and girls who moved into Abilene to take over the cash added their bit to the perpetual riot. To keep order over everything were policemen like Bat Masterson and Wild Bill Hickok.

As the railroads moved farther west, the junction of cattle trail and payday riot moved out from Abilene to Newton, which was to become famous as "Shootin' Newton," and on to Dodge City. The next fifteen years have been worked over by novelists, movie writers, playwrights, and the high dreams of small American boys until they have become encrusted with the gilt gingerbread and stardust that until then had belonged to King Arthur and Sir Lancelot.

The cattle from the Southwest were shipped to Chicago where in turn they were, for the most part, transshipped on the hoof to eastern cities. However, certain of the more enterprising companies slaughtered and dressed the beef in the cold months from October to March, froze the meat, and shipped the meat, either frozen or smoked, to eastern cities in an attempt to undersell local butchers. Business, pouring into Chicago and out, erupted. McCoy had transported thirty-five thousand longhorns in 1867; in the following year, the total was three hundred thousand. Two years later it rose to three quarters of a million.

Philip Danforth Armour

G. F. Swift

The packers in Chicago dominated the meat industry through the invention of the refrigerator car. Armour and Swift were butchers from the East who came west in the '70's when they practically monopolized the business through the ruthless tactics which were considered quite proper at the time.

Each spring the new calves were branded to identify the owners. On the open range the herds multiplied at a high rate, but the railroads allowed the ranchers to ship all the cattle they could handle to the Chicago yards.

2. THE INVENTION OF THE REFRIGERATOR CAR

Pressure on the slaughterers was so great that they extended the winter slaughtering season by working during the spring and summer in ice houses. They had discovered that chilled meat, whether frozen in summer or winter, would stay fresh for as long as a month. The invention of the refrigerator car consisted simply of putting one of the slaughterers' ice boxes on wheels.

George Henry Hammond is credited with being the first to see the possibilities of such a car. Hammond was inspired by the success of William Davis, a fish dealer who had been shipping fish from Lake Superior to Detroit. He had Davis build a car for him in which he sent a load of frozen dressed beef to Boston sometime during 1867. The Davis car was primitive in design. The meat lay directly on the ice, so that it arrived somewhat discolored. This was unfortunate because refrigerated meat was given a bad name in the East for some time. The following year a patent was taken out by J. Tiffany for a car which had bunkers and tanks for ice and heatproof doors. Technically, the problem was the circulation of the refrigerated air. By 1872, refrigerator cars were designed so that ice was carried in V-shaped containers at the ends of the car. By 1882, ice loads were replenished three or four times during a trip from Chicago to New York. More than a ton of ice was added at each loading.

The advantage of the refrigerator car was that the contents of two cars, expertly packed, were the equivalent of three cars of livestock, each containing nineteen head of cattle.

By means of the refrigerator car, the Chicago meat dealer extended his factory right down into the freight yards of New York, Boston, Philadelphia, even, after a while, to London and Paris.

The railroads at first rebelled against the idea of refrigerator cars; greater revenue could be derived from shipping live cattle. But meat dressed on a mass scale in Chicago could undersell in New York meat that had been slaughtered and dressed by individual butchers in New York. The aggressive Chicago meat dealers who drove hard to capture the market were Swift, Armour, Hammond, and Cudahy. They became so powerful by the 1880's that they were able to wipe out or absorb all the smaller slaughtering houses. They built their own

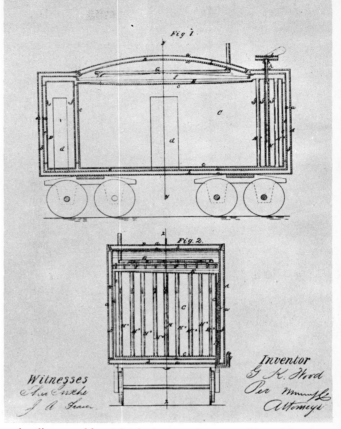

UNITED STATES PATENT OFFICE.

GEORGE K. WOOD, OF MORRISTOWN, NEW JERSEY.

IMPROVED REFRIGERATING-CAR.

Specification forming part of Letters Patent No. **76,285**, dated March 31, 1868.

To all whom it may concern:

Be it known that I, GEORGE K. WOOD, of Morristown, in the county of Morris and State of New Jersey, have invented a new and Improved Refrigerator-Car; and I do hereby declare that the following is a full, clear, and exact description thereof, which will enable others skilled in the art to make and use the same, reference being had to the accompanying drawings, forming part of this specification.

This invention relates to a new and improved construction of a refrigerator-car, as hereinafter fully shown and described, whereby the interior of the car may be kept at a low temperature and in a dry state, with conditions which insure the keeping of edibles, more especially meat, in perfect state of preservation for a long period of time.

The invention further relates to a novelty in the construction of the car, whereby provisions at different stations on the route may be placed in the car without allowing the external air to come in contact with provisions previously placed in it.

In the accompanying sheets of drawings, Figure 1 is a longitudinal vertical section of my invention, taken in the line *x x*, Fig. 2; Fig. 2, a transverse vertical section of the same, taken in the line *y y*, Fig. 1.

Similar letters of reference indicate corresponding parts.

A represents the body of the car, which is double-walled, the space between the two walls *a a* being filled with a suitable non-conducting material *b*. The top and bottom of the car are constructed precisely like the sides, the top having a hinged portion, to serve as a lid, B.

Within the body A there is inserted a chamber, C, the sides and top and bottom of which (designated by *c*) are constructed of metal; and D is a smaller chamber, also inserted within the body A, and constructed precisely like C. These chambers, of which there may be two or more, have each a separate door, *d*, and a space, *e*, is allowed between the chambers, as well as all around between them and the inner wall *a* of the body A, at the top and bottom as well as at the sides, as shown clearly in Fig. 1.

The top of the chamber C is slightly depressed to form a basin, E, to receive the water from the ice, the latter resting on a grate, *f*, over the basin, the space between the basin and inner double wall being made, by means

of an arch, sufficiently ample to form an ice-chamber.

The water is discharged from the basin E through a pipe, F, the lower end of which is bent upward, as shown at *g*, Fig. 2, to form a seal to cut off the external atmosphere from the basin E.

The object in having a plurality of chambers is to admit of provisions being put into the car at different stations on a route without allowing the external air to come in direct contact with provisions previously taken in. For instance, if the main chamber C be filled at the station from whence the car starts, it will not be opened before the car reaches its point of destination, the chamber D being opened to receive additional freight.

I would remark that the doors *d d* should be made with double walls, backed in any suitable manner, and made to fit tightly when closed, so as to avoid the ingress of external air.

In the chamber C there is placed a series of upright hollow pillars, H*, which communicate at top and bottom with the dead-air space *e*. These pillars have hooks attached for the purpose of suspending meat to them. Similar hooks are attached to the sides.

The object of this arrangement is to have the meat or other provisions thus suspended in contact with a cool surface and cool air; and, besides this, it admits of a large number of carcasses of meat being suspended in the chamber without being crowded together, as would frequently be the case were no provision made to suspend them anywhere rather than to the metallic sides of the chamber C.

The smaller chamber D may also be provided with similar pillars H*, for the same purpose.

I claim as new and desire to secure by Letters Patent—

The pillars H*, arranged or placed within the provision-chambers, any or all of them communicating above and below the dead-air space between said chambers and the sides of the car, substantially as and for the purpose set forth.

The above specification of my invention signed by me this 21st day of November, 1867.

GEO. K. WOOD.

Witnesses:
J. A. FRAZER,
ALEX. F. ROBERTS.

An early, but not too successful, car was George Wood's. It was compartmented, so that partial loading or unloading would not let in too much warm air, and it relied on hollow pillars to circulate air cooled by ice.

---

fleets of refrigerator cars because the railroads refused to furnish them. The monopoly of refrigerator cars had been forced upon them, but they in turn used the power of this monopoly to force the railroads to carry the cars at a price they themselves set. More than that, the monopoly was able to demand that the railroads carry no other refrigerator cars but those which the big packers set on the roads. This meant that all fruits and vegetables being shipped from anywhere in the country had to go on the monopoly's cars.

With the power which came from the railroad's submission, the big packers turned to the men who raised the herds, the producers of their "raw material." At the stockyards, buyers of the "big four" would act according to a preconceived plan. Three buyers would lounge up to the yards at the arrival of a new cattle shipment, but refuse to make an offer. The following day a buyer from the fourth company would appear and, because no one else seemed interested, he could set any price he wished. After the purchase, the meat was shared equally by all four slaughterhouses.

The expression "cattle is king" was no longer applicable to the Texas ranchers, but to the Chicago butchers, who had cornered the market on both transportation and processing. Just as the rancher and his men had been given their day of glory and glamour in *Leslie's Weekly,* so now Armour and Swift moved onto the pages of *Scribner's* and *Harper's* for adulation of the new rich. One dissenting voice was raised in Upton Sinclair's novel, *The Jungle.* It made Upton Sinclair famous, but in the long run it did not affect the big packers. Nothing could touch them. They owned the nation's meat, and the nation had no intention of changing its eating habits. By the time *The Jungle* was written, the thirty-five thousand head of cattle shipped to Chicago in 1867 by McCoy had reached the astronomical figure of almost ten million hogs a year and as many head of cattle.

The histories of both the Pullman car and the refrigerator car have one thing in common. The original inventors—Woodruff, Tiffany, Davis and others—are barely remembered today; while the names of the entrepreneurs who had the daring and ruthlessness to exploit the inventions have become enshrined in American legend. Thus, again, the American Dream was translated into reality by men who believed that any American could get what he wanted if he tried hard enough—and let the devil take the hindmost.

3. CHICAGO BEEF GOES EAST

The cattle market in Chicago during the 1870's. Big pens held the steers shipped from the ranchers. Buyers from the great packing houses made their selections and offers here.

Slaughtering was done by men on platforms over the cattle chutes. Each man had a spear which he drove into the back of the animal's skull. Some spears had trigger and spring devices to insure a more reliable blow.

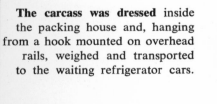

The carcass was dressed inside the packing house and, hanging from a hook mounted on overhead rails, weighed and transported to the waiting refrigerator cars.

Refrigerator cars, cooled by ice stored in compartments, were drawn up to the slaughterhouse platform and the meat was carried directly aboard (right).

Within the cars, the dressed beef was again hung on hooks so that the cooled air could circulate freely. A car of refrigerated beef carried fifty per cent more beef than one car containing a live shipment.

Long trains of loaded "reefers" moved eastward out of Chicago to the coastal cities where Chicago beef undersold meat produced by the local packers.

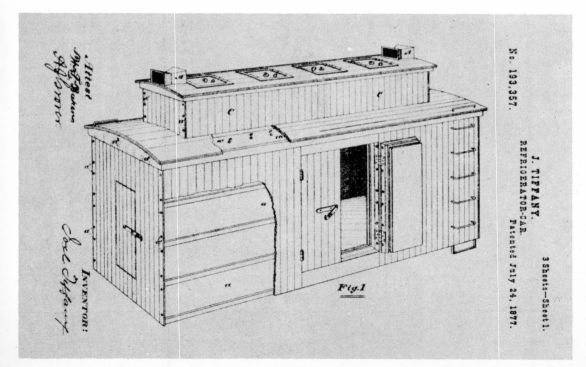

The first really successful refrigerated car was patented by Joel Tiffany in 1877. He later made several improvements, and referred to his car as a "Summer-Winter Car," but railroad men called them simply "reefers."

Cattle herds grazing on the western plains made it hard for immigrants who wanted to fence in farms. Wooden fences imported into the treeless area were easily smashed.

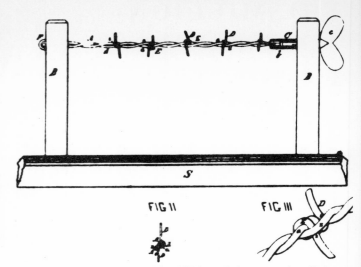

Barbed wire was invented in 1874, and drove cattle off the open range. Glidden's improvement over previous attempts lay in the special barbed spur wound about the wire strands.

Reapers and mowers, such as this Champion, found new markets when the Great Plains were opened to farming.

The Corn Exchange and Grain Market of Chicago rivaled the Stock Exchange in New York. Most of the wealth of the expanding West flowed through Chicago which had replaced Buffalo as the western metropolis of the United States.

THE MILLION-ACRE FARM

1. BARBED WIRE

The architects of the Centennial had taken the nation's measure; and the most eloquent statement of America's condition on the Republic's hundredth birthday was this: the largest building at the Centennial was not Agricultural Hall.

After the Main Building, in acreage, came Machinery Hall. The agricultural building was third. This was the single statistic that revealed how far Thomas Jefferson's agrarian republic was already passing into the limbo of men's dreams.

In 1876 the population of America was increasing at a fantastic rate, but the population engaged in agriculture had fallen sharply. Yet the production of foodstuffs in America was greater than it had ever been before. The wheat harvest of 1840 had amounted to 85,000,000 bushels. At the beginning of the Civil War, that figure was doubled, of which more than a third was exported. By 1890 the American wheat crop was doubled again to become one-sixth of the entire world's production. In America, at the turn of the century, wheat could have been measured in mountains.

The staggering acceleration of American grain production in the last quarter of the nineteenth century was due in great part to the invention of barbed wire in 1874 and the transformation of McCormick's 1831 reaper into the post-Civil War harvester.

The successful introduction of barbed wire, in itself a seemingly minor piece of ingenuity, put an end to an era more decisively than any of the great plagues which had spread through Europe in the Middle Ages.

In the twenty years after the Civil War, cattle grazing on the great treeless plains west of the Mississippi created a seemingly impregnable industry and society. The cattle empire was born when the untended longhorns of Texas multiplied themselves to almost five million head during the distracting years of the war. At the end of the war the railroads began to move west from Kansas City, and Texans discovered that cattle could winter on the plains north of Texas just as well as the buffalo had done before them. Cattle from Texas surged north in a flood until the new "cow country" extended from the Rio Grande to Canada, from the Mississippi to the foothills of the Rockies. The land was for the most part untenanted and unfenced. The great herds of cattle foraged, multiplied, and then carried themselves by the millions to the railheads for shipment and slaughter.

The scrawny, vicious longhorn of Texas was soon replaced by a meatier breed, descendants of the small herds driven west by the Oregon settlers. These shorthorns were driven back out of Oregon through Idaho and Wyoming, and within several years had completely replaced the Texas steer even in Texas.

The profits of American cattle raising were so enormous that capital was attracted not only from the cities east of the Mississippi, but from London, Paris, and even St. Petersburg in Russia. However, the steady stream of gold depended on one thing—thousands and thousands of miles of free open range.

The railroads, whose shipments of beef had made possible the butcher's bonanza, were also to spell its doom. The railroads had been built originally for the immediate profits to be found in construction contracts awarded by the heads of railroads to themselves in their private capacity as heads also of newly formed construction companies. The railroad promoters had never envisioned any great income from freight or passenger traffic until the land in the vicinity of the railroads could be built up. Accordingly, the railroads had acquired from the government huge grants of land on their right-of-way, now being grazed.

The income for hauling beef was an unexpected windfall, but even while the railroads were taking in the gold, they went ahead with their original plans to sell their land as farm sites. They sent agents throughout Europe offering inducements to prospective settlers from Germany, Russia, England and Scandinavia. One agent descended on Iceland like the Pied Piper and induced one-third of the total population to migrate. And while the railroads were selling off their grants, the United States government was offering, through the Homestead Act of 1862, one hundred and sixty acres of free land to any citizen who could prove five years' residence and cultivation on a site in the public domain. The Great Plains were in the public domain.

For a decade or so, the incoming rush of settlers stayed on the periphery of the great range. In a region completely barren of trees and rocks, no fence could be built, and no homesteader could hope to prosper when cattle could range freely over his plowed land and graze contentedly in his corn and his wheat. Barbed wire, which would have been meaningless in New England or the South, burst upon the West in the mid-70's with all the force of a cataclysm.

The cattle rangers fought the homesteaders with violence. Two decades of unchallenged access to streams and water holes now made the cattlemen feel that ancient rights were being violated by pirates; but the railroads, for each shipment of eastbound beef, carried west new waves of homesteaders, and each homesteader carried a deed that had the law behind it. The lines of barbed wire were strung east and west, south and north, and the rangers were fenced into successively narrower and narrower confines.

Wood's Self-Raking Reaper

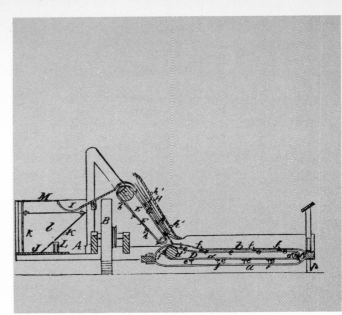

The Marsh Harvester patent drawing (No. 21,207. 1858).

Mann Harvester

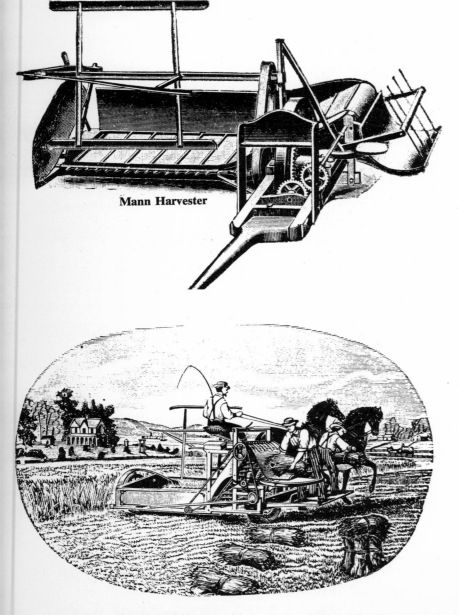

Marsh Harvester

2. REAPER INTO HARVESTER

The open range went the way of the buffalo, the Indian, and the fur trader in the ghostly parade that had begun two and a half centuries earlier, two thousand miles to the east on the Atlantic beaches.

The new western farmer came armed with installment-bought equipment that would have seemed marvelous even to McCormick's generation. The reaper, by its ingenuity, had drawn the attention of other inventors to other agricultural problems. John Deere's steel plow had been replaced by the still tougher steel plow of James Oliver; and even that plow was now a multiple tool, capable of cutting several furrows at one time. The hand hoe, which had softened and mulched the earth turned over by the plow, had now become the horse-drawn harrow which did the same job more efficiently. Hand sowing of grain, which had fed the wild birds more often than the farmer, was a thing of the past. The western farmer now walked behind a machine which bored holes into the ground; and, from a hopper, the machine dropped the right number of seeds into the holes and then covered the holes. Such drills had been patented in the 1840's but only after the Civil War did they begin to achieve popular success.

Plowing, hoeing, planting, and harvesting by hand had all been replaced by intricately-geared machines which converted the power of straining horses into

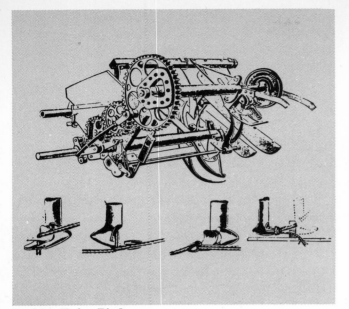

Appleby Twine Binder

Marsh Harvester and Appleby Binder

Belt separator

human judgment and effort. Nevertheless, the American farm was still the place for back-breaking chores. Reaped wheat had to be gathered into bundles and tied. On June 19, 1849, U. S. Patent No. 6,540 was granted to the Manns on a machine attached to a reaper that carried cut grain on an endless belt to one side where it was packed to form a bundle that was then dumped upon the ground. This was improved by Marsh, whose 1858 patent, U. S. No. 21,207, allowed standing room for a man to ride along so that he could bind the bundles with twine before dumping them. The hand binder was replaced in 1871 by Sylvanus D. Locke of Wisconsin who was granted U. S. Patent No. 121,290 on an ingenious arrangement of steel fingers which wrapped wire around the bundle, twisted the wire into a knot, and then cut it free. Wire proved objectionable, and in 1879, John F. Appleby, with U. S. Patent No. 212,420, added an automatic twine binder to the Marsh improvement of the Mann machine which had been added to the reaper developed by McCormick.

Thus, in the forty-five years that elapsed between the McCormick and the Appleby patents, over 200,-000 inventions had been registered and recognized by the United States government.

Numbers describe the growth of the reaper business: in 1840, three machines were made; in 1850, 3,000; in 1860, 20,000; in 1870, 30,000; in 1880, when the cord binder came into general use, 60,000; and in the single year of 1890, two companies alone made more than 200,000 agricultural machines.

Traction engine and gang plow

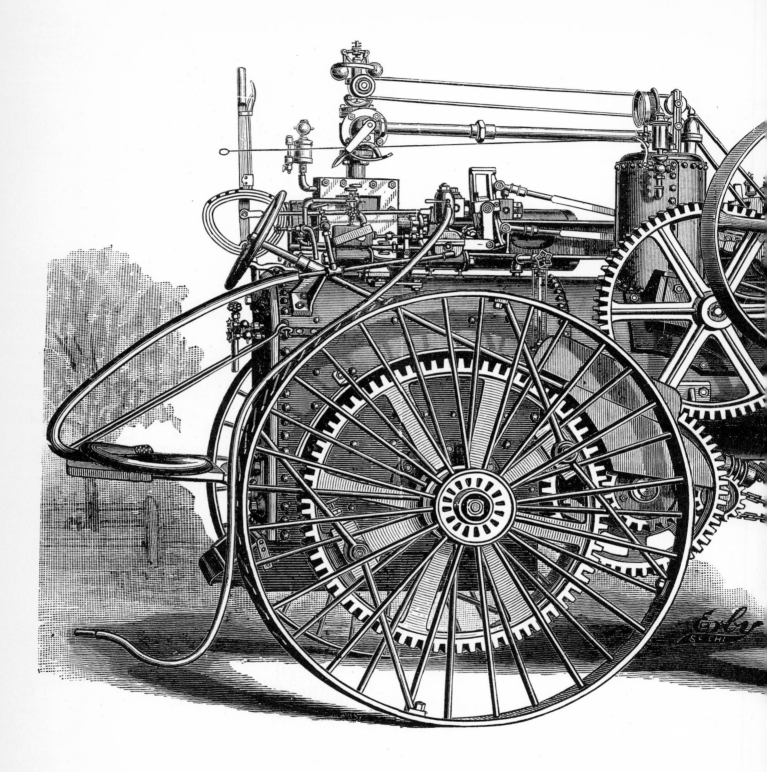

3. BONANZA!

The versatility of the machines made possible western farms that extended over thousands of acres, and the very size of such farms in turn demanded a still higher rate of productivity. Steam engines whose driver wheels before the day of the caterpillar tread were anywhere from two to ten feet wide made monster steam tractors on such farms as Glenn's 45,000 acres of wheat, Dalrymple's 70,000 acres in North Dakota. One 50,000-acre farm employed 282 self-binding reapers for its harvest.

These huge "bonanza farms," absentee owned and run as businesses, were different from anything ever seen before. In the Red River valley of North Dakota, where the land was as flat as a lawn, the average bonanza farm was 7,000 acres. The land was bought in large tracts from the railroad company. The average farm was divided into sections. Crews working at one end of the farm might not see the crews working in other sections from one season's end to another. The average yield was twenty bushels to an acre, giving an annual yield of 140,000 bushels. The 1897 valuation of a single average bonanza farm was over $200,000. In the machine shop were ten four-horse plows, eight four-horse seed drills, six harrows and seven binders. There were three steam-driven threshing machines. The farm had its own railroad which ran across the field.

A standard feature of every bonanza farm was the grain elevator which had first been introduced in Buffalo in 1842 so that the grain could be stored against market fluctuations. The average Red River farm had elevators with capacity of over 100,000 bushels.

On such a farm, most of the workers were migrants who earned nine to twelve dollars a week during harvests which lasted ten days in any particular region. Permanent hands received twenty-five dollars a month. Fifty men were employed during the plowing season; forty of them were discharged when the season was ended. The total cost of growing and yielding an acre of grain in such an operation was $3.75. Gross income per acre was $10.45. After discounting improvements, maintenance, and depreciation, the net profit was $2.50. The era of bonanza farms ended at the turn of the century when they were broken up, at a profit, into smaller units in anticipation of rising costs.

In breaking up, the bonanza farms were simply responding to conditions which had already hit the smaller farmer. With all the increase of productivity, and the rise in national wealth, the farmer's percentage of the nation's income was disproportionately small. Time saved by the new machines was used to work additional land, driving the price of food to still lower levels. Farm life was not easy and the younger people left for the cities.

Self-propelled steam engines, like this popular 1886 Case model, permitted farming on a mass-production scale.

Seeding a 50,000-acre bonanza farm in 1897 by machine. Four horses pulled each drill twenty-five miles a day.

Bonanza farm reaping and binding. Machines were pulled by four-horse teams. One farm might have ten binders.

4. MASS-PRODUCTION FARMING

In desperation, the farmers made a political organization out of the fraternal society, the Patrons of Husbandry, which had been founded in 1867 to demonstrate that farming was the backbone of the nation, and to make farm life more comfortable and attractive. Through the Grange, as the Patrons of Husbandry were called, farmers made war against the railroads, against the produce buyers, and everyone else who was fattening on the benefits of the farm. The courts were flooded with Granger cases.

The American farmer at the 1876 Centennial was

Shocking a sea of wheat. Crews working on different parts of a bonanza farm might not see each other for weeks.

Steam threshers were fed by two wagons, one on each side. These steam engines were replaced by gasoline tractors.

a worried man who looked at the mechanical wonders produced by his nation, and convinced himself that somehow everything was going to turn out all right. Seventeen years later, in 1893, he went to the Columbian Exposition at Chicago and saw a far more beautiful fair with mechanical marvels that made the exhibits at Philadelphia seem like primitive crudities in retrospect. To take his mind off his own special troubles, he rode somberly on Mr. Ferris' giant wheel and then went to see Little Egypt dance the Hootchy-Cootch. She, at least, made him smile.

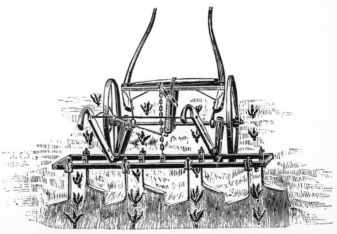

Beet cultivators were among the wide variety of machines that followed the reaper in the mechanization of farming.

THE AGE OF THE MACHINE

Edison invented a magnetic ore separator that was widely used to work ores with low iron content. Pulverized ore was dropped past an electro-magnet. Iron ores were attracted to one side of a barrier and collected.

Molten iron balls were squeezed to remove the last traces of impurities such as silicides, carbides and phosphides. As more and more carbon was oxidized out of the molten metal, the iron turned into steel. The rise of the American cities and the building of bridges created a great demand for structural steel.

242

1. THE MAKING OF STRUCTURAL STEEL, 1895

The steam-hammer shown here struck a blow of 125 tons on molten iron. The beating made the steel dense and homogeneous, and further forced impurities out of the mass. The steam-hammer could also come down so gently that it could rest on an egg without breaking it.

The rolling mill was as important as the steam-hammer in finishing products of iron and steel. After a bloom or an ingot had been heated to the proper temperature, it was passed through cast-iron rollers, turning at high speed, to give it proper shape.

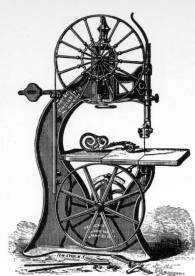

The Mohawk Dutchman, a band saw, familiarized Centennial-goers with the intricate patterns that could now be cut from wood.

The band saw was to create a special era in American architecture called "American Carpenter Renaissance."

The Ingersoll Rock Drill made possible the underwater widening of Hurl-Gate, north of Manhattan.

The interior of Machinery Hall, showing the great guns of the Krupp Works, shipped to impress the world with Germany's military power. Halfway down the Hall, in the British exhibit, can be seen a model of the steam-hammer, one of the marvels of the century. Small boys who saw the great hammer wanted to become "stationary engineers."

The Hoe "Web Printing Machine" printed 25,000 sheets an hour, the result of a thirty-year search for a high-speed cylindrical press.

2. MACHINERY HALL—
PRIDE OF THE CENTENNIAL

Machinery was the pride of the Centennial Exhibition of 1876, and the pride of Machinery Hall was the great Corliss Steam Engine which supplied the power for all the machines on display. America in 1876 was in love with machinery and everything connected with it. The awe which men felt towards mechanical power was also extended to the men who controlled it.

"As one leans over the railing around the visitors' platform and looks down into the area below, it seems difficult to imagine that the quiet attendants, who so leisurely pile the coal into the furnaces and try the various gauge cocks, are the active agents in whose control is the generation of that mighty power, steam . . . And yet so it is. Neglect on their part and all would stop; the great wheels would remain silent, the busy hum would cease, the machinery would lose its life."

To the nineteenth-century American, the more mechanical power man controlled, the closer he seemed to be approaching command over destiny. The feeling towards machinery was almost religious in fervor. In the 1870's the machine that most captured men's imagination was the great steam-hammer which could deal a blow of hundreds of tons and also could be brought down so gently that it could rest on a delicate pocket watch without cracking the glass crystal. The steam-hammer was the ultimate in man's subtle control over power.

The steam engine in general was a machine of exquisite refinement. Its existence was made possible only by the invention of tools that could shape and cut metal with microscopic precision. The basic tool for shaping metal by 1876 was the lathe; but one hundred years earlier, the lathe was almost as primitive as it had been a thousand years before. At the time of the American Revolution, both in England and America, wood was the only material that could be turned on lathes with any success; and since the development of Watt's steam engine coincided with the founding of the Republic, he was unable to have the pistons of his first large engines turned out on a lathe for him. His early pistons were so irregular that leakage of steam through the open spaces between the badly fitted parts almost completely counteracted any of the improvements he made in design.

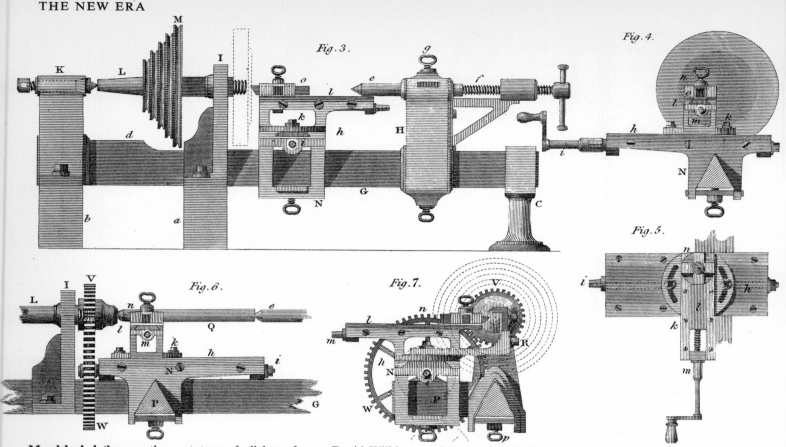

Fig. 3.

Fig. 4.

Fig. 5.

Fig. 6.

Fig. 7.

Maudslay's lathe was the prototype of all later forms. David Wilkinson, of Pawtucket, R. I., also designed a slide-rest, with less success.

3. THE LATHE, THE PLANER AND THE MILLING MACHINE

The steam engine revealed the need for metal shaping machinery of greater delicacy than the hammer, chisel, and file. The need was met by an English inventor whose stature in his own field was as great as Watt's in steam. This machine designer, Henry Maudslay, was truly an artist. His nearest American counterpart was his contemporary, David Wilkinson of Pawtucket, Rhode Island. Maudslay and Wilkinson attacked the same basic problem—from different levels of skill, with different national resources to draw on, and for very different purposes.

The potter's wheel was a flat circular platform that rotated at a fairly uniform speed. On the rotating surface, a mound of soft clay could be shaped by the potter's hands into a symmetrical shape. If he held his fingers tightly against the clay, a certain amount of clay would be removed evenly all around as the wheel turned. The ancients shaped wooden poles in somewhat the same way. The driving wheel was turned on its side, and rotated a wooden bar. The wood worker, holding a chisel in his hands, placed the edge against the spinning surface. The circular cut made was dependent on the firmness of his grip.

No machinist's hand was steady enough or strong enough to hold a scraping tool against a turning piece of iron for more than a few minutes at a time. Nor could he maintain a constant pressure. Yet the Industrial Revolution was impossible until a way could be found to hold a cutting tool against metal so that machines of iron could be built. The solution to this problem was one of the greatest inventions of the nineteenth century.

Describing the principle of Maudslay's invention, his disciple, James Nasmyth, wrote in 1841: "Up to within the past thirty years, nearly every part of a machine had to be made and finished to its required form by mere manual labor . . . Then a sudden demand for machinery of unwonted accuracy arose . . . and but for the introduction of the principle which I am about to describe, we could never have attained to one-thousandth part of the bright object . . . which has since been so wonderfully realized.

"The principle to which I allude consists of a *substitution of a mechanical contrivance in place of the human hand* for holding, applying, and directing the motions of a cutting tool . . ."

This contrivance was called the slide-rest. It was a moving metal carriage, in which a cutting tool was rigidly clamped. This tool holder was clamped to the lathe and, by means of accurately threaded screws, could be made to move both along the length of the lathe and at right angles to it on tracks. When a metal rod was rotated very rapidly so that it touched the edge of the cutting tool held rigidly by the tool holder, a fine, even strip was sliced away with perfect symmetry. If the tool were screwed in still further, a deeper cut was made. On the other hand, if the cutter was slowly moved along the length of the spinning rod, the entire surface was smoothly peeled away in the form of a long thin spiral. By means of the slide-rest, a lathe could put a very even face on a piece of metal, and a perfect cylinder of any desired diameter could be turned out of a rough bar.

One of the most brilliant of Maudslay's achievements was the screw-cutting lathe in which he used the principle of the slide-rest to make a machine cut a spiral groove along a length of metal rod. He could make the groove as deep as he pleased or at whatever pitch he pleased. The result was a perfectly threaded screw, made to an accuracy that had been unknown before. The importance of truly threaded screws, whether an eighth of an inch, two feet, or six inches in diameter, cannot be exaggerated. In any machine that depends on a screw-thread mechanism for movement, the accuracy of the movement is dependent on the accuracy of the screw thread. Screws for new lathes were made on lathes designed to cut spiral grooves of any desired pitch; screw-cutting lathes reproduced themselves.

Maudslay adapted the slide-rest to another kind of machine called a planer. In the planer, the work to be cut was clamped in place on a horizontal bed that could move back and forth in a flat plane underneath a tool held in a slide-rest. With each pass, the tool was moved slightly to cut a new strip from the surface of the work. Intricate nonsymmetrical shapes could be made on the planer. In America, around the same time, Eli Whitney was achieving a similar effect by passing metal slabs beneath a rotating cutter. Whitney's milling machine was a form of continuously operating chisel.

In a single lifetime, Maudslay worked out all the basic forms of modern machine tools. By 1830, Maudslay and his apprentices had tried every variation of the slide-rest, and English machine tools were unequaled in the world.

But American machine tools eventually overtook and then surpassed the English lead, in spite of the fact that there was no one American inventor of Maudslay's stature. The development of the American machine tool was steady and evolutionary: the accumulation of one small refinement after another. Six decades of American competence and adaptability was in the end equal to one generation of Maudslay's genius. The reason was to be found in the very different ends to which machine tools were put in the two countries.

Sellers' planing machine worked on Maudslay's principles. Eli Whitney had invented a milling cutter, and Blanchard had invented a copying lathe for irregular shapes.

American metal-turning lathes, by the 1870's, were as good as English machines, and were developed by a slow step-by-step accretion of shop-proven knowledge.

4. THE MACHINES THAT MAKE MACHINES

The slide-rest was one of the greatest mechanical inventions of the 19th century. The straining figure on the left is using the primitive lathe in which human muscle power forces a cutting tool against the rotating work. The relaxed man on the right is using Henry Maudslay's great invention.

Detail of Maudslay's slide-rest shows the cutting tool delivering a smooth, even curl. The cutting tool is clamped in a carriage (S) that can be slid along the work with great precision by a hand-turned crank (H). An automatic feed was obtained by fitting a collar (O) on the work, which turned a star (X) one notch at a time. (X) and (H) are on the same shaft. (K) is a second sliding carriage, and moves transverse to the work.

Maudslay's screw-cutting machine used the slide-rest to thread a rod with great precision. A gear (W) rotated with the work and drove a small gear (w) which made the tool traverse the length of the work, cutting a spiral groove on each pass. These 1840 pictures show the uses of one of England's greatest 19th-century prides.

Maudslay's slide-rest was also used to cut gears. The work did not rotate, but was turned one position at a time on an index (D). The cutting tool (R) was mounted on a slide-rest and driven by a pulley arrangement. The handle (S) made the cutter traverse the work and cut a gear tooth.

A planer of smooth metal surfaces also embodied the slide-rest principle. The work (W) was slid back and forth beneath a tool. A crank (L) deepened the cut, while another crank (H) moved the tool across the surface. The modern machine tool was perfected by two generations of English genius: Maudslay and Bramah.

249

5. INTERCHANGEABLE PARTS, REPLACEABLE MEN

While the English were able to make machine-making machinery of enormous precision, their engines were turning out products on a one-at-a-time basis. In America, the system of mass production started by Eli Whitney at the beginning of the century slowly diffused throughout New England. Whitney had been faced with the fact that he was unable to get skilled machinists. The use of precision machinery was only incidental to his plan for making guns on the principle of interchangeable parts.

After David Wilkinson patented the American version of a slide-rest, the next important contribution to lathe design was made in 1818 by Thomas Blanchard whose profile, or "copying" lathe was designed to duplicate irregular shapes—specifically gunstocks. It was truly American in inspiration because the goal was primarily mass production.

The principle of mass production was used in the making of cheap brass clocks and, after that, for sewing machines. Because volume of production, not precision, was the American goal, tolerances at first had to be very loose. To meet competition, a finer mass-produced product had to be developed and this in turn

demanded closer tolerances. Individual machinists were forced to make continual improvements in precision in their machines. Each improvement was in itself small, but over a period of years the accumulated body of experience began to equal in value the single force of Maudslay's genius. The method of manufacture by interchangeable parts had become so widespread and so unique to this country that when an English Army commission in the 1850's placed an order for rifles made in American armories, they spoke of guns being made according to the "American system of manufacture."

The search for American precision reached the point where, in 1851, Brown and Sharp could bring out a commercial vernier caliper reading to a thousandth of an inch.

In 1854, Robbins and Lawrence of Windsor, Vermont, developed a turret lathe—the "turret" being a multiple tool holder in which several different tools could be held at once so that a succession of operations could be performed on the work without unclamping it. After each operation, the turret was rotated to bring another tool to bear. Like the copying lathe of Blanchard, the purpose of the turret lathe was volume production.

In 1864, William Sellers, president of the Franklin Institute and head of one of Philadelphia's outstanding machine companies, proposed to standardize screw

Steelworkers: Noontime. American steel was continually improved to meet the demands of the machine tool industry for harder s

threads to the point where they might be made interchangeable not only from one machine to another, but the screws made by various manufacturers would be interchangeable. This was adopted the following year by the United States government. Thirty years later the screw thread became internationally standardized.

Frederick W. Taylor, in 1880, began work in Sellers' factory on the physics of metal cutting. The result of his work was high-speed tool steel.

In the very era in which the American admiration for the great inventor was reaching its zenith, American machine tool practice was proving that the concerted work of many men, none of whom was blessed with genius, could perform the same function as genius. In the very era when individual American inventors were building enormous corporations to produce, develop, and market their products, American corporations were learning that it was possible to get along without the individual inventor.

By the turn of the century, many large companies had begun the system of the "industrial research laboratory." In machinery, electricity, and other fields of human ingenuity, the mass of lesser men was moving in. American machine design had done without its Robert Fulton, its Edison, and it was nevertheless leading the world. Whitney's system was revealing its hidden corollary: not only were machine parts interchangeable, so were men.

The Corliss bevel-gear cutting machine embodied all the principles of the slide-rest and the lathe on a massive scale. Foreigners were deeply impressed by it.

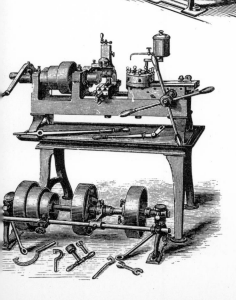

American machine tools had developed a character of their own by 1876. The turret lathe (left) was an American invention, as was the universal grinder (upper left). The universal milling machine (upper right) had only recently been developed, but it retained Eli Whitney's principles. The surface grinding machine (right), like the others, was free from the elaborate disguise of "Minnehaha" design.

THE MACHINE TO REPLACE THE PEN: 1

An early typewriter was conceived by William Burt in 1829. Paper was clamped to a roller. The letters were mounted on plungers held in springs on a circular carriage that was rotated by hand. The action was slow.

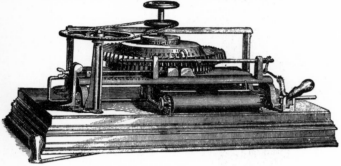

The American Typographic Machine was only a slight improvement. The carriage moved, a single handle worked all the letters, but the type, still in a circular carriage, had to be moved by hand.

The first modern typewriter was designed by C. L. Sholes, Carlos Glidden, and S. W. Soule, embodying two ideas: the carriage moved one space to the left when a letter was printed, and the keys worked on a "piano-forte" action.

Lillian Sholes demonstrated her father's typewriter. Sholes, a Wisconsin printer, worked for years to perfect the machine, patenting it in 1867. He worked for a time with Edison, but sold out to Remington.

THE TYPE-WRITER.

WHAT "MARK TWAIN" SAYS ABOUT IT.
Hartford, March 19, 1875.

GENTLEMEN: Please do not use my name in any way. Please do not even divulge the fact that I own a machine. I have entirely stopped using the Type-Writer, for the reason that I never could write a letter with it to anybody without receiving a request by return mail that I would not only describe the machine, but state what progress I had made in the use of it, etc., etc. I don't like to write letters, and so I don't want people to know I own this curiosity-breeding little joker. Yours truly,

SAML. L. CLEMENS.

Mark Twain was the first author to use a typewriter and wrote a humorous testimonial for it. The machine was first offered to ministers and authors without too much success. No one thought of its office possibilities.

Philo Remington

The Remington No. 2 was an improved model over the original and began to find favor. The first "noiseless" machine had a heavy glass case enclosing the action.

Sholes hit upon the idea for the typewriter in his search for a machine to print numbers on tickets and book pages. In the early 1870's he worked with Edison who was interested only in a printing device for a telegraph system. Neither Edison nor Sholes foresaw the use of the "writing machine" in business offices.

The Sholes machine in 1873 was brought to the attention of Philo Remington, the son of the firm's founder, who was looking for a product that could be mass produced to take up the post-war slack in the arms industry. The typewriter seemed promising if only a market could be found for it.

Thirteen years later, in 1886, this market was not yet developed. Remington's financial difficulties forced the sale of the typewriter company to independent interests. Mass production techniques were expanded, and the machine began to find its way into business offices. By the early 1890's, the boom was on. Sholes' total earnings from his invention were $12,000.

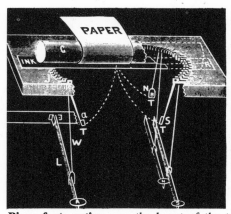

Piano-forte action was the heart of the typewriter. When a key was pressed, a lever made a letter strike the roller. All the letters struck at exactly the same point.

The aligning room of the Remington Typewriter Company, now independent of the Arms and Sewing Machine Company. Mass production was introduced, and in the early 1890's, forty men worked in this room alone.

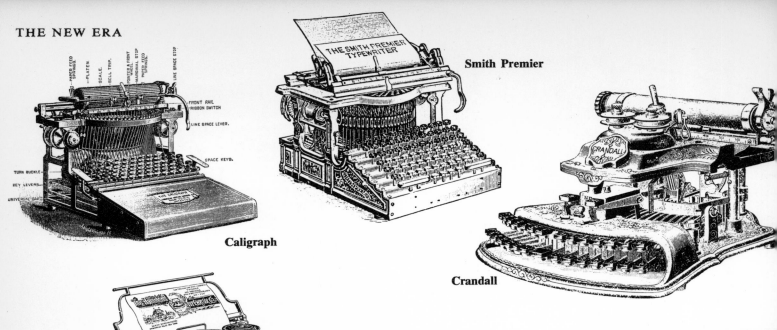

Caligraph

Smith Premier

Crandall

Hammond

2. THE REMINGTO

Philo Remington sold out too soon by a year. All the spade-work he had done in trying to develop a market finally paid off—for his successors. The growing centralization of business made for large offices with enormous amounts of paper work, and here, rather than among ministers and writers, the mass market proved to be. Remington's success encouraged other manufacturers, and within a short time dozens of modified forms began to appear.

The two basic requirements of a typewriter: a carriage that

LIFE WITH A TYPEWRITER

Women followed the typewriter into the American business office. Fourteen years after the Centennial, the typewriter and the telephone were standard equipment. So was the young lady secretary. Here are two illustrations from the *Illustrated Phonographic World* from a time when the word "phonograph" meant a method of writing from dictation.

DAUGHTER: Charlie Huggard kissed me last night.

MOTHER (*indignantly*): What! That shorthand teacher fellow! That's outrageous. Did you sit on him for it?

DAUGHTER: I was.

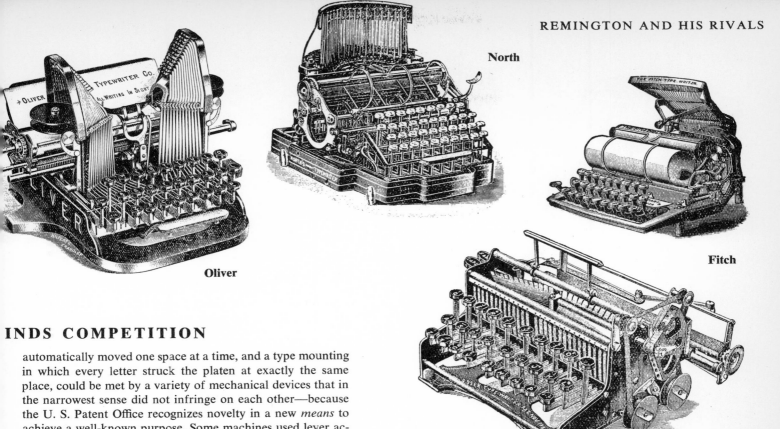

North

Oliver

Fitch

Essex

INDS COMPETITION

automatically moved one space at a time, and a type mounting in which every letter struck the platen at exactly the same place, could be met by a variety of mechanical devices that in the narrowest sense did not infringe on each other—because the U. S. Patent Office recognizes novelty in a new *means* to achieve a well-known purpose. Some machines used lever actions that differed only slightly from the Remington, some even went back to Burt and used a rotatable type wheel that was actuated by levers.

UNCLE SAM'S TYPEWRITER

The flood of typewriters in the early 1890's almost drowned America with conflicting claims. This cartoon was *Harper's* view of a situation where every make was supposed to be the government's exclusive choice.

Blowing machinery at the Centennial caused a lot of merriment; compressed air machinery was new to America.

Drilling the Mt. Cenis tunnel suggested to Westinghouse in 1866 the use of compressed air to actuate a railroad brake.

GEORGE WESTINGHOUSE

1. THE STOLID YOUNG MAN

"For six months, thus, the Exhibition continued open —a time long to be remembered by those who passed through it—and listened to the strains from Gilmore's band, or heard the tones from the grand organ swelling up and dying away in the distance. . . . One could not but feel the immense pleasure and benefit given to the masses of our people . . ." Everyone found something to admire, and every exhibit attracted its share of the crowd. "To foreigners, our railway exhibits were most interesting, presenting the peculiar features of a system differing in many respects from anything in their own countries."

One thing different about American railways was an increasing measure of safety unknown to the rest of the world. In the Machinery Building, between Bean's brake-shoe and Z. Cobb and Son's elliptic steel springs was the display of the Westinghouse Air Brakes Company of Pittsburgh, Pennsylvania; automatic brakes, vacuum brakes, air compressors, speed indicators, engine governors, engines.

The Centennial marked the beginnings of the careers of a number of brilliant young men, but few were as young or as brilliant as George Westinghouse. In 1876, he was thirty years old, and for several years he had been the president of a company capitalized at more than half a million dollars. In the year of the Centennial, thirty-eight per cent of the 15,567 American locomotives and the 14,055 passenger cars were already equipped with his air brakes.

There were other bright young men whose works

This railroad accident at Angola, New York, was typical of too many tragedies in the days when there was no adequate system of signaling or braking. In one such accident, Westinghouse came to understand the need for a brake.

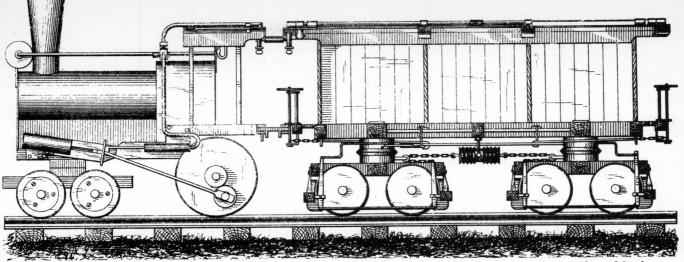

Westinghouse's first idea was to use steam pressure to force a brake to engage. Not only had it been tried before, but it was impractical: the steam condensed in the long pipes before exerting pressure on the brake-shoe.

were on exhibition at the fair—Alexander Graham Bell and Thomas Edison, but George Westinghouse was unique because his career was to mark an end of one era and the beginning of another. He founded a complex corporate structure that was only the reflection of his own creativeness. He had nothing in common with the Hills, Leland Stanfords, or the Drews of the railroad manipulations. He did not believe with Pierpont Morgan in the building of trusts simply for the sake of bigness. Westinghouse was in the tradition of Robert Fulton and Eli Whitney, and he was almost the end of the line. He was a beginning in this sense: the great corporation which he created would go on, becoming even more powerful after his forced resignation at the end of a lifetime of creativeness and service. Westinghouse, the corporation, would get along without Westinghouse, the man.

Westinghouse had been born in 1846 in a small Vermont town. His father had a shop for the manufacture of farm machinery and the boy learned the laws of gears, pistons, and cams. In 1861, at fifteen, he ran off to join the army, following his beloved older brother, but his father marched him home. Three years later he entered the navy. After the war, he fulfilled a promise to his father to enter college. One year was the time it took for him to come in conflict with the president of Union College, and Westinghouse happily retreated to the outside world where school work would not interfere with his inventions.

He was a tall, heavy boy with stolid features. A man who had worked with him for many years said of his first impression of Westinghouse, "He did not appeal to me as being a wizard. He seemed to be a plain human being with lots of initiative and nerve. He met my ideas of what an engineer should be."

Westinghouse's calm voice and matter-of-fact manner hid a complex talent in a complicated man. Almost as soon as he left college, he began work on his first important invention. In the same years when George Pullman and others saw there was room for passenger comfort on railroad travel, when Tiffany and Swift saw the profits in mobile refrigerators, Westinghouse was one of the men who were appalled by the fearful accidents which were then considered among the normal hazards of life. Thirty years of railroading had developed neither adequate signaling nor braking systems. A train was brought to a stop by the action of brakemen stationed along its length who frantically turned hand wheels on each car in response to whistle toots from the engineer.

Westinghouse said, "My first idea of braking apparatus came to me in this way: a train upon which I was a passenger in 1866 was delayed due to a collision between two freight trains. If the engineers of those trains had had some means of applying brakes to *all the wheels of their trains,* the accident might have been avoided."

The idea that came to his mind was a type of railroad brake that had been tried in the earliest days of railroading: a braking device attached to the coupling mechanism. As the locomotive slowed, the cars would tend to ride forward on their couplings. The rearward motion of the coupling on each car would then apply brakes locally. He discovered that this idea had been fully anticipated and was a failure.

"My next thought was the placing of a steam cylinder under each car with a pipe connection extended from the locomotive so that steam could be transmitted to all the cylinders; but it required little experimentation to disclose it would be impossible."

About the same time he had reached this conclusion, he came across a magazine article describing the building of the tunnel in Mount Cenis in Switzerland, using compressed air which exerted a uniform pressure through three thousand feet of pipe. Compressed air promised to be his answer.

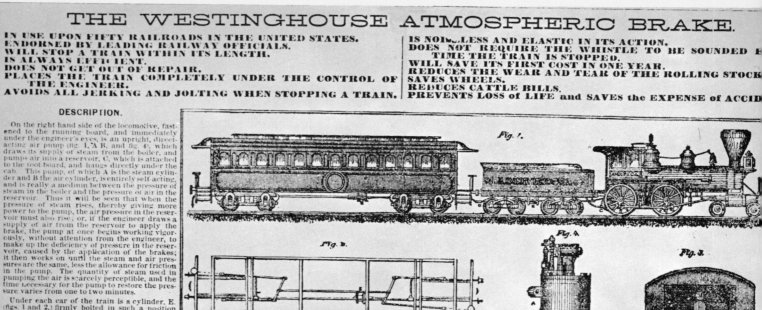

THE WESTINGHOUSE ATMOSPHERIC BRAKE.

IN USE UPON FIFTY RAILROADS IN THE UNITED STATES.
ENDORSED BY LEADING RAILWAY OFFICIALS.
WILL STOP A TRAIN WITHIN ITS LENGTH.
IS ALWAYS EFFICIENT.
DOES NOT GET OUT OF REPAIR.
PLACES THE TRAIN COMPLETELY UNDER THE CONTROL OF
THE ENGINEER.
AVOIDS ALL JERKING AND JOLTING WHEN STOPPING A TRAIN.

IS NOISELESS AND ELASTIC IN ITS ACTION.
DOES NOT REQUIRE THE WHISTLE TO BE SOUNDED E
TIME THE TRAIN IS STOPPED.
WILL SAVE ITS FIRST COST IN ONE YEAR.
REDUCES THE WEAR AND TEAR OF THE ROLLING STOCK
SAVES WHEELS.
REDUCES CATTLE BILLS.
PREVENTS LOSS of LIFE and SAVES the EXPENSE of ACCID

DESCRIPTION.

On the right hand side of the locomotive, fastened to the running board, and immediately under the engineer's eyes, is an upright, direct-acting air pump (fig. 1, A B, and fig. 4), which draws its supply of steam from the boiler, and pumps air into a reservoir, C, which is attached to the foot-board, and hangs directly under the cab. This pump, of which A is the steam cylinder and B the air cylinder, is entirely self acting, and is really a medium between the pressure of steam in the boiler and the pressure of air in the reservoir. Thus it will be seen that when the pressure of steam rises, thereby giving more power to the pump, the air pressure in the reservoir must also rise; or, if the engineer draws a supply of air from the reservoir to apply the brake, the pump at once begins working vigorously, without attention from the engineer, to make up the deficiency of pressure in the reservoir, caused by the application of the brakes; it then works on until the steam and air pressures are the same, less the allowance for friction in the pump. The quantity of steam used in pumping the air is scarcely perceptible, and the time necessary for the pump to restore the pressure varies from one to two minutes.

Under each car of the train is a cylinder, E (figs. 1 and 2,) firmly bolted in such a position that the piston acts on the lever now used for the ordinary hand-brake, and not at all interfering with hand-braking.

The pressure of air is conducted to these cylinders from the reservoir, C, under the locomotive, by a line of three-quarter inch gas-pipe, running the entire length of the train, and the connection with each cylinder is made from the main line with a quarter-inch elbow. From each end of a car the pipes are extended by three-ply rubber hose, which are connected, when the cars are coupled together, by an ingenious coupling, D, (figs. 1 and 5,) so arranged that when the parts, G and H, (fig. 5,) are united, the air passes freely through them. But should any of the cars become detached from any cause, the coupling, which is held together by stiff springs, pulls apart, the valve closes, the escape of air is prevented, and the brake remains effective on the rest of the train. Or should the brake have been applied, and afterwards a car become detached, the valves of the coupling on the detached car immediately close, and the brake continues applied, thus preventing a car from running back on a grade.

An air gauge, J, (fig. 3) placed immediately above the steam gauge, indicates to the engineer the amount of pressure in the reservoir; and the entire management of the train is placed in his hands by means of the three-way cock, F, by simply turning which he can instantly and effectively stop the train, without that unpleasant jerking and bounding noticeable on all trains where hand or other brakes are used, or can as quickly release the brake or graduate it to any desired speed.

While the brake is so adjusted that the engineer can, by a simple movement of his hand, apply it with its utmost force, as in case of accident, yet it is impossible for him to get such force as to break anything or even lock or slide the wheels.

The brake is applied instantly to all the cars of a train alike, so that, in running into an obstruction, the train would be perfectly taut, and could stand a considerable blow; or, in case of an anticipated collision, the train could be stopped, the brake released, and the train backed out of danger at once.

The cases are numerous where railway officers have testified to the prevention of accidents by the use of this brake. Many engineers, who

have become accustomed to its use, say they would be unwillin without it.

To all alike—travelers, officials, and employees—it recommen by supplying a long-felt need, and practically proves its claime safety and economy which its use insures.

N B.—*We will furnish any railroad company with a complete set o for one train, to be paid for only when the BRAKE is found perfectly sat For farther particulars apply to* RALPH BAGALEY, SECRETA *ner of Liberty and 25th Street, Pittsburg, Pa.*

Fig. 1.

Fig. 2.

Fig. 4.

Fig. 3.

Fig. 5.

WESTINGHOUSE AIR BRAKE

NATIONAL RAILWAY PUBLICATION COMPANY, PHILADELPHIA.

The air brake was one invention that did not have to wait long for its general adoption by the public. This 1872 advertisement was placed only six years after Westinghouse first conceived the idea and began experiments.

2. THE SAFETY BRAKE

"At that time, no compressed air apparatus of importance had been in operation. The apparatus needed for a demonstration was, however, laboriously constructed in a machine shop in Pittsburgh, being finally completed in the summer or early autumn of 1868." The first successful compressed air brake had these essential parts:

1. An air pump driven by the steam engine, which would compress air into a main reservoir to about sixty or seventy pounds per square inch;

2. A pipe leading from this reservoir to a valve mechanism for the engineer's control;

3. A line of pipe which passed under all of the cars for the length of the train, with connections between cars made by flexible couplings;

4. Cylinder and piston devices on each car to actuate the brake-shoes.

To stop his train, then, the engineer let compressed air from the locomotive reservoir into the train pipe and thus to the brake cylinders. To release the brakes, the compressed air in the pipes was discharged into the atmosphere.

When Westinghouse had completed his experimental apparatus, he invited railway officials to watch it in operation. W. W. Card of the Panhandle Railroad offered Westinghouse the Steubenville accommodation train—a locomotive and four cars. On the day of the trial, a drayman disregarded all warnings and found himself astride the track with the train bearing down on him. In panic, the horses fled, and he was thrown down on the track, where he lay unconscious.

"Tate, the engineer, who had just been turning over in his mind the most effective way of bringing the train to a standstill at the first station where it was to halt, reached instinctively for the brake valve and gave it a mighty twist. The air rushed out of the compressor, through the pipes into the cylinders beneath the cars,

Railroad safety was a major interest of Westinghouse. Besides the air brake, he began to make signals.

The interior of a switch tower, showing the operation of interlocking switches in a system of block signals.

Emergency halts were the least of the functions of block signals which were designed to keep rail traffic moving.

and the pistons brought the brake-shoe with force against the wheels. The train came to a stop four feet on the safe side of the unhappy driver."

This successful demonstration enabled Westinghouse to capitalize the Westinghouse Air Brake Company at $500,000. He was only twenty-three years old.

The conditions for an ideal railroad brake were fully met by Westinghouse, with the exception of two:

1. If a part of the train comes loose from the rest, the brakes must come automatically into play;

2. The failure of the brake apparatus in one or more cars must not interfere with the action of the brakes on the rest of the train.

Westinghouse met these two objections ingeniously. Instead of having compressed air actuate his brakes, he decided to reverse his entire scheme. The brakes were now continually *kept* from bearing on the wheels by compressed air. To stop the train, the engineer *decreased* the air pressure, and the brake-shoes then collapsed against the wheels, actuated by individual reser-

voirs of compressed air mounted under each car. If the train were to part anywhere, the sudden decrease in air pressure would automatically apply the brakes.

For the next few years Westinghouse continued adapting his air brake to the various conditions to be met in traffic. His competitors were driven out of the market, not because of any financial manipulation, but simply because the Westinghouse brake was infinitely superior to anything else.

Brakes and safety were uppermost in Westinghouse's mind, and he sought a signaling system that would be as automatic in operation as his air brake. The art of signaling was almost unknown in the United States. The Union Switch and Signal Company which he founded in 1880, at the age of thirty-four, sold complete systems whose purpose was not necessarily to stop trains but to keep them moving at such speeds as to give best results and service and cost. His block signal system was improved over the years, but not basically changed.

3. THE WESTINGHOUSE UTILITIES

With two major companies in profitable operation, Westinghouse found himself at the age of thirty-seven, in 1883, with time on his hands. He decided to sink a small gas well on the grounds of his estate, "Solitude," in the handsome residential section of Pittsburgh. Two months later, a small vein was tapped. Westinghouse said he'd prefer the well to be a little larger so that he could have enough gas for his house and for friends.

Another vein was struck at fifteen hundred feet, and Westinghouse urged them to keep digging. Suddenly they "struck such a volume of gas that it blew the tools out and ripped off the casing head with such a roar and racket that no one could hear his own ears within a block." The gas was lighted, and for the next few weeks the elegant neighborhood was lit with Westinghouse's private torch. Westinghouse now became seriously interested in natural gas as a fuel and organized the Philadelphia Company which became large enough to meet the needs of the people of Pittsburgh, Allegheny City, and the entire vicinity. Westinghouse devoted himself to the engineering aspects and took out thirty-eight patents. He invented the gas meter, the automatic cutoff regulator, and a leak-proof piping system.

George Westinghouse

Then once again he looked around for something new; and once again he found it. Westinghouse, more than any other man, must be credited with the introduction of alternating current as a power source.

In terms of power, a high voltage producing a low current is no different from a low voltage producing a high current. However, power at low currents can be transmitted over great distances with much greater economy than at high current, because low current power requires much less bulk of wire. On the principle discovered by Joseph Henry, it was possible to transform alternating current from high to low voltage and back again, not possible with direct current.

The first electrical transformer in the modern sense had only recently been developed by a Frenchman named Gaulard, backed by an Englishman named Gibbs. The device, so far not developed beyond a laboratory scale, was then called a "secondary generator." Westinghouse was the first American to realize its possibilities, and he introduced alternating current practice to the United States by buying the patent of Gaulard and Gibbs so that he could manufacture transformers of his own improved design. Being as much entrepreneur as engineer and inventor, he set to work to popularize alternating current.

Here he met with sharp competition from Edison and others who were deeply committed to direct current power. Westinghouse entered New York, offering lighting and factory power. Edison and his supporters played up every fatal electrical accident and blamed it on high voltage transmission. Just at that time, too, the State of New York introduced electrocution by alternating current as a means of capital punishment. To New Yorkers, AC now became synonymous with certain death. Westinghouse fought back with this statement: "The alternating current will kill people, of course. So will gunpowder, and dynamite, and whisky, and lots of other things; but we have a system whereby the deadly electricity of the alternating current can do no harm unless a man is fool enough to swallow a whole dynamo."

Westinghouse was a shrewd inventor, a fighter, a leader, but his contemporaries called him a poor administrator. However, this was a judgment passed in the days when American business was tending to monopoly in spite of the Sherman Anti-Trust Act; Westinghouse believed in the older American principles of open competition. For a long time he held his own against the utilities. At one point during negotiations with Coffin, president of the General Electric Company, Coffin confided how he had squeezed out the two inventors on whose patents General Electric was based. Westinghouse said contemptuously to Coffin, "You tell me how you treated Thomson and Houston. Why should I trust you after what you tell me?"

Westinghouse refused to enter any trust or combine. In the end he paid for his independence. After 1900, when he was in his sixties, Morgan's financial manipulation forced him out of the companies which he had founded, and the Westinghouse Company made peace with its competitors. He died shortly after.

George Westinghouse was in the direct tradition of the early American engineers, and with him the tradition reached its high point. After him, the American engineer became less and less an entrepreneur—and more generally a salaried employee. The times were changing. Westinghouse stood at the exact point of balance. His career was the personification of the nineteenth-century American dream and its end.

Natural gas for illumination was developed by George Westinghouse for the Pittsburgh area before he became interested in electricity. He invented the gas meter and automatic safety valves so that gas could be used in the home.

Electric cooking and ironing were first brought to public awareness in the Columbian Exposition of 1893 where George Westinghouse was trying to popularize alternating current.

Streetcars were driven by alternating current carried by underground conductors. Each car carried a plow that extended through a slot in the street to make contact.

A war of generators took place in New York during the 1890's. Edison was committed to direct current; Westinghouse moved in with alternating current. Edison knew better, but claimed that AC was dangerous. Westinghouse fought back.

4. WESTINGHOUSE AND THE
GROWTH OF THE CITIES

The Bowery at Night, painted in 1895 by W. Louis Sontag, shows how George Westinghouse participated in the late 19th century rise of the cities. The clanging streetcars were

powered by Westinghouse generators; the stores were lit by either his alternating current lines or Edison's direct current; the elevated railroad, shortly to be electrified, was running safely over the heads of city dwellers because of the Westinghouse air brake. The homes that were lit by gas were metered on principles also developed by him.

Daguerre (standing) and Niépce (seated) worked together to invent a system of photography.

Fox Talbot, in England, at the same time developed another process. This used the system of "positive" and "negative," but was less well known.

John William Draper, American scientist, made the first portrait by photography in 1840.

When a mixture of oxide of chrome and .... it is also converted into basic chromate of lead and oxide of lead.

It is therefore chromate of lead, which is often employed in organic analysis, from which this latter mixture is derived.—*Journal für Praktische Chemie,* No. 2. 1840.

PORTRAITS IN DAGUERREOTYPE.

Professor Draper, of the University of New York, informs us in a note dated March 31st, that he has succeeded during the winter in procuring portraits by the Daguerreotype, and that they have all the beauty and softness of the most finished mezzotint engraving, and only require from 20 to 45 seconds for execution.

METEOROLOGICAL OBSERVATIONS FOR APRIL, 1840.

Chiswick.—April 1. Slight rain: cloudy. 2. Hazy: very fine. 3. Cold dry haze: frosty at night. 4—6. Very fine. 7. Fine: stormy showers at night. 8. Slight showers. 9. Cloudy and cold. 10—12. Very fine. 13—17. Fine but very dry. 18. Clear, hot and dry. 19. Hazy: very fine. 20. Very fine. 21—23. Cloudy and fine. 24. Very fine. 25. Very hot, nearly cloudless, and excessively dry. 26, 27. Hot and dry. 28. Excessively hot for the period of the season. thermometer 81° in the shade. 29, 30. Very fine: hot and dry. This .... for a high ....

Draper's achievement was noted in scientific journals. He also daguerreotyped the moon.

Dorothy Catherine Draper, as photographed by her father in daguerreotype. This was the first portrait ever made with the subject's eyes open.

PHOTOGRAPHY

1. PAINTING
WITH SUNLIGHT

"The Centennial Photographic Company had erected upon the grounds, almost opposite Machinery Hall on the east, the largest studio that was ever known in America. . . . Here a motley crowd used to be assembled. There were Tunisians, Algerians, Turks, Chinamen, Japanese, Africans, Germans, Austrians, Italians, Frenchmen, Spaniards, and Arabs, all jabbering in their native tongues, scrambling for their turns in their national way, showing their international measure of push and enterprise in getting ahead, giving evidence of their several dispositions as circumstances required. A true babble, indeed, in a most picturesque site. Day by day, nearly 700 heads were taken off for the purposes named."

Indeed photography at the Fair was among the most important exhibits. One hundred and thirty-eight American firms displayed supplies and pictures. Schreiber and Son of Philadelphia exhibited a glacé embossing press. The official catalogue listed views of the oil regions, views of the Holy Land, architectural views, and just plain photographic views. In the America of 1876, photography was popular and widely accepted even though there had not been one important American contribution to the art so far.

More than a century earlier, photography had become a possibility when chemists noticed that light decomposed the salts of silver. In 1802, Humphry Davy and Thomas Wedgwood, son of the founder of the famous porcelain works, showed that a hand or a leaf placed upon a sheet of paper coated with a solution of silver nitrate would leave a clear imprint when exposed to light. The silhouette would last a little while before fading. In France, some twenty years later, Daguerre, an artist, solved the problem of the fading image when he found that he could replace the activated silver of silver iodide salts with mercury. He hit upon a method of "fixing" his picture when he came across some results of Sir John Herschel, who explained the chemical action of hyposulphites on silver salts.

While Samuel Morse was in France in 1838 trying to promote his telegraph, he met Daguerre. The two inventors made a contract. Daguerre agreed to promote Morse's telegraphy in France, and Morse undertook to spread the use of the daguerreotype in America. Morse opened one of the first portrait studios in America to increase his income. At the beginning it was a success, but the length of time for a sitting was too much for his subjects, and the project failed. Still, a number of studios for making Daguerre portraits were opened at the time; and one New Yorker, Philip Hone, wrote, "I went this morning by invitation of M. Francis Gourand, to see a collection of the views made by the wonderful process lately discovered in France by M. Daguerre. . . .

"The pictures are extremely beautiful—they consist of views in Paris, and exquisite collections of the objects of still life. The manner of producing them constitutes one of the wonders of modern times, and, like other miracles, one may almost be excused for disbelieving it without seeing the very process by which it is created."

The first photographic portrait in a modern sense was made by Professor John W. Draper, a physicist and an astronomer of New York University. In the following year, 1840, he took the first picture of the moon. It was small, not well focused, but it was the forerunner of America's main contribution to photography: its application to astronomy.

Daguerre's discovery was considered one of the great scientific achievements of his time. It was announced by Arago to the Academy.

Daguerreotype parlors were opened in every major city in the U. S., England, France, and Germany. Improvements were made in the chemistry of photography every year, but no major contribution came from America until the advent of George Eastman.

George Eastman as a boy photographer carrying the usual burden of equipment needed for the wet plate process.

Beautiful detail and texture could be caught by the wet plate process in the hands of an artist like O'Sullivan.

2. GEORGE EASTMAN

Just as the mid-century telegrapher's life seemed full of glamour to Thomas Edison, the 1870's offered the dare-devil photographer as another adventurer who did difficult things with courage in far places. During the Civil War, Matthew Brady had taken his camera and chemical wagons to the front lines oblivious of death and danger and returned with thousands of war pictures which were shocking in their realism.

His assistants all became heroes in their own turn in the next decade. Alexander Gardner followed the Union Pacific Railroad west to Promontory Point. T. H. O'Sullivan explored the 40th parallel with the U. S. cavalry, dragging equipment up the Sierra Nevadas. In Panama, he photographed Commander Thomas Oliver Selfridge's jungle expedition. Back in the American West, his camera explored the unknown Grand Canyon.

The early photographers were artists; they were also chemists who dragged laboratories with them; they were lean, hardbitten men of high adventure. At least they seemed so to a meticulous young bank clerk of Rochester, New York, who dreamed of making a photographic exploration of Santo Domingo.

George Eastman, sole support of his widowed mother and two sisters, had for eight years worked his way up from messenger boy, through insurance clerk, to bookkeeper in the Rochester Savings Bank. Each year, since his father's death, young Eastman had conscientiously totted up his annual savings—thirty-seven dollars in the year he earned three dollars a week, more each year with each raise until finally his bank book showed five thousand dollars. He settled for half his dream. Instead of a photographic expedition to Santo Domingo, he took a camera and hundreds of pounds of equipment to Mackinac Island.

"My layout," said Eastman about photography in the 1870's, "had in it a camera about the size of a soap box, a tripod which was strong and heavy enough to support a bungalow, a big plate holder, a dark tent, a nitrate bath and a container for water." This list did not include a heavy mass of glass plates which also had to be transported.

The method of photography which Eastman learned had been unchanged since the 1850's. A large plate of glass (during the Civil War, Brady had used pieces of windowpane from demolished houses) was washed chemically clean. Then in the darkness of a light-proof tent, the glass was coated with a collodion solution of an iodide, bromide or whatever halide suited the photographer's fancy. While the collodion was still tacky, the plate was soaked for about five minutes in a solution of silver nitrate; then, still wet, it was put into a light-tight plate holder, mounted in the camera which had already been prepared for the shot, exposed, and then returned to the tent, where it was washed with pyrogallic acid to remove all the silver salts which had not been activated by light.

The whole process had to be carried out before the original collodion was completely dry. For this reason, the process was called "wet plate" photography.

For some years, England, the center for the art, had been trying to coat glass with a collodion solution which could be used in the dry state. These dry plates, if perfected, would remove ninety per cent of the photographer's burden. He could prepare all his plates before going into the field, and develop them when he arrived at his home laboratory. The *British Journal of Photography* carried a new formula in almost every issue. Richard Leach Maddox in 1871 substituted gelatin for collodion because, as he later said, he couldn't stand the smell of ether involved in the preparation of collodion. Eastman, the avid amateur, read every publication on photography he could lay hands on; and in 1877, when he was twenty-three years old, began to experiment himself.

"Finally I came upon a coating of gelatin and silver bromide that had all the necessary photographic qualities. . . . At first I wanted to make photography simpler merely for my own convenience, but soon I thought of the possibilities of commercial production."

Forty years had passed since Daguerre's discovery. Americans had been enthusiastic practitioners of the art, but until Eastman, no American had made any contribution to its technology. Eastman gave up his bank job and went into business with one of his mother's boarders, Henry A. Strong, to manufacture dry plates. The first patent, "An improved process of preparing gelatin dry plates for use in photography and apparatus thereof," was issued in England, July 22, 1879, and in the United States in the following April. Eastman sold his English patent for twenty-five hundred dollars; this was his capital for his American factory.

In the 1880's, young Americans looked at the Singer Sewing Machine Company, at the McCormick Harvester Company, at the cheap clock factories of New England, and gravely repeated to each other that the secret of American manufacture was quantity production by machinery, a low price for a wide market, and get-up-and-go advertising.

For all the talk though, Eastman and his one-flight-up factory was one of the first to put these methods to use in making a nonmechanical product. But a few months after its first shipment, the Eastman Dry Plate Company was on the verge of disaster. Plates which had remained for some time on the dealers' shelves lost their sensitivity. Eastman guaranteed to make up the loss, shut down manufacture, and made an intensive search for the cause of failure.

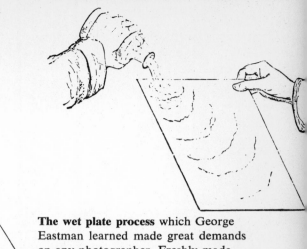

The wet plate process which George Eastman learned made great demands on any photographer. Freshly made solutions had to be poured evenly on clean glass just before exposure. Some of Matthew Brady's famous Civil War pictures were made on windowpanes from shell-wrecked houses. A photographer had to know chemistry and optics besides the laws of composition. The wet plate process stemmed from Fox Talbot rather than from Daguerre.

The discovery of celluloid by Hyatt led Eastman to try to experiment with film as a substitute for glass.

UNITED STATES PATENT OFFICE.

JOHN W. HYATT, JR., AND ISAIAH S. HYATT, OF ALBANY, NEW YORK.

IMPROVEMENT IN TREATING AND MOLDING PYROXYLINE.

Specification forming part of Letters Patent No. **105,338**, dated July 12, 1870.

We, JOHN W. HYATT, Jr., and ISAIAH S. HYATT, both of Albany, in the county of Albany and State of New York, have invented a new and Improved Process of Dissolving Pyroxyline and of Making Solid Collodion, of which the following is a specification:

Our invention consists, first, of so preparing pyroxyline that pigments and other substances in a powdered condition can be easily and thoroughly mixed therewith before the pyroxyline is subjected to the action of a solvent; secondly, of mixing with the pyroxyline so prepared any desirable pigment, coloring matter, or other material, and also any substance in a powdered state which may be vaporized or liquefied and converted into a solvent of pyroxyline by the application of heat; and, thirdly, of subjecting the compound so made to heavy pressure while heated, so that the least practicable proportion of solvent may be used in the production of solid collodion and its compounds.

The following is a description of our process: First, we prepare the pyroxyline by grinding it in water until it is reduced to a fine pulp by means of a machine similar to those employed in grinding paper-pulp. Second, any suitable white or coloring pigment or dyes, when desired, are then mixed and thoroughly ground with the pyroxyline pulp, or any powdered or granulated material is incorporated that may be adapted to the purpose of the manufacture. While the ground pulp is still wet we mix therewith finely-pulverized gum-camphor in about the proportions of one part (by weight) of the camphor to two parts of the pyroxyline when in a dry state. These proportions may be somewhat varied with good results. The gum-camphor may be comminuted by grinding in water, by pounding, or rolling; or, if preferred, the camphor may be dissolved in alcohol or spirits of wine, and then precipitated by adding water, the alcohol leaving the camphor and uniting with the water, when both the alcohol and the water may be drawn off, leaving the camphor in a very finely-divided state. After the powdered camphor is thoroughly mixed with the wet pyroxyline pulp and the other ingredients, we expel the water as far as possible by straining the mixture and subjecting it to an immense pressure in a perforated vessel. This leaves the mixture in a comparatively solid and dry

prevent the pyroxyline from burning or exploding during the remaining process. Third, the mixture is then placed in a mold of any appropriate form, which is heated by steam or by any convenient method, to from 150° to 300° Fahrenheit, to suit the proportion of camphor and the size of the mass, and is subjected to a heavy pressure in a hydraulic or other press. The heat, according to the degree used, vaporizes or liquefies the camphor, and thus converts it into a solvent of the pyroxyline. By introducing the solvent in the manner here described, and using heat to make the solvent active, and pressure to force it into intimate contact every particle of the pyroxyline, we are able to use a less proportion of this or any solvent which depends upon heat for its activity than has ever been known heretofore. After keeping the mixture under heat and pressure long enough to complete the solvent action throughout the mass it is cooled while still under pressure, and then taken out of the mold. The product is a solid about the consistency of sole-leather, but which subsequently becomes as hard as horn or bone by the evaporation of the camphor. Before the camphor is evaporated the material is easily softened by heat, and may be molded into any desirable form, which neither changes nor appreciably shrinks in hardening.

We are aware that camphor made into a solution with alcohol or other solvents of camphor has been used in a liquid state as a solvent of xyloidine. Such use of camphor as a solvent of pyroxyline we disclaim.

Claims.

We claim as our invention—

1. Grinding pyroxyline into a pulp, as and for the purpose described.

2. The use of finely-comminuted camphor-gum mixed with pyroxyline pulp, and rendered a solvent thereof by the application of heat, substantially as described.

3. In conjunction with such use of camphor-gum, the employment of pressure, and continuing the same until the mold and contents are cooled, substantially as described.

JOHN W. HYATT, JR.
ISAIAH S. HYATT.

Witnesses:
WM. H. SLINGERLAND,

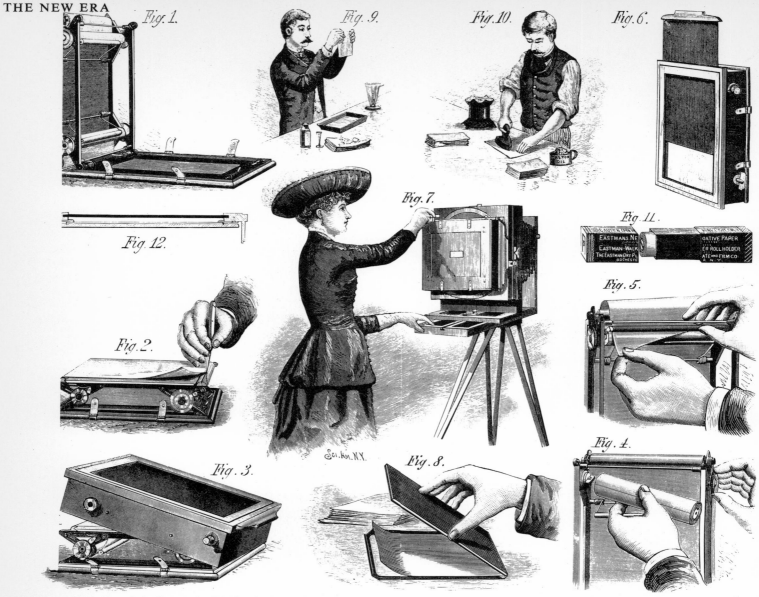

Fig. 1.—Roll Holder Thrown Back. Fig. 2.—Cutting off the Film. Fig. 3.—The Case Partly Raised. Fig. 4.—Putting in the Spool. Fig. 5.—Inserting the Free End. Fig. 6.—The Case—Slide partly drawn. Fig. 7.—Operat-ing the Holder. Fig. 8.—Single Film Carrier. Fig. 9.—Developing. Fig. 10.—Making Films Transparent. Fig. 11.—The Package. Fig. 12.—Cross Section of Slide Aperture.

Once the dry plate process was perfected, Eastman produced a coated film mounted on a roller that could be adapted to any camera. The *Scientific American* hailed the invention and instructed readers in its advantages and use.

The Kodak # 1 was Eastman's method of popularizing the use of film by amateurs after professionals turned it down. The Kodak took a circular picture, had a fixed focus, with a felt stopper for time exposures. Price was $25.

3. THE EASTMAN KODAK

Eastman doubted his own techniques and went to England to teach himself the art all over again by working in a dry plate factory there. All the time, however, he was checking his own research notes and finally realized that the error was not in his formula, but in an impurity in the gelatin he had used. He reopened his factory, and business soared.

By 1884, the photographer had to carry only a bundle of glass plates along with his camera, but Eastman began to seek a substitute for glass. He found that he could coat paper with a solution of collodion and then coat this transparent film with photographic emulsion. His aim had been to use paper only as a temporary backing for a film which he could then strip away when dry. But he could find no collodion film strong enough to support itself without paper backing. However, he

The cartoon panels contain the following captions:

TAKING THE COASTERS.

PORTRAIT OF A FRIEND.

OUR NEIGHBOR'S DOG.

A BOW CAUGHT ON 5TH AVENUE

HE LIGHTED THE FLASH-LIGHT WITH A FUSE

EFFECT OF A FLASH-LIGHT ON THE UNINITIATED.

STUDY OF UNCLE JOHN IN SUNLIGHT.

AT A FRIEND'S REQUEST HE IS TAKEN RIDING HIS NEW BRONCHO.

AND IS WAITING FOR IT TO GO OFF.

TOMMY AND ETHEL IN THEIR DONKEY CART

2ND ATTEMPT AT UNCLE JOHN. THE FILM SLIPPED.

3D ATTEMPT AT UNCLE JOHN HE GETS TIRED.

"DON'T YOU WORK NO DETECTIVE CAMERER ON ME! I'M ON TO THAT RACKET!"

A.B.FROST.

Everyone recognized his own mistakes as a photographer in this cartoon of the 1890's. The small "detective" camera had an instantaneous popularity. In the development of film, Eastman used Reichenbach, a trained chemist.

found that the paper-backed film could be used to take a picture, and the developed film stripped from the paper to make a negative. Here was a new marketable product. Probably not even Eastman guessed at the potential size of that market.

With W. H. Walker, he designed a lightweight mahogany roll-holder to fit any camera. Eastman then offered photographers a continuous strip of paper-backed film which would do away with the necessity for dragging around a load of plates. Commercial photographers and serious amateurs were reluctant to take up the new development: the grain of the paper showed in the picture.

Eastman now faced a choice: either give up the development of film or find an entirely new market. With the same care with which he had kept his private accounts and his firm's books, he analyzed the requirements for creating a new kind of photography.

Until then, the actual taking of pictures was only the smallest part of photography. Eastman concentrated on just that moment in which the shutter was opened and closed.

He designed a simple, fixed-focus camera with which anyone could snap a picture of a friend without having to know the intricacies of focusing, lighting, and composition, or the high mysteries of chemical development. His camera, which he called the Kodak because it meant nothing in any language, loaded with enough Eastman film to take one hundred snapshots, was to sell for twenty-five dollars. When the film was exposed, the camera and a ten-dollar bill was to be sent to Rochester. The photographer would get back prints of his hundred pictures and his camera loaded for another hundred shots. Eastman's slogan, which he himself invented, was, "You press the button, we do the rest."

4. EASTMAN—
THE METICULOUS
PHILANTHROPIST

Eastman's success was sensational, his aim for international distribution was fulfilled, and within a short time, the Kodak was so successful that Gilbert and Sullivan had a girl Kodaker sing, in their opera, *Utopia, Limited:*

> To diagnose our modest pose
> The Kodaks do their best:
> If evidence you would possess
> Of what is maiden bashfulness,
> You only need a button press—
> And we do all the rest.

The success of the Kodak camera did not deceive Eastman. He had opened a new photographic market, but he had still not solved the problem of photographic film. He employed Harry M. Reichenbach, a young chemist, to devote his entire time to the research. Under Eastman's direction, Reichenbach developed one collodion solution after another, seeking the strength and resiliency required to make a film independent of paper backing. Finally, they repeated the discovery of Hyatt,

who had found that camphor mixed with nitrocellulose would produce a tough, smooth, transparent substance called celluloid.

The details of proper proportions and additives were worked out, and patents granted in 1889 and 1892 to the Eastman Dry Plate and Film Company described a film composed of nitrocellulose and 60 per cent solution of camphor, modified by a solution of fusel oil and amyl acetate to control the behavior of the camphor. Eastman foresaw what the celluloid film would do for the Kodak camera, and in 1892 he incorporated the Eastman-Kodak Company in New Jersey with a capitalization of $35,000,000. The company developed a daylight loading film cartridge, and then a daylight developing machine so that film no longer had to be returned to the factory. The Eastman Company's slogan was modified to "You press the button, we do the rest (or you can do it yourself)."

Eastman enlarged his laboratory staff to include chemists, physicists and mathematicians. Under the direction of Mees, this corps of scientists turned out a staggering volume of work ranging from photographic improvements to the most abstract problems of molecular structure and relativity. During the First World War, the Eastman laboratories were one of the handful of companies that made it possible for the chemical

The Kodak was so popular that competitors paid him the compliment of using the name in their advertisements.

George Eastman in 1890 was already a rich man, making a product that was world famous. He was 36 years old.

industry in the United States to develop from a licensed dependent of Germany into the foremost in the world.

Eastman's contribution was more than a mere mechanical contrivance. Photography became the greatest educational medium in the world since the invention of the printing press. Edison's kinetoscope was only a plan on paper until the invention of film.

As a man, George Eastman was a many-sided character, reticent, sensitive, and generous. In the era of violent labor strife, Eastman was the first American to grant dividends on wages to his working staff; he introduced profit sharing. He was a man of contradictions: he had the bookkeeper's meticulous concern about the last penny in the column—but he could also think in terms of millions of dollars. To protect himself from the impulse to lose himself in every petty detail, he deliberately kept aloof from his staff. He set high standards for performance, trusted his people implicitly, acknowledged their right to their individual dignity as human beings, and was ruthless with failures. He must always have been at war with himself. He never married. During his lifetime, he systematically gave away his fortune of a hundred million dollars to universities and clinics. As an anonymous "Mr. Smith," he gave an enormous endowment to M. I. T. His identity was not disclosed until years later.

Urbane and solitary, he was at last able to indulge the impossible boyhood dream of the photographic expedition to distant places by making a number of hunting trips to Africa which were organized, however, with meticulous solicitude for the tiniest detail. Once he was filming a charging rhinoceros. Everyone but the hunter and Eastman fled, and Eastman stood there with the Kodak movie camera at his eye. The hunter fired only when the great animal was fifteen paces off. Eastman was still taking pictures. When asked why he didn't cut and run, the boy adventurer who wanted to go to Santo Domingo merged with the million-dollar-business executive. He said: "You've got to trust your organization."

Eastman took every one of his philanthropies with great seriousness, analyzing each request to see whether it would fit into his over-all plan for advancing American culture and education.

By the time he reached his seventies his health was failing and he could look around and see that he had given away practically all of his wealth as he had planned, an estimated $100,000,000, that things were turning out exactly as he had calculated. There was very little left to come that would surprise him. To his friends, he wrote: "My work is done. Why wait?"

Then he shot himself.

"Anybody can take a picture now" complained the members of the photography cult when Eastman gave the public the Kodak and the "snapshot." The muddy road above is marked with wagon tracks. Autos were still to come.

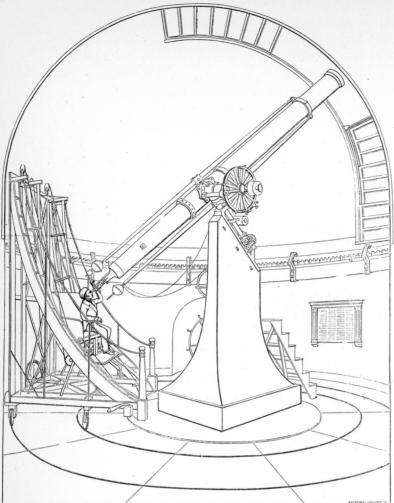

A movable chair facilitated observations by Harvard astronomers. The seat could be moved up and down by a handcrank, as well as around a circular track.

Donati's comet of 1858 seen in the night sky over the Harvard Observatory, situated on the highest point of Cambridge—Bond Street—named after the first director.

The Halsted Observatory at Princeton. Solar studies here by America's famous astronomer, Young, inspired George Hale who later built the 200-inch telescope.

On Tuesday, the 28th of February, 1843, a brilliant body resembling a comet, situated near the Sun, was seen in broad daylight, by numerous observers in various parts of New England. It was discovered on the same day at Waterbury, Salem, and Wolcott, Conn.; New Bedford, Braintree and Haverhill, Mass.; Woodstock and Rutland, Vt.; Plymouth and Concord, N. H.; Gray and Portland, Me., and doubtless also in many other places from which no announcement has been received.

From Drs. G. L. Platt and M. C. Leavenworth, and Messrs. S. W. Hall, Alfred Blackman, and N. J. Buel, of Waterbury, who in common with a large part of the adult population of that town, observed this remarkable phenomenon with great interest, the following particulars have been obtained. The comet was there first noticed as early as half past seven o'clock in the morning, the sky at the time being quite clear. It was seen as late as 3 P. M.; after which time the sky was considerably obscured by clouds and haziness. The appearance was that of a luminous globular body with a short train;—the whole taken together being estimated at two or three degrees in length; its position, east of and below the Sun. A comparison of the various diagrams made by observers at Waterbury, gives the place of the nucleus of the comet at 10 A. M., Feb. 28, in R. A. $345\frac{1}{4}°$, S. decl. $9°$; but as the diagrams are not entirely consistent, this determination cannot be relied upon within about one degree in each element. It is greatly to be regretted that the observations were not more precise, but it is to be hoped that accurate determinations were made by navigators in various parts of the world, by some of whom the comet was undoubtedly detected on that day.

Great public interest in astronomy was roused by the appearance of the 1842 comet. Bostonians contributed a fund used to buy the first Harvard telescope.

Obtaining sidereal time at the Astronomical Observatory at Washington. Many American astronomers were trained here.

The Chronometer Room of the Astronomical Observatory kept the country's time by means of Morse's telegraph.

ASTRONOMY

1. HARVARD OBSERVATORY

In addition to the more frivolous exhibits at the Centennial, there was Exhibit No. 282 by O. G. Mason of New York: "Photographs of the Moon." Within the thirty-six years that had passed since Draper's first picture, scientific astronomical photography had taken long strides, and Draper's work was recognized in 1876 by the American Academy of Science, which presented its highest award, the Rumford Medal, to him for "Researches on radiant energy."

The president of the Academy, the Honorable Charles Francis Adams, enumerated Draper's achievements. He had established experimentally that all solid substances become incandescent at the same temperature—about 977° F.; he was the first to show that the spectrum of an incandescent solid was continuous; he was the first to show that the radiation from a heated body increases with its temperature, and that the major portion of that radiation is invisible (infra-red and ultra-violet); he was the first to apply the daguerreotype process to taking portraits; and he was one of the earliest researchers in absorption spectra, particularly on the effect of growing plants.

In 1876 there was one achievement of Draper's that didn't seem important enough to be specifically mentioned; yet it was to be shown within a few years to have pointed the way to one of the most revealing bodies of research in the century. After having taken a photograph of the moon, Draper, a few years later, was the first man to photograph the solar spectrum.

Americans in the first half of the nineteenth century were deeply interested in the science of astronomy. In 1839, President Quincy of Harvard University induced William Cranch Bond, a self-instructed astronomer and the proprietor of a successful chronometer manufacturing business, to take over the duties of Astronomical Observer to Harvard University, without salary. Bond was the first of a line of men who were to make the Harvard Observatory an institution of international fame. In the 1840's Bond raised enough money from the citizens of Boston to buy a fifteen-inch refracting telescope and a building in which to house it.

The first picture of a star in close proximity to the moon. Whipple and Black, on June 8, 1857, made this collodion plate which proved for the first time that the intrinsic brightness of a star was far greater than that of the moon. Until this picture was taken, it was thought that the "diffused light in the vicinity of the moon would overpower the actinic effect of a star."

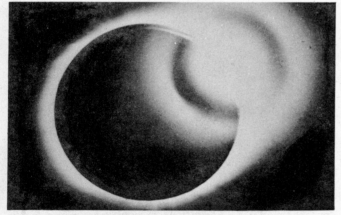

The first photograph of the "diamond ring" effect—a flare of light at the moment following total eclipse of the sun.

The solar eclipse expedition of Harvard at Shelbyville, Ky., in 1869, where the "diamond ring" photograph was taken.

2. THE COSMIC DAGUERREOTYPE

Within a few years after the building was opened, a professional Boston daguerreotypist named Whipple took a photograph of the moon that was much superior to the Draper picture. That night in December, 1849, Bond wrote in his notebook: "On the evening of the 18th, just as we were commencing observations on Mars, Messrs. Whipple and Jones came to take a daguerreotype of the moon. Very much against our inclinations, we unscrewed the micrometer . . ." No mention was made of satisfaction or dissatisfaction with the picture. Six months later, Whipple and Jones returned and successfully took a picture of a star, hitherto considered impossible because of the weak light source.

On March 2, 1851, the *Harvard Journal* reveals, "Succeeded in daguerreotyping Jupiter about 11 P.M. —took six plates more than 24 hours old—" In 1852, Whipple took a great many more pictures of the moon, stars, and various clusters. About that time it became apparent that the detail of the pictures could be improved if the telescope were focused for direct exposure to a plate.

Rutherford began stellar photography in New York at Columbia in 1864, and in May of 1872, William Draper's son, Henry, made the first successful photograph of the spectrum of a star. He found four of the Fraunhofer lines which had hitherto been seen only in the sun.

3. ASTROPHYSICS

The transition from positional astronomy to astrophysics was made in the United States when Edward Charles Pickering of Beacon Hill became the director of the Harvard Observatory in 1877. Pickering's appointment had caused considerable resentment among astronomers because his training was that of a physicist. He had taught physics at M. I. T. and had been the first man to create a laboratory where students could learn physics by means of experiments. When Pickering came to astronomy, he brought with him all the techniques and attitudes of the laboratory physicist.

Pickering's first approach was to find a precise, quantitative standard of measure for the brightness or luminosity of stars. The first man ever to make a quantitative measure of light had been Count Rumford—his instrument he had called a photometer. Pickering's photometer was an instrument made by the famous telescope maker at Cambridge, Alvan Clark, which superimposed the image of the star being investigated upon the image of the pole star.

Just about that time, Huggins in England introduced the newly developed dry gelatin plates into celestial photography. This suggested to Pickering the possibility of using the camera as a really quantitative piece of apparatus in astronomy. The working life of an astronomer was neither simple nor comfortable. When he examined the sky at night, he was exposed for hours in the open air, summer and winter. When Pickering introduced astrophotography on a large scale, he made it possible for an astronomer to see far more of the night sky than he had ever seen before. Day after day, examination of exposed plates revealed things never noticed before. The great application of astrophotography by Pickering was to the examination of spectra. He placed a large prism over the objective of the great telescope, transforming the instrument into an enormous spectroscope. Since each star was itself a point source, a single photographic plate with one exposure would show the spectrum of every star in the telescopic field. Pickering and his assistants, in a very short time, collected the spectra of thousands of stars.

Shortly before this, Angelo Secchi of the Observatory of the Collegio Romano had examined some star spectra and had divided all stars roughly into four classes. Pickering wanted to reduce this classification to precise quantitative terms and, with his assistants, he evolved the category of grading stars which is still in use.

For purposes of convenience, Pickering divided all stars into fourteen classes, the first numbered "A" and the last numbered "N." As the basis of classification he selected the intensity of the hydrogen spectral lines in the star. Those stars with the most intense hydrogen

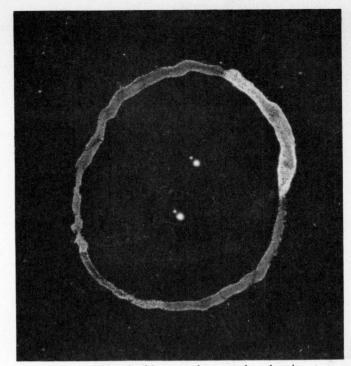

One of the earliest double star photographs, showing two successive exposures of Alcar-Mizar. This was taken by the wet plate process, May 8, 1857, with Harvard's 15-inch refractor. The picture is an enlargement of the original, and the roughly drawn loop was a fine pen line drawing by the astrophotographer around the two images of the double star.

Solar studies in the 1870's began to disprove the idea of the sun as a habitable sphere surrounded by a glowing gas.

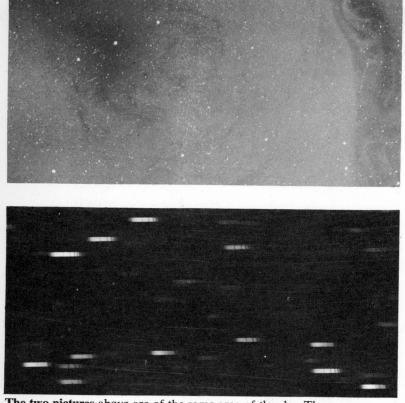

The two pictures above are of the same area of the sky. The upper one is the direct photograph. The lower one is the same field taken with a prism in the front of the telescope.

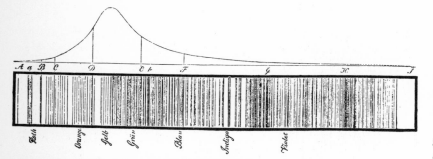

Star spectra reveal the composition of a star. In 1814, Fraunhofer, a Bavarian, analyzed the spectra of the sun, and found it striated with black lines that were always in the same position. Forty years later, the Fraunhofer lines were shown to be due to the presence in the sun's outer atmosphere of almost all the elements known on earth. Pickering of Harvard was one of the first to bring this spectroscopic technique to the study of stars.

Edward Charles Pickering, of the Harvard Observatory. He had been trained as a physicist at M.I.T. With Simon Newcomb and Charles Young, he became one of America's greatest astronomers.

lines were in class A; those with the least were put into class N. As the work progressed, several changes were found to be necessary. Some classes—C, D, and H—had to be discarded because they were based on photographs that were out of focus and were, in fact, duplications of other classes. A new class of star, tentatively called "O" because it looked as if the spectra were faintly banded, had to be placed at the beginning of the whole sequence. The final formulation gave the classes in this order: O, B, A, F, G, K, and M, and astronomy teachers were giving their students the mnemonic aid, "Oh, Be A Fine Girl, Kiss Me Right Now."

What was particularly important about this formulation was that these classifications turned out to be direct measures of the temperatures of the star—class O being white-blue stars, ranging through yellow stars, down through the reds in M. These temperatures in turn gave valuable information for all subsequent theories for the constitution of stars.

Maria Mitchell of Vassar was the first woman professor of astronomy, but under Pickering's directorship, many more women began to work in this field. In his classification work, two women were brilliant assistants; and since then, astronomy has been one of the few exact sciences in which American women are numerous. It all started with Pickering's violent temper. The spectra classification was extremely tedious, and Pickering's male assistant was falling into carelessness out of boredom. Pickering exploded with anger one day and said, "Damn it, my cook can do a better job than that!" He brought her in, and Wilhelmina Fleming did superbly for the next thirty years. Another woman, Annie Jump Cannon, classified over 200,000 stars.

Pickering's selection of hydrogen concentration was a remarkable insight because the prevalent theory of star constitution was radically different from what it became later. It was assumed, for example, that the sun was either a solid or a fluid body, not incandescent, surrounded by a vast incandescent atmosphere.

Pickering's astrophysics was to dispel the notion expressed by the famous French physicist, Arago, who had said, "If this question were simply proposed to me, 'Is the sun inhabited?' I should reply that I know nothing about the matter. But if anyone asks of me if the sun *can* be inhabited by beings organized in a matter analogous to those which people our globe, I hesitate not to reply in the affirmative."

The use of photography in positional astronomy in the last quarter of the nineteenth century resulted in the discovery of thousands of new nebulae.

Just as the century had seen steam and then electricity give man tools and power he had never dreamed of possessing before, so the camera had given the cosmos an extension it had never, to man's knowledge, possessed before.

FIRST MODERN PHYSICIST

"I intend to devote myself to science," wrote Henry Rowland to his sister with the seriousness of a young man of twenty, in 1868. "If she gives me wealth, I will receive it as coming from a friend, but if not, I shall not murmur." One of America's finest experimental physicists, Rowland was to become the guiding spirit of the new Johns Hopkins Graduate School. Peppery and vivacious, he took particular pleasure in four of his many publications. The first was a straight-faced hoax on the editors of the *Scientific American* when he was twelve years old. The second was the discovery of the laws of the magnetic circuit—the magnetic analogue of Ohm's law for electricity, unappreciated by all his contemporaries but Clerk Maxwell. The third was his elegant proof that electric currents were simply electrically charged bodies in motion—an experiment that proved what had been only an hypothesis until then. The fourth was his invention of a machine that would rule twenty thousand straight lines to an inch on glass with absolute precision. These "gratings" proved to be far more sensitive for spectroscopic studies than the prism. Rowland's gratings became world famous. Four decades of spectroscopic analysis were to culminate in one of the great intellectual revolutions of human history—the formulation of the quantum theory in the early years of the twentieth century. Henry Rowland marks the beginning of the long line of modern experimental physicists of America.

THE LICK OBSERVATORY

The Lick Observatory's great refracting telescope on Mt. Hamilton, California, was built by Alvan Clark and Sons in 1888. The supporting column and base were of iron, and weighed 25 tons. This rested on a masonry foundation which formed the tomb of the wealthy miner, James Lick, the donor. The telescope tube was 52 feet long, 4 feet in diameter in the middle. The object glass was 36 inches in diameter. The steel dome was 75 feet in diameter, and the moving parts weighed 100 tons. The conditions imposed by the trustees said: "It must be superior to and more powerful than any telescope made." A few years later, it was surpassed by the Yerkes telescope, donated by the Chicago traction magnate Charles Yerkes, which had an object glass that was 40 inches in diameter. Joseph Henry was one of the men who prevailed on Lick to make the bequest that gave great impetus to American astronomy.

Alvan Clark, a miniaturist, began his telescope-making career by building a small one for his sons. His interest deepened, and soon his lenses equaled Europe's best.

277

The "string" telephone was a toy by which sound was transmitted through the mechanical vibration of a string and a diaphragm.

VISIBLE SPEECH

AS A MEANS OF

Communicating Articulation to Deaf-Mutes.

By A. GRAHAM BELL,

Member of the Philological Society, London, Eng.

From the American Annals of the Deaf and Dumb, January, 1872.

THE system of "Visible Speech" was invented by my father, Mr. A. Melville Bell, professor of vocal physiology; and it constitutes a new species of phonetic writing, based, not upon sounds, but upon the actions of the vocal organs in producing them.

The plan originated fully a quarter of a century ago; and the germ of the invention was published in the first edition of "The Principles of Speech," (1849.)

The idea conceived was that of representing the sounds of all languages by means of one alphabet, the characters of which should reveal to the eye the organic formation of the sounds. Although my father's professional duties as a corrector of the defects of utterance directly favored the study of the organic formation of sounds, still, the difficulties in the way of carrying out the idea were so great that it was not until 1864 that the plan took definite shape. Then, indeed, a scheme of letters was produced which claimed to be so perfect as to represent *any sound the human mouth could utter.*

Linguists and men of science were invited to test the truth of this assertion. The invitation was accepted;

Bell, a philologist, was seeking a scientific method of teaching deaf mutes to speak.

ALEXANDER GRAHAM BELL

1. FAMILY OF PHILOLOGISTS

Every Sunday the gates of the Centennial were closed in deference to the Philadelphia Sabbath, but on the Sunday of the twenty-fifth of June, in the worst heat wave of 1876, the judging committee in top hats and frock coats sweated through its weary round, appraising the exhibits, led by the indestructible Dom Pedro. At noon, the judges were relieved to hear that they were examining the last display for the day. A tall, pale young man, responsible for a Visible Speech exhibit down the way, looked at them wistfully. Dom Pedro glanced at him and remembered that they had met in Boston a few weeks before on the Emperor's whirlwind survey of American schools.

"Mr. Bell!" he said, holding out his hand. "And how are your pupils?"

Mr. Bell said that they were all very well, but that he was disappointed because he had come all the way from Boston that very morning to have his work judged, only to be disappointed.

"Then we'll see it tomorrow," said the Emperor.

"I won't be here. I've got to get back to my classes in Boston."

"Then let's see what you have right now," said the Emperor, taking Bell's arm; and the rest of the committee, sighing, followed along.

Bell claimed to have a telegraph which could transmit human speech. On the table before the committee, he said, was the receiver. On the other side of the building was the transmitter. He called his device a telephone. If the committee would only listen, he would go to the transmitting booth and they would hear him over the wires. In a few minutes, the committee heard a disembodied voice from the horn of the small instrument, delivering: "To be or not to be . . ." in the best elocutionary manner. The judges, particularly Sir William Thomson, the Atlantic cable engineer, were delighted. Sir William himself walked over to the transmitting booth and gave his own recitation: "Aye, there's the rub." Sir William's voice was clearly recognizable. The audience cheered. The heat was forgotten as each committeeman took his turn singing and speaking to the others across the deserted fair grounds.

The year before, when Bell was twenty-eight, the idea of the telephone had been only a vague plan in his mind. His main mechanical interest was a multiple telegraph—a means by which several telegraphic messages could be sent simultaneously over a single wire. In the wet spring of 1875, he went to Washington to see about a patent, even though the multiple telegraph was not working out too well. Tormented by indecision, he decided to ask for an expert opinion from the foremost scientist in the country, elderly Joseph Henry of the Smithsonian. Bell strode up and down Henry's office, dripping rain all over the rug as he explained what he had done and what he was hoping to do. Henry listened politely until Bell mentioned a seemingly unimportant observation, then he came alive at once to the implication. He got out of his chair saying, "Well, where's your apparatus? Let's see it!" The next morning Henry examined Bell's array of batteries and coils and wire for some time. Then he said: "Under no circumstances should you think of giving up." Bell was so moved by this encouragement that for the rest of his life, with his fabulous income from the telephone, he was to play Henry to other men's Bell, saying that he was simply paying an old debt.

Alexander Graham Bell was born on March 3, 1847, in Edinburgh, the second of three sons, to Alexander Melville Bell, one of the foremost proponents of the nineteenth-century art of elocution. He introduced to phonetics a system called Visible Speech, in which written symbols represented certain basic sounds, so any foreign language—Chinese or Choctaw—written in phonetic symbols, could be spoken by someone familiar with the system. In *Pygmalion*, George Bernard Shaw used Melville Bell's system to transform Eliza Doolittle from a "guttersnipe" into a lady.

Aleck Bell grew up in Edinburgh surrounded by music and a love for the sound of the human voice. The Bells were never silent. At fourteen, Aleck was sent to London for a year, to live with his fastidious grandfather, the first Alexander Bell, the very founder of the art of elocution, and the author of *Elegant Extracts,* a book of high-minded readings to be found on the parlor table of any nineteenth-century family with the least pretension to culture. The grandfather was appalled by what he considered a shocking lack of education. Grandfather Bell drove the boy through his own library from book to book and carried him off to his speech-teaching classes. Night after night the old gentleman stood before the pale boy until satisfied with the boy's rendition of "To be or not to be . . ."

At the end of the year Aleck Bell returned to Edinburgh determined to carry on his grandfather's work; and in order to become self supporting as soon as possible, he applied at sixteen for a position as a pupil-teacher of music and elocution at a school in Elgin. By the next year he was the resident master in the Weston House Academy.

During the next ten years Alexander Graham Bell did intensive research in acoustics and the physics of speech. Aleck Bell's two brothers died and Bell became assistant to his father, then professor of elocution at the University of London. Alexander Graham Bell worked with such intensity that by the spring of 1870 he was on the verge of a breakdown. His father interrupted his own career to take his son to Canada where he would regain his strength.

That autumn Melville Bell was offered a position in Boston which he could not accept because of a previous commitment to teach in Canada. He suggested that his son take his place. In the autumn of 1871, Aleck Bell joined the staff of the Boston School for the Deaf.

This was the Boston of Mr. Longfellow, Mr. Emerson, and Mrs. Julia Ward Howe; and the elegant young gentleman from London's intellectual circles was made to feel very much at home. In appearance he was the personification of the romantic fictional hero of the day—tall, slender, very pale, with dark expressive eyes, subject to infernos of feeling, both of gaiety and despair.

Besides teaching at the school, there were private lessons "for the correction of stammering and other defects of utterance and for practical instruction in Visible Speech, conducted by Alexander Graham Bell, member of the Philological Society of London."

With all this, he still found time to work on a problem that promised a ready fortune from Western Union to the inventor who could send several messages simultaneously over the same wire. In that way, telegraph traffic could be increased without putting up additional lines. Bell's approach came from his knowledge of acoustics.

Bell knew that if a musical note were sounded near several different tuning forks, only the fork tuned to that particular note would start vibrating. He reasoned that if he were to send over a wire an electric current vibrating with the frequency of a musical note, an electromagnetic tuning fork tuned to that note would respond. If he were to send several such electrical notes over the same wire at the same time, and there were several different electromagnetic tuning forks connected to the receiving end, the currents would sort themselves out, each fork vibrating with its own frequency. Bell's plan for a musical telegraph could send as many messages simultaneously as there were notes in the musical scale.

Alexander Graham Bell came to America in his early twenties to regain his health. Within ten years, he gained a fortune.

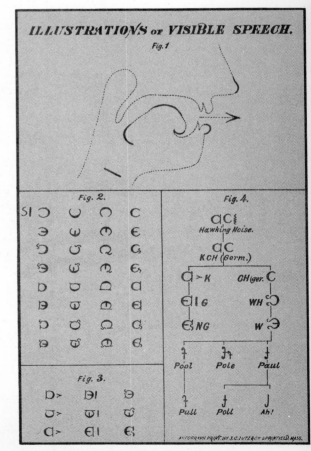

Bell's father invented this chart to teach deaf mutes the use of lips, tongue, and larynx.

machine, the muscles of our arms are made to *vibrate* at a rate corresponding to the making and breaking of the primary circuit.

Now the thought struck me that if we could make the direct and reversed induced impulses succeed one another as regularly as the crests and depressions of waves, then an electrode applied to the ear so as to induce a vibration in the membrane tymp. *should create the sensation of sound without the aid of any intermediate apparatus.*

I have had an instrument made and the experiment seems a success.

A number of permanent magnets were arranged upon a cylinder, which was revolved in front of electro-magnets.
[*See illustration.*]

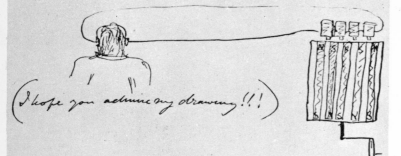

(I hope you admire my drawing!!!)

On filling my ears with water and applying the wires (protected of course) as in the diagram, a soft musical note was heard. The sound stopped the moment the electrical circuit was broken. The wires employed were very short, so that the noise of the rotating cylinder (conducted mechanically along the wire) almost drowned the musical note. The latter thus appeared like an *over-tone.*

Two ladies who were present submitted to the experiment and heard the note as clearly as I did. A gentleman, however (who could not distinguish over-tones in music), heard nothing more than the *noise.*

I want your co-operation. Can we arrange for a meeting on Saturday morning at your rooms? I am anxious to see the results of your experiments.

Yours sincerely,

A. GRAHAM BELL.

DR. C. J. BLAKE,
Hotel Berkeley.

Bell drew cartoons in letters to his parents to illustrate his work. They were made part of the patent trial record.

SALEM, MASS., May 24, 1875.

DEAR PAPA AND MAMA:

I am so immersed in telegraphy and science that I find it impossible to write freely about anything else, but I feel that at the present time you can scarcely be inclined to listen to anything I have to say on such subjects.

Since I gave up professional work and devoted myself exclusively to telegraphy, I have been steadily gaining health and strength, and am now in a fit state to encounter Mr. Gray or anyone else. The patents that have been granted to me without opposition are, —

1st. The principle of converting a vibratory motion into a permanent make or break of a local circuit.

2nd. The special form of "vibratory circuit breaker" put in illustration.

3rd. The autograph telegraph.

The autograph arrangement is rapidly approaching completion. Already I can copy handwriting *quite legibly,* though not yet neatly. The rate of transmission by means of my instrument will be exactly ten times more rapid than "Bakewell's Autograph Telegraph," in which the rate is 300 letters per minute. When 3000 letters per minute can be sent, my telegraph will be the most *rapid* as well as the ...

56   TRANSMISSION OF SIGNALS WITHOUT A BATTERY.

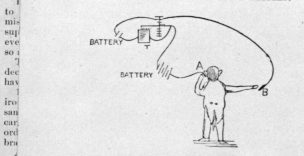

BATTERY

BATTERY

A
B

Two thin strips of brass (A and B) are connected with the wires coming from my Transmitting Instrument, T, and from the Battery. On holding A to my ear I hear nothing, but the moment that I touch B with my finger a musical note is heard to proceed from A!!

Truly, the more I study electricity and magnetism the more I feel the truth of Hamlet's saying, "There are more things," etc.

I fear that this telegraphic business may force me to remain the greater portion of the summer here, but I cannot tell yet, so many details have to be worked out. My inexperience in such matters is a great drawback. However, Morse conquered his electrical difficulties although he was only a painter, and I don't intend to give in either till all is completed.

With dear love,

Yr affectionate son,

ALECK.

2. BELL, THE INVENTOR

In a short time Bell was able to interest a number of wealthy Bostonians in his invention, men whom he met through his work with the deaf. Gardiner Greene Hubbard, a successful lawyer, was one of these. His daughter Mabel had lost her hearing as a result of scarlet fever. She and Bell fell in love; but she was never, as legend has it, Bell's pupil.

Besides his work on the musical telegraph, Bell was seeking a way to show deaf persons how vocal sounds should be made. He experimented with a device in which a membrane, vibrating with sound, made a stylus trace the sound waves on a rotating drum. To widen his knowledge of vibrating membranes, Bell spent a year experimenting with the human ear at the Massachusetts Eye and Ear Infirmary and gradually conceived the idea of the telephone in the conclusion "that it would be possible to transmit sounds of any sort if we could only occasion a *variation in the intensity of an electric current exactly like that occurring in the density of the air* while a given sound is made."

Nothing in the existing science of electricity could serve him as a precedent. Moses G. Farmer, a successful electrical inventor of the period, went without sleep for a week in anger with himself when he read of Bell's telephone. He said, "If Bell had known more about electricity, he never would have invented the telephone!" He missed the point. There was far more to the telephone's conception than electricity; only an expert in acoustics could have worked out the problem.

Bell's first assistant, and the man who was to build all of his apparatus in those early years, was a young Bostonian named Thomas A. Watson, who said of Bell: "One day when I was hard at work . . . a tall, slender, quick-motioned man with a pale face, black side whiskers, and high sloping forehead came rushing over to my workbench . . . bringing to me a piece of mechanism which . . . had not been made as he directed.

"He was the first educated man I had ever known intimately, and many of his ways delighted me."

In 1875 Bell's twenty-four-hour schedule included teaching deaf children, lecturing to teachers on his father's system of Visible Speech, perfecting his harmonic telegraph, and running out to Cambridge to visit Mabel Hubbard, whose father disapproved of Bell's suit as much as he approved of his ideas. Of all his projects, the one that seemed least likely for immediate success was the telephone—yet it was to be the first to come to fruition.

Through an accident on a warm June afternoon in 1875, exactly one year before the successful demonstration at the Centennial, Bell discovered the means to make his telephone. He and Watson had been working on the harmonic telegraph.

3. THE TELEPHONE

The receiver and the transmitter were in two different rooms. Both consisted of a number of springlike metal strips that were clamped only at one end. The strips were of different lengths, so that each one would vibrate at a different musical note. Watson, at the transmitter, was having trouble with one metal reed whose free end had become stuck. As he worked on it, he kept touching the other reeds, which set up a jangling noise. Although the line was supposed to be dead, Bell's very acute hearing picked up the faint jangling sound at the receiver. He immediately guessed what was happening and ran into Watson's room.

"What are you doing?" he shouted. "Don't change anything!"

Watson started to explain his trouble, but Bell excitedly pointed out that they had found exactly what they had been working for all along. The stuck reed was working like a primitive diaphragm. The conventional method of operation had been for the vibrating free end of the reed to make and break an electrical contact; instead, its slight movement was now *inducing* its own vibrations in the electromagnet directly behind it.

This was the difference between the telephone and every other telegraphic device that had preceded it. Telegraphy transmitted sharply defined *pulses* of current, each pulse having the same intensity, even though the current pulse for a *dash* was longer than for a *dot*. A telephone required a *continuous current* whose intensity could *vary* exactly as the sound waves in the air.

An electrician could have known every facet of circuit behavior, but only an acoustician would have been aware of the exact nature of the continuously varying current required for telephony.

That night Bell gave Watson directions for the first true electric speaking telephone: a tiny drumhead whose center was to be adapted to one of the springs. To concentrate the sound, a small flaring horn was mounted over the drumhead. Within a very short time, Watson completed Bell's apparatus, and it worked, although very feebly.

This was essentially the form of the telephone for which Bell made his patent application. It was granted March 7, 1876, only a few months before the Centennial.

In order to devote himself to the telephone, Bell had to defy his prospective father-in-law, who saw the telephone only as a toy. To Mr. Hubbard, the harmonic telegraph promised an immediate return.

To get money, Bell, who was as stubborn as he was impetuous, refused to approach either his father or his prospective father-in-law and instead went to a Cana-

Bell's first telephone—1876

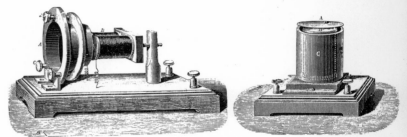

Bell's first telephone, 1876—a schematic diagram

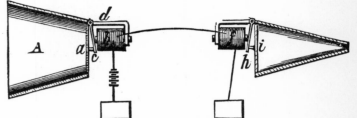

Bell's second telephone: transmitter and receiver

Commercial form of Bell's telephone

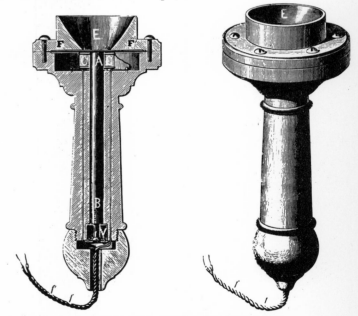

THE EVOLUTION OF THE TELEPHONE

The basic principle of the Bell telephone was the conversion of continuously varying sound waves into continuously varying electric currents. Until Bell, experimenters had used circuits in which the current was made and broken, losing the smooth variation required for reproduction of speech. The receiver reconverted the electrical variations into sound. In the commercial form of Bell's instrument, the same diaphragm served for transmission and reception. This was the standard shape of the earpiece until the French telephone.

Bell spoke and sang to his assistant Watson from Salem, March 15, 1877, to demonstrate how the new telephone could transmit and receive the human voice. Reporters made notes of everything he said and did and checked later.

Reporters were also with Watson in Boston. When their notes were compared with those taken in Salem, people could see that there had been no deception.

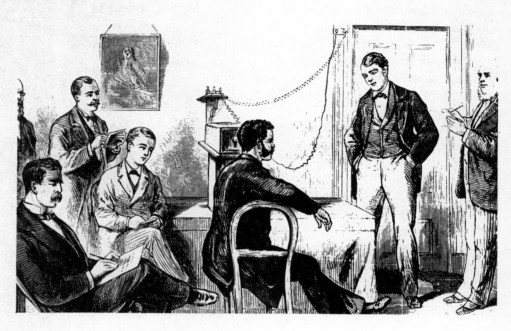

The telephone was a sensation in Europe because of clever publicity. It was a feature of many great industrial fairs.

3. THE TELEPHONE (continued)

dian named George Brown, offering him the English rights to the telephone in return for twenty-five dollars a month for six months. Because of this commitment, Bell had to agree to postpone applying for an American patent until after Brown had made an English application. Brown thought so little of the telephone that he let the agreement lapse without telling Bell. Bell continued to postpone his American application, driving his prospective father-in-law frantic, because even though Hubbard didn't think much of the telephone himself, it *was* an invention and ought to be protected.

Bell's application was ready for submission and finally, beside himself, Mr. Hubbard himself entered the application for Bell. Just two hours later, Elisha Gray, another electrical inventor, filed a caveat with the Patent Office, stating that he *intended* to invent a telephone based on certain stated principles, which turned out to be somewhat similar to Bell's. The generally accepted statement that Bell and Gray both invented the telephone at the same time is based on a misunderstanding of the nature of a caveat. Gray, as an American citizen, could file a caveat with the United States Patent Office; Bell, still a British subject, did not have that right. Bell applied for a patent on an invention that was already working; Gray served notice that he intended to make such an invention.

Three months after Bell's patent was granted, the Committee of Awards congratulated him at the Centennial. One of the members of that committee was Elisha Gray, who was as delighted with the invention as the other judges. Neither on that occasion nor for some time to come was he to claim that he had invented a telephone prior to Bell. The conflicting statements that came later were made during patent litigations which were notoriously acrimonious.

Bell's patent was the most valuable patent ever issued by the government. For decades thereafter it was the subject of attacks by every major electrical and telegraph company in the United States.

At one point during President Cleveland's administration, a conspiracy which included the Attorney-General of the United States, several senators, ex-senators, and an ex-governor of the State of Tennessee, deliberately tried to use the power of the United States government to break the Bell patent on behalf of a private corporation. In the corporation, which existed only on paper, the Attorney-General of the United States secretly held stock amounting to a million and a half dollars. In terms of the business ethics of the day, this attempted piracy was unusual in only one way—it failed.

In 1877, Bell improved his telephone. The diaphragm was a thin disc of iron, mounted in front of a pole-piece of an electromagnet. As sound waves made the diaphragm vibrate, the movements of the iron induced a continually varying current in the magnet which was then sent along a wire to the receiver. In the Bell telephone, the receiver and the transmitter were identical. Shortly thereafter Watson came across a permanent magnet that was superior to the electromagnets. By the time the Bell telephone came into commercial use and for decades thereafter the shape of the earpiece was determined by the length of the cluster of permanent magnets within the hard rubber tubular envelope.

With all the diverse projects in which the young man was involved, there was one that was even closer to his heart than the telephone—the outrageous idea of flight by a heavier-than-air machine. "I fancy," said Watson, "that if Bell had been in easy financial circumstances, he would have dropped everything and gone into flying machines at that time."

Telephones were at first sold to individuals for their own private circuits, as shown in this ad.

Telephoning operas, concerts, and other musical events were also suggested as proper uses.

The switchboard, central station, and the rented telephone service were all part of Bell's plan.

4. "HELLO, CENTRAL"

Few revolutionary inventions have been adopted by the public as rapidly as the telephone. Very adroit promotion put the telephone into commercial use within five years from the time Bell's patent was granted.

The crowds at the Centennial who had seen the telephone were completely unimpressed, but scientists saw the invention in its proper aspect. On January 13, 1877, Joseph Henry, the Secretary of the Smithsonian Institution, chaired a meeting of the Philosophical Society in Washington at which Bell demonstrated his telephone. He read a paper in which he described how he had been given the use of some long-line telegraph wires, over which he had carried on a telephonic conversation from Boston to Portland, Maine. The telephone was subject to storms of noise owing to induction from nearby wires, and Bell had to shout at the top of his voice, "Ahoy, ahoy, Watson, are you there?"

Up to this point, Bell's expenses had been paid by both Gardiner Hubbard and Thomas Sanders, whose deaf son had been Bell's private pupil. Bell now offered his patent to Western Union for one hundred thousand dollars so that he could pay off his debts and get married. Western Union was not interested.

Bell made demonstrations of his invention in Salem, Boston, and New York; and the newspapers began to treat him with respect. These demonstrations were in the popular tradition of lectures on "Useful and Enlightening Subjects Combining Entertainment and Education for All." Bell, of course, was an experienced lecturer, and most of the early transmission consisted of performances on musical instruments, and the always popular part-singing. Audiences seemed far more impressed by the ability of the telephone to combine the voices of the members of a quartet, each singing into his own transmitter, than by the fact that there was transmission of a human voice at all.

One year after the Centennial, on July 11, 1877, Bell and Mabel Hubbard were married at her home on Brattle Street, and the young couple sailed for England. Colonel Reynolds of Providence, Rhode Island, had arranged to promote the English rights; American rights were left in the hands of Hubbard and Sanders. In England, Bell's triumphal tour was made easier by the fact that Colonel Reynolds had secretly hired a dashing lady journalist named Miss Kate Field, who invited her friends of the press to a delightful *Matinée Téléphonique* and arranged a demonstration before the Queen and the Royal Family at which all the royal visitors sang, recited and asked each other if they were there.

The promotion was going so well that Western Union decided to take another look at the telephone. Orton, Western Union's president, made the rational decision that if a hearing teacher could invent the electric telephone, a couple of expert electricians like Thomas Edison, Elisha Gray, and others could invent an even better one. Early in 1879, Western Union formed the American Speaking Telephone Company and went into business, ignoring the Bell Associates. The Bell Associates got some money from Sanders' relatives, formed the New England Telephone Company and, through Gardiner Hubbard, went truculently to court to fight back. Toward the end of 1879, Western Union came to terms with Bell's backers and formed a joint company. Western Union was amply satisfied with twenty per cent, for which they would supply wires, circuits, and equipment. The Bell Associates supplied the Bell patent. In December of 1879, stock in the Bell Company went to $995 a share, and from that moment on Alexander Graham Bell was an extremely rich young man.

Bell knew exactly what he had invented, its importance, and its future. He wrote to his backers in March, 1878, outlining with brilliant foresight the future course of commercial telephony. In this letter he described the method and means of building a telephone network in a large city, and the use of a central switchboard. From a promotional point of view, he stressed the desirability of placing telephones, free of charge, in the most important shops in each town, both as a convenience to subscribers and as a pressure on other businesses to subscribe.

From this one letter came most of the phraseology connected with the telephone, including the phrase which died only with the appearance of the dial phone: "Hello, Central."

Once Bell had pointed the way, innumerable inventors added improvements. By 1900 there were more than three thousand patents related to the telephone. In the United States alone, only twenty-four years after the Centennial Exhibition, there were 1,580,101 telephones, doing a gross business of $5,760,106.45. Dividends from that sum amounted to $3,882,945.

In 1888 Bell became an American citizen. From France he received the coveted Volta prize of fifty thousand francs, which had been founded by Napoleon and awarded only once before. He received the Legion of Honor; and for his subsequent work on acoustical physiology he was awarded an honorary medical degree from Heidelberg. He used the money from the Volta prize to found the Volta Institution at Washington for commercial research on the telephone, phonograph, and other means of electric communication. He himself plunged into a hundred different projects which included sheep breeding, aviation, and hydrodynamics. He was not interested in any financial rewards for himself, but found his greatest pleasure in helping men like A. A. Michelson, Langley and Glenn Curtiss, just as Joseph Henry had once helped him.

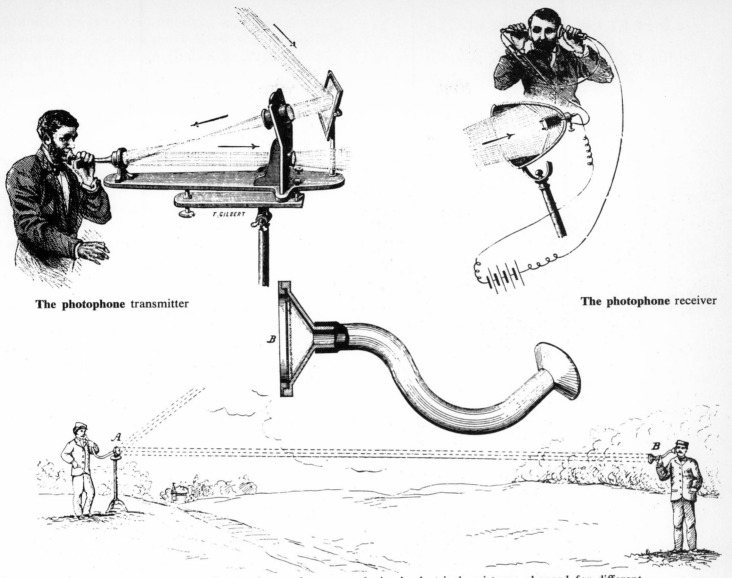

The photophone transmitter

The photophone receiver

Bell's photophone made sound waves vibrate a beam of reflected sunlight. The receiver changed the varying light intensity back into sound. Bell found that selenium's electrical resistance changed for different light intensities, and equipped his radiophone receiver with the first true "photoelectric" cells.

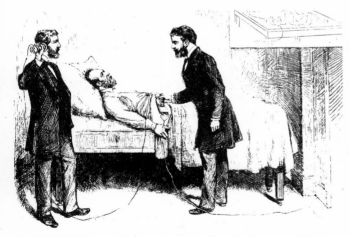

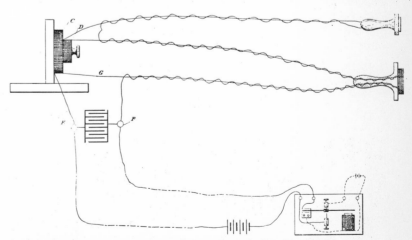

When President Garfield lay dying, shot by an assassin's bullet, Bell invented a special electrical circuit which would make a click in a telephone when a probe was brought near the imbedded bullet which had to be removed. The nation waited breathlessly while he made his experiments in vain.

The circuit failed to detect Garfield's death bullet because Bell's instructions were not followed. The balanced circuit responded in the presence of any metal; and the steel bed spring, which should not have been present, interfered with the tests. Bell's circuit remained in use until the X-ray.

THE WIZARD OF MENLO PARK: 1

Edison sold fruit, papers, and candy as a boy to make money and ride free to Detroit where he could read in the library. A French illustrator has dealt imaginatively with the cars.

"Black Friday," the gold panic of 1869, which Edison watched from the Western Union booth top, gave him the idea that the telegraphed news of gold was worth more than gold itself.

Guests at Edison's second marriage gaped at the inventor's marvels while his experiments made him forget the ceremony. His first wife had been his laboratory assistant.

"The electromagnetic shunt . . . invented by Mr. Edison . . . to produce a momentary reversal of live current at the instant when the battery is thrown off . . . deserves award as a very important step in land telegraphy."

The Mr. Edison who received this Centennial award was twenty-nine years old, a man of medium height, with gray eyes in a head that was abnormally large. His fair hair was unruly, his bearing aggressive, and his manner quick and tough. Even then he was known to his assistants as the Old Man.

His place of business was in a small town called Menlo Park in New Jersey. He had been married five years to a young girl named Mary Stillwell; and in addition to many telegraph patents, he had to his credit a variety of other inventions. He had been in and out of deals with Jay Gould, and he had already earned and spent close to two hundred thousand dollars.

Thomas Alva Edison was born in 1847 to parents in comfortable circumstances in the small village of Milan, Ohio. His family tradition was vehemently nonconformist. Thomas Edison himself had only a few months of formal schooling. His mother educated him at home. At school he had been thought to be feeble-minded because he refused to recite in class. He was growing up in the same world as Tom Sawyer. With the same proclivity for turning a profit, twelve-year-old Edison made six hundred dollars by peddling vegetables, but he fell in love with chemistry. He set up a laboratory in the basement of his house, with every bottle labeled "Poison." At fifteen, he began selling newspapers.

He was cocky and shrewd. Once he was asked, "Were you one of those boys who used to sell candies in boxes that had false bottoms half an inch thick?" "The bottoms to my boxes," said Edison, "were always one inch thick."

Actually Edison was a poor businessman. In later years, when talking to Nernst, the German physicist, he took his usual position that an invention wasn't worth developing unless it had immediate commercial value. Nernst had invented an electric light, which was only briefly popular until it was superseded by Edison's carbon filament lamp. Nernst, the academician, listened to the practical man and then asked how much Edison had made out of the carbon lamp. "Not a dime," said Edison. "I made $250,000," said Nernst.

The Civil War absorbed some fifteen hundred telegraphers, and the railroads were looking for new operators. Edison was not fit for war service because of complete deafness in one ear, and so in his mid-teens he joined one of the most romantic brotherhoods of his time.

Edison traveled around the country adopting the careless dress, casual swagger, and toughness of the corps. Telegraphers worked hard, made a lot of money, drank heavily, and boasted that they never saved a cent. Edison became one of the fastest receivers and transmitters of his time, but he had neither discipline nor loyalty to his employer. His earliest inventions were mechanical contrivances designed to make the line superintendent think he was working when he was really sleeping.

Edison was actually a sensitive, creative man, who was always hiding his true self behind a façade of cyncial toughness—whether as a telegrapher or financier. A London employee of his, George Bernard Shaw, in later years used some of his attributes in creating the hero of his novel, *The Irrational Knot*.

In 1868, at the age of twenty-one, Edison slouched into the Western Union office in Boston, chewing tobacco, wearing on the back of his head a battered, arrogant relic of a Confederate soldier's hat. A friend had recommended him for the job.

"Here I am," he said.

The superintendent looked him up and down. "And who the hell are you?"

"Tom Edison," he drawled in a tone that made every operator turn, seething with resentment.

The superintendent immediately put him on the New York receiver, and wired New York to put on its fastest operator. For four hours steadily Edison sat at the stuttering key, and his pen never missed a stroke. Every so often, because he knew what was going on, he would languidly break in on the New York operator and tell him to get up a little speed. The New York operator was the first to give in.

Young Thomas Edison

Edison went to Boston with bigger ideas for himself than being merely the fastest, toughest telegrapher in the business. In 1869, he invented a telegraph for office communication, but there were better ones on the market. He drifted to New York, penniless, during the Stock Exchange wars waged by Jay Gould. Prices fluctuated so wildly that few of the telegraphic stock tickers could keep up. In one frenzied office where Edison was hanging around for a job, the ticker broke down. The superintendent, the operator, and all the brokers went into panic. From Edison's experience with his own machines he recognized the trouble. He told the superintendent and the man screamed at him, "Fix it, fix it! Only be quick!"

In two hours the entire system was working again, and on the spot Edison was appointed general manager of the Gold Indicator Company, at the fantastic salary of three hundred dollars a month. The high point of Gould's raid on the gold market occurred on the morning of "Black Friday," September 24, 1869. Edison watched the spectacle from the Western Union telegraphic booth in the Stock Exchange and saw men go crazy as fortunes in speculation were lost.

He saw that the surest wealth in gold lay not in its changing value but in selling information about its fluctuations—which was the function of the stock ticker. Better stock tickers were still to be invented. In the winter of 1869 the telegraphers' paper stated that "T. A. Edison has resigned his situation and will devote his time to bringing out his inventions."

Edison went into the business of invention with a partner named Pope, and they called themselves by a name that had never before been used in this new sense: "electrical engineers."

Their first assignment was Edison's plan to improve the stock ticker. The Gold and Stock Telegraph Company asked Edison the price of the patent. Edison had originally decided to ask the outrageous price of five thousand dollars, so he could back down to his real price, three thousand. But at the direct question, the tough, swaggering, hard-bitten man lost his twenty-two-year-old nerve. "Make me an offer," he said. "How would forty thousand dollars strike you?" Edison nearly fainted, then ran down to the bank where the clerk, as a joke, cashed the check in small bills. Edison stayed awake with the money all night in fear of robbers. By morning his spirit was broken. He humbly sought advice and was informed of another great invention—the bank account.

He immediately went to work with a staff of fifty men, manufacturing stock tickers in Newark, New Jersey. Edison's staff, from the beginning, included names to become famous in electrical engineering. At one time or another on Edison's payroll were Schuckert, the founder of the great Siemans-Schuckert works in Germany; Kruesi, who was to become the chief engineer of General Electric; Kennelly, who would discover the Kennelly-Heaviside layer; Acheson, who was to invent carborundum; and Fleming, who was to invent the radio tube.

Edison devoted himself to telegraphic invention until Jay Gould took over Western Union.

"Then," said Edison, "I knew that no further progress in telegraphy was possible, so I went into other lines."

2. INVENTIONS TO ORDER

Menlo Park, Edison's laboratory, as an Italian newspaper showed it when Edison demonstrated his electric lamp.

History was made on the day that Edison went into the business of "inventions to order." His shop set the pattern for the great commercial laboratories which dominated research in the following century.

In 1876, after six years in Newark, Edison moved his laboratory to Menlo Park which, even when he employed up to one hundred men, was essentially a one-man affair. Edison's diversity of interest, sense of detail, and powers of concentration were unequaled.

The same problem—multiple telegraphy—that was attracting Bell in Boston was directly attacked by Edison. Using more conventional methods than Bell, Edison successfully developed the duplex, the quadruplex, and finally in 1875, the sextuplex telegraph. His agreement with Western Union gave them first call on his services and a first option on his patents. On order from them, he broke the monopoly of the Page patent electric relay by inventing the "electromotograph," which worked chemically rather than by magnetism. The Page patent, having lost its power, was put on the market and Western Union bought it. Edison's multiple telegraphy increased the value of Western Union by fifteen million dollars. In 1877, Western Union refused to buy Bell's telephone patent and called on Edison to invent an alternative method.

In his experiments on the quadruplex telegraph, Edison had found that he could change the electrical resistance of a powdery mass of carbon by changing the mechanical pressure on the carbon. His first attack on the telephone was to replace Bell's system of transmission. Bell used an iron membrane that vibrated under the impact of sound waves. This motion produced a vibrating magnetic field, which in turn induced a vibrating electric current. Edison replaced the magnetic circuit with a carbon button placed immediately behind the diaphragm; when the diaphragm vibrated under the impact of sound waves, the varying pressure against the carbon made the resistance to the current vary with the same frequency, resulting in a sympathetically fluctuating current. Since one could use a strong battery, Edison's system gave a far more powerful signal than Bell's transmitter. Bell and Western Union pirated each other's best features while they scrambled for subscribers. The Bell Company used Edison's mouthpiece, and Western Union used the Bell receiver.

In his own mind, Edison had set twenty-five thousand dollars as the figure he wanted for his carbon transmitter. Before he could state it, Western Union offered him one hundred thousand. This was only one year after Western Union had refused to pay the same amount to Bell for a clear title to the entire telephone field. Edison compounded the comedy of errors by agreeing to accept, only on one fantastic condition—that Western Union would pay him six thousand dollars a year for the seventeen years of the life of the patent. He did not calculate that if he accepted the one hundred thousand dollars in a lump and put it into a conservative investment, his money would earn him six thousand dollars a year. Western Union had only to deposit the one hundred thousand dollars in a bank and let Edison have the interest. Since they retained their capital, at the end of the seventeen years, in effect, they got his invention for nothing.

Later it was discovered that Edison's patent application was in conflict with the transmitter of a similar

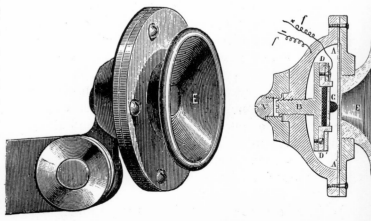

Edison's telephone transmitter surpassed Bell's. Sound waves in the mouthpiece (E) vibrated against a carbon button (C) and changed its electrical resistance.

The roads and paths were lined with wooden poles bearing lamps whose soft light at night delighted visitors.

chalk cylinder. When a signal current passed from the rod to the rotating chalk cylinder on which it rested, the frictional drag varied with the changing current. This change in drag set up a vibration in the diaphragm which generated audible sound waves. Mechanically the device had many faults, and Edison intended it to be no more than a counter-move in a complicated patent war. His strategy was correct because the British recognized this as novel and freed him from interference by Bell. The two companies then followed the classic pattern and amalgamated to fight the British Patent Office, which proposed to take over all telephone companies as a state monopoly. Very shortly thereafter, Western Union and Bell associates formed a single international company.

When Edison had used this property of moistened chalk to get around the relay patent for Western Union in 1875, he was paid one hundred thousand dollars. The telephone application in 1877 earned him another hundred and fifty thousand dollars.

"Invention to order" earned Edison large sums of money, but he was sometimes led into manufacturing the devices he had invented. "I was a poor manufacturer," he said, "because I could not let well enough alone. My first impulse on taking any apparatus into my hand, from an egg beater to an electric motor, is to seek a way of improving it. As soon as I have finished a machine, I'm anxious to take it apart again in order to make an experiment. That's an expensive mania for a manufacturer."

What Edison wanted was this: "My one ambition is to be able to work without regard to the expense. What I mean is that if I want to give up a whole month of my time and that of my whole establishment to finding out why one form of a carbon filament is slightly better than another, I want to do it without having to think of the cost. That galls me. I want none of the rich man's usual toys. I want no horses or yachts—I have no time for them. What I want is a perfect workshop."

design described by Emile Berliner, and after fourteen years of litigation, the broader patent was granted to Berliner, who had sold it to the American Bell Telephone Company. However, Edison's device served its purpose in the rough-and-tumble warfare in the early days of telephony.

In the same year, 1877, Edison was called upon again in a similar situation in the English phase of the Telephone War. There the equitable piracy between the Bell and Edison forces was halted by the stringent British Patent Office, and Edison was restrained from using the Bell receiver. Edison's English company frantically cabled Edison for advice. He told them to hang on for a few more weeks.

He had drawn on an incidental discovery in telegraphy research for the solution to the transmitter problem; now he fell back on another find he had made in 1875 for the "electromotograph": moistened chalk became slippery when it carried an electric current. Edison used the phenomenon in his telephone receiver this way: one end of a light rod was connected to the center of a diaphragm, while the other end of the rod rested on the surface of a rotating

The crank in Edison's telephone receiver rotated a chalk cylinder (right) hidden inside the box. The chalk had to be damp.

Rotation of damp chalk cylinder (A) pulled lever arm (C) when pulses of current made (A) less slippery.(C)pulled a diaphragm (D).

An electric locomotive of Edison's impressed visitors to Menlo Park. The engineer told *Harper's* it would soon go 200 miles an hour.

Edison's first laboratory, where the incandescent lamp was developed. A tube of mercury was used to draw air from the bulb.

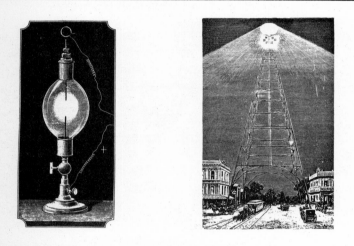

EVOLUTION OF THE ELECTRIC LAMP

Many attempts had been made to make an electric light before the 1870's. The first was Sir Humphry Davy's in the Royal Institution. A cellar full of voltaic batteries maintained an arc between two carbon pencils, as shown. Because of lack of good vacuum apparatus, no oxidizable material could be 'used. In 1840 Sir William Groves used a coil of platinum wire made incandescent by electricity, but slight fluctuations of current burned out the wire. The arc light, improved over Davy's 1810 design, became the 1860 blinding light used in the streets of New York, Cleveland and even San Jose, Cal. (above). However, the arc light was totally impractical for home lighting. It glared, flickered and was uneconomical except in the very large installations. Edison's incandescent electric lamp (right) domesticated electricity.

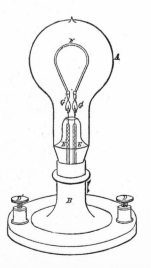

3. LIGHT AND POWER

The greatest drawback to the widespread use of carbon arc lighting was the lack of an efficient and inexpensive source of electric power. This was solved in 1867 by Gramme, who invented the self-exciting dynamo to give steady direct current. Around the same time another invention also changed the course of electric lighting development: the invention of an efficient vacuum pump by Sprengel. Many substances that would oxidize in air when incandescent could be operated safely within a vacuum.

In 1878, Edison's attention was drawn to the unsolved problem of electric lighting for home use. Any electric light would have to compete in cost, candle power, and convenience with the gas jet. Before beginning any laboratory research, Edison made an exhaustive study of the gas industry. Still on paper, he designed a central electric power plant and a method of running radiating lines to private homes and shops; he then made calculations on the cost of copper and the other materials which would enter into the manufacture of a lamp and the generation of power from steam-driven dynamos.

The analysis of these figures not only determined the dimensions of the lamp, but also made it clear that the price of a lamp would have to be forty cents.

When he had satisfied himself that the problem was soluble in his own terms, he went to work on a lamp in which a carbon filament was sealed in an evacuated glass globe on which he was granted patent No. 223,-898 on January 27, 1880. In itself the conception was not particularly novel except to the extent that the Edison design differed from its predecessors. Edison's contribution was his fantastically exhaustive analysis

Edison's multipolar dynamo was as important an engineering development as the electric light.

In 1880, Edison utilities used underground power cables. Connections were soldered and covered with a bath of tar.

of materials and his discovery, in the least possible time, of the most efficient and reliable form of carbon for his filament. The first filaments were carbonized sewing threads. These remained incandescent for forty hours. He examined every possible material that contained carbon: foodstuffs, tars—in all, six thousand variations of vegetable fiber. Of the vegetable fibers, bamboo was the best, and of the bamboos, one form, the binding leaf of a Japanese palm leaf fan, gave the best results. On the last day of 1879, he ran special trains to bring three thousand people to see a demonstration of hundreds of small electric lamps burning in his shop and on the roads in the neighborhood—all fed by underground mains from a central dynamo.

Edison's prestige was so great that even before his first patent was granted in 1880, the news that he had solved the problem of electric light caused the stocks of gas companies to fall sharply. Each succeeding demonstration caused gas stocks to fluctuate, and at one point the London Stock Exchange went into complete panic.

But Edison's calculations could not stop with the development of a lamp. "Everything is so new that each step is in the dark," he said. "I have to make the dynamos, the lamps, the conductors, and attend to a thousand details the world never hears of." He thought in terms of gas engineering: the dynamos were the equivalent of gas reservoirs; his insulated wires laid through the streets were the analogue of gas conduits; his electric meters had to be invented to replace the gas meters for measuring consumption.

Edison designed the two-phase generator to solve the problem which some of the leading electricians of the time thought impossible. It was not believed, by the very men who ridiculed Edison for his lack of theoretical knowledge, that dynamos could be designed which

would take care of the ever-changing electric load as lights were turned on and off by users in different parts of a house and in various houses on the same street. Edison's dynamo was built in direct violation of every contemporary tenet of design, and he was proved right.

He now began the production of dynamos, cables, lamps, and fittings. He called Samuel Insull from England to be his business manager and gave Insull his start in the utility industry. Most of the subsidiary factories, when put on a producing basis, were sold to a group headed by Henry Villard, who had made his fortune in western railroads, and the new corporation was called the Edison General Electric Company.

Edison held on to the lamp manufacturing company, not because of his desire for profits, but purely out of pride. He had promised himself that the whole operation would not be of commercial value until the cost of lamps could be forty cents, and he had to justify himself in his own eyes. He went to work mechanizing his method of production. In the first year his lamps cost him $1.25 apiece. The next year they cost him $1.10; but the third year he was producing them at a loss of only ten cents. The following year he was clearing three cents per lamp, and with that profit he was able to make up the total loss to date. When the cost of the lamp was down to twenty-two cents, he sold out.

Just as the casual, laconic kid had slouched into the Boston office of the Western Union, knowing that he was the best telegrapher in the outfit, now Mr. Thomas Edison, world-famous inventor, could look about him at the great manufacturers and financiers and know that he could do a job of large-scale manufacturing better than any of them. What was more, he didn't give a damn about the profit for which they were all breaking their necks.

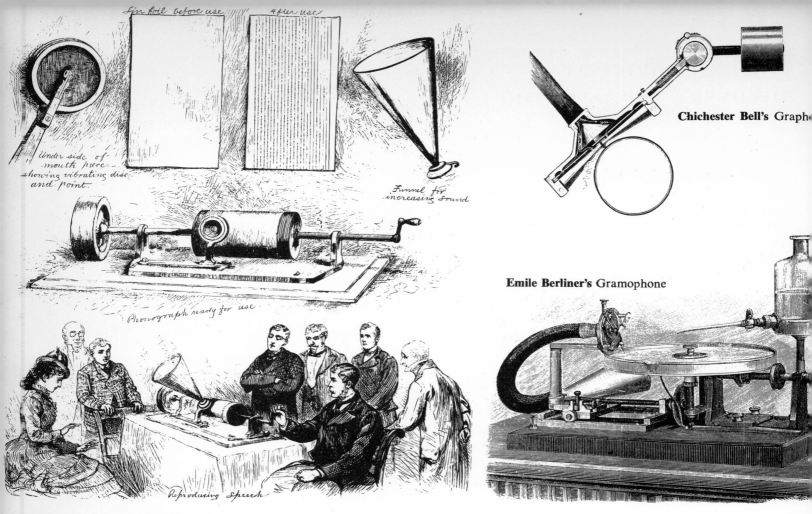

Edison's original phonograph

EVOLUTION OF THE PHONOGRAPH

Harper's Weekly, 1877, gave a complete description of the newly invented phonograph to its readers. Tinfoil was wrapped around a cylinder, and the vibrating sound wave was inscribed in it with a needle. Bell's improvement consisted of cutting the sound track into a cylindrical record made of shellac, while Emile Berliner invented the modern form of flat disc records in which the track was etched chemically. They were called "plates." The Bell and Berliner patents were combined finally to form the Columbia Gramophone Company. The Victor Company was based on Edison's patent. These two were the parent companies of the two great competing 20th-century entertainment corporations, Columbia and RCA.

Edison's improved phonograph

4. EDISON'S ORIGINAL DISCOVERY AND INVENTION

In the same year that Edison finished his telephone work, he made a rough sketch at his desk of a piece of apparatus, then looked at it for a moment to gauge the amount of time required to build it. Edison's machinists were paid on a piecework basis, and so at the side of the sketch he wrote $18. He handed it to John Kruesi. The mechanism was quite simple and in the last stages of assembly; Kruesi casually asked Edison what it was supposed to be.

"A talking machine," said Edison. And Kruesi burst out laughing at the Old Man's joke.

When the machine was finished, Edison set it up and shouted into a horn, "Mary had a little lamb." He then made a few adjustments, and in a squeaky voice the horn shouted back to him the same words. Kruesi leaped back in amazement.

The fact that Edison's electric light, telegraph, telephone, and dynamo were original variations of known devices in no way detracts from his stature. Most men work in the tradition marked out by predecessors. Newton followed Kepler; Franklin followed Hawksbee; and Willard Gibbs followed Clausius.

However, it sometimes happens that an individual will mark out the beginning of a path which has not been touched before. The phonograph, a machine to record, indefinitely store, and then reproduce at will, human speech, or music, was completely novel as a conception. The Patent Office, in its usual search for the prior art, could find nothing that even remotely anticipated Edison, even though the means he used were combinations that were not new.

Edison was led to the possibilities of a talking machine when he worked out a method of recording telegraph messages on the surface of a flat rotating disc by having a stylus make a spiral recording of the message's dots and dashes. To reproduce the telegraphic message, a level arm was placed in the groove on the tin disc, and as the disc rotated, the arm rose and fell according to the markings which it reproduced. One day Edison cranked the machine at a very high rate, and the lever arm set up an audible vibration. Edison immediately realized, by analogy with some of his telephone experiments, that if he attached the lever arm to a diaphragm, sound waves of a varying pitch could be generated.

The sketch which he gave to Kruesi called for a rotating cylinder, to be cranked, about which a sheet of tin could be wrapped. As the cylinder revolved, it was moved along between two small horns which were fixed in position. One horn was a mouthpiece. It contained a flexible diaphragm which contained a tiny stylus that rested lightly on the tin cylinder. When one spoke into the mouthpiece and rotated the cylinder, the vibrations of the diaphragm traced a bumpy path on the tinfoil. To reproduce the message, the mouthpiece was rotated out of the way, the cylinder was returned to its starting point, and the other horn, which contained a much more delicate diaphragm and a far lighter stylus, was moved into position. As the crank was turned, the second stylus set its diaphragm into vibration, and sound waves were sent out.

In the next model, one diaphragm and stylus was used both for recording and, with the addition of a horn to act as a megaphone, for playing.

The public's first awareness of the phonograph came when Edison gave a demonstration in 1877 to a few friends. They saw a simple-looking machine which astonished them by saying, in what seemed like a somewhat human and somewhat unearthly voice: "Good morning! How do you do? How do you like the phonograph?"

Edison was delighted with his invention, and he suggested ten possible uses for his instrument:

1. Letter writing and all kinds of dictation without the aid of a stenographer.
2. Phonographic books that would speak to blind people.
3. The teaching of elocution.
4. Reproduction of music.
5. A family record to be a registry of remarks and reminiscences by members of a family in their own voices.
6. Music boxes and toys.
7. Clocks that would announce the time.
8. The preservation of languages by exact reproduction of the manner of pronouncing.
9. Educational purposes.
10. Connection with the telephone to make a permanent record of conversations.

Just as Edison had improved Bell's telephone, now Bell and his associates improved on Edison's work and developed the graphophone, in which a wax cylinder was substituted for tinfoil, and instead of having the stylus make vertical indentations, it cut a groove in the cylinder as it revolved. The quality of the graphophone was much higher than Edison's machine, and the Columbia Gramophone Company was founded to exploit it.

Still a third form, the gramophone, was invented by the same Emile Berliner whose work on the carbon telephone transmitter resulted in a broader patent than Edison's. Berliner introduced the flat disc of a hardened plastic material. By the turn of the century, the phonograph and all its variations had achieved broad acceptance, and most of the predictions made by Edison almost a quarter of a century earlier were beginning to come true.

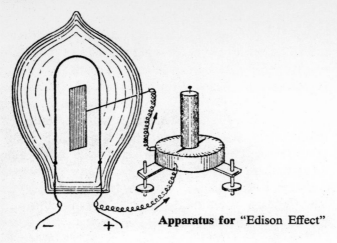

Apparatus for "Edison Effect"

5. THE EDISON EFFECT

The phonograph was one of the inventions of which Edison was most proud. He performed another piece of work that was to prove subsequently of far greater importance: he was the first to detect the flow of free electrons through evacuated space. For a quarter of a century, his notes went unnoticed, until they were re-examined at the end of the century, and then the "Edison Effect" was to lead the way to the development of the radio tube and the radio industry.

In 1883, when Edison was working with carbon filaments, he noticed that the inside of the bulbs became gradually blackened. The deposit of carbon on the bulb was uniform except for a fine clear line on one side near the filament support, as if the support itself cast a shadow. Edison surmised that the carbon deposit on the glass was coming from the filament, but he was unable to give any mechanical explanation for the "shadow." In a test lamp, he inserted a small metal plate between the two legs which supported the carbon filament. The metal plate could be connected either to the high or low voltage side of the filament. When connected to the positive leg, the plate drew a small current, he discovered. When the plate was made negative, no plate current flowed.

Thirteen years later, in 1896, the discovery of the electron by J. J. Thomson suggested to Fleming, Edison's young assistant, that the half-forgotten phenomenon observed by Edison meant that the incandescent carbon filament boiled off electrons, which were attracted across the evacuated space by the positively charged plate. When the plate had been negatively charged, the electrons had been repelled. Fleming's variation of Edison's apparatus was to surround an incandescent filament with a metal wall which was positively charged. This permitted the passage of the positive half of every cycle of alternating current, and was the first electron rectifier.

By the turn of the century, Edison's great creative-ness began to wane. His work became more dogged and less versatile, even though he invented a new form of storage battery in 1903, and a new process for separating iron from low-grade ores in the decade between 1890 and 1900. In 1891 he invented the kinetoscope—a device for showing in succession pictures of motion on a continuous strip of film.

The U. S. Patent Office granted Edison 1,093 patents during his lifetime, the largest number ever given to one man.

His first wife had died and he had remarried. He lived a more conventional life, and the ghost of the boy who had swaggered into the Boston office of Western Union arose only occasionally during interviews with newspaper men. The older Edison loved the boy he had been long ago. The world was moving very fast, but whatever it was that had driven Thomas Alva Edison to work for days on end around the clock seemed to have lost its sting. Engineers and chemists working for the giant corporations he had helped to build were taking over his work, and the new explanations of the physical world were incomprehensible to him. Young men who had worked for him had grown up to a world fame of their own, to the directorships of great companies, to knighthoods, to Nobel prizes. It was all going very fast, but never once did Edison use the heartbreaking words of the tired and lost: "I guess I've lived too long." He lived to be an old man, but he never stopped working, he never lost his pride, and he was never defeated.

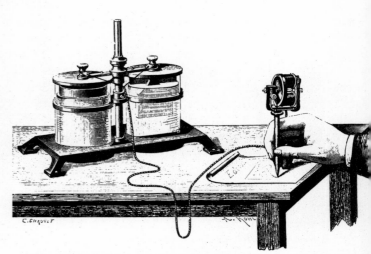

Edison's electric pen, patented in 1877, was for a long time in general use for making manifold copies of manuscripts. The operator drew a design or message with an electromagnetically vibrated stylus, and this became the stencil for the printing of many copies. It was very useful until the development of the typewriter and carbon paper. A later form, as a percussion hammer, was to be used by dentists. Edison also invented gummed paper, tried to produce artificial rubber from goldenrod, improved the electric storage battery, built electric automobiles. He always considered himself a chemist.

6. THE INVENTION OF MOVING PICTURES

Fig. 2.

In the second figure, the right leg is bending at the knee, so as to lift the foot from the ground, in order that it may swing forward.

Fig. 3.

The next stage of movement is shown in the *left* leg of figure 3. This leg is seen suspended in air, a little beyond the middle of the arc through which it swings, and before it has straightened

Fig. 4.

The foot has now swung forward, and, tending to swing back again, the limb being straightened, and the body tipped forward, the heel strikes the ground. The angle which the sole of the foot forms with the ground increases with the length of the stride; and as this last surprised us, so the extent of this angle astonishes us in many of the figures, in this among the rest.

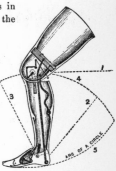

Oliver Wendell Holmes, in a sense, started the train of thinking that led to the invention of motion pictures. The enormous number of wounded men in the Civil War led to a demand for artificial limbs. Prosthetic devices could be neither useful nor comfortable until they let a man walk with something that approached the normal gait. Very little was known about the details of human locomotion, and Dr. Oliver Wendell Holmes of Boston undertook the analysis. He studied photographs of men caught in stride and demonstrated for the first time how the different parts of the leg and foot came into play.

MUYBRIDGE PHOTOGRAPHS ANIMAL LOCOMOTION

The interest created by Holmes' study of the human gait raised a number of questions for artists, anatomists, and finally, photographers. An argument over the question of whether a horse's four feet were ever off the ground all at the same moment led two wealthy Californians to hire the services of an Americanized English photographer, Edward Muybridge, to settle the problem for them. Muybridge decided to do it by a novel application of photography. He had a horse gallop over a measured path, on one side of which was a bank of cameras. Across the path at intervals were fine threads, which the horse broke as he galloped through them. Each torn thread released the shutter of a camera, and an instantaneous photograph was taken. The complexity of the work can be understood when it is realized that Muybridge had to use wet plates.

Results of the test were historic because it revealed something never noticed before: the gait of a galloping horse had never been correctly portrayed by artists. Muybridge became fascinated by the technique and set to work to improve it. Artists who had seen the work on the horse gait, particularly Thomas Eakins of Pennsylvania, were excited by the possibilities.

Muybridge was given a grant and brought to the University of Pennsylvania in 1883 to develop the technique. To insure the project's scientific character, a commission was set up composed of various members of the departments who would be interested in such work. The commission included physicians and an anatomist, a physicist, engineers, and of course Eakins of the Academy of Fine Arts.

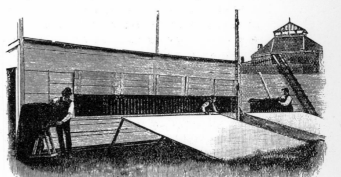

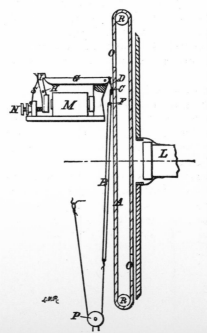

The camera house of the Muybridge project was a shed with room for twenty-four cameras side by side. Large reflectors threw sunlight on a straight track forty-nine feet away on which the subject moved. The cameras were set off by an ingenious electromagnetic timing circuit; and each camera had a patented shutter (left) which was like a roller shade. Two openings (O) passed across a lens (L) when an electromagnet (M) released the shade which had been held in position by the tension of a rubber band (B), fastened at (C). Exposure time was controlled by the elasticity of B.

MUYBRIDGE PHOTOGRAPHS ANIMAL LOCOMOTION (continued)

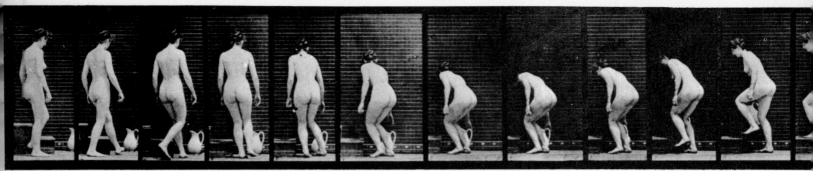

A strip of pictures showing successive positions of a human being in motion, made by Muybridge. His folio consisted of hundreds of these, and when they were published, artists and illustrators studied them. American illustration, as a result, began to show more fluidity and naturalness in drawing human beings.

THE PICTURE STORY OF ALEXANDER BLACK

One of the earliest picture stories was worked out by Alexander Black in the 1890's. He considered himself the inventor of the "picture play."

Over a period of years he had been illustrating fiction, when it began to be clear to him that fiction and photography would best supplement each other if each was "devised with a regard for the demands and limitations of the other . . . The pictures must do more than illustrate . . . In the first place, the pictures would be primary, the text secondary . . . Again the pictures would not be art at all, in the illustrator's sense, but simply the art of the *tableau vivant,* plus the science of photography."

Black worked out a story, devised sets for the background of the action, and got professional actors to pose in dramatic positions. He arranged his pictures in the proper sequence to tell his story, showed them through a magic lantern to capacity audiences, and with each picture went his narration. His audiences were captured by the illusion and felt they were actually seeing moving pictures.

"Miss Jerry" had a story far in advance of any continuity of the early Edison pictures. The heroine was described as a "girl of Eastern birth" raised out in the Colorado mine camps, where she had been called "The Princess of Panther Mine." Here are the first three tableaux with Black's narration:

(Top) "When the story opens, Holbrook and his daughter have been in New York for five years enjoying the fruits of the miner's success . . . The first cloud of misfortune . . . is a letter from the mine reporting probable disaster. The miner and his daughter must make some radical change in their way of living . . ."

(Center) "When she surprises him . . . he starts guiltily, slipping the letter into his pocket, muttering some commonplace about being late for the office. But she reads trouble in his face; and the Colorado postmark on the envelope which he has not taken from the table, confirms her suspicions of trouble at the mine."

(Lower) "On the same morning, Kate, the maid, announces in much excitement that there is a 'pirate in the hall.' The 'pirate' lounges in . . . and drawls, 'I guess this *is* Jerry!' 'Is this you, Pink?' exclaims the girl. 'Waal, I'll be hanged if I'd knowed yer, Miss Jerry, yer got to be such a woman!'"

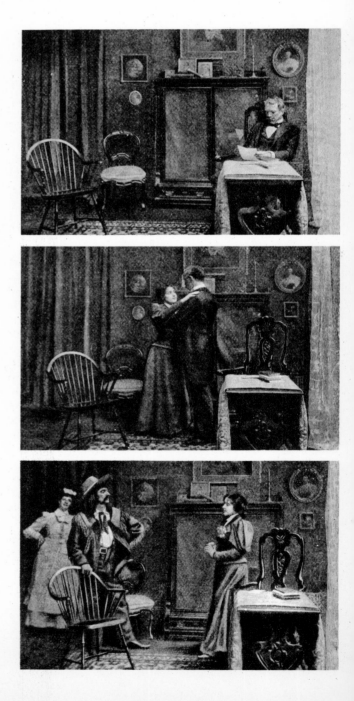

EDISON'S KINETOSCOPE

Two patents were granted to Edison in the spring of '93. One was for an electrically propelled road vehicle which became the famous "Edison Electric": the glass-enclosed coach which was to roll with silent and vibrationless elegance along the city streets for the next twenty years, a favorite with ladies who could not stand the noisy, smelly, jouncing gasoline cars.

The second Edison patent, that spring, was to help found an industry called the "movies," to be responsible for one of the most radical changes in the diffusion of knowledge since the invention of the printing press. Edison had, eighteen months earlier, patented a camera—U. S. No. 403,-534 for "taking a large number of photographs of a moving object in such a manner that any two successive pictures are almost identical in appearance."

The 1893 invention was a means to show the pictures which had been taken or, as the patent put it: "The present invention relates to apparatus for using photographs which have been taken in rapid succession of an object in motion, by means of which a single composite picture is seen by the eye, said picture giving the impression that the object photographed is in actual and natural motion."

"The film 3, on which a large number of photographs of a moving object have been taken . . ." is a statement that reveals his indebtedness to the recent invention of photographic film by George Eastman. Several years later, in a patent suit, a federal judge apportioned the credit for inventing motion pictures equally between Edison's camera and Eastman's film; and Edison was always the first to give his friend Eastman his due.

Edison's projector, in its earliest form, used a film in the form of "an endless belt or band" passed back and forth over rollers 36, 37 (right). "This band is advanced at the proper speed by the reel 38 on the shaft 39 driven through the belt 40 by any suitable motor. The film passes over the pulley 41, under the light spring 42 through the slit 43 and over the reel 38. In order to get a sufficiently long strip or tape—say several hundred feet—the rollers 36, 37 may be multiplied to any desired extent.

Edison's projector was not as successful as his camera. While the patent specifically states that it could be used to project the picture on a screen, it was used as a viewer for one person at a time in penny arcades. He improved Thomas Armat's projector and marketed it as the Vitascope. He also demonstrated how a film of moving pictures could be synchronized with a phonograph record to make "talking pic-

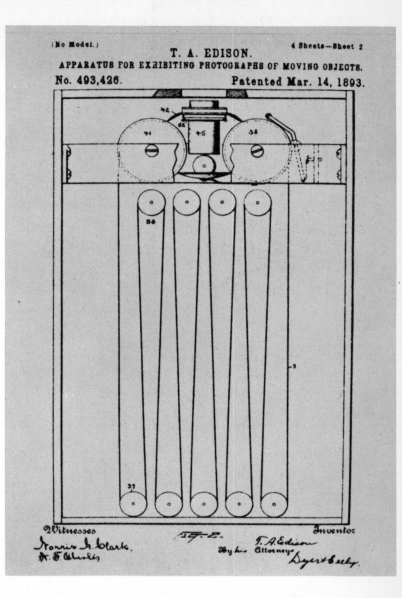

tures"; and although this system was long since obsolete by the 1920's, a similar plan was used in the first commercially successful "talkies."

Edison himself took an active hand in the production and casting of the early motion pictures, and he had a special fondness for cowboy stories.

JENKINS' PHANTASCOPE

The projector which turned out to be most widely used and to serve as the model for later improvements was the Phantascope invented by Jenkins specifically for screen projection for an audience of many people. Jenkins also was one of the earliest workers in mechanical television which used a moving disc, as originated by Nipkow, for scanning. Jenkins' television was made obsolete by the development of electronic scanning devices by Farnsworth and Zworykin. Jenkins never repeated the success he had with his motion picture projector, but it undoubtedly was a factor in popularizing the new entertainment.

J. WILLARD GIBBS

1. WITNESS TO
THE WORLD OF CHANGE

The speaker on the platform was the great British scientist, Clerk Maxwell. His attentive audience: Queen Victoria and an international gathering of the most famous figures of European science. His subject: the brilliant work being done by an unknown young American—"Professor Willard Gibbs of Yale College, U. S. A." The place was London; the year, 1876.

The music, uproar, and frenzy of the Centennial Exposition at Philadelphia kept Americans from noticing that another important nation was also putting itself on exhibition—the international nation of science. Two sister queens, Victoria of England and the Empress of Germany, went through the same rites in South Kensington that Dom Pedro and President Grant had performed at Philadelphia, and the first International Loan Exhibition of Historic Scientific Apparatus was officially opened.

Maxwell's speech on Gibbs was a remarkable tribute from a man at the height of his fame; but Maxwell foresaw that Gibbs would some day be ranked with the immortals of science. Only a few months earlier, Maxwell had announced that because of the obscure American, "problems which have long resisted the efforts of myself and others may be solved at once."

Ordinarily, such enthusiastic sponsorship by a great man before a select audience of experts should have brought Gibbs instant recognition. It did nothing of the sort. No single advance in science can be appreciated without a knowledge of the field which it illuminates. In 1876, neither American nor European scientists had sufficient information on chemical and physical processes to appreciate Gibbs's work. For that reason the London papers did not report Maxwell's speech, and so no mention appeared in any American paper. At the time, Gibbs knew nothing about it. All the talk at 121 High Street, New Haven, was about the coming summer vacation to be spent at a boarding house either in the Adirondacks or in the White Mountains.

That year, Josiah Willard Gibbs was thirty-seven, a slender, bony-faced, bearded man with piercing blue eyes and a quiet sense of humor. He had been professor of mathematical or theoretical physics at Yale for five years. He was unmarried and lived with his sister and her family. To her children, he was their Uncle Will who made the salad, stoked the furnace, took them all for sleigh rides, and told wonderful stories. Later, they were to realize that he was a famous man; but never from any remark he himself ever made. If he had known about Maxwell's speech, he probably would have said nothing at all about it. In his lifetime, he was to receive nineteen awards and honorary degrees, including the highest international prize for scientific achievement; but even his closest friends never knew the full list until they read his obituary in the newspapers.

Josiah Willard Gibbs, the physicist, was born in 1839. He was of the same generation as George Pullman, Pierpont Morgan, and John Rockefeller. He grew up in the same America, was subject to the same influences and values—and went a way that was different from them all.

He came of a New England family, distinguished in scholarship for six generations, which included one Harvard president, one secretary of the Massachusetts Colony, and the first president of Princeton. Gibbs's father was an outstanding theologian.

When he was ten years old, he went to a small private school, half a block from his home in New Haven. He was a shy, quiet boy, who followed the others, never a leader and never an outsider. In 1854, when the time came for his entrance examination for Yale, he went to one of the professors, a family friend, and confessed that even though he knew he was prepared, he wasn't applying; he was afraid he would never pass the oral inquisition by the committee. Professor Thacher sympathetically asked where he would fall down and what his answer would be if the examination were a private interview. Gibbs spoke very freely, then somewhat reassured, rose and asked when to return for the exam. Thacher laughed and told him that the examination had just been held; Gibbs was now a member of the college.

In the years just before the Civil War, Yale students were organized in secret societies with violent rites of initiation. They were in a continual state of open warfare with the town. In Gibbs's freshman and senior years, two townsmen lost their lives fighting student mobs. Some of the undergraduates carried pistols. At one point the town was so maddened that a group of men tried to seize the cannon of the local militia to blast the collegians.

In the school, cheating was flagrant. During one examination, a student drilled a hole through the floor beneath his seat and passed his questions to another student on the floor below who looked up the answers in a book. A harassed professor giving an examination called out, "Look sharp there, Mr. Monitor, another student has just escaped through the window!"

Through all this, Gibbs took part in the student life and still maintained his own standards of scholarship. He received his bachelor's degree in 1858.

These were also the years of emergence for the Sheffield Scientific School. A department for graduate studies in science had been founded in 1847; but the degree of Ph.D. was not instituted for advanced work until 1861. Gibbs was to become America's greatest theoretician in science, but his training was along the lines of American practicability. In 1863, he became the first American ever to receive a Ph.D. in engineering and his doctoral thesis was *On the Form of the Teeth of Wheels in Spur Gearing*. He was immediately given a three year appointment as tutor in the undergraduate college.

Gibbs's father died in 1861, leaving an estate valued at $23,500 to be shared among the children. This gave Gibbs a small independent income for life.

Classes during the war were at their most turbulent; and Gibbs was remembered by some of his students of that period as having a hard time maintaining discipline. This was no real reflection on Gibbs—Abraham Lincoln and his generals were having a difficult time maintaining discipline, too.

During his tutorial years, Gibbs worked on his main interest: engineering. He made extensive notes on steam turbines and invented a railroad brake to be actuated by a train's inertia. His patent was U. S. No. 53,971, granted March 24, 1866. When his appointment at Yale ended, Gibbs went abroad with his two sisters. This was the turning point of his career; in Europe he received the advanced training that prepared him for the great work of his life.

His first stop was at the Sorbonne and the Collège de France, where he loaded himself up with sixteen hours of lectures a week under the mathematical physicists Duhamel and Liouville, and became familiar with the works of Laplace, Poisson, Lagrange, and Cauchy. The following year he went to Berlin, where he studied under Kundt and Weierstrasse. After a year in Berlin, he went to Heidelberg where courses were being offered by Kirchhoff, Cantor, Bunsen, and Helmholtz, all outstanding men from whom he learned still more about theoretical physics.

About the same time, other American students abroad were William James, who lived very near Gibbs in Heidelberg, and Henry Adams, who was later to apply Gibbs's theoretical physics to a treatment of history.

The turbulent social activities of American colleges were only one facet of American student life; the serious American scholars abroad were another. However, in Europe, too, student life in those years was violent even though it was to be hopelessly sentimentalized in *The Student Prince*, the *Prince of Pilsen*, and du Maurier's *Trilby*. A contemporary American visitor, Mark Twain, in *Innocents Abroad*, saw little glamour in the German dueling societies. The life of European students was, as in America, the surface ferment of societies in tension. Germany under Bismarck was on its way to war with France

Gibbs was a student at Yale during the 1850's when student life was violent and uproarious. Some undergraduates carried pistols.

under Napoleon—only two years after Gibbs returned to New Haven.

Gibbs had moved undeflected through the years at Yale; in the same way he worked apart from the furor in Europe. He lived with his sister, who married while they were abroad, but Gibbs shared his father's house with her and her husband when they all returned to New Haven. On July 13, 1871, in the minutes of the Yale Corporation meeting was this statement: "Mr. Josiah Willard Gibbs, of New Haven, was appointed Professor of Mathematical Physics, without salary, in the Department of Philosophy and the Arts."

This was the first such chair to be set up in America. In that same year, the first such chair in Europe was set up at Cambridge for Clerk Maxwell, who was already famous while Gibbs had published nothing but his doctoral thesis and had applied for a patent on a railroad brake. Only an intimate knowledge of Gibbs's potential ability and a shrewd guess as to what he would probably do, had led Yale to make the appointment.

Gibbs's first plunge into serious work showed his complete identity with his time: as an engineer he studied a problem which bore directly on the most practical subject of the day—the efficiency of steam engines. In this respect, he was a man of the same era as Rockefeller, Vanderbilt, and Pullman. But once he had entered the work, he became his own man, and another Gibbs appeared, the Gibbs who had studied under Helmholtz, Liouville, and Weierstrasse.

His attack broadened. The particular problem of steam and water became generalized to include all matter. The brilliant engineering insight deepened into some of the most profound scientific truths ever to be set forth by an American scientist.

Gibbs's doctoral thesis (above) was in the highly practical field of mechanical engineering.

2. THE IMPORTANCE OF GIBBS'S WORK

Before Newton, men had thought of equilibrium as the state of balance in which all things were finally motionless. An upright pillar of a Grecian temple was in equilibrium because all the forces on the pillar—its own weight, the weight of the frieze above it, the sideways thrust of horizontal beams—were so perfectly adjusted, one to another, that the pillar would stand forever.

Isaac Newton expanded the idea of equilibrium to include motion. Out in space, a planet moved forever in a certain definite orbit because of the forces acting on it. Therefore, said Newton, the motion was in equilibrium with the force that created it.

Newton saw that a force acting on a body gave it an acceleration that depended on the body's mass. Not only did Newton's law describe the motion of planets in the night sky, it was found to describe the motion of bodies moving along the surface of the earth; it described how gears mesh, how wheels turn, how pistons rise and fall; and it predicted what combinations of machines would never work.

Newton's statement created one of the great intellectual revolutions of all time. Willard Gibbs's work was of equal magnitude. Gibbs extended the concept of equilibrium to include the way in which matter changed its state—its very identity. Ice becomes water, water becomes steam, steam becomes oxygen and hydrogen. Oxygen combines with nitrogen and becomes ammonia. Every process in nature is a process of change; and the laws of such change were discovered by Gibbs. Just as Newton founded the science of mechanics, Gibbs created the science of physical chemistry, to which all other chemistries became subordinate.

Within fifty years after Gibbs's work, chemistry had pervaded the world's greatest industries. Steel had become chemistry, along with the baking of bread, the making of Portland cement, the mining of salt, the manufacture of petroleum fuels, paper, tungsten filaments, cloth, and a hundred thousand other articles whose reaction had been analyzed, corrected, or predicted, using the results of Gibbs.

Gibbs's work was used to explain the action of volcanoes, the physiological processes in blood, the electrolytic action of storage batteries, and the manufacture of fertilizers.

In the half century after his death, the Nobel prize was awarded four times for work based directly on some facet of Gibbs's results.

Gibbs studied change. Just as Newton had to find the measure of motion that would most truly fit his theory of dynamic equilibrium, so Gibbs had to find the measure of a substance's condition, which would tell him whether it would, or would not, change into something else.

Helmholtz in Germany influenced generations of American physicists who had to go abroad for advanced science study.

France was the center of studies in light. This physics lecture hall in the Sorbonne was world famous.

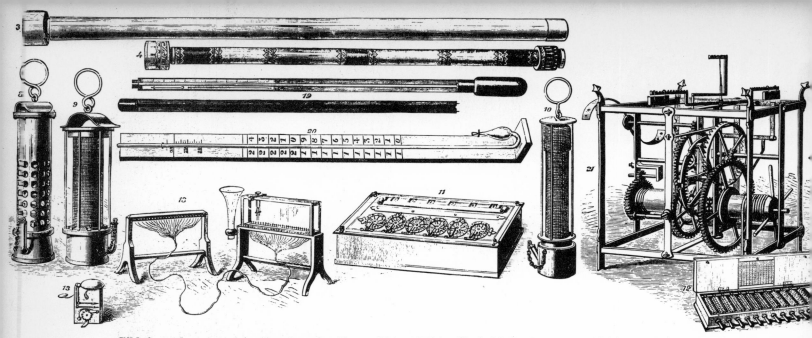

Gibbs's work was explained to the scientific world in 1876 by Clerk Maxwell at the exhibition in London of historic scientific

3. GIBBS'S WORLD
OF CHANGE

A piece of matter is actually an enormous number of tiny particles in motion, each particle requiring a Newtonian equation of its own. When ice melts into water and becomes steam, the type of motion for each particle changes. Each change would require still an additional set of Newtonian equations of motion. In a chemical reaction, a mass of hydrogen gas permeates a mass of nitrogen, and each nitrogen atom becomes associated with three hydrogen atoms. The new constellation has new modes of motion. Newtonian mechanics could never solve these problems.

The key to motion which Newton used was a body's acceleration, proportional to the force acting on the body. The key Gibbs used was a particle's velocity, which is proportional to its energy. The study of energy is called thermodynamics. Gibbs said: "The laws of thermodynamics . . . express . . . the behavior of systems of a great number of particles."

The higher the temperature of a molecule, the more energy it has. The more energy it has, the greater its velocity. The pressure exerted by a gas is simply the sum of repeated collisions of individual gas molecules against the walls of the container. Therefore, the greater the velocity of a molecule, the more pressure it exerts on the walls of its container. If the walls are not rigid, this greater velocity makes the molecules diffuse outwards in an expanding volume. Expanding gas molecules can push a piston, which in turn performs mechanical work. For these reasons, the measurement words of thermodynamics are *energy, pressure, volume, temperature,* and *work.*

Count Rumford had shown that one form of en-

ergy could be converted into another. Twenty years later, the twenty-eight-year-old son of a wealthy Bonapartist family, Sadi Carnot, said that in spite of all the ways in which energy transforms itself, the total sum of energy in the universe remains constant, but by the 1840's, experimental evidence made it clear that in every energy transformation, a certain amount of energy became unavailable for further transformation.

Water, when heated at constant volume into steam, loses a certain amount of the heat to the internal structure of the molecules. Liquid ammonia, going through the same transformation into gaseous ammonia, loses a different amount of heat. The name of this property of internal absorption of heat is *entropy*. The numerical measure that is important is the *change* of entropy in any reaction. The change of entropy that takes place when a liquid boils at constant volume is simply the heat of vaporization divided by the boiling point. In general, the change in entropy for any reaction is obtained by simple arithmetic: the number of calories of heat required to make such a change, divided by the number of degrees of temperature at which the heat is applied. Gibbs added *entropy* to the measurement words of thermodynamics.

In the two examples given above, a single component—water in one case, ammonia in another—went through a single change of phase: from liquid to gas. Gibbs extended this treatment to include several components existing together, so that one could treat mixtures of liquids and mixtures of solids. It was when he extended this still further to include components which could combine with each other that he finally found the equations which described chemical reactions and their equilibrium.

For such systems, Gibbs defined new quantities related to entropy, which allowed him to predict in advance whether or not a chemical or physical change would take place; and if it did take place, how far

Key to Objects in Illustrations Above: **1.** Tycho Brahe's quadrant **2.** Sir Francis Drake's astrolabe **3.** Galileo's second telescope **4.** Galileo's telescope **5.** Newton's telescope **6.** Jansen's compound microscope, 1590 **7.** Galileo's microscope (occhialino) **8.** Sir Humphry Davy's first safety-lamp **9.** Third safety-lamp **10.** Davy's improved safety-lamp **11.** Pascal's adding and subtracting machine,

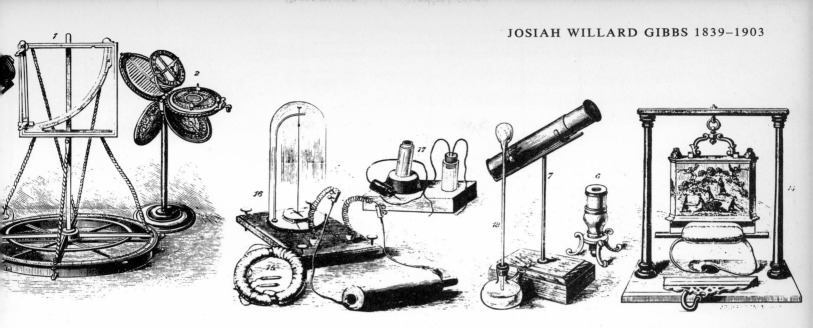

uments (key below). Even this impressive sponsorship failed to attract profound study of Gibbs's work during his own time.

the reaction would go. These quantities he called chemical potentials. Just as entropy was a physical property of a substance, so was chemical potential.

Gibbs's famous Phase Rule grew out of these studies. He devoted only four pages to its development, without giving any concrete physical example. Within the next fifty years, other scientists wrote books and monographs—a total of eleven thousand pages—on Gibbs's Phase Rule, describing applications to mineralogy, petrology, physiology, metallurgy, and every other field of science.

Gibbs's Phase Rule stated the conditions which had to hold for a number of compounds to exist together in equilibrium in various phases: liquid, solid, or gaseous. Dutch chemists were the first to give this rule its concrete application, until it became recognized as the most important single linear equation in the history of science.

In World War I, two disciples of the Gibbsian analysis—Haber, a German, and Freeth, an Englishman—both used the Phase Rule to work out for their separate governments the supremely important problems of manufacturing nitrates for explosives. Science countered science, and war was reduced once again to what it must always be—individual men in uniform, fighting and dying in the mud.

Besides thermodynamics, Gibbs's vector algebra was an important contribution. In nature there are many quantities which must be described, not only by number, but by direction. A downward force of fifty pounds obviously creates far different results from an upward force of fifty pounds. The expression "fifty pounds" is physically ambiguous unless the direction of the force is also specified. In three-dimensional space, each directional quantity must be defined by three coordinates. Gibbs's vector algebra simplified reference to space. A more generalized Gibbsian vector, the *dyadic,* was destined to become a powerful tool

in a science only being born in Gibbs's last years and to remain unknown to him—relativity.

In his early studies on equilibrium, Gibbs treated matter as a continuous mass. Later on he faced the reality that matter was made up of minute particles in motion. He redefined his thermodynamics from a new point of view, in which he treated their behavior on a statistical basis: Newtonian mechanics became statistical mechanics.

Starting with absolutely independent assumptions, he found through his statistical mechanics new meanings for entropy and the other related quantities which had proved so powerful on his first derivation. On the basis of the classical second law of thermodynamics, Gibbs's contemporaries had predicted that the "end of the world" would come when the entropy of the universe approached its maximum value; that is, all the energy of the universe would pass beyond the bounds of convertibility to useful work. This was called the "heat death" and was terrifyingly described in fiction by H. G. Wells in "The Time Machine." Gibbs's statistical mechanics revealed that this was not necessarily so. A low probability of "survival" might conceivably be increased.

Newton had no knowledge of the constitution of planets or stars. His equations for their motions were independent of their nature and, as far as he went, everlastingly true. Gibbs and his contemporaries knew nothing of molecular structure. He realized this and wrote: "One is building on an insecure foundation who rests his work on hypotheses concerning the constitution of matter." Like Newton he saw with an exalted vision, and so his statistical mechanics has survived every new revelation of atomic and nuclear physics. Gibbs came as close to the fundamental truths of nature as only the greatest scientists had before him, as any man is ever likely to come in the future.

1642   **12.** The "Napier Bones," for division and multiplication, about 1700   **13.** Sömmering's electric telegraph, 1809   **14.** Faraday's magneto-electric induction apparatus   **15.** and **16.** Faraday's later apparatus   **17.** Forbes's apparatus   **18.** Galileo's air thermometer **19.** Dalton's mountain barometer   **20.** Dalton's apparatus for testing the tension of ether vapor   **21.** Ancient Swiss clock, Dover Castle

4. THE SERENE
AND HAPPY MAN

"Towards us children, Uncle Willard was all kindness and generosity." "Willard Gibbs was the happiest man I ever knew." "If I were asked what was Willard Gibbs's most striking characteristic, I should unhesitatingly reply, 'his serenity.'" "I needed advice, and I knew that he could help me, not alone because he was a great scientist, but because I felt that he was a kindly, sympathetic, and understanding man." So said his nephews, nieces, friends, and students.

He was a quiet man of medium height, slender and assured. He had a Yankee face, and he looked distinguished with the neat beard that was in fashion at the time. He spoke rapidly in a voice that was high and urbane. A man with quick perceptions and a thin vein of irony, he was remembered by children only for his gentleness. His eyes were brilliantly piercing. He had a taste for nonsense, a talent for fun, and little interest in meeting people outside his own circle.

Gibbs was one of those men with whom modesty is a passion. On the basis of Gibbs's papers, Clerk Maxwell had a three-dimensional representation of Gibbs's curves cast in plaster and sent to him. As a compliment from one great scientist to another, it could not be surpassed. By his students, who knew perfectly well where the plaster model had come from, he was asked: "Who sent you the model?" "A friend," he replied shortly. "Who is the friend?" "A friend in England."

One of the mysteries about Gibbs is how Maxwell, at the height of his fame in England, had the time and discernment to become familiar with Gibbs's papers, even as they were appearing in the obscure *Transactions of the Connecticut Academy of Science.* Only within recent years has the mystery been solved. Maxwell learned of Gibbs's work in a very straightforward manner—through the mail. Gibbs, the man who stood accused of caring so little for approval of his work that he published it as obscurely as possible, personally sent reprints of each paper to the most eminent scientists of his day. Gibbs had a special mailing list of 507 names, representing twenty different countries. During his working life he wrote twenty monographs, personally sending each one to those names on the list for whom the research would have the most meaning.

Gibbs's papers are difficult to read and to follow. He made few preliminary notes and carried his researches in the back of his mind until they reached the acme of refinement. When the time came to write down his theories, the intermediate steps of his reasoning seemed no longer important to him.

People who are unaware of the time required for a profoundly new idea to penetrate into general thought, are inclined to be dismayed that ten to twenty years passed before Gibbs's work was widely understood and utilized. In the three centuries of modern science, there have been fewer than a dozen ideas in science as profound as Gibbs's studies of equilibria; and in every case, at least two decades were required for all the implications of the new science to be understood. In Gibbs's case, his colleagues at Yale admittedly did not understand his work, yet they certainly were aware of his genius.

As a man, Gibbs is truly understandable only when one realizes that within the privacy of his own inner creativeness he lived a complete life. His work was his justification for living, and he was happy because he knew very well that his work was high on the scale of greatness. His last years were troubled, not only by the death of his sister and closest friend, but just as deeply by the advent of the revolutionary new physics, radioactivity, X-rays, the reality of the electron. He did not know how these unexpected revelations would fit in with the universe as he understood it. At one point he was so depressed that he shook his head in bewilderment and said to some students that perhaps it was time he passed on. He was tired, lonely, and the justification for living seemed gone.

Gibbs's worry was needless. His work absorbed quantum mechanics. Of all the great theories advanced in the nineteenth century, his is the only one to stand without serious modification.

The mystery of Gibbs is not whether or not he was a misunderstood or neglected genius. As genius goes, his time dealt with him gently and generously. The mystery of Gibbs is this: how did it happen that pragmatic America, in its most materialistic years, produced a great theoretician? There was never one before him. There has never been one since.

American scientists have been experimentalists. The countries of Europe, whose cultural heritage America shares, have all produced great theoreticians. America has produced only one. Gibbs died at the dawn of the twentieth century, leaving no heir. America has searched Gibbs's life as if to blame him for his difficult papers, his reluctance to be more aggressive in disseminating his truths in more useful forms, his inability to surround himself, like Agassiz, by hordes of devoted students. In the end, none of these are Gibbs's failures; they are flaws in America itself; and until America can produce another Willard Gibbs, it must continue to search itself.

Gibbs is a measure of what American science can be. Was he simply a brilliant accident, or a prediction of what is to come? That this question has gone unanswered for half a century is itself a doleful, brooding answer.

JOSIAH WILLARD GIBBS LLD
PROFESSOR OF MATHEMATICAL PHYSICS
IN YALE COLLEGE MDCCCLXXI TO
MCMIII   DISCOVERER AND
INTERPRETER OF THE LAWS
OF CHEMICAL EQVILIBRIVM

Gibbs became a legendary figure at Yale during his last years when world honors and recognition came to him. His name and Yale were synonymous in the domain of science. This bronze plaque does not exaggerate Gibbs's serene strength.

The great tangent galvanometer of Cornell University was an impressive piece of apparatus at the turn of the century. The electrification of the United States was in its second decade, and electrical engineering had become a booming profession. The great galvanometer was a precision instrument for the measurement of large and small currents, but the young men who learned electricity in the 1890's were going to have to accommodate themselves to the great changes brought about by the advent of electronics. The new era began in 1907 with De Forest's "audion."

ndividualists

In 1899 journalists and orators were busily seeking a theme to symbolize the end of the nineteenth century. Hardly anyone, at the time, found it in an event which had occurred that very year in New York—the death of Horatio Alger, Jr.; yet most of the beliefs, dreams, aspirations of post-Civil War America were embodied in that shelf of literary works which included *Andy Grant's Pluck, Sink or Swim, Phil the Fiddler,* and *Bound to Rise.*

In Horatio Alger's nineteenth-century America, a penniless young boy, by honesty and courage, by industry and frugality, would "make the grade." It was an America of small, independent businessmen, honest farmers, where the sun shone every day.

So thoroughly did Horatio Alger reflect the popular belief, that the biography of every currently successful American was written in Alger terms. Andrew Carnegie, whose income in 1900 was twenty-three million dollars, had started at thirteen as a mill boy at $1.20 a week. John D. Rockefeller had begun work as a $4.00-a-week lad. Thomas Edison was presented as an Alger boy; and even Alexander Graham Bell, the highly trained philologist, son of three generations of literate upper-class Englishmen, and son-in-law of one of New England's wealthiest lawyers, was still presented as the penniless, untrained boy inventor who had managed by pluck and luck to evolve that marvelous, money-making machine—the telephone.

For a long time after the death of Horatio Alger, Americans who had grown up on his books would look with uneasy puzzlement at the twentieth-century America in which they lived out their day-to-day lives. Less and less did it seem like the country where they had been born.

The world that replaced Horatio Alger's America actually began eleven years before his death with the remarkable event in 1888 that was destined to shape the new face, heart, and mind of America: the holding company. As far as the future of American invention was concerned, the evolution of the holding company was of decisive importance.

James B. Dill, a New Jersey lawyer, had been asked by the governor for a way to increase the state's income and so attract large corporations to the state. Dill suggested the deceptively simple-looking law which would permit New Jersey corporations to buy and own stock in other corporations. In other states this was illegal, because it made people uneasy. An America of individualists demanded individual responsibility; corporations were too anonymous.

Dill's New Jersey law was the better mouse-trap supreme: companies rushed to incorporate themselves anew under the New Jersey dispensation, for the law brilliantly solved a problem which had been tormenting certain American businessmen for a decade.

In 1879, John D. Rockefeller and the owners of twenty-six other oil companies had put the stock of all the companies into the hands of a committee of three trustees who operated the twenty-seven companies as a single unit and represented ninety per cent of all oil refined in the United States. With this enormous leverage, retail prices could be controlled as well as the costs of raw materials. Competitors, non-members of the group, were literally forced out of business. The "trust" was an economic steamroller. Other industries—sugar, meat, rubber, and railroads—decided to follow the same pattern. However, these trustee-controlled industries were so ruthlessly efficient in fixing wages, prices, and competition with small business that the protests of the victims—rival businessmen and the exploited public alike—called for the passage, in 1890, of the Sherman Anti-Trust Act. The act was only gingerly enforced, but nevertheless, it was

The last testament of Alfred Bernhard Nobel (1833–1896), expressed his century's idealism by requesting that the annual income from the major part of his fortune amassed by his invention of dynamite be divided into five portions and awarded as prizes for high achievement in physics, chemistry, medicine and physiology, literature of an uplifting nature, and the promotion of peace among nations.

on the books as a latent threat.

The New Jersey holding company law made it no longer necessary for competing companies to form the kind of "voluntary associations" that were frowned upon by the Sherman Anti-Trust Act. A holding company, by buying stock, could control any number of competing companies and perform the same function as a trust. As matters turned out, it could do far more.

The holding company was begun simply as a scheme to make big money. Stock in holding companies could be sold to the public for far better prices than the shares in any of the subsidiary corporations. Moreover, as the number of acquisitions went on, shares in a holding company would increase in value every time a new company was absorbed. Combination was the order of the day and millionaires were produced overnight with the mushroom appearance of such huge companies as American Steel and Wire, American Tin Plate, and United States Steel. The early American holding company became more than a stock-selling, competition-killing scheme largely because of the personality of one man—J. P. Morgan.

Morgan welcomed the holding company because he believed that "competition is the death of trade." He also believed that any corporation which had his backing had to be properly and efficiently managed. Morgan was a man whose snobbishness and arrogance were massive, but so was his integrity. If he sold stock, it had to be—comparatively speaking—"worth the money." Corporations under his control had to be run according to his plan. When George Westinghouse refused to come to terms with the Morgan-dominated General Electric Company, Morgan's influence made Westinghouse's own Board of Directors oust him after a lifetime of service. Morgan was the most powerful American at the turn of the century.

However, when a large industrial corporation is efficiently run with the accent on the production of goods, it becomes far more than the aggregate of the small businesses it has absorbed. Specialization in various departments begins to take place, and the result is a close integration of many widely different production patterns. It works, grows, feeds itself, and, what is important to American science and invention, becomes an important contributor to technology.

Power in America stemmed from possession of the productive power of the machine. The giant corporation, the organization of diversified but cooperating units which was the outgrowth of the holding company, turned out to be ideally suited to the management of these large aggregates of production machinery. Thus, as the decades of the twentieth century unrolled, the huge corporation was to emerge as the century's social and economic unit.

Just as the feudal age—based on the power of land—determined the feudal personality, so the Cor-

poration Age was to develop a new American personality. The 1950 grandson of the 1900 independent businessman was to be a corporation executive.

In 1900 the individual, independent, American businessman, no matter how he felt about trusts, could still sympathize with William Rockefeller when he refused to divulge details of his business during the course of a government lawsuit. The general feeling was "the way I run my business is my own business." In 1954, however, the grandson of the 1900 big businessman would have grown up with the habit of being subordinate to someone else. In his day-to-day working life at the office, plant or laboratory, there was always someone to whom he was responsible, to whom he would have to report. The way he ran his business—his department—was the business of every one of his superiors. He would no longer be an intense individualist; he would be versed in the techniques of "getting along with the group."

The average income for a 1900 American was about $500 a year; an unskilled worker got $1.50 a day; shopgirls earned about $6.00 a week in large cities; the average working day was ten hours; the average work week was six days.

In 1900 the American scientist couldn't possibly conceive of the day when he would be anything but one of America's most independent individualists. A. A. Michelson refused to have an assistant who was not completely under his domination. Graduate students irked him to the extent that he called in Robert Millikan to relieve him of the burden of training these younger scientists in his own laboratory. George Hale, who grew up in the international fellowship of astronomers, was unwittingly to create the conditions in America that would foster the birth of the academic "research team" of the mid-century, because the great telescopes which Hale built could not possibly be reserved for the researches of a single individual. To justify the expense of building the mammoth observatories, groups of astronomers had to work together, each group taking turns at the instruments for their own individual problems. Later on in the century, other great research installations, like cyclotrons or other high voltage accelerators, costing millions of dollars, would impose this same pattern of cooperation on large numbers of individual scientists.

Irving Langmuir, in the laboratories of General Electric, would be the first American scientist to prove the possibilities that resided in large-scale coordinated research and development. Other corporation laboratories would prove to be just as successful.

America was to proliferate its new social forms with the speed of light during the twentieth century; but those who lived through it saw only the day-to-day change and scarcely realized what was happening.

A. A. MICHELSON

1. THE ELEGANT INTELLECTUAL

"It would seem," said *The New York Times* in the spring of 1879, "that the scientific world of America is destined to be adorned with a new and brilliant name."

The name was Albert Abraham Michelson; the prediction, made when he was twenty-seven, proved correct. Michelson was the first American to win the Nobel prize in physics.

Of all Michelson's contradictory qualities, the one that was most pervasive was elegance: elegance in technique, elegance in intellectual analysis of physical problems, elegance of presentation, and elegance in appearance. In 1894, when acting as host to a group of scientists at the dedication of the Ryerson Laboratory at Chicago University, this is the appearance he made: "With his jet-black hair, his attractive hazel eyes, his faultless attire, and his elegant and dignified bearing, he made a striking figure."

Another quality was his disconcerting honesty about his own motives and those of others. A man once asked Michelson's associates whether certain criticisms of the scientist were true. The colleagues said, "Don't ask us, ask him. He'll tell you." The man took the advice and came back looking shocked—"He certainly told me!"

He smiled easily, he had deep personal charm, and he was intensely individualistic; he knew exactly what he wanted to do and did it. Nothing diverted him from his goal, no matter who or what had to be sacrificed. He knew everything there was to be known about the special fields in which he was interested; he frankly admitted his utter ignorance of everything else. He was generous with praise when his admiration was aroused and ruthless in criticism of careless work or intellectual pretense.

To most of his closest friends, he was "like the sea on a summer's day—serene, illimitable, unfathomable." Yet beneath the serenity he was a man of deep

Albert A. Michelson

impulsiveness and powerful feelings. In 1898, during the hysteria over the sinking of the *Maine,* a meeting of students at the University of Chicago was called by the president to listen to two outstanding members of the faculty. No one knew then or ever discovered afterwards what the *Maine* was doing in Havana Harbor, nor on whose orders she was sent. Certainly there was no evidence then or later that the explosion was caused by the Spanish. Van Holst, the historian, counseled patience and objectivity until all the facts were in. Michelson, the scientist, who had made a creed of precision and suspended judgment, with blazing eyes and choked voice, emotionally demanded that the United States declare war immediately.

His first marriage ended, disastrously and his feelings about it were so strong that forty years had to pass before he could bring himself to ask his divorced wife, through his lawyer, to forgive him for any pain he might have caused her.

Michelson was born in 1852 in a small town on the German-Polish frontier, and was brought to this country at the age of two. This was only five years after the gold rush to California began and Michelson's family went to San Francisco over the Isthmian route across Panama. They settled first in the mountain town of Murphy's Camp in Calaveras County, celebrated by Bret Harte and Mark Twain. Later, they moved to Virginia City, Nevada, at the height of its excitement caused by the finding of the Comstock Lode. Michelson's father ran a dry-goods store.

For his schooling the boy was sent to San Francisco where he boarded with the high school principal, who taught science. Michelson developed a love for scientific apparatus and received three dollars a month to take care of the school's laboratory equipment.

He knew his career was to be in science. His mother wanted him to study medicine but his father suggested Annapolis, and so the quick, brilliant-eyed boy took the examination for the congressional appointment. He tied with another applicant who had more political influence.

Michelson was determined to be a midshipman and so, entirely on his own, he went to Washington to see President Grant. The ten appointments-at-large at the

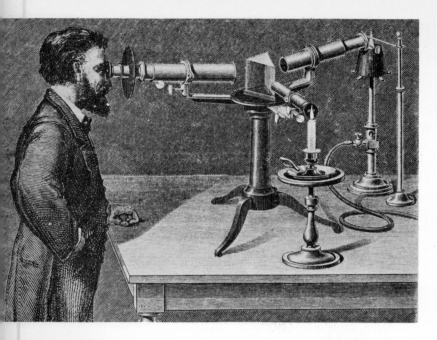

DEPENDENT AMERICAN SCIENCE

Nineteenth-century American physics students studied from texts in which experiments were performed by scientists bewhiskered in the French fashion. This was because most of the textbooks used in the United States were translations of Ganot's physics or a book by Deschanelles. Not until the end of the century were there American texts equal to the foreign classics.

After the Civil War, American universities began to establish graduate departments, and both Johns Hopkins and the University of Chicago were founded expressly to stress graduate work, but many American college graduates who wished to do advanced work in any science—physics, chemistry, or medicine—went abroad for their doctorates until the outbreak of the First World War.

When Michelson first entered physics, his interest in light was derived from brilliant work done abroad. Spectroscopy (above) was a very recent technique developed by Bunsen and Kirchhoff of Germany. Even the basic laws of optics (below) were being re-examined in terms of Maxwell's equations. The great 19th-century names in light were mostly French: Fresnel, Cornu, Fizeau, Foucault.

President's disposal were all taken but Grant's naval aide suggested that the boy go on to Annapolis on the chance that one of the ten applicants might fail the entrance examination. Michelson sat in the Commandant's office for three days, but none of the applicants failed. He then announced that he was going back to Washington to see Grant again, but Grant forestalled him. An additional appointment was made just so that Michelson could become a midshipman.

After graduation from the Academy in 1873, Ensign Michelson was made instructor of physics and chemistry. While a member of the Annapolis faculty, he performed the experiment which first gave him his international reputation as a physicist: he measured the velocity of light with an accuracy that had never been achieved before, using apparatus that he had built for slightly over ten dollars.

The following year he married Margaret M. Heminway and shortly afterwards he went abroad to study optics in France. There he first designed the apparatus which would produce the results that led to Einstein's theory of relativity.

In the 1870's it was assumed that the physical laws of the universe had all been described. Nothing remained for future physicists except further refinements in measurement. Michelson completely accepted Lord Kelvin's thesis of "the unlikelihood of future discoveries coming from other work than that involving the sixth place of decimals."

However, it was from exactly such measurements that Michelson proved all existing theories of matter to be inadequate. If the main questions were answered, the answers were all wrong.

In 1892 Michelson was one of the outstanding American scholars and scientists invited to join the faculty of the newly-endowed University of Chicago,

Dress parade at Annapolis when A. A. Michelson was a midshipman in 1870. After graduation, he remained to teach.

which was to stress advanced work by graduate students. Michelson's reputation attracted many graduate students but he discovered that he was a lone wolf by temperament. He couldn't share his work or his time, and it was not until he himself brought Robert Millikan there as his assistant that a large body of graduate research was organized. Shortly after Millikan arrived in 1905, he reported that Michelson called him in and said:

"If you can find some other way to handle this thesis business I don't want to bother with it any more. What these graduate students always do with

The Naval Observatory at Annapolis where Michelson made his first measurement of the speed of light at the age of 26.

my problems, if I turn them over to them, is either to spoil the problem for me because they haven't the capacity to handle it as I want it handled, and yet they make it impossible for me to discharge them and do the problem myself; or else, on the other hand, they get good results and at once begin to think the problem is theirs instead of mine, when in fact the knowing what kind of problem is worthwhile to attack is in general more important than the mere carrying out of the necessary steps. So I prefer not to bother with graduate student theses any longer. I will hire my own assistant by the month, a man who will not think I owe him anything further than to see that he gets his monthly check. You take care of the graduate students in any way you see fit and I will be your debtor forever."

From that time on, Michelson devoted himself purely to research and the few lectures that were necessary for his courses. He took no part in the departmental administration, attended no faculty meetings, and followed an intensely concentrated daily schedule with his personal assistants in the laboratory that ended promptly at four o'clock, when he went to the Quadrangle Club for tennis or billiards. He was a good violinist and a sensitive colorist as a painter. His physical coordination was remarkable. It was said that "there was more satisfaction in being defeated by his gracefulness than winning from another opponent."

Perhaps the best measure of the man is in the choice of his first research, for few feats are as daring in conception as the attempt to measure the speed of light. For eons, men thought light was instantaneous. Long before such concepts as photosynthesis, light was synonymous with life; and the symbol of light was the sun. Michelson's was a Promethean mind.

13. *On a method of measuring the Velocity of Light ;* by ALBERT A. MICHELSON, Ensign U. S. Navy, Instructor in Physics and Chemistry, U. S. Naval Academy. (From a letter to the Editors.) —The following method of measuring the velocity of light dispenses with Foucault's concave reflector, and permits the use of *any* distance. In the figure, S is a division of a scale ruled on glass; M, a revolving plane mirror; L, an achromatic lens; S″, a fixed plane mirror, at any distance from L.

The point S is so situated that its image S′ reflected in the mir-

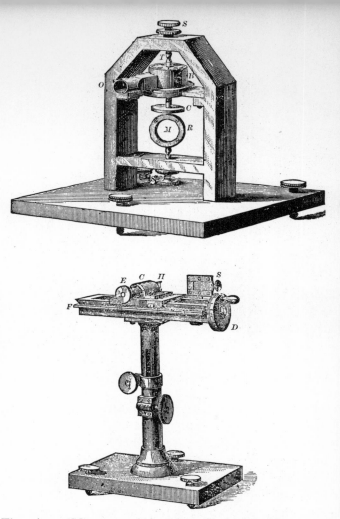

ror M, is in one focus of the lens L, while the image of S′ coincides with the mirror S″, which is placed at the conjugate focus. With this arrangement, when M turns slowly, the light from S″ is reflected back through the lens, so that an image is formed which coincides with S. When, however, the mirror rotates rapidly, the position of M will have changed while the light travels from M to S″ and back again, so that the image is displaced in the direction of rotation of the mirror.

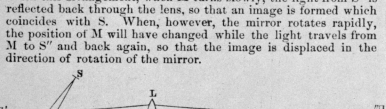

Let V be the velocity of light; D, twice the distance M S″; n, the number of turns per second; r, the distance M S and δ the deflection; then V is found by the formula $V=\dfrac{4\pi rnD}{\delta}$.

In a preliminary experiment the deflection amounted to five millimeters when the mirror revolved 128 times per second.

II. GEOLOGY AND MINERALOGY.

1. *On the Limestones of the Falls of the Ohio*, by JAMES HALL. 16 pp. 4to. Advance sheets of vol. v, part 2, of the Paleon-

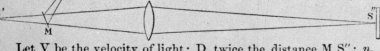

The American Journal of Science, 1878, printed Michelson's first note on his method for measuring the speed of light. His apparatus, a revolving mirror (above) and observation slit (below), were drawn for the complete paper of 1882.

The mirror (M) was made by Alvan Clark. A turbine wheel (T) was driven by high pressure air. (R) was a cast-iron frame. This mirror was an inch and a quarter in diameter. In later experiments, he used multi-faced mirrors.

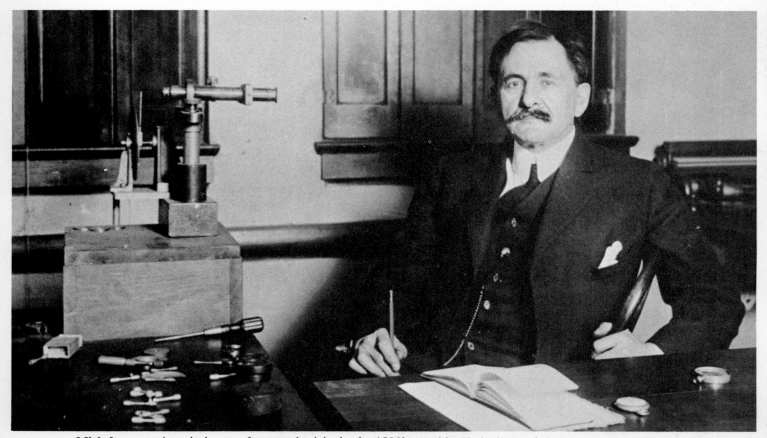

Michelson was America's most famous physicist in the 1890's. His reputation for elegance in experimentation was world wide. He had an artist's temperament, a sense of beauty, an outspoken tongue, and an eye for attractive women.

2. THE SPEED OF LIGHT

Not until the seventeenth century did anyone successfully attempt to measure the speed of light. Then the young Dane, Roemer, observed that the shadow of one of Jupiter's moons periodically appeared on the planet's surface, sixteen minutes and thirty-six seconds earlier than when it was observed at another time of year. Roemer decided that the reason for the time difference was that at one point of the year, the earth was closest to Jupiter; six months later, it was at its greatest distance. Roemer reasoned that the few minutes' difference was the time required for light to travel across the earth's orbit. When he divided this distance by sixteen minutes and thirty-six seconds, his answer was 186,000 miles per second.

Not until one hundred and seventy-three years later, in 1849, was it possible to measure the speed of light passing between two points on earth. The distance selected was ten miles. Fizeau, the French scientist, performed the experiment by sending pulses of light to a distant mirror and measuring the time taken for their return. Light was chopped into pulses by passing a beam through the edges of a toothed wheel that was rotating at high speed. When the wheel spun rapidly enough, a pulse of light that passed through an opening would reach the distant mirror and return in the same time that the wheel had turned a tiny arc —the width of one opening. Fizeau's wheel had 720 teeth and made exactly 25 revolutions per second. Knowing the distance to the mirror and back, he calculated the speed of light as 194,000 miles per second.

Some twenty years later, when Michelson was teaching at Annapolis, the problem of the speed of light had taken on a new and crucial importance. Maxwell's recently expounded electromagnetic theory of light stated that the velocity of light would be less in water than it was in air. Newton's corpuscular theory insisted that the velocity in water was *greater* than in air. In the 1860's and '70's the measurement of this difference constituted the most crucial experiment in physics; science required a method of measuring light velocities in any medium with great accuracy.

Michelson said: "The fact that the velocity of light is so far beyond the conception of the human intellect, coupled with the extraordinary accuracy with which it may be measured, makes this determination one of the most fascinating problems that fall to the lot of the investigator."

The velocity of light was also important to many astronomical problems of navigation, and so Simon Newcomb, the distinguished American astronomer, had been working on the problem with the aid of an appropriation from Congress. In 1877 the young ensign suddenly thought of a method which would allow him to make the measurement with the simplest of apparatus. His result appeared in the *American Journal of Science* six months later, May, 1878.

That summer, Michelson's father-in-law gave him two thousand dollars to improve his apparatus. The path of the light beam was extended over thirty times to 700 meters, the deflection of the image was 13.3 centimeters instead of only two. Maxwell had predicted that the velocity of light should be 300,000 kilometers per second. Michelson's result was 299,-895 plus or minus thirty. He had corroborated Maxwell with an accuracy of one part in ten thousand.

Throughout his entire life, he continually came back to this measurement, attempting in countless ways to refine it still further. In 1926, when he was seventy-four years old, he used a system in which a beam of light was sent from Mt. Wilson twenty-two miles to Mt. San Antonio and back. His rotating mirror was made with the highest precision, and it was driven by specially designed methods. He corroborated his earliest measurement.

Two years later, in 1928, at the age of seventy-six, he obtained the funds to measure the speed of light in vacuum, with the joint support of the Mt. Wilson Observatory, the University of Chicago, the Rockefeller Foundation, and the Carnegie Corporation. F. G. Pease and F. Pearson were his assistants. The United States Coast and Geodetic Survey marked out and surveyed the distances for the huge apparatus on the Irvine ranch. The vacuum was to be in a steel tube almost a mile long. The tube was three feet in diameter and came in sixty-foot sections of rolled and corrugated steel sheet. By means of multiple reflections, the light was to travel a path eight miles long, accurate to one part in a million. The entire system was pumped out to one fifteen-hundredth of the earth's atmosphere, and evacuation took forty-eight hours. Every time something needed adjustment, vacuum had to be broken and the long pumping process begun all over again.

His first apparatus at Annapolis had cost ten dollars; this cost fifty thousand dollars. It was Michelson's most ambitious project. As the work went on, his health began to fail. Pearson made the direct measurements under the guidance of the dying man. Hundreds of observations were made throughout 1930. Altogether almost three thousand observations were made. The velocity of light in vacuum turned out to have a mean value of 299,774 kilometers a second.

The very last paper under Michelson's name was to have exactly the same title as his first, published at Annapolis in 1878: "On a Method of Measuring the Velocity of Light."

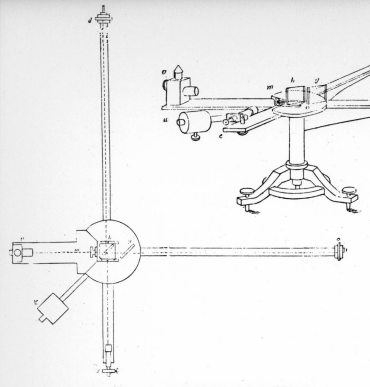

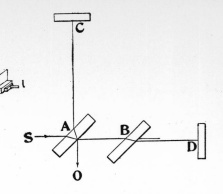

3. THE ETHER DRIFT

Michelson was one of the great masters of instrumentation. While his measurements of the velocity of light were classics of precision, his masterpiece was a device so sensitive that it measured distances as small as a single wave length of light as easily as the diameter of a star two hundred and fifty times bigger than the sun. With it, Michelson gave Einstein the first experimental confirmation of the revolutionary theory of relativity.

Michelson invented this instrument—the interferometer—in 1880, two years after his first measurement of the velocity of light, when he was only twenty-eight years old.

The measure of the brilliance of a scientist is how deeply he plunges into the most difficult problems of his time. Michelson met that test. The most exciting development of his time was Maxwell's theory which demanded that the universe be flooded with a substance called *ether*. The very first proponent of the ether had been Christian Huyghens some two hundred years earlier. By Maxwell's time the ether had been given many other properties.

Sir Oliver Lodge, one of the pioneers of wireless, thought of the ether as "one continuous substance filling all space; which can vibrate light; which can be sheared into positive and negative electricity, which in whirls constitutes matter, and which transmits by continuity and not by impact every action and reaction of which matter is capable." Since every theory in nineteenth century physics depended on the existence of the ether, Michelson determined to find out whether it actually did exist.

The heart of Michelson's method depended on the same phenomenon that explained the iridescent colors

seen in a thin film of oil floating on a puddle of water. Most of the sunlight is reflected from the upper surface of the oil film, while some of the light penetrates the film and is reflected from the lower surface. At certain angles, the two light reflections interfere just as water waves can cancel or reinforce each other depending on whether the trough of one wave coincides with the crest or the trough of another. (The different colors that make up white light have slightly different wave lengths.) In the interference of light, some colors cancel and one sees a black streak on the oil; where the colors reinforce, one sees the streaks of chromatically pure prismatic colors.

Michelson's interferometer, first conceived in France, split a beam of light into two parts, just as sunlight is split in two by the two surfaces of the oil film. Michelson made the separate beams of light traverse separate paths and then brought them back together again. If the two light paths were even slightly different—as if one had been reflected from the top of thin oil film and one from the slightly lower surface—the observer would see a pattern of "fringes" of light, alternate bright and dark bands of light.

As long as he knew the wave length of his light, he could then calculate the infinitely small difference between the paths which the two beams traveled. The brilliance of Michelson's conception was that the two beams of light were made to travel at right angles to each other before being rejoined. If one beam of light traveled in the direction of the earth's motion through space—which meant motion through the ether—and the other beam traveled at right angles, there should be a discernible difference between the paths, just as if two equally powerful swimmers were sent into a mile-wide river in which a strong current was flowing downstream. One man would be told to swim across and back; the other

ART. XXI.—*The relative motion of the Earth and the Luminiferous ether;* by ALBERT A. MICHELSON, Master, U. S. Navy.

THE undulatory theory of light assumes the existence of a medium called the ether, whose vibrations produce the phenomena of heat and light, and which is supposed to fill all space. According to Fresnel, the ether, which is enclosed in optical media, partakes of the motion of these media, to a ...

... will be ...

Assuming then that the ether is at rest, the earth moving through it, the time required for light to pass from one point to another on the earth's surface, would depend on the direction in which it travels.

... the interpretation of these results is that there is no displacement of the interference bands. The result of the hypothesis of a stationary ether is thus shown to be incorrect, and the necessary conclusion follows that the hypothesis is erroneous.

This conclusion directly contradicts the explanation of the ...

All 19th-century physics depended on the existence of an ether. At 29, Michelson stated (above) that the hypothesis was incorrect. His faith in his own measurements was firm.

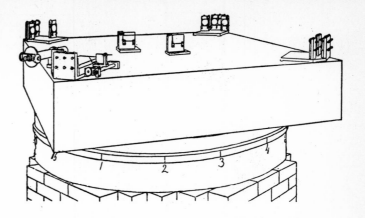

The interferometer was so sensitive to vibration that it had to be mounted on a block of concrete that floated in a cylindrical, brick-enclosed trough of mercury.

man to swim one mile downstream and back. The cross-river swimmer would be carried downstream a little more on both crossings and would return considerably farther down the bank from where he had left. The other swimmer would go down very quickly and have a hard time getting back. The time taken for the up-and-down-stream swimmer would be longer than that for the cross-river swimmer. From the time taken by each swimmer, one could calculate just how fast the current was flowing.

Michelson's light experiment with the interferometer depended on just this principle, and the fringe pattern would tell just how fast the ether was moving with respect to the earth. Michelson set up his delicate apparatus and found no sign of motion through an ether. He had such enormous confidence in his delicate measurements that he was able to fly in the face of every theory and scientist of his day. In his paper which appeared in the *American Journal of Science* in 1881, he stated flatly, "the hypothesis of a stationary ether is thus shown to be incorrect."

For the most part, Michelson's conclusion was violently rejected. Two men, Fitzgerald of Dublin and Lorentz of Leyden, independently offered a suggestion that would preserve the ether theory providing science would accept the radical notion that objects—like one arm of an interferometer—moving against the ether were contracted in length along the line of their motion, depending on how closely their velocity approached the speed of light. At ordinary speeds the amount of shrinkage was practically zero; at half the speed of light the shrinkage could amount to almost fifteen per cent.

Most physicists found the Lorentz-Fitzgerald contraction as fantastic as Michelson's conception and preferred to withhold judgment until further evidence was produced. In 1901 Kaufman showed that electrons emitted by radium seemed to increase their mass as the velocity of their ejection approached the speed of light. To young Albert Einstein, who had been born only two years before Michelson's experiment, the matter could be resolved by starting from completely new postulates:

1. All the laws of physics are the same in all systems having a uniform motion with respect to one another. Therefore, *an observer in one system cannot with any experiment detect the motion of that system by any measurements that are confined only to that system.*

2. The velocity of light in any system is independent of the velocity of the source of light.

3. This means that the velocity of light must be independent of the relative velocity of the source of light and the observer.

Stating this mathematically in 1905, Einstein's special theory of relativity indicated that the Lorentz-Fitzgerald contraction was real, but that the contraction had nothing to do with the ether. Furthermore, the mass of any object must increase as its velocity approaches the speed of light.

In Einstein's system, no point in the universe makes a better starting point for measurement than any other. All motion can be measured only in relation to the observer who performs the measurement. In the same way, there is no point in time to which any observer can refer as the beginning. Time and position are all relative to the observer: hence the theory has been called Einstein's relativity as opposed to Newton's relativity which contained absolutes of time and position. In 1919 Einstein's general theory was given further support by an astronomical observation, and for the first time the general public's attention was focused on the man who had been doing spectacular work for over twenty years.

At Mt. Wilson Observatory, Michelson mounted an 800-lb. interferometer on the 100-inch telescope to measure the diameter of the star Betelgeuse. He showed that the giant star had a diameter 250 times that of our sun.

4. THE GREAT PRECISIONIST

The interferometer of Michelson which started this revolutionary trend in physics was also used by him in 1920 at Mt. Wilson to measure, for the first time, the diameter of a star, using principles he had suggested as early as 1890. The interferometer can also be used for the measurement of distances that could not be detected under a microscope. For example, ball bearings in the automobile industry can be tested for perfect roundness with an accuracy of one part in ten thousand. Modern American production methods which depend on absolute precision owe much to the standards set by Albert Abraham Michelson.

Michelson was an artist. The thought processes and the temperament of the scientist and the artist are identical. The particular art form to which a creative man is drawn depends on the specific shape of his talent. The mathematician and theoretical physicist are similar to the poet and musician. The experimentalist is more like the painter and sculptor.

"One comes to regard the machine as having a personality," he wrote. "I had almost said a feminine personality—requiring humoring, coaxing, cajoling, even threatening. But finally one realizes that the personality is that of an alert and skillful player in a fascinating game, who will take immediate advantage of the mistakes of his opponent, who 'springs' the most disconcerting surprises, who never leaves any result to chance but who nevertheless plays fair, in strict accordance with the rules he knows, and makes no allowance if you do not. When *you* learn them and play accordingly, the game progresses as it should."

An instrument as delicate as the interferometer was the echelon spectroscope, created in 1898 for the analysis of spectral lines with an accuracy that had never been achieved before. When he reached what he considered the limit of optical precision in that field, he turned to the even more challenging problem of designing diffraction grating superior even to the masterpieces of Rowland. Michelson thought he could build a ruling engine in a few months; he took eight years to produce a six-inch grating containing 110,000 lines. This was fifty per cent better than anything that had been produced up to that time.

In 1919, to solve the problem of tides in the earth, he set out to measure the rigidity of the planet. This was the first time that he ever undertook a problem

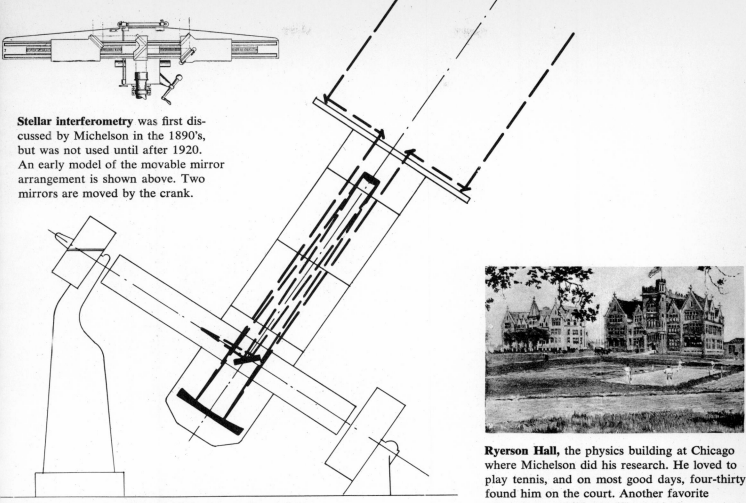

Stellar interferometry was first discussed by Michelson in the 1890's, but was not used until after 1920. An early model of the movable mirror arrangement is shown above. Two mirrors are moved by the crank.

Beams of light from the opposite tips of the star follow the optical paths shown in this plan of the 1920 set-up.

Ryerson Hall, the physics building at Chicago where Michelson did his research. He loved to play tennis, and on most good days, four-thirty found him on the court. Another favorite relaxation was billiards. His physical coordination was remarkable. He also painted.

at anyone else's suggestion. He buried two six-inch iron pipes, five hundred feet long, ten feet under the ground, one running east and west, and the other running north and south. He established his observation chamber where the two pipes met. The pipes were half-filled with water. Using interference methods, he made precise measurements of the variations of the levels of the water as miniature tides were produced in the pipes by the sun and the moon. If the earth had a semi-liquid structure, there would be no observable change in the water level. On the other hand, if the earth were absolutely rigid, small tides should be developed in the pipes. He measured shifts in the pipe tides of eight-thousandths of a centimeter which was what would be expected from a body that had a fifty per cent rigidity.

During the First World War, Michelson, at the age of sixty-five, rejoined the navy with the rank of lieutenant commander to develop optical equipment. His range-finder became standard equipment.

Besides the Nobel prize in 1907 and the Draper medal in 1910, he won the Copley medal of the Royal Society and many honorary degrees from American and European universities. From 1901 to 1903 he was

president of the American Physical Society, of the American Association for the Advancement of Science in 1910, and of the National Academy of Physical Sciences for four years from 1923.

He lived a long, rich, full life that covered the high tide of nineteenth-century physics and the years of deep confusion of the first decades of the twentieth century; and he saw the beginnings of the new light that clarified science with the advent of relativity and wave mechanics. During his lifetime, American physics ceased being provincial and rose to the level of the most advanced European countries.

He died just when a new era was dawning, for in the same volume of the *Scientific Monthly* in which his younger colleague, Robert Millikan, wrote his brief biography, there appeared a notice describing the Fifth Washington Conference on Theoretical Physics:

"An unexpected event . . . was the first information in this country given Professors Bohr and Fermi regarding the chemical discovery of Professor Hahn and his co-workers of disintegration of uranium into the comparatively light element barium . . . with the attendant release of approximately two hundred million electron volts of energy per disintegration."

5. THE INTERFEROMETER

Michelson's interferometer measures distances with a precision thousands of times greater than the finest optical microscopes. Light from a concentrated source (top) is made parallel by a lens beneath it and then split in two by a half-silvered mirror set at 45°. One half travels

horizontally to a fixed mirror (above), the second half passes down through the half-silvered mirror to a 45° mirror below which directs it horizontally to a movable mirror. Both beams are reflected and rejoin at the half-silvered mirror where they are directed (right) to the

observer who sees a pattern of light and dark bands. As the lower mirror is moved left or right, the pattern of bands shifts so that the amount of movement can be calculated with fantastic accuracy. In the ether-drift experiment, the split beams of light did not travel parallel paths.

THE HORSELESS CARRIAGE

1. SELDEN'S PATENT

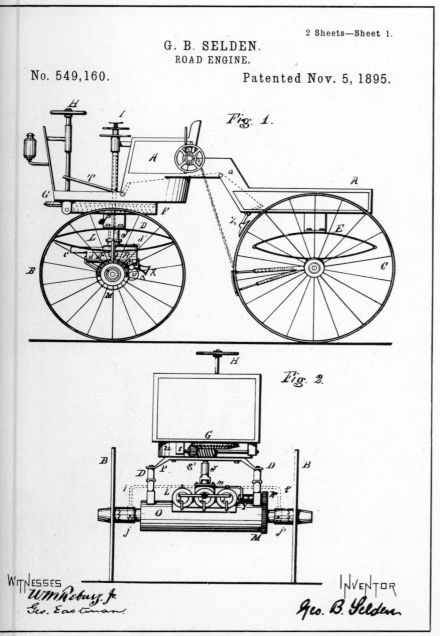

2 Sheets—Sheet 1.

G. B. SELDEN.
ROAD ENGINE.

No. 549,160.

Patented Nov. 5, 1895.

Fig. 1.

Fig. 2.

WITNESSES
W M Rebury Jr.
Geo. Eastman

INVENTOR
Geo. B. Selden

The first gas engine automobile patent ever granted was Selden's front wheel drive.

This is the way it looked to the public late in the fall of 1903: seventy million dollars were saying that U. S. Patent No. 549,160 was valid, while a mere twenty-eight thousand dollars were saying that the patent had no meaning at all—that, in fact, the "trust" was attempting to use the patent to enforce a monopoly.

The seventy million dollars was supposed to be the aggregate strength of the Association of Licensed Automobile Manufacturers and the Electric Vehicle Company. The twenty-eight thousand dollars was the working capital of the small automobile company known as Ford Motor. The patent in question belonged to George B. Selden and was assigned to the Association who was defending it. An eight year war between the "tyrannical trust" and the "struggling little" company began in the courts on October 22, 1903, in the Southern District of New York.

In actual fact, the situation was not at all that one-sided. The inventor, George B. Selden, had been paid only ten thousand dollars for his patent by the Electric Vehicle Company against the promise of royalties from most of the manufacturers of gasoline-driven vehicles. The Ford Motor Company, by September 30, 1903, had sold $142,481.72 worth of automobiles.

However, it was the next year that the public read Ida M. Tarbell's stories of the machinations of the oil trust led by the Standard Oil Company and exposés by other writers revealing the lurid inner workings of other trade combinations. It was good policy for Ford to appear as the underdog in the fight of the "little fellow" against the "interests." The case was bitterly fought on both sides. It dragged through the courts for years, filling thirty-six volumes with testimony.

By September, 1909, when the District Court was ready to hand down a decision, the financial balance between the "trust" and the "little" independent had radically changed. In 1909 alone, the Ford Motor Car Company had sold slightly over nine million dollars' worth of automobiles, from which it derived a net income of three million dollars — twenty times the amount of profit which the owners of the Selden patent had taken in nine years from the total aggregate of royalties after paying off Selden.

Rose Wilder Lane's 1915 biography, *Henry Ford's Own Story,* gave the Ford version which was the one that was still popularly accepted: "As a poor, hard-working mechanic, (Ford) fought weariness and poverty and ridicule to build his motor car; as an unknown inventor, still poor, he had struggled for a foothold in the business and got it; now he was in for a long, expensive legal battle before he should be able to feel secure in his success." This could have been applied to Selden with far more truth than to Ford. The public was also told that Ford had a gasoline carriage on the road long before Selden even applied for his patent. This, of course, was false. Selden applied for his patent in the year that Ford was only sixteen years old.

Court records of patent trials are notoriously deceptive when it comes to giving a proper evaluation of a patent. It is the business of lawyers on either side to stress only the points which they feel are favorable to their clients, and to confuse and decry the points that count against them. Moreover, the decision of the court reflects the popular passions of the moment, the shrewdness of a lawyer capitalizing on the weakness or confusion of a given witness, and the judge's limited ability to understand the technical points involved. In the case of the patent of George B. Selden, advertising and partisan passion have been mistaken for history. Although the Circuit Court of Appeals decided in favor of Ford, the patent of George B. Selden was never declared invalid. As a matter of fact, the Selden patent had an important historical function.

Among the students at the Yale Sheffield Scientific School in the years when Willard Gibbs was an instructor, was a nineteen-year-old veteran of the Civil War, the son of an upstate New York judge. In Selden's second year of college, his father's illness forced him not only to leave school, but to give in to his father's wish that he study law. In 1871, he was admitted to the bar, but his interest in engineering naturally turned him to the practice of patent law.

During the years when he was preparing for the bar, and for the first few years thereafter, he worked on a number of trivial inventions. During this time, too, he was also playing with the idea of a "horseless carriage" which could be run on a small, lightweight engine. For three years, from 1875 to 1878, he designed a number of engines to be driven by steam, ammonia, carbon bisulphite, and finally a mixture of nitrous oxide and kerosene. None of these proved satisfactory. In 1878 he built a crude, three-cylinder, internal combustion engine designed to burn one of the fractions of hydrocarbon liquid that was distilled from crude petroleum. This operated successfully. On this engine he applied for a patent, May 8, 1879.

Selden's patent was the first one on record anywhere of a combination of an internal combustion engine with a carriage. He knew that he was far ahead of his time, but since he understood the intricacies of the American patent system, he decided to keep his patent from being issued until the time when the public would be ready for such a machine. His seventeen year monopoly would begin to run from the date his patent was issued, not from the date his application was filed. He could keep his application alive by continually filing amendments. With each new amendment, the Patent Office would have to begin its action all over again. Any application that might be filed later than his would be declared an infringement on him. He wanted this protection while he set out to raise money from friends to finance the great invention.

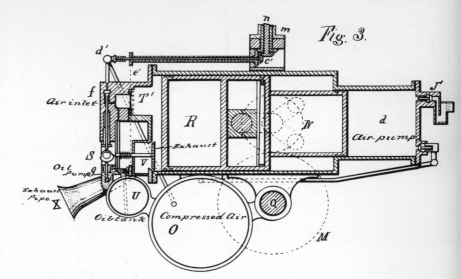

Selden's engine used "hydrocarbon" as fuel. He did not specify either gasoline or kerosene.

George B. Selden in his workshop, around 1909. He was a good engineer, but was not a practiced mechanic.

J. M. Studebaker in his Wagon Tire Shop at Hangtown, Cal., before Studebaker became one of the most famous wagon builders in America. His sons built autos.

Cugnot built the first self-propelled steam wagon as a carriage for artillery. Napoleon saw no future in steam locomotion and withdrew his support.

2. ENGINES FOR HORSES

George Selden was by no means the first man to experiment with internal combustion engines. Priestley's work on gases led others to realize that a combustible gas, when set afire in a closed chamber, produced a violent increase in pressure. This sudden expansion of gas could drive a piston fitted to form one end of a cylindrical chamber. A reciprocating piston, as in a steam engine, could be used to turn a shaft.

Even before the steam engine was put into a usable form, there had been experiments with gunpowder as the explosive material. An explosion—or combustion —engine had this advantage over a steam engine: no cumbersome boiler was required. John Stevens of Hoboken thought of an explosion engine and one was actually built by a temporary assistant, the French emigré Brunel, who later became a famous engineer in England and whose son built the "Great Eastern."

In 1769, Joseph Cugnot in Paris built a self-propelled steam carriage which ran three miles per hour. An early patent was taken out by Philip Lebon in France in 1799; his design set forth the principle of using the explosion of coal gas.

In the succeeding years, other inventors, both English and American—Wellman, Wright, Johnston, and Barnett — designed variations and minor improvements. In Wright's engine, 1833, the gas was ignited by a burning gas jet. Johnston's engine, about the same time, used hydrogen mixed two to one with oxygen as fuel. The explosion created water vapor which condensed and formed a partial vacuum, helping the piston to descend again. Johnston's idea was ingenious, but oxygen and hydrogen were prohibitively expensive at the time.

The electric spark as a means of ignition was added in 1857 by Barsanti and Mattuci. Three years later, the spark system was used by Lenoir to ignite the vapors from hydrocarbon compounds, thus starting the cumulative line of invention down a new track that was to lead to the most usable hydrocarbon of all—gasoline.

The combustion engine was subjected to its first searching theoretical examination by the Frenchman, Alphonse Beau de Rochas, in 1862. He was the first to establish the principle of the four cycle engine that was to become almost universally adopted.

In 1867, two young Germans, Nikolaus Otto and Eugen Langen, built an engine that had a greater efficiency and more fuel economy than Lenoir's. It was an atmospheric engine in which the explosion took place on only one side of the piston. When the exploded gases had been condensed to form a partial vacuum, the pressure of the atmosphere drove the piston back down into position for another explosion. The piston rose rapidly, but fell slowly, giving an uneven, convulsive rhythm. Six years later, in 1874, Otto designed a new, smoother engine based on the four cycle principle of Beau de Rochas—and it became famous as the "silent" Otto.

In the meantime, in 1872, George Brayton of Boston patented an engine that was the first actually to use petroleum as a fuel. Brayton's engine was essentially a hot air engine and was quiet in operation. By the time of the Centennial Exhibition at Philadelphia, Brayton's engine was preferred by many in America over any foreign design. By this time, Selden's application had been in the Patent Office for six years, continually kept alive by amendments.

The history of steam-driven road vehicles shows one of the rare examples of mechanical progress being held up for half a century by legal measures. Oliver Evans's *Orukter Amphibolos* had lumbered and groaned through a stretch of woods, paddled up the river, and

Trevithick and Vivian built an early steam coach in 1801. Oliver Evans's partisans say that Trevithick copied his design for high-pressure steam engines.

The American velocipede, said Hiram Maxim, made the public conscious of horseless locomotion long after the means were available for self-propelled carriages.

then rolled around Center Square for a flamboyant curtain call before ending forever a short career as a self-propelled land vehicle. Richard Trevithick, in England, built a road steam engine in 1803 which was later mounted on a track. In 1825, Thomas Blanchard of Springfield, Massachusetts, built another, but nobody wanted to buy it.

In the United States, roads were so dreadful that any form of road engine experimentation was close to moon-madness. The English situation was very different. Yet, no matter how good the English roads were, they had been designed for horse-drawn traffic and foot passengers and could not support the weight of the early steam-powered carriages.

In 1831, when the first English railroads were being set up, Sir Charles Dance organized a steam carriage route between Gloucester and Cheltenham. The distance was nine miles. Sir Charles's ornate bus made it in forty-five minutes, four times a day on schedule. Walter Hancock ran five beautifully ornamented steam buses in a regular service from Stratford to Paddington. In 1836, in only twenty weeks, Hancock's line carried 12,760 passengers and covered 4,200 miles. The owners and drivers of conventional horse-drawn stages complained that the three-ton steam buses were ruining the roads and highways. Popular prejudice against the puffing road steamers and the influence of the stage owners combined to pass the Locomotive Act of 1836, which posted such heavy road tolls for the steam carriages that they could no longer afford to operate. Also, it required that all self-propelled vehicles be preceded by a man carrying a red flag in the daytime or a red lantern at night. By that Act, popularly called "The Red Flag Act," England relinquished her lead in self-propelled road vehicles. The Act was not repealed until 1896, and then only after gas engine carriages were already on the roads in France, Germany, and the United States.

The first known operative gas-engined vehicle was built by Marcus, a German, in 1860. In 1865 the Frenchman, Lenoir, drove twenty-four kilometers in three hours. Then in 1885, Gottlieb Daimler and Karl Benz simultaneously and independently attached small gas engines to tricycles.

Working independently in America, a number of men, who had only the vaguest idea of what was going on abroad, also were experimenting with Otto-engined carriages—Charles Duryea, a mechanic; Henry Ford, working for the Edison Company; and Haynes, collecting bills for the gas company.

In 1886 Duryea constructed a light buggy driven by a two-horsepower steam engine, but never completed it. In 1891, he made drawings of another carriage—this time to be driven by a gasoline engine—and began work on it with his brother. The "buggyaut" ran successfully on April 19, 1892. In 1894, still another carriage, powered by a four cycle engine, was built by the Duryea brothers.

This model was put on the road in March or April of 1895. It ran daily throughout that hot summer and, in the fall of that year, it won a race against expensive, heavily-built, imported German cars in the *Chicago Times-Herald* race. A Duryea Motor Wagon Company was organized, and built thirteen cars in 1896.

Elwood Haynes built a gasoline carriage in 1893 that was successfully tested in 1894. Charles B. King built and ran a horseless wagon in Detroit in March, 1896. Two months later, Henry Ford ran his "autocycle" in the same city, the lightest gasoline engine carriage built so far. Duryea's "buggyaut" weighed 700 pounds, Haynes's weighed 820, King's was extremely heavy—1,300 pounds, but Ford's was only about 500 pounds. That year too, 1896, Alexander Winton built an automobile.

By 1895, Selden knew that the time for which he had waited sixteen years had finally come.

3. DEATH
OF A MONOPOLY

Selden was no mechanic. His ideas were sound, his understanding was clear; but tools were only lumps of metal in his hands. For sixteen years, he had tried hard to raise money to pay the cost of development.

For one thing, he was not interested in building merely a model car. He had no illusions that the sight of one gasoline buggy would immediately create a market for itself. The history of steam carriages was well known to him: they had all been more or less isolated experiments, and they were considered cantankerous freaks. Selden wanted to raise sufficient backing to cover not only the cost of the necessary experiments, but he wanted enough left over to carry on a business through several years of adversity.

A second cause for Selden's failure was that the bicycle had not yet attained the wide popularity which was to come much later. The bicycle not only improved American roads, but accustomed the public to the revolutionary idea of horseless travel. The third reason for Selden's trouble was his own personality. He had a genial, kindly nature; but he had entered a profession that didn't suit him, and continued disappointment with the automobile filled him with a barely suppressed impatience that sharpened a tongue already direct enough.

Selden had to stand by helplessly while more able mechanics were beginning to drive carriages with the new type of engine. In France and Germany, "automobilism" was becoming the fashion among the sporting rich, and finally when Levasseur won a sensational road race from Paris to Bordeaux in 1895, Selden knew that the time had come to have his patent issued.

"The object of my invention," says his patent, "is a safe, simple, and cheap road locomotive, light in weight, easy to control, and possessed of sufficient power to overcome any ordinary inclination."

His vehicle was to have a propelling wheel, a steering mechanism, a receptacle for liquid fuel (of the hydrocarbon type), a power shaft connected with the propelling wheel, a disconnecting device to vary the speed, and an unencumbered body for passengers. The engine was to be placed on the front axle beneath the seat, although other positions were possible. It was the opinion of the Englishman Dugald Clerk, the foremost expert on gas engines, that the Selden patent was valid and that the device described was operable.

The Selden patent came to public notice in a roundabout way. Beginning in 1895, the Pope Manufacturing Company, realizing that its bicycle business was falling off, turned to Hiram Maxim for experimentation on gasoline- and electrically-driven carriages. The company had both types on the market by 1899, only one year after the first American-made gasoline carriage was sold. That date is March 24, 1898. However, the electric carriage proved more popular because of its quiet, its lack of vibration, and its ease of handling. By 1899 there were only fifty gasoline engine automobiles in the entire country, foreign-made and domestic.

A group of New York businessmen, headed by William C. Whitney, was interested in starting a fleet of electrically-driven cabs, and approached the Pope Company with the contract. This discussion led to broadened plans in which the Pope Manufacturing Company and the New York syndicate were to join forces in the manufacture of electric and gasoline cars.

While the deal was pending, the New Yorkers made an investigation of the patent situation and discovered the existence of the Selden patent. Maxim wanted to fight the patent, but the New York group decided that

THE FIRST AMERICAN AUTOMOBILE

Chas. Duryea's "buggyaut" was the first American-built car. Duryea did not know of Selden's patent.

J. Frank Duryea, in 1895, won a race against imported cars. It was steered by a tiller.

it would be easier, cheaper, and safer in the long run to buy out Selden. An agreement with Selden was reached and the new company, the Columbia and Electric Vehicle Company, was given a license by Selden for ten thousand dollars and a percentage of what royalties could be collected from other manufacturers.

Columbia and Electric Vehicle circularized the manufacturers of automobiles, informed them that the Selden patent existed, and that licenses were available to any manufacturer who would pay the royalty. The first resentment was overcome when Alexander Winton, by now the most successful automobile manufacturer in America, decided to come to terms. With Winton went Elmer Apperson, of the Haynes-Apperson Company, the Auto-Car Company, and the Charles Duryea Power Company. This settlement was reached, however, only after they had gone on trial and the court had sustained the Selden patent.

Very liberal terms were granted to the manufacturers. They were not asked to pay royalties on any cars produced before the time of the agreement. More than that, they were allowed to deduct the cost of the recent trial from a royalty agreement. Two-fifths of the income was to go to a newly formed organization called the Association of Automobile Manufacturers, and one-fifth to Selden. Peace was formally declared in March of 1903.

Only a few manufacturers were left outside the agreement and, one by one, they came to terms. The Ford Company and one or two others were the exceptions. Ford would have been glad to avoid any kind of trouble by joining the association, but he had been told, incorrectly, that they would not grant him a license under the patent because he was "an assembler and not a builder of cars." To Ford, this was a personal insult. His partner, James Couzens, was just as angry. When a representative of the association came to the Ford partners, Ford told him angrily, "Tell Selden to take his patent and go to hell with it." The representative said, "You men are being foolish; the Selden crowd can put you out of business—and will." Couzens laughed. Ford, at this point, completely lost his temper. He stood up, shook his finger at the representative and shouted, "Let them try it!"

During the years in which the litigation dragged out, both sides attacked each other in the press with advertisements and with threats. This was how the Ford Motor Company first came to public notice. The course of the trial was confused by hammering away at trivial and often irrelevant points. The Ford lawyer tried to make the Selden patent look ridiculous by comparing the basic conception, which dated from 1879, with practices of 1910. On the other hand, the Selden forces overstated their case, even though they insisted that what they were patenting were "general principles." In the end the courts decided the Selden patent was valid, but that the Ford motor car was sufficiently outside its scope, as was every other automobile being manufactured in this country at the time—thirty-three years after the original conception.

The A.L.A.M. then broke up, because no further royalties had to be paid to Selden. On the other hand, the Selden patent would have had only one more year to run anyhow. The financial loss to Selden was not quite so serious as it might have been.

That the Selden patent was bound to be superseded by other improvements was, of course, just as inevitable as the improvements on the McCormick reaper. The argument made against the Selden patent was that it patented "no new device" and that it described only a combination of known elements. However, the American patent law is very explicit on the point, and there is no doubt that the Selden patent, when filed in 1879, was a highly original and ingenious conception.

ILT BY THE DURYEA BROTHERS

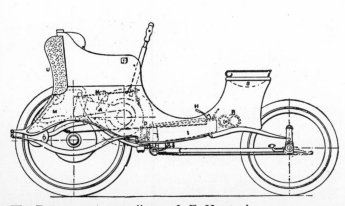

The Duryea car, according to J. E. Honans' 1905 *Self-Propelled Vehicles.*

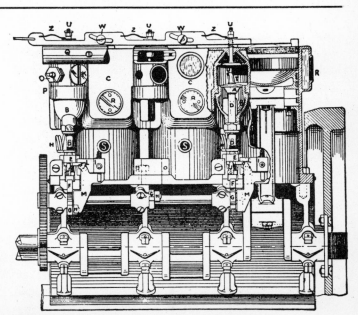

The Duryea engine, according to R. T. Sloss's 1906 *Book of the Automobile.*

America's greatest contribution to the automobile was mass production. The first steps by Ransom Olds were developed by Henry Ford in 1914 at Highland Park. Bodies were slid down a chute to fall on the chassis.

4. THE ASSEMBLY LINE

The automobile really became an American institution when it entered the stage of mass production. The "Father of Automotive Mass Production" was Ransom E. Olds who had started business on a shoestring in 1899 on East Jefferson Avenue in Detroit. Olds built an "assembled" car. The Dodge brothers' machine shop made his engines. The Lelands, father and son, made his transmissions. The "Merry Oldsmobile" looked like a buggy steered by a tiller—crude and spidery compared with the massively built, elegant French cars; but its cost was less than four hundred dollars against five to ten thousand for the imported models.

In 1901 Olds turned out four hundred and twenty-five cars; and in the following year he turned out twenty-five hundred. He was the first to preach and practice the idea of a cheap car for the masses.

The popularity of the Oldsmobile was largely due to its smooth performance, and the Lelands—transmission builders—were responsible for that. The Lelands were master machinists. To them, precision was a religion. They soon left Olds and started their own company—Cadillac—and were the first by many years to use interchangeable parts throughout. Leland was sixty years old when he built his first Cadillac. He established the mechanical standards for the entire industry. He sold Cadillac to General Motors in 1909, continued as manager for eight years, and then designed another high standard mass-produced car—the Lincoln—which he eventually sold out to Ford.

Henry Ford made several unfortunate starts in the motor car industry. For a while, in 1899, he was chief engineer of the Detroit Automobile Company, but failed to make a salable car. He was fired and replaced by the Lelands, whose car was so superlative that the company changed its name to be identical with Leland's product—the Cadillac Motor Company. It is said that Henry Ford never forgave Leland, and that he bought Lincoln Motors twenty years later just for the satisfaction of kicking out the old man.

Whatever Ford's early failures at manufacturing may have been, however much the credit for the financial success of the Ford Motor Company may be traceable to Ford's partner, James Couzens, there is no doubt that Ford himself carried the idea of mass production to its ultimate form. When Olds, against his better judgment, gave up the cheap car on the insistence of his directors, Ford took over the field. Mass

The 1914 Ford chassis and engine were tested for performance and then driven to the bottom of the chute

where the body fell into place, was fastened, and then the finished car was driven away ready for sale.

production in the modern sense was the subject of intensive experiments in 1913, and was finally made standard Ford practice the following year.

In a million ways, the face of America was shaped by the motor cars. New cities, towns, farmlands, mines, entire industries owe their existence to the automobile. Wherever there was solid ground on which a wheel could turn, the automobile penetrated. Fulton's steamboat developed the river-side of America; automobiles covered the land.

The network of highways that converted backwater towns into shopping centers was created because of the automobile. The building of the vast dormitory suburbs to house city workers was due to their accessibility to the automobile. With the unmanageable traffic congestion in the cities, the suburbs were to become autonomous units by the mid-century when the large office establishments began to move out of the towns to regions where there were ample parking facilities.

The second half of the nineteenth century was the era in which the giant city came into being—the urbanization of America. Because of the automobile, the second half of the twentieth century may very well mark the reverse trend—the suburbanization of America.

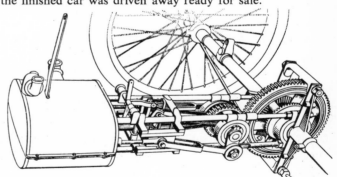

Engine and spur-drive connections of the Stanley Steam Carriage. An example of early direct-connected drive.

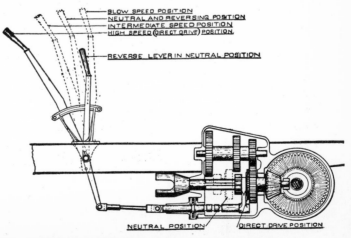

The "sliding transmission" of an early Packard. The chain drive of the 1890's soon became obsolete.

Robert A. Millikan in 1891 was teaching physics at Oberlin College even though he had started out to be a classics scholar. He went into physics simply for the money— six hundred a year.

ROBERT MILLIKAN

1. THE SCIENTIST IN SPITE OF HIMSELF

Late in the spring of 1889, Professor John F. Peck, who taught Greek in the small Ohio college of Oberlin, requested one of his classical scholars to learn enough physics to give the elementary physics course the following year.

"But I don't know any physics."

"Anyone who can do well in my Greek can teach physics."

"All right," said the student, "but you'll have to take the consequences."

The consequences were two of the most fundamental researches in twentieth-century physics. Robert Millikan, who accepted the assignment because he needed the money, never went back to his classical studies.

Robert Millikan was born in 1868 in Illinois, the son of a minister. He grew up in the small river town of Maquoketa, Iowa. "My father and mother brought up a family of six—three boys and three young girls—on a small-town preacher's salary of thirteen hundred dollars a year," he said. "We wore two-piece suits of blue jeans and no shoes from the close of school at the end of May until its beginning in September. Our yard contained about an acre of ground in which Father and his three boys raised potatoes, corn, melons, and garden truck. . . In the winter we boys sawed ten sticks of four-foot wood a day so long as the ten cords lasted. In vacation, we were required to work mornings in the garden, but the afternoons were free for play."

They swam in the river, played baseball, milked the cows twice a day, got up at three in the morning to greet the circus, became expert gymnasts on homemade parallel bars, and never heard that it was possible for a grown man to make a living out of spending his time in a laboratory working on something called "physics." To be "physicked" meant to be given a cathartic.

In the Maquoketa high school, the only physics course was given by the principal who spent his summers locating water with a forked hazel stick, and anyhow didn't take much stock in all that nonsense in the textbook. How could sound be made up of waves? Nonsense, boys, all nonsense! On the other hand, Millikan was to remember his algebra teacher with respect for the rest of his life. When Millikan was eighteen, he entered Oberlin College; his grandmother's brother had been a founder.

During his second year in college, he took another course in physics which was as dull as his first in high school. His backyard training in games and athletics won him a part-time job as student instructor of gymnastics, and the income from his second teaching assignment—physics—further helped pay his expenses. Millikan, however, was a conscientious teacher, and he plowed through the available texts to keep ahead of his students. There were only two books which were then widely used in American colleges: translations from the French of Ganot and Deschanelles. Under this forced pressure, he really learned his subject.

On graduation in 1891, he continued to teach physics at Oberlin at an annual salary of six hundred dollars only because he saw "no other immediate opening in that depression year." However, the Oberlin faculty took his role in science far more seriously than he did and, without his knowledge, sent a transcript of his record to Columbia University. The Columbia fellowship of seven hundred dollars was

Michael Pupin of Columbia University was the first real physicist Millikan ever knew. Pupin had a powerful personality and his influence on Millikan was decisive.

A country boyhood was Millikan's preparation for a career in science. At Oberlin, he taught gymnastics and physics.

granted, and Millikan accepted, because again there was no other way to get that much money. At Columbia, for the first time, he met men who were truly interested in physics and, by contagion, he decided to try to make himself a true scientist—although for years he was plagued by inner doubts about his ability.

In 1893, America was backward in pure science. Only men who had been trained in Europe had a real awareness of what research should properly be. In the Columbia physics department, there was only one such man. Professor Michael Pupin, Cambridge trained, was a powerful influence on Millikan, as he was on every other young scientist who met him. "My course in optics with Dr. Pupin was an eye-opener," Millikan said. "He was the first man I had ever seen who knew analytical processes well enough to come to class day after day without preparation and do his thinking in terms of equations. Watching him inspired me to see if I could learn to do it myself."

When Millikan's Columbia fellowship in physics expired, he was not reappointed; Pupin was in the Engineering School and had passed over Millikan in favor of an engineering candidate. When Pupin realized that Millikan was left without resources, he really began to take an interest in him. It was Pupin, the following year, who advised Millikan to go abroad to study in Germany. When Millikan confessed that he could not afford it, Pupin loaned him the money. He would have made an outright gift, but Millikan insisted on signing a note.

Just before Millikan went abroad, he met one other man who was to exercise a decisive influence in his life: during a summer session he went to the newly opened University of Chicago where he met A. A. Michelson who impressed the young graduate student more than anyone else he had met thus far.

Fortunately for Millikan, he was in Europe when

the series of experiments were made which culminated in the great explosion of all the classical theories; 1895 and 1896 were the years when the names of Becquerel, Roentgen, Curie and Thomson were news in science.

The ferment was still going on in the summer of 1896 when Millikan received a cable from Michelson offering him an assistantship at the University of Chicago. Millikan was then twenty-eight. "I hocked my trunk and clothes with the captain of one of the boats on the American Transport Line, telling the company I would pay the captain the fare before I removed my belongings from the boat in New York."

During the next dozen years, he took part in the intellectual vitality that marked Chicago during the first decade of the century. The University of Chicago was attracting the young men whose names during the coming years were to become famous. There was George Hale, the astronomer, James Breasted, the historian, Stephen Leacock, the economist, Robert Lovett and dozens of others. In Millikan's boarding house were two other young men: Thorstein Veblen and Harold Ickes.

Millikan's first years in Chicago were devoted to writing some of the first acceptable American textbooks on physics and raising his young family. Michelson turned over to him all the administrative and educational chores for which the older man had no temperament.

Not until Millikan was almost forty years old did he turn seriously to research. Then the problems that he selected were those that had so stirred the world of science during his earlier years in Europe. Millikan, who had become a physicist in spite of himself, was to perform two experiments that are still classics of elegance of conception and execution. His Nobel prize was well deserved.

The University of Chicago in 1896, where Millikan was called by Michelson, was an experiment in education.

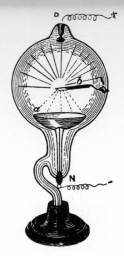

A Crookes tube in 1879 in which a strip of platinum (*b*) is made red hot by the passage of current between the bowl-shaped cathode (*a*) and an anode (D). In a partial vacuum, this current was said to consist of *cathode rays*. The nature of these rays was the subject of decades of research. Some physicists called them the "fourth state of matter."

J. J. Thomson of Cambridge analyzed all the previous data on cathode rays, then did his own brilliant experiments.

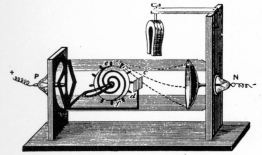

Cathode rays (*c*) were known to have definite mass because their bombardment against the vanes (*e, d, f*) caused the wheel to spin. They were also known to have electric charge because they could be deflected by magnetic fields.

Thomson's 1897 classic paper summed up all the evidence on cathode rays and came to the conclusion that electricity was the motion of negatively charged particles—*electrons*.

THE

LONDON, EDINBURGH, AND DUBLIN

PHILOSOPHICAL MAGAZINE

AND

JOURNAL OF SCIENCE.

[FIFTH SERIES.]

OCTOBER 1897.

XL. *Cathode Rays.* By J. J. Thomson, *M.A., F.R.S., Cavendish Professor of Experimental Physics, Cambridge**.

THE experiments† discussed in this paper were undertaken in the hope of gaining some information as to the nature of the Cathode Rays. The most diverse opinions are held as to these rays; according to the almost unanimous opinion of German physicists they are due to some process in the æther to which—inasmuch as in a uniform magnetic field their course is circular and not rectilinear—no pheno-

2. THE MYSTERIOUS FOURTH STATE OF MATTER

Looking back over his life, Millikan said that the luckiest thing that had ever happened to him was that Pupin did not take him on as his assistant. Otherwise he never would have gone abroad and found himself in Europe in the years when modern physics had its true beginnings.

On January 4, 1896, Wilhelm Konrad von Roentgen read a paper before the Würzburg Physico-Medical Society in Würzburg, then repeated it at the anniversary meeting of the German Physical Society in Berlin. His announcement created a sensation in two sciences. Roentgen described the discovery of an entirely new form of radiation which permitted him to photograph objects hidden beneath opaque, solid shields. He showed a photograph of parts of his own living skeleton—the bones of his hand. To the medical world, the phenomenon of the Roentgen rays was a miracle that had to be put to diagnostic work at once. To the world of the physicist, the explanation of the phenomenon seemed far more important at the moment than its use. The search for this explanation was to prove the first leap into the atomic and sub-atomic world.

The marvelous rays discovered by Roentgen had a history going back some forty years in European science. In 1853, a French physicist named Masson played a high voltage electric spark on a glass vessel from which most of the air had been evacuated. The flask suddenly was filled with a bright, unearthly purplish glow. Hittorf and Crookes made further investigations of this beautiful phenomenon during the 1860's and '70's. The invention of the same highly efficient vacuum pumps that allowed Edison to invent an incandescent lamp also allowed Crookes to observe the weird vacuum glow at lower and lower pressures. The nature of the glow changed as the pressure inside the glass flask was reduced to a hundredth and then a thousandth of the atmosphere outside. It brightened, then broke into isolated blobs of light, and finally diminished and disappeared altogether. When the vacuum was sufficiently thorough, the glow in the tube was gone, but the glass walls of the vessel itself began to shine with a ghostly greenish light.

Crookes's tube was shaped like a long pear. In either end he sealed a metal plate. He established that the glow in the tube was due to the passage of *rays*, as he called them, through the vacuum between the two metal discs—the electrode—when the metal plates were attached to a source of high voltage. The rays were called *cathode rays*, and the tube was called a cathode ray tube. Crookes noted also that the mysterious rays seemed to act as if they had mass and velocity. He did not understand their nature, and he referred to them as "a fourth state of matter," neither liquid, gaseous, nor solid.

It further was established that the cathode rays were electrical in nature because a magnet held outside the tube could cause the cathode rays to bend in an arc within the tube. An electric force outside the tube would also cause the cathode rays to be deflected. Other investigators showed that the cathode rays could be brought outside the tube if they were made to strike a very thin foil of aluminum; however, their penetration through the air outside the tube was very limited.

Some physicists actually thought that the "fourth state of matter" was the mysterious ectoplasm described by spiritualists. For a while the market in ghosts took an upward turn.

In the autumn of 1895, Konrad von Roentgen was performing some experiments with a Crookes tube which was wrapped tightly in black paper so that none of the glow would escape. By accident, he happened to notice that in the completely dark room, with the tube so shielded, "a paper screen washed with barium-platinum-cyanide lights up brilliantly and fluoresces equally well, whether the treated side (of the paper) or the other be turned toward the discharge tube."

The paper screen was almost *six feet away* from the apparatus. Roentgen knew that the cathode rays would make such a coated sheet fluoresce, but this piece of paper was far beyond the range of any cathode ray that had ever been recorded. He soon found that all substances were more or less transparent to the mysterious new rays. Only lead seemed opaque to it. He found that he could activate photographic dry plates and films, and this made photography possible with the new rays. He traced back the source of the rays. They came from the spot on the glass where the cathode rays impinged at high vacuum. He then said that the new rays could be generated whenever cathode rays struck any solid body. To prove it, he designed a tube which would give a more intense form of this radiation which, for lack of a better name, he called "X-radiation"—X, the unknown.

Within a few months of Roentgen's announcement the medical world was using his tube in a hundred different ways to analyze fractures, deep-seated wounds, and the inner structures of the human body. The scientific journals of the leading countries were filled with articles by physicists, repeating Roentgen's experiments and offering new explanations. Roentgen himself still did not understand the phenomenon and offered the explanation that these were "longitudinal vibrations in the ether."

His discovery made physicists study the phenomenon of fluorescence more closely.

ON A NEW FORM OF RADIATION.*

BY PROF. WILHELM KONRAD RÖNTGEN.

1. If we pass the discharge from a large Rühmkorff coil through a Hittorf or a sufficiently exhausted Lenard, Crookes, or similar apparatus, and cover the tube with a somewhat closely-fitting mantel of thin black cardboard, we observe in a completely-darkened room that a paper screen washed with barium-platino-cyanide lights up brilliantly and fluoresces equally well whether the treated side or the other be turned towards the discharge tube. Fluorescence is still observable 2 metres away from the apparatus. It is easy to convince oneself that the cause of the fluorescence is the discharge apparatus and nothing else.

2. The most striking feature of this phenomenon is that an influence (*Agens*) capable of exciting brilliant fluorescence is able to pass through the black cardboard cover, which transmits none of the ultra-violet rays of the sun or of the electric arc, and one immediately inquires whether other bodies possess this property. It is soon discovered that all bodies are transparent to this influence, but in very different degrees. A few examples will suffice. Paper is very transparent;† the fluorescent screen held behind a bound volume of 1,000 pages still lighted up brightly; the printer's ink offered no perceptible obstacle. Fluorescence was also noted behind two packs of cards; a few cards held between apparatus and screen made no perceptible difference. A single sheet of tinfoil is scarcely noticeable; only after several layers have been laid one the top of each other is a shadow clearly visible on the screen. Thick blocks of wood are also transparent; fir planks 2cm. to 3cm. thick are but very slightly opaque. A film of aluminium about 15mm. thick weakens the effect very considerably, though it does not entirely destroy the fluorescence. Several centimetres of vulcanised india-rubber let the rays through.‡ Glass plates of the same thickness behave in a different way, according as they contain lead (flint glass) or not; the former are much less transparent than the latter. If the hand is held between the discharge tube and the screen, the dark shadow of the bones is visible within the slightly dark shadow of the hand. Water, bisulphide of carbon, and various other liquids behave in this respect as if they were very transparent. I was not able to determine whether water was more transparent than air. Behind plates of copper, silver, lead, gold, platinum, fluorescence is still clearly visible, but only when the plates are not too thick. Platinum 0·2mm. thick is transparent; silver and copper sheets may be decidedly thicker. Lead 1·5mm. thick is as good as opaque, and was on this account often made use of. A wooden rod of 20 × 20mm. cross-section, painted white, with lead paint on one side, behaves in a peculiar manner. When it is interposed between apparatus and screen it has almost no effect when the X-rays go through the rod parallel to the painted side, but it throws a dark shadow if the rays have to traverse the paint. Very similar to the metals themselves are their salts, whether solid or in solution.

3. These experimental results and others lead to the conclusion that the transparency of different substances of the same thickness is mainly conditioned by their density; no other property is in the least comparable with this.

The following experiments, however, show that density is not altogether alone in its influence. I experimented on the trans-

---

* Preliminary Communication to the Würzburg Physico-Medical Society. Published by Messrs. Stahel, of Würzburg, who will shortly also issue an English edition.

† By the "transparency" of a body I denote the ratio of the brightness of a fluorescent screen held right behind the body in question to the brightness of the same screen under exactly the same conditions, but without the interposing body.

‡ For brevity's sake I should like to use the expression "rays," and to distinguish these from other rays I will call them "X-rays."

to this conclusion, and I have, therefore, sought another explanation.

There seems at least some connection between the new rays and light rays in the shadow pictures, and in the fluorescing and chemical activity of both kinds of rays. Now, it has been long known that besides the transverse light vibrations, longitudinal vibrations might take place in the ether, and according to the view of different physicists *must* take place. Certainly their existence has not up till now been made evident, and their properties have not on that account been experimentally investigated.

May not the new rays be due to longitudinal vibrations in the ether?

I must admit that I have put more and more faith in this idea in the course of my research, and it behoves me therefore to announce my suspicion, although I know well that this explanation requires further corroboration.

Würzburg. Physikal Institut der Universität, *December*, 1895.

Roentgen's discovery of X-rays in 1895 is another classic research. He named the new radiation in his third footnote, but believed they were longitudinal waves in the ether.

SÉANCE DU LUNDI 24 FÉVRIER 1896,

PRÉSIDENCE DE M. A. CORNU.

PHYSIQUE. — *Sur les radiations émises par phosphorescence.*
Note de M. HENRI BECQUEREL.

« Dans une précédente séance, M. Ch. Henry a annoncé que le sulfure de zinc phosphorescent interposé sur le trajet de rayons émanés d'un tube de Crookes augmentait l'intensité des radiations traversant l'aluminium.

» D'autre part, M. Niewenglowski a reconnu que le sulfure de calcium phosphorescent du commerce émet des radiations qui traversent les corps opaques.

» Ce fait s'étend à divers corps phosphorescents et, en particulier, aux sels d'urane dont la phosphorescence a une très courte durée.

» Avec le sulfate double d'uranium et de potassium, dont je possède des cristaux formant une croûte mince et transparente, j'ai pu faire l'expérience suivante :

» On enveloppe une plaque photographique Lumière, au gélatino-bromure, avec deux feuilles de papier noir très épais, tel que la plaque ne se voile pas par une exposition au Soleil, durant une journée.

Becquerel's discovery of radioactivity was the third great event of the 1890's, coming a month after X-rays. His first note shows that he thought he was seeing a new kind of phosphorescence.

AN ACCOUNT OF THE SESSIONS OF THE ACADEMY OF SCIENCE
SESSION OF MONDAY, FEBRUARY 24, 1896
M. A. CORNU PRESIDING
PHYSICS—*On Radiations Emitted by Phosphorescence*
by HENRI BECQUEREL

"At a previous meeting, M. Ch. Henry announced that the sulphate of phosphorescent zinc interposed in the path of rays coming from a Crookes tube increased the intensity of the radiations passing through the aluminum.

"In addition, M. Niewenglowski recognized that commercial calcium sulphide emits phosphorescent rays which will penetrate opaque bodies.

"This fact extends to many phosphorescent bodies and, in particular, to those uranium salts in which the phosphorescence has a very short duration.

"With crystals of the double sulphate of uranium and potassium, I was able to make the following experiment:

"One wraps a Lumiere gelatine bromide photographic plate with two sheets of very thick black paper so that the plate cannot be exposed by the sun.

"One puts on the outside of the sheet of paper a disc of the phosphorescent material and exposes the whole to the sunlight for several hours. When one next develops the photographic plate, one discovers that the silhouette of the phosphorescent substance appears in black on the negative. If one slips a coin or a metallic screen pierced with a stenciled design between the phosphorescent material and the paper, one finds the image of the stencil or the coin appearing on the negative.

"One can repeat the same experiments by interposing between the phosphorescent material and the paper a thin sheet of glass, which will exclude the possibility of a chemical reaction due to the vapors which might emanate from the substance heated by the rays of the sun.

"One must conclude from these experiments that the phosphorescent substance in question emits radiations which penetrate paper opaque to light, and reduce silver salts."

3. RADIOACTIVITY AND THE PHOTO-ELECTRIC EFFECT

One month after the announcement of the discovery of X-rays, Henri Becquerel performed an experiment on the fluorescing properties of the double sulphate of uranium and potassium. When certain substances were exposed to light and then took on a gleam of their own, they were said to fluoresce. Many such substances were known, and Becquerel's uranium preparation was among them.

In Becquerel's experiment, uranium salt was exposed to sunlight and then its fluorescent properties were measured. At one point, however, the weather became cloudy and he put away his preparation for several days. By chance it happened to be lying in a drawer on a pile of photographic plates, and by still further chance, he decided to check the quality of his photographic plates before he began the experiment.

The first plate, which happened to be the one lying on top, was the one he developed; and to his annoyance he found that it seemed to have been exposed to light. However, something about the pattern of the exposure made it look as though some kind of shadow had been cast on the plate. Checking back, he found that if one looked at the pattern with some imagination, one could vaguely make out a shadow of the metal disc which had held his uranium preparation. Ordinarily, Becquerel would have discarded the plate without thinking any more about it. But all the talk of X-rays had made every physicist alert. Becquerel decided to check.

He took his preparation of the uranium salt, exposed it once more to light, and put it away in a dark drawer mounted on a photographic plate which was encased in black paper. Once again the uranium sulphate caused the plate to fog.

For several months Becquerel thought that the uranium sulphate had to be exposed to sunlight to bring about the effect, which was sufficiently marvelous in itself. No one had realized that light from a fluorescent substance could penetrate opaque objects.

However, he soon discovered that a sample of the uranium sulphate salt which had *not* been exposed to the sun was capable of activating a photographic plate with undiminished intensity. The effect was more and more marvelous. He next discovered that if he used pure uranium which was not fluorescent, the results were even more intense than when he used the uranium compound. Fluorescence could also be discarded. He next discovered that these invisible rays from uranium possessed the property of discharging electrically charged bodies exactly as Roentgen had discovered with the X-rays. He called this completely new phenomenon "radioactivity."

Becquerel rays, as they were called, were as marvelous in their way as the X-rays of Roentgen and attracted just as much interest among physicists. Two of Becquerel's associates, Pierre Curie and his wife Marie, went to work on the problem. After some time they discovered that there were other chemical elements which had the same property and both of them were new to science. One was called polonium, after Mme. Curie's native country. The other element was called radium.

The great classical theories of physics seemed shaken to their foundations. X-rays at first appeared to deny Maxwell's laws until, after several years, Roentgen and others showed that there was no violation of the ether theory because X-rays could be made to exhibit all the normal optical qualities of reflection, refraction, and interference. The phenomenon of radioactivity observed by Becquerel seemed to put an end to the beautiful theory of the conservation of energy. How was it possible for a substance to produce energy continually without any apparent source of supply?

A curious discovery had been made in 1887 when Heinrich Hertz found that ultra-violet light, shining on one electrode in a high voltage circuit, could make a spark jump much farther than when no ultra-violet light at all was shining. J. J. Thomson demonstrated that this was because the ultra-violet light was creating a negative charge on the metal surface. This was called the "photo-electric effect."

Just as the discovery of X-rays had made physicists examine the phenomenon of fluorescence more closely, so it made them re-examine the nature of the cathode rays. There were two schools of thought: the Germans tended to believe that the cathode rays within the tube were vibrations of the ether; the English physicists tended to believe that the cathode rays were electrically charged particles, as predicted by Benjamin Franklin. J. J. Thomson was the foremost exponent of the English school of thought.

In 1897, Thomson published the classical paper called "Cathode Rays," in which he reviewed all the experiments on cathode rays to date and described

several of his own. He announced that the particle whose movement under high voltage had been called a cathode ray was in reality a negatively charged particle much smaller than the smallest atom. Using a name suggested by Stoney, Thomson called the particle the "electron." He insisted that the photo-electric effect was no more than the emission of these electrons from metal surfaces by ultra-violet light. He also claimed that one of the components of the Becquerel rays was also an electron.

The assertions of Thomson seemed fantastic to a generation of scientists who did not at all accept the hypothesis that matter was composed of atoms. The suggestion that there was a particle still smaller than the atom created a furor. Some men were willing to accept the idea that electricity consisted of the movement of very small electrically charged particles, but it remained to prove that such a particle had a definite mass and a definite electric charge. An experiment was needed to prove once and for all the truth of the atomic theory of matter and that the existence of electrons was real.

One German in the 1890's that did not accept the ether theory of X-rays was Albert Einstein, who had been profoundly impressed by Michelson's experiment with the interferometer. Another German that did not accept the ether theory was Max Planck, who made an equally radical suggestion: radiant energy—light—was to be thought of in terms of "quanta," or tiny packets. Einstein used Planck's "quantum theory" to explain the photo-electric effect and wrote down a beautifully simple equation that summed it all up. At the time, Einstein's suggestions about the photo-electric effect were given little credence.

Millikan, one of several American graduate students in Europe at the time, was to be the man who, after years of reflection, would perform the two crucial experiments of his time: one would prove the validity of Thomson's theory of the electron; the second would prove Einstein's theory of the photo-electric effect, and that the quantum theory was more than a mathematician's dream.

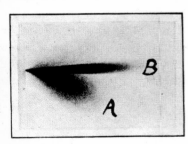

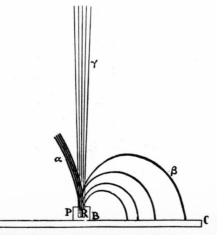

Becquerel rays were examined photographically by placing a pinpoint of radioactive matter on a plate between the poles of a magnet. First only 2 smudges appeared, called *alpha* and *beta*. Stronger magnetic fields showed three kinds existed. Intense work started on identification.

Magnetic analysis soon showed that beta rays were electrons; gamma rays, some kind of light; alpha rays, atomic fragments.

Pierre and Marie Curie isolated the radioactive elements, discovering radium, polonium, and thorium.

4. THE ELECTRON ON THE OIL DROP

"At the end of my first decade at the University of Chicago (1906) I was still an assistant professor," wrote Robert Millikan. "I had two little boys, was building a home which I hoped I could finance through book royalties, but I knew that I certainly had not attained a position of much distinction as a research physicist."

The textbook on which he had been working was sent off to the publishers, and finally he started intensive work on a new phase of his career in science.

"Everyone was interested in the magnitude of the charge of the electron . . . though its value had never been measured up to this time. . ."

Many attempts at this crucial measurement had already been made by J. J. Thomson, but after a decade of work, Thomson's assistant, H. Wilson, reported that eleven different measurements had given eleven different answers.

Before starting on his own, Millikan first duplicated the Cambridge method. The theory of the Cambridge experiment was this:

The mass of a body was determined by measuring its downward thrust on a balance pan due to gravity. If a particle was electrically charged and an upward-pulling electric force could be made exactly equal to the downward pull of gravity, the particle would be in a state of balance and a physicist could calculate the amount of electrical charge. If the charge were due to a single electron, one would then know the charge of the electron.

The Cambridge theory was sound enough, but physicists had been unable to devise an apparatus for dealing with single particles. Instead they observed the average behavior of a cloud of electrically charged water droplets. In a partially evacuated chamber, a fog of water vapor was created. The top of the chamber was connected to a voltage supply. The fog took a certain time to settle. When the fog was irradiated by X-rays, the droplets became charged, and the upward pull from the high-voltage chamber-top was supposed to keep the droplets from falling. In practice, none of the delicate conditions required for balance could be met.

Millikan sought a new approach. The fault was not in the apparatus, but in the way the apparatus was being used. He made a number of small changes that . . . *"made it for the first time possible to make all the measurements on one and the same individual droplet:"*

"To take the first steps in the . . . improvements, in 1906 I built a ten-thousand-volt small storage battery —at that time quite an undertaking—that would produce a field strong enough to hold the upper surface of Wilson's cloud suspended 'like Mohammed's coffin.' When I had everything ready and had . . . formed the cloud, I threw on the electric field by turning a switch. *What I saw happen was the instantaneous and complete dissipation of the cloud*—in other words, there was no top surface of the cloud left to set cross hairs upon, as Wilson had done and as I had expected to do. This complete dissipation of the cloud by throwing on the powerful electric field between the upper and lower plates seemed at first to spoil my experiment. . .but when I repeated the test I saw that I had something before me of much more importance. . .for repeated tests showed that whenever the cloud was thus dispersed by my powerful field, a few individual droplets would remain in view."

Under the very strong electric field, he had inadvertently swept the region clean of all but the extremely few particles that were in the most perfect balance of mass and electrical charge. Actually, the droplets swept out of the chamber had been those that had confused all previous measurements.

"When I held the electric field on and watched through my short focus telescope. . .the behavior of these balanced droplets, some of them would begin to move slowly down, and then as they lost weight by evaporation, would stop. . .turn. . .and begin to move slowly upward as the force of gravity upon them diminished through evaporation. . ." "When the electrical field was suddenly thrown off, the 'balanced drops,' appearing merely as stars in a dark field, would all then start to fall, but some of them slowly and some of them much more rapidly, *these latter being those that had been suspended because they had carried on their backs two, three, four, five, etc., electrons, instead of only one. . . Here, then, was the first definite, sharp, unambiguous proof that electricity was definitely unitary in structure."*

Actually this last observation, at the time, was far more important than the measurement of the electron's charge.

He finished these first measurements of the charge of the electron in September, 1909, and took them at once to the meeting of the British Association for the Advancement of Science at Winnipeg. Although he was not on the program, he was given an opportunity to speak. He had no illusions, however, that his results were anything but preliminaries to the answers that could be obtained from more refined techniques.

"Riding back to Chicago from this meeting I looked out the window of the day coach at the Manitoba plains and suddenly said to myself, 'What a fool I've been to try in this crude way to eliminate the evaporation of water droplets when mankind has spent the last three hundred years in improving clock oils for the very purpose of obtaining a lubricant that will scarcely evaporate at all!'

"When I got back to Chicago, I met Mr. Michelson at the entrance of the laboratory and we sat down on the doorstep to chat. I asked him how accurately he thought he had measured the speed of light. He replied that I could count on its value to about one part in ten thousand. 'Well,' said I, 'I have in mind a method by which I could determine the value of . . . the charge on the electron to one part in one thousand, or else I am no good.'

"I went at once to the shop and had the mechanic build me an air condenser consisting of two circular brass plates some ten inches in diameter and held about six-tenths of an inch apart. . . . In the center of the upper plate were drilled a few small half-millimeter holes, through which oil droplets, sprayed . . . with an atomizer, might find their way into the space between the plates, to which the terminals of my ten-thousand-volt battery could be applied. . . ." He planned to charge the oil droplets with a beam of X-rays just as he had done previously with water.

For three years, from 1909 to 1912, he devoted himself to the oil-drop experiment.

"It was fascinating to see with what complete certainty one could count the exact number of the electrons sitting on a given drop, whether it was one or any number up to a hundred, for this involved merely putting the drop in question through a long series of up-and-down trips, each accurately timed, and then computing the least common multiple of a fairly long series of speeds.

"To get the data needed on one particular droplet sometimes took hours. One night Mrs. Millikan and I had invited guests to dinner. When six o'clock came, I was only halfway through with the needed data on a particular drop. So I had Mrs. Millikan apprised by phone that 'I had watched an ion for an hour and a half and had to finish the job,' but asked her to please go ahead with dinner without me. The guests later complimented me on my domesticity because what they said Mrs. Millikan had told them was that Mr. Millikan had 'washed and ironed for an hour and a half and had to finish the job.'"

Millikan published his results in the fall of 1910 and received enormous attention throughout the world of physics. The German school which included Roentgen, the discoverer of X-rays some fifteen years earlier, changed their attitude completely. Their spokesman was the great physical chemist Ostwald, who wrote in 1912: "I am now convinced. . . . Experimental evidence . . . sought in vain for hundreds and thousands of years . . . now . . . justify the most cautious scientist in speaking of the experimental proof of the atomic theory of matter."

Robert Millikan in 1908 had still to achieve his great results in electron research. He was forty. His two sons, Clark and Glenn, grew up to become scientists too.

Millikan's apparatus for measuring the charge on the electron gave results so conclusive that the last doubters of the atomic theory of matter were forced to surrender.

Michelson and Einstein visited Millikan in 1931. Michelson corroborated Einstein's relativity. Millikan proved Einstein's

5. THE REVOLUTION IN LIGHT

In 1921 Albert Einstein was awarded the Nobel prize for having conceived the theory that explained the "photo-electric effect." Two years later Robert Millikan was awarded the Nobel prize for having performed the experiment that proved Einstein's theory. Einstein's theory had first been advanced in 1905; Millikan's great experiment was performed almost a decade after that. The double award marked the success of one of the most profound revolutions in physics.

Isaac Newton had enriched the science of physics with two theories: the first described the laws of motion of ponderable bodies; the second described light as being composed of very tiny particles of radiant matter. The first of Newton's contributions caused

Millikan, approaching seventy, worked with a new generation of physicists, Paul Dirac and Robert Oppenheimer.

Millikan's cosmic ray ionization chambers were used in a world-wide research that found a new particle—the meson.

quantum theory of light.

him to be hailed as a genius. The prestige of his genius supported the far weaker corpuscular theory of light, even though it explained only two of the known phenomena of light. Reflection, according to Newton, was simply the elastic bouncing of the light particles from the reflecting surface; and refraction, the bending of light as it passed from a rare medium like air to a denser medium like water, was due to a change in momentum as the light particle passed through the surface of the denser medium. Newton's theory of light could not explain interference, diffraction, or polarization.

By the beginning of the eighteenth century, the wave theory of light put forward by Newton's con-

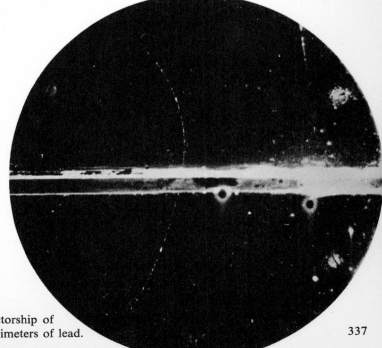

The positron, positive electron, was discovered in 1932 by Carl Anderson from cloud chamber measurements during Millikan's directorship of Cal Tech. The particle is moving upwards, in an arc, through six millimeters of lead.

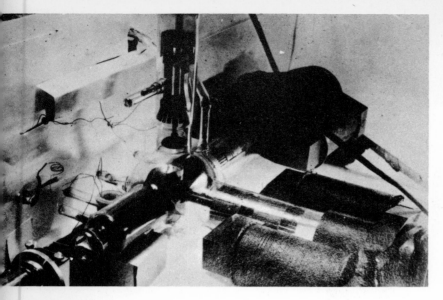

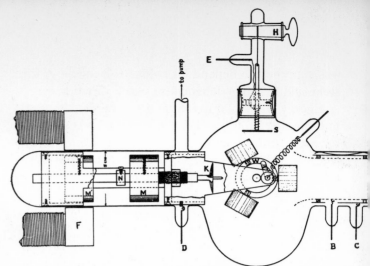

In Millikan's "vacuum barber shop," a grinder (K) cut clean surfaces on photo-electric metals mounted on turntable (W). A contact plate (S) measured "work function." External magnetic coils (left) brought the tools into play.

temporary, Huyghens—that light consisted of a vibration in the ether—began to come to the fore. The great French physicist Fresnel demonstrated mathematically that if light were truly a wave phenomenon, then all the observed behavior could easily be explained. Half a century later, James Clerk Maxwell strengthened the wave theory of light by demonstrating dramatically that light was a vibration of electric and magnetic waves. Not until the last decade of the nineteenth century did there appear to be any discrepancy in Maxwell's theory.

In 1887 Hertz had noticed that light—particularly ultra-violet light—would cause metal surfaces to become electrically charged. Thomson showed that the positive charge on the surface was due to the instantaneous emission of negative electrons from the metal.

One physicist who seemed aware that this involved a contradiction in the wave theory of light was Albert Einstein; and in 1905 he suggested that the "photo-electric effect" could be explained only by a return to the corpuscular theory of light with certain important modifications.

To Einstein, the contradiction was this: The more light that was shone on a metal surface, the greater the number of electrons that were given off; but the *individual energies of the electrons were not affected* by the intensity of light even though Maxwell's theory said that this was the measure of light energy.

Einstein offered this explanation: A beam of light was composed of a stream of tiny corpuscles or pulses of energy. The energy of each pulse was proportional to its *color* or, in classical terms, its frequency—not its amplitude, as Maxwell had said. When light struck solid matter, some of these Einsteinian corpuscles of energy were absorbed. The absorbed energies in some cases were great enough to allow electrons to escape from the atoms in which they had been held. The en-

ergy of these liberated "photoelectrons" should, therefore, be identically equal to the energy of the captured light corpuscle, called "quanta," less the amount of energy needed to extricate the electron from the atom. This last quantity, the "work function," could be measured by direct means.

Einstein stated this in the form of an equation that connected the *velocity* of an emitted photoelectron with the energy of the captured light quantum and the work function.

"Such a corpuscular theory," said Millikan, "had nothing back of it of an experimental sort except Lenard's observation in 1900 that the energy with which electrons are ejected from a zinc plate seemed to be independent of the intensity of the light. . . I think it is correct to say that the Einstein view of light quanta, shooting through space in the form of. . . pulses, or as we now called them photons, had practically no convinced adherents prior to about 1915. . . Nor in those earlier stages was even Einstein's advocacy vigorous or definite."

Millikan himself was far from convinced, but because the Ryerson Laboratory at Chicago under Michelson was so deeply committed to experiments based on the wave theory of light, he decided to test Einstein's hypothesis once and for all.

"As soon as I returned to my laboratory in the fall of 1912, I. . .went at the problem of designing new apparatus. . .to get a convincing answer to the problem of this Einstein photo-electric equation, and I scarcely expected. . .that the answer, when and if it came, would be positive; but the question was very vital, and an answer of some sort had to be found. . . I began. . .photo-electric work in October, 1912, and it occupied practically all my individual research time for the next three years."

The crux of Einstein's theory was the way energy

was supposed to depend on color, or frequency. Einstein said that this dependence was a direct one:

Energy was equal to frequency multiplied by a certain number; and the "certain number" was the same for every color; it had to be a constant of nature. Einstein used the symbol h for the number out of deference to his colleague, Max Planck.

Some years earlier, Max Planck had been able to solve a hitherto insoluble theoretical problem in radiation by arbitrarily replacing the term for energy with another term that included frequency and this very constant. Planck had written the number as h and regarded the whole operation as a mathematical convenience adopted simply to make the problem "come out." Einstein perceived that Planck inadvertently had done considerably more: because Planck's "mathematical convenience" had solved a problem, it was possibly a true statement and meant what it said.

Einstein gave it literal meaning and so his photoelectric equation was the first direct application of the new quantum theory. Millikan decided to subject Einstein's theory to these three questions:

1. Did the energy of a light quanta actually equal h times the frequency of light?

2. Was h really a constant for all colors?

3. Did Einstein's photo-electric equation agree with what occurred in nature?

For the experiment Millikan designed an ingenious apparatus which he was later to call his "vacuum barber shop." Inside a glass vacuum chamber he had a turntable which could be rotated by means of a magnet outside the chamber. On three faces of the turntable were samples of three highly reactive metals—sodium, potassium, and lithium—each of which responded to light of different frequencies. Because the experiment would depend so crucially on the nature of the surface of each metal sample, the vacuum chamber also contained a small polishing device which could be brought to bear on the metal surfaces by magnets outside.

White light from a lamp source was refracted into its spectrum by means of lenses and a prism. The different pure colors were played in turn upon a narrow slit so that Millikan could observe the effect of only one color at a time upon the metal surfaces. As each pure color shone in on the metal surface, Millikan measured the number of electrons that came off and their energy. The number of electrons coming off each second was simply the current. He measured their energy by determining how much electrical force was needed to stop them. If a body of unknown weight requires a force of five pounds to be held in the air, one can say that the body weighs five pounds. Following the same reasoning. Millikan determined electron velocity by measuring the force required to cancel it out. Knowing this velocity, he was able to calculate

the energy of the electrons emitted for each color. When this was repeated for all the various portions of the spectrum, he was then able to plot a curve showing the electron's energy dependence on color—or frequency. His result gave conclusively positive answers to the three questions he had asked Einstein's theory. The direct measurement of Planck's constant turned out to be 6.57×10^{-27} erg seconds.

America had waited a long time for such a man as Millikan. His researches were of the first rank; as a teacher at Chicago he took the time to train and encourage the young men with whom Michelson had no patience; as administrator at California Institute of Technology, he trained several generations of young scientists to a level of achievement which would put an end forever to the necessity for young Americans to go abroad for scientific training. With Robert Andrews Millikan, American science came of age.

A DIRECT PHOTOELECTRIC DETERMINATION OF PLANCK'S "h."[1]

BY R. A. MILLIKAN.

I. INTRODUCTORY.

QUANTUM theory was not originally developed for the sake of interpreting photoelectric phenomena. It was solely a theory as to the mechanism of absorption and emission of electromagnetic waves by resonators of atomic or subatomic dimensions. It had nothing whatever to say about the energy of an escaping electron or about the conditions under which such an electron could make its escape, and up to this day the form of the theory developed by its author has not been able to account satisfactorily for the photoelectric facts presented herewith. We are confronted, however, by the astonishing situation that these facts were correctly and exactly predicted nine years ago by a form of quantum theory which has now been pretty generally abandoned.

It was in 1905 that Einstein[2] made the first coupling of photo effects and with any form of quantum theory by bringing forward the bold, not to say the reckless, hypothesis of an electro-magnetic light corpuscle of energy $h\nu$, which energy was transferred upon absorption to an electron. This hypothesis may well be called reckless first because an electromagnetic disturbance which remains localized in space seems a violation of the very conception of an electromagnetic disturbance, and second because it flies in the face of the thoroughly established facts of interference. The hypothesis was apparently made solely because it furnished a ready explanation of one of the most remarkable facts brought to light by recent investigations, viz., that the energy with which an electron is thrown out of a metal by ultra-violet light or X-rays is independent of the intensity of the light while it depends on its frequency. This fact alone seems to demand some modification of classical theory or, at any rate, it has not yet been interpreted satisfactorily in terms of classical theory.

While this was the main if not the only basis of Einstein's assumption, this assumption enabled him at once to predict that the maximum energy

[1] An abstract of this paper was presented before the Am. Phys. Soc. in April, 1914. (PHYS. REV., IV., 73, '14.) The data on lithium were however first reported at the meeting of the Am. Phys. Soc. in April, 1915. (PHYS. REV., VI., 55, '15.)
[2] Ann. d. Phys. (4), 17, 132, 1905, and (4), 20, 199, 1906.

---

10. SUMMARY.

1. Einstein's photoelectric equation has been subjected to very searching tests and it appears in every case to predict exactly the observed results.

2. Planck's h has been photoelectrically determined with a precision of about .5 per cent. and is found to have the value

$$h = 6.57 \times 10^{-27}.$$

RYERSON PHYSICAL LABORATORY,
UNIVERSITY OF CHICAGO.

Millikan's Nobel prize-winning research begins with a remarkable tribute to Einstein's intellectual daring. The results are stated with the terseness of certainty.

The Wright glider of 1902 was one of the most important steps in man's evolution of flight. Not until the Wrights worked out the structural, aerodynamic, and control problems for gliders, did they feel ready to attempt powered flight.

THE WRIGHT BROTHERS

1. FLIGHT AT KITTY HAWK

Steady winds from the northeast and long swells of the Atlantic Ocean roll incessantly onto the sand bars and beaches of the Carolina coast. The beaches are windstripped, desolate, and lonely. A sand bar separates Albemarle, Pamlico, and Roanoke Sounds from the ocean, and one stretch of it has a name—Kitty Hawk.

On the cold, bleak morning of December 17, 1903, two men pushed back the doors of a temporary shelter to look out at the weather. They were brothers, named Orville and Wilbur Wright. They were lean, thin-faced men, wearing conventional business suits and high starched white collars. Orville, thirty-two, was a shade over five feet ten, about an inch and a half taller than his thirty-six-year-old brother Wilbur. Orville had a mustache, and sometimes he liked to tease. Wibur had a poker-faced, wry Ohio sense of humor. Orville, being the younger brother, every so often reminded Wilbur to say "we" when he said "I."

The surf pounded, ice floes moved down Albemarle Sound, and the white beach sand flew on the twenty-seven-mile-an-hour wind.

At ten o'clock in the morning it was clearly useless to wait any longer in the hope that the wind might soften. The two brothers sent up a flag to the top of a mast as a gathering signal to the men at the small U. S. Life-Saving Station south of the camp on the hundred-foot sand dune called Kill Devil Hill. While waiting for the men to come, the brothers dragged out their "flying machine"—a biplane with white muslin wings, about forty feet across. The stretched rectangles of cloth were called "aeroplanes." Earlier, on March 23 of that same year, the Wrights had written to the U. S. Patent Office: "Our invention relates to that class of flying machines in which the weight is sustained by the reactions resulting when one or more aeroplanes are moved through the air edgewise at a small angle of incidence."

The flying machine was intended to take off from a little two-wheel truck, made from bicycle wheel hubs, that fitted a rail made of two-by-fours.

The Wrights, leaning against the wind, were laying track when the five men arrived from the station to help and, by witnessing one of the most historic events of all time, to achieve footnote immortality: J. T. Daniels, W. S. Dough, A. D. Etheridge, W. C.

Brinkly, and a boy from Nag's Head, Johnny Moore.

"The biting cold made work difficult," wrote Orville Wright in his diary that day. "We had to warm up frequently in our living room, where we had a good fire in an improvised stove made of a carbide can."

About twenty-five minutes after ten, the engine was started, and the propellers turned slowly during warm-up. At exactly ten-thirty-five, Orville, squinting against the wind, climbed through the wire struts of the machine and lay face downward with his hips in a special cradle alongside the roaring engine. The cradle could be moved slightly from side to side, and its motion controlled the lateral movement of the machine. In addition, he grasped a small lever which controlled climb or dive.

Wilbur stood on the sand next to the machine holding onto a wing tip to balance it. With the engine racing, Orville slipped the release that had been holding the machine in position and it began to roll forward, with Wilbur walking, then trotting, then running alongside. When he began to stumble, he let go. The first heavier-than-air self-powered flying machine was in the air under the control of a human passenger.

From the moment the machine started, Orville "found the control of the front rudder quite difficult. . . (It) had a tendency to turn itself when started so that (it) . . . turned too far on one side and then too far on the other . . ." Because of the rudder, the machine began to dart toward the ground when it had risen only ten feet. Orville got it under control and flew a hundred feet, when suddenly the machine glided down and landed. The time of the first powered flight under human control was twelve seconds. In his diary that day, Orville noted only that the "flight lever for throwing off the engine was broken and the skid under the rudder cracked."

During those twelve seconds, however, Orville was well aware that he was making history, and years later he described his feelings this way: "The motor close beside you kept up an almost deafening roar during the whole flight, yet in your excitement, you did not notice it till it stopped."

The two brothers spent half an hour dragging the machine back to the track and making the necessary repairs. At eleven o'clock, Wilbur made the second flight. His course was very much like Orville's. The machine flew low and wobbly, rising and falling for 175 feet before it came down to the blowing sand.

The wind was beginning to ease off and, with the aid of the men from the life-saving station, the machine was put back on the track for a third try. At eleven-twenty, Orville took off.

"When out about the same distance as Will, I met with a strong gust from the left which raised the left wing and sidled the machine off to the right in a lively manner. I immediately turned the rudder to bring the machine down, and then worked the end control. Much to our surprise, on reaching the ground the left wing struck first, showing the lateral control of this machine much more effective than on any of our former ones."

Twenty minutes later it was Wilbur's turn to make the fourth trial. At just twelve, the machine took off, and now it was under much better control. It flew evenly for eight hundred feet, when it began to pitch and suddenly darted to the ground. "The front rudder frame," wrote Orville, "was badly broken up, but the main frame suffered none at all. The distance over the ground was 852 feet in fifty-nine seconds."

The two brothers and their five helpers carried the machine back and set it down on the sand for a few minutes, while Wilbur discussed what had happened in the last flight. Suddenly a gust of wind came up, raised the wing of the machine and started to spin it over. Everyone rushed to hold it down.

"Mr. Daniels, having had no experience in handling a machine of this kind, hung on to it from the inside, and as a result he was knocked down and turned over and over with it as it ran. His escape was miraculous, as he was in with the engine and chains. The engine legs were all broken off, the chain guys badly bent, a number of uprights and nearly all the rear ends of the ribs were badly broken."

A complete reconstruction job was necessary, and so the two Wright brothers knocked off for lunch, knowing that they were not only the first men to fly in a machine that rose and maintained itself in level flight under its own power, but what was far more important, they were the first men to fly with a complete system of control. For another fifty years these principles, which they had worked out entirely by themselves, were to remain the essential laws of flight control.

In their shack on the windy dunes, Orville cooked the lunch and Wilbur, as usual, washed the dishes.

The engine of the first plane was built by the Wrights themselves. The metal cylinder on top of the intake manifold is the carburetor, made from an old tomato can.

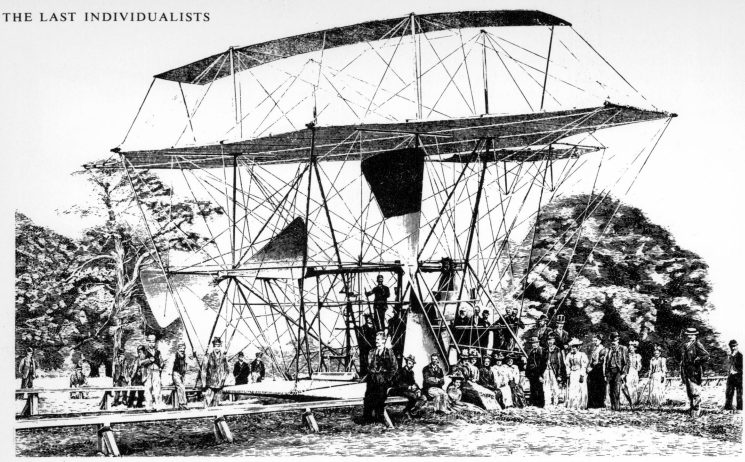

SIR HIRAM MAXIM'S ENORMOUS, STEAM-DRIVEN MULTIPLANE, 1894

Sir Hiram Maxim attempted powered flight in the 1890's with the most massive flying machine that had ever been built. Its 360-horsepower engine was not to be matched for many years. The wing structure of the $200,000 machine was based on kite principles. Unlike the Wrights, Maxim had not sought a sytem of controlling an inherently unstable machine. He relied on pure power. The 8000-pound machine was designed to test-run along a track, with another set of guide rails above the wheels to keep the machine from flying. In 1894, the 4000 square feet of wing and the great steam engine developed so much lift that the guide rails were smashed and the machine would have taken off if Maxim hadn't cut the power. As it was, the machine was wrecked. He never attempted to fly again.

The first radial gasoline engine built by Manly for Langley's 1903 aerodrome weighed 150 pounds, developed 52 hp.

2. THE WRIGHTS' PREDECESSORS

A true pioneer in heavier-than-air flight was Sir George Cayley (1773–1857) who, wrote Orville Wright, "knew more of the principles of aeronautics than any of his predecessors, and as much as any that followed."

There were four main schools of thought about heavier-than-air flight: the ornithopter school copied the motion of flapping bird wings; a second school imitated the box kite, which has inherent stability; a third group studied gliding birds like gulls and hawks. The fourth busied itself with helicopters.

In the 1890's, Sir Hiram Maxim and Samuel Langley developed flying machines that were powered kites, but their machines lacked the very stability they had counted upon. Langley, the Smithsonian's director and an outstanding scientist, built small-scale machines that flew.

Langley's first aerodrome, steam-engine powered and catapulted from a specially built houseboat on the Potomac, also lacked a system of wing control. This quarter-sized model flew successfully.

Samuel Langley (right), director of the Smithsonian, and his assistant, Charles M. Manly.

Langley's ill-fated 1903 model just before launching. Models of this aerodrome had flown successfully, and there was every reason for high expectations. Adverse newspaper publicity on the crash made Congress cut off support.

Otto Lilienthal, world-renowned glider, died in a crash in 1895. He led the way for the Wrights.

FLYING MACHINES.

INTRODUCTION.

HAVING in a previous volume treated the general subject of "Aerial Navigation," in which a sketch was given of what has been accomplished with balloons, I propose in the following chapters to treat of Flying Machines proper —that is to say, of forms of apparatus heavier than the air which they displace; deriving their support from and progressing through the air, like the birds, by purely dynamical means.

It is intended to give sketches of many machines, and to attempt to criticise them.

We know comparatively so little of the laws and principles which govern air resistances and reactions, and the subject will be so novel to most readers, that it would be difficult to follow the more rational plan of first laying down the general principles, to serve as a basis for discussing past attempts to effect artificial flight. The course will therefore be adopted of first stating a few general

Octave Chanute's *Flying Machines* of 1895 was the textbook which the Wrights studied.

ing. Even with light winds of 4-5 m velocity per second (9 to 11 miles per hour), we can with some little practice glide along at the slight angle of 6° to 8°, as is shown in the line *b f*.

The greatest velocity of the wind at which I dared to start was about 7-8 m. per second (15 to 18 miles per hour). In these flights I often had a very interesting though not dangerous struggle with the wind, in which I sometimes came to a state of absolute rest, and was suspended in the air at one point for several seconds, almost exactly as the falcons of the Rhinow Mountains are. Sometimes I was suddenly lifted from such a position of rest many meters in a vertical direction, so that I became alarmed lest the wind should carry me off altogether. As, however, I never ventured out except when such gusts were exceptional, I was always able to continue my flight and to land safely. The line *b g* shows a wavy course, brought about by gusts, during which I rose to the height of my point of starting.

I want to emphasize particularly that the results obtained in actual sailing agree well with my small-scale experiments on the supporting power of arched surfaces. During a calm it is quite feasible, with proper practice in placing the wings, to

Lilienthal's account of his flights inspired a generation that became the war aces of 1914.

AEROPLANES.

AEROPLANES—*i.e.*, thin fixed surfaces, slightly inclined to the line of motion, and deriving their support from the upward reaction of the air pressure due to the speed, the latter being obtained by some separate propelling device, have been among the last aerial contrivances to be experimented upon in modern times.

The idea of obtaining sustaining power from the air with a fixed, instead of a vibrating or a rotating surface is not obvious, and it was not till 1842 that an aeroplane, as we now understand the term, consisting of planes to sustain the weight, and of a screw to propel, was first proposed and experimented with. All aviators must have occasionally seen and marveled at the performances of the soaring varieties of birds, sailing in every direction at will upon rigidly extended wings (a performance concerning

Chanute's book led the Wrights to study soaring birds and their methods of wing warping.

3. ORVILLE AND WILBUR

On Decoration Day, 1899, Wilbur Wright, at thirty-two, wrote a letter to the Smithsonian Institution saying:

"I have been interested in the problem of mechanical and human flight ever since, as a boy, I constructed a number of bats of various sizes after the style of Cayley's and Penaud's machines. My observations since have only convinced me more firmly that human flight is only a question of knowledge and skill, just as in all acrobatic feats."

Looking over the letter before it was sent out, Orville thought, "Why doesn't he say *we?*"

The close partnership between Orville and Wilbur did not begin until they were in their teens. There were five children born to Milton and Susan Wright. The mother died early and the father, a bishop of the United Brethren Church, raised his family. The two oldest sons, Lorin and Reuchlin, married and left home. The third child, Katherine, took care of her two younger brothers. Wilbur and Orville considered her their mother.

Both boys were marvelously proficient with their hands. They joined kite clubs and became so expert that they began to make kites for sale to the other boys. Thirteen-year-old Orville built a printing press, and seventeen-year-old Wilbur added improvements to it.

Katherine finally left them and entered college at Oberlin. In 1892, with the invention of the "safety" bicycle, the two brothers, who were by now inseparable, set up a shop of their own in Dayton, Ohio.

Wilbur Wright was a serious and thoughtful young man, while Orville, like Katherine, saw life as a time for laughter. When Orville was twenty, he wrote his father about a politician at a political rally: "A few minutes' look at him and I was satisfied and left. If he is an honest man, he ought to sue his face for slander."

Wilbur never did go to college. He and Orville read about the glider experiments of Otto Lilienthal, and the work of Samuel Pierpont Langley. They fell in love with the idea of human flight and married it. By the early 1890's, man had reached the point of utter impatience with every means of animal locomotion. Small, compact steam engines and electric motors had finally been mounted on carriages; and primitive "automobiles" were rolling over city streets in the same years that men attacked the lower air.

The Smithsonian Institution replied to Wilbur Wright's 1899 letter by sending a number of pamphlets and books and suggesting others. Wilbur Wright wrote: "When we came to examine these books, we were astonished to learn what an immense amount of time and money had been expended in futile attempts to solve the problem of human flight. . . . Men of the very highest standing in the professions of science and invention had attempted the problem: Leonardo da Vinci; Sir George Cayley, one of the first men to suggest the idea of the explosion motor; Professor Langley, secretary of the Smithsonian Institution; Dr. Bell, inventor of the telephone; Sir Hiram Maxim, inventor of the automatic gun; Mr. Thomas A. Edison . . . and a host of others."

The Wrights argued aviation vehemently from the time they sat down to their supper till it was time to go to bed. Their housekeeper heard their voices going along, then suddenly burst out, and then fall quiet, as if they would never speak to each other again. After a while, one would say, " 'Tisn't either," and the other would say, " 'Tis, too." They enjoyed themselves hugely.

At length they built a glider that weighed fifty-two pounds and had a wing span of seventeen and a half feet. A space eighteen inches wide was left at the center of the lower surface, where the operator would lie like a boy on a sled. To the Wright brothers, the art of gliding meant that a man would have to use his balance and muscular control to keep the winged surfaces facing into the wind. In their analysis of past gliding experiments, they found that no one could claim more than a few minutes in the air over years of trials. No man could ever have learned to walk with only a few seconds a day of practice. To learn to fly, they should go where there was constant wind, and slopes free of trees, so they could spend hours soaring. They wrote to the Weather Bureau, describing their needs. The Weather Bureau named, among others, a place called Kitty Hawk in North Carolina.

Joseph J. Dosher at the weather station at Kitty Hawk wrote Wilbur Wright on August 16, 1900: "In reply to yours of the third, I will say the beach here is about one mile wide, clear of trees or high hills, and extends for nearly sixty miles, same condition. The wind blows mostly from the north and northeast September and October. . . . You could not rent a house here, so you'll have to bring tents."

On September 23, 1900, Wilbur wrote to his father, "I have my machine nearly finished. It is not to have a motor, and it is not expected to fly in any true sense of the word. My idea is merely to experiment and practice with a view to solving the problem of equilibrium." He reassured his father that there was no danger. In these first experiments, the glider was flown as a kite with strings manipulating the rudder.

The machine flew perfectly, even when loaded with seventy-five pounds of chain to simulate the weight of a passenger.

The following year, they began experiments on free gliding with a man in control of the machine, but the data on previous gliders proved to be wrong.

Wilbur Wright wrote in his diary on July 30, 1901, "The most discouraging features of our experiments so far are these: The lift is not much over one-third that indicated by the Lilienthal tables . . . we find that our hopes of attaining actual practice in the air are decreased to about one-fiftieth of what we had hoped. Five minutes practice in free flight is a good day's record."

On their return to Dayton in 1901, the Wrights decided to check all the previously accepted data on wing camber and aerodynamics. They built a wind tunnel out of an old starch box. Wilbur Wright had been invited by Octave Chanute to speak on gliding to the Western Society of Engineers. Before his talk, Wilbur and Orville tested the action of wind pressure on more than two hundred types of miniature wing surfaces in their tunnel. They proved that the leading edge of the wing should not be sharp as had been previously thought, that deeply cambered wings were inefficient, that unless a flying machine could glide and soar without an engine, it would never be stable in flight with an engine. Wilbur's lecture was reprinted in the "Annual Report" of the Smithsonian Institution.

After their wind tunnel experiments, the Wrights went to Kitty Hawk for the third time. The new glider was vastly different from their previous models. The wing span was ten feet greater. The chord was only one-sixth of the span, instead of one-third. The new glider had a tail which consisted of vertical planes. They had already had experience with "tailspin," and Orville decided that the tail must be movable to counteract the turn of the machine about its vertical axis. The model was a success and proved the correctness of their system of controls.

In March, 1903, they applied for a patent, and that autumn they took a new machine to Kitty Hawk—this time powered with a motor.

They were ready really to fly.

One of Chanute's gliders piloted by Herring, who became an enemy of the Wrights and Curtiss.

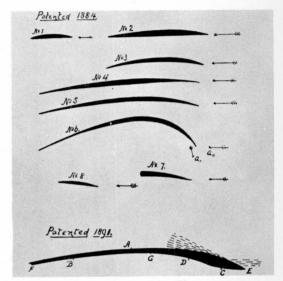
Phillips' airfoils, described by Chanute, gave the Wrights an insight into aerodynamics.

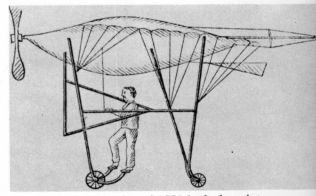
Goupil's flying machine of 1883 looked quaint but it was accompanied by engineering study.

tion. As the sustaining surface was 290 sq. ft., we then have, using the table of "lift" and "drift" heretofore given, the following estimate :

RESISTANCE OF THE GOUPIL AEROPLANE.

Drift 10°. . . . . . 290 × 0.85 × 0 0585 = 14.42 lbs.
Body . . . . 26.9 × 0.85 ÷ 10 = 2.28 "
Edge of wings . . 19.7 × 0.2 × 0.85 ÷ 3 = 1.11 "

Total 17 81 "

which agrees closely with the amount said to have been ascertained by experiment ; but when we come to calculate the lifting force we have :

Lift 10° — 290 × 0.85 × 0 332 = 82 lbs.,

while the apparatus is said to have actually lifted 440 lbs., or more than five times as much !

Chanute analyzed Goupil's data, and the Wrights learned to calculate the forces of flight.

4. THE CONQUEST
OF THE AIR

The simple precepts by which the wingless human biped was able to master flight through the planet's atmosphere were set down some ten millenia after the same creature had come crawling out of caves in the receding polar ice sheet.

The enunciators of the new principles were named Orville and Wilbur Wright. Their revolutionary information was given to the world in the form of a long, detailed, stilted letter to a subordinate bureau of their government. This bureau studied the letter for three years and then released it to mankind at large—in a scarcely-read bureau gazette, immediately following the description of a new form of haystacker. On May 22, 1906, the great teachings were revealed in the following form:

> 821,393. FLYING-MACHINE. Orville Wright and Wilbur Wright, Dayton, Ohio. Filed Mar. 23, 1903. Serial No. 149,220.
>
> *To all whom it may concern:*
> Be it known that we, ORVILLE WRIGHT and WILBUR WRIGHT, citizens of the United States, residing in the city of Dayton, county of Montgomery, and State of Ohio, have invented certain new and useful Improvements in Flying-Machines, of which the following is a specification.

Mankind had already attempted to fly with four different kinds of apparatus: 1. a balloon filled with lighter-than-air gas which would rise but could not be controlled so that men in balloons were blown on the wind like winged seed; 2. a machine in imitation of a bird's flapping wings—an ornithopter; 3. a helicopter, which would be capable of flight without forward motion; 4. a variation of a kite in which a curved plane of cloth—called an "aeroplane"—was held aloft by the streaming motion of air and which, when adapted for men, was called a glider. In these a man could ride down from a hilltop in a gentle gliding fall. Most attempts of this sort had ended in death for the operator. Nevertheless, the Wrights wrote:

> Our invention relates to that class of flying-machines in which the weight is sustained by the reactions resulting when one or more aeroplanes are moved through the air edgewise at a small angle of incidence, either by the application of mechanical power or by the utilization of the force of gravity.

The Wrights realized that there were three essentials to flight by man: 1. a lightweight engine; 2. the form of a smooth plane surface against which the air would stream and support the weight of the engine and a man; 3. and lastly, a means to control the movements of such a machine through the air. The Wrights interpreted the disaster of Langley and Maxim to mean that the first two could easily be solved, but disaster had always resulted from lack of control. To them, control was crucial and so they wrote:

> The objects of our invention are to provide means for maintaining or restoring the equilibrium or lateral balance of the apparatus, to provide means for guiding the machine both vertically and horizontally, and to provide a structure combining lightness, strength,

The Wrights had carefully studied the behavior of birds in soaring flight and noted how buzzards and gulls could remain aloft for long periods at a time.

The Wrights had noted: "No bird soars in a calm. A bird soars *on* the wind, and *facing* into the wind because the air streaming past the upper and lower surface of the curved wing creates a lifting force on the underside of the wing. And so they stated:

> the air. The relative movements of the air and aeroplane may be derived from the motion of the air in the form of wind blowing in the direction opposite to that in which the apparatus is traveling or by a combined downward and forward movement of the machine, as in starting from an elevated position or by combination of these two things, and in either case the operation is that of a soaring-machine, while power applied to the machine to propel it positively forward will cause the air to support the machine in a similar manner. In either case owing to the va-

To fly safely, a man must have a way to restore equilibrium to his flying machine. The Wrights noticed that birds twisted their wing tips and thus changed the angle at which the leading edge of the wing met the air stream. The Wrights intended to give a similar control to human flyers to meet the changing conditions of the wind. Ropes were stretched from the operator's cradle to the edge of the wings so that he could warp the wing, raising one side and lowering the other, at will.

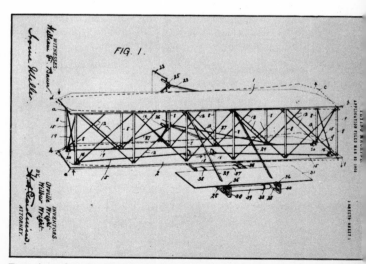

Drawings for the Wrights' 1903 patent. Dark blotches in left view show diagonal lay of muslin to prevent wrink-

obvious manner. By reason of this construction it will be seen that with the particular mode of construction now under consideration it is possible to move the forward corner of the lateral edges of the aeroplane on one side of the machine either above or below the normal planes of the aeroplanes, a reverse movement of the forward corners of the lateral margins on the other side of the machine occurring simultaneously. During this op-

atmosphere that side presenting the largest angle of incidence, although being lifted or moved upward in the manner already described, at the same time meets with an increased resistance to its forward motion, and is therefore retarded in its forward motion, while at the same time the other side of the machine, presenting a smaller angle of incidence, meets with less resistance to its forward motion and tends to move forward more rapidly than the retarded side. This gives the machine a tendency to turn around its vertical axis, and this tendency if not properly

However, the Wrights were well aware that there were other methods by which the form of wings could be distorted to give control, and they protected themselves against imitation by stating:

of the machine to either side. We wish it to be understood, however, that our invention is not limited to this particular construction, since any construction whereby the angular relations of the lateral margins of the aeroplanes may be varied in opposite directions with respect to the normal planes of said aeroplanes comes within the scope of our invention. Furthermore, it should be under-

ing the machine to turn. The movement of the rudder hereinbefore described prevents this action, since it exerts a retarding influence on that side of the machine which tends to move forward too rapidly and keeps the machine with its front properly presented to the direction of flight and with its body properly balanced around its central longitudinal axis.

This control also gave them the means to turn the flying machine while in the air. If one wing were warped in such a way that it had more lift, the flying machine would tend to turn on its side and fly in a circular path. However, when a wing was given more lift, it was also given more drag which would turn the flying machine in the wrong direction. The Wrights understood that the function of an aerial rudder is not to turn the machine, as a ship is turned, but simply to hold it straight while the wings are being inclined.

These methods of control proved to be completely successful in every experiment made by the Wright brothers and their followers. Even the improved controls suggested by Alexander Graham Bell and Glenn Curtiss who built flying machines with rigid wings and "ailerons" were predicted by the Wrights when they wrote:

We do not wish to be understood as limiting ourselves strictly to the precise details of construction hereinbefore described and shown in the accompanying drawings, as it is obvious that these details may be modified

The Wright patent had sixteen claims which fully described all the means of control for a flying machine. Claim No. 7 covers the rudder of the flying machine which remained unchanged in principle for almost fifty years:

7. In a flying-machine, the combination, with an aeroplane, and means for simultaneously moving the lateral portions thereof into different angular relations to the normal plane of the body of the aeroplane and to each other, so as to present to the atmosphere different angles of incidence, of a vertical rudder, and means whereby said rudder is caused to present to the wind that side thereof nearest the side of the aeroplane having the smaller angle of incidence and offering the least resistance to the atmosphere, substantially as described.

flight. It will be observed in this connection that the construction is such that the rudder will always be so turned as to present its resisting-surface on that side of the machine on which the lateral margins of the aeroplanes present the least angle of resistance. The reason of this construction is that when the

lateral margins of the aeroplanes are so turned in the manner hereinbefore described as to present different angles of incidence to the

The Wright brothers considered themselves to be scientists. Yet, at the same time, they were anxious for great wealth. The conflict between the two drives was to torment them for the rest of their lives. But of one thing they were very sure: the flying machine was one of the greatest gifts man had ever given to man because at last it would mean the end of all wars. No longer could armies conceal their movements from each other, no longer were civilian areas safe from explosives dropped by enemy aircraft, and so rational men would now have no alternative but to find the means by which all the peoples of the world would live together in harmony.

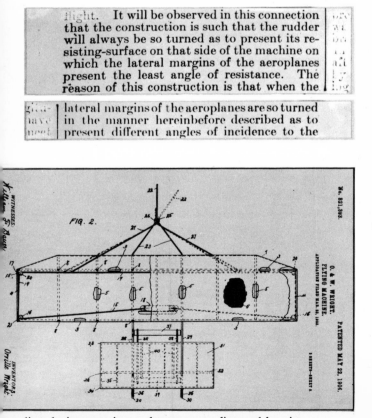

ling during warping and to serve as diagonal bracing for the wing structure. Patent describes a glider.

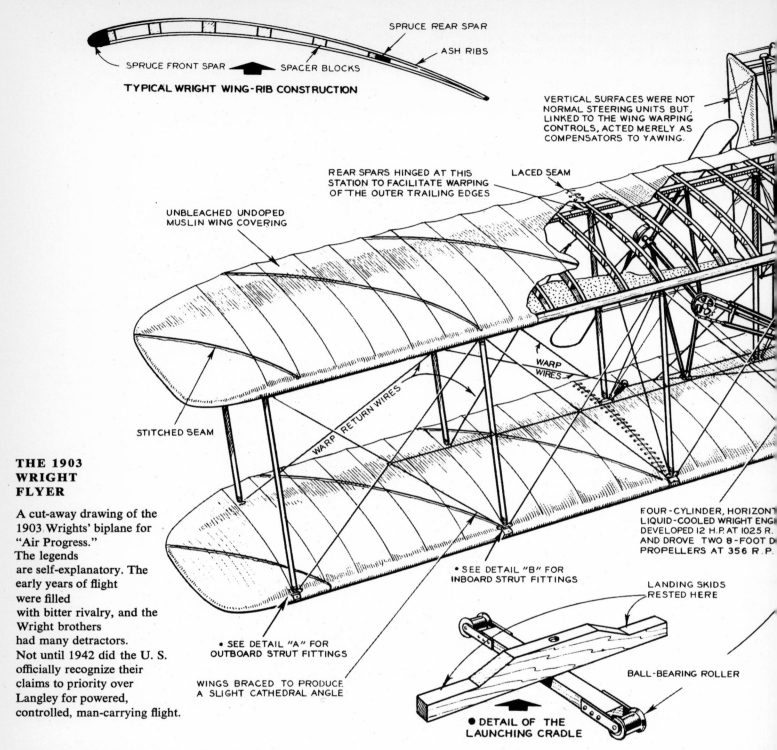

SPRUCE REAR SPAR

ASH RIBS

SPRUCE FRONT SPAR → SPACER BLOCKS

TYPICAL WRIGHT WING-RIB CONSTRUCTION

VERTICAL SURFACES WERE NOT
NORMAL STEERING UNITS BUT,
LINKED TO THE WING WARPING
CONTROLS, ACTED MERELY AS
COMPENSATORS TO YAWING.

REAR SPARS HINGED AT THIS
STATION TO FACILITATE WARPING
OF THE OUTER TRAILING EDGES

LACED SEAM

UNBLEACHED UNDOPED
MUSLIN WING COVERING

WARP
WIRES

WARP RETURN WIRES

STITCHED SEAM

**THE 1903
WRIGHT
FLYER**

A cut-away drawing of the
1903 Wrights' biplane for
"Air Progress."
The legends
are self-explanatory. The
early years of flight
were filled
with bitter rivalry, and the
Wright brothers
had many detractors.
Not until 1942 did the U. S.
officially recognize their
claims to priority over
Langley for powered,
controlled, man-carrying flight.

FOUR-CYLINDER, HORIZONT
LIQUID-COOLED WRIGHT ENGI
DEVELOPED 12 H.P. AT 1025 R.
AND DROVE TWO 8-FOOT D
PROPELLERS AT 356 R.P.

• SEE DETAIL "B" FOR
INBOARD STRUT FITTINGS

LANDING SKIDS
RESTED HERE

• SEE DETAIL "A" FOR
OUTBOARD STRUT FITTINGS

BALL-BEARING ROLLER

WINGS BRACED TO PRODUCE
A SLIGHT CATHEDRAL ANGLE

● DETAIL OF THE
LAUNCHING CRADLE

5. THE WRIGHT BOYS
IN EUROPE

A year before the Wrights applied for their patent,
accounts of their gliding experiments appeared in several journals. Captain Louis F. Ferber, the French
aeronaut, expressed his admiration for the Americans
and procured a machine similar to theirs. Within a
short time after the Wrights made their first powered
flight, the French mounted engines in their American
gliders and powered flights were made in flying machines *du type Wright*. In 1905, the Wrights built a
still heavier machine driven by a twenty-horsepower

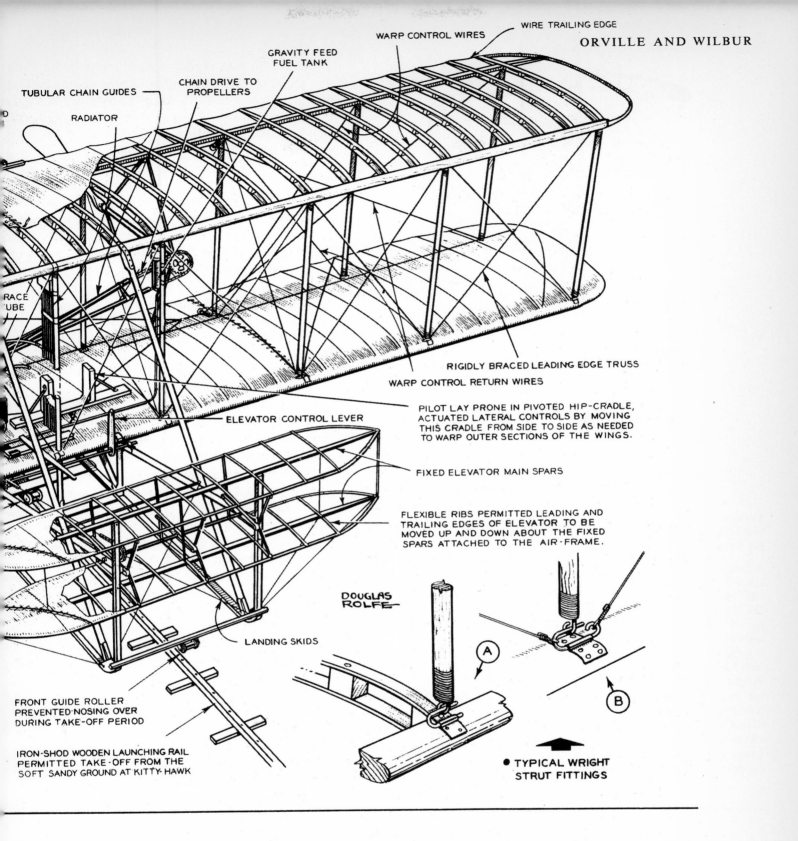

WIRE TRAILING EDGE

WARP CONTROL WIRES

GRAVITY FEED
FUEL TANK

CHAIN DRIVE TO
PROPELLERS

TUBULAR CHAIN GUIDES

RADIATOR

RACE
UBE

RIGIDLY BRACED LEADING EDGE TRUSS

WARP CONTROL RETURN WIRES

PILOT LAY PRONE IN PIVOTED HIP-CRADLE,
ACTUATED LATERAL CONTROLS BY MOVING
THIS CRADLE FROM SIDE TO SIDE AS NEEDED
TO WARP OUTER SECTIONS OF THE WINGS.

ELEVATOR CONTROL LEVER

FIXED ELEVATOR MAIN SPARS

FLEXIBLE RIBS PERMITTED LEADING AND
TRAILING EDGES OF ELEVATOR TO BE
MOVED UP AND DOWN ABOUT THE FIXED
SPARS ATTACHED TO THE AIR-FRAME.

DOUGLAS
ROLFE

A

B

LANDING SKIDS

FRONT GUIDE ROLLER
PREVENTED NOSING OVER
DURING TAKE-OFF PERIOD

IRON-SHOD WOODEN LAUNCHING RAIL
PERMITTED TAKE-OFF FROM THE
SOFT SANDY GROUND AT KITTY-HAWK

● TYPICAL WRIGHT
STRUT FITTINGS

engine. In September that year, they made fifty successful flights, and on October 5, they flew 24.2 miles in thirty-eight minutes.

The Wrights formed a company with licensed subsidiaries in England, France, and Germany. The Wright Brothers became *Wright Frères* and the *Gebruder Wright*. In Europe, they were famous. Their acquaintance was sought by Edward VII of England in 1908, and King Alfonso of Spain took a lesson from Wilbur in the use of the controls. At international air shows, which began in 1909 at Reims, Wright planes demonstrated that it was possible to fly higher than the fifty or one hundred feet which had been achieved in the early years of aviation and soared up to altitudes awe inspiring to spectators.

Wright-trained European pilots made flights that covered a hundred miles, but what always impressed the spectators more than anything else were the figure eights, the perfect circles, and the gentle landings made possible by the Wright controls.

Wilbur briefing two Wright-trained fliers, Johnstone and Brookins, famous names in American aviation.

6. THE CREATURES
OF THE AIR

By the time the First World War started, only eleven years after the glorious December morning at Kitty Hawk, Orville and Wilbur Wright had passed from the pride of that first achievement, through the tangle of angry patent litigation with Glenn Curtiss, to the bitter tragedy of Wilbur Wright's death in 1912. Wilbur's last will left fifty thousand dollars apiece to his brothers Reuchlin and Lorin and to his sister Katherine, while the residue was left to Orville, "who, I am sure, will use the property in very much the same manner as we would use it together in case we would both survive until old age."

Orville, who lived until 1948, never recovered from the heartache over his brother's death. Even though he succeeded Wilbur as president of the Wright Company, he sold out to a syndicate shortly after Wilbur's funeral. Ironically, this syndicate was also to buy out the Wrights' bitterest rival—Glenn Curtiss.

Glenn Curtiss, the Wrights' rival, was no villain. Before he became interested in aviation he was a builder of motorcycle engines in Hammondsport, New York, and in 1907 he established himself, on a motorcycle, as the "fastest man on earth" by being the first to travel at a speed that exceeded two miles a minute. His motorcycle engines were used in the first American dirigibles as early as 1903, but he took no interest in aviation until his 1907 speed record brought him to the attention of sixty-year-old Alexander Graham Bell who was experimenting along lines of flight that were the reverse of the Wrights'. Bell was looking for the ultimate in stability: a flying machine that could practically stand still and hover in the air. He had reached a point in his kite experiments where powered flight was the next step. The brilliant young engine builder was pressed to join Bell's Aerial Experiment Association, a cooperative of young men who worked with Bell on aviation problems in the manner of a science research team.

The Aerial Experiment Association closely studied the methods set forth in the Wrights' patent. In 1908, when the Wrights were conquering Europe, Bell and Curtiss attempted to improve on the Wrights' design. Instead of wing warping for control, Curtiss built independently-hinged tips called "ailerons" and won many prizes, although none of his flights compared with the Wrights'. His "ailerons" were declared an infringement by the court, and the wording of the decision hurt Curtiss because he felt that he had been called a pirate. His pride was as deeply involved as the Wright brothers' who mistakenly thought that Curtiss was a "mountebank" because of his exhibition flying. Actually, Curtiss had been trying only to arouse the American public from its apathy towards aviation by putting on demonstrations that would demand attention. His main interest was the development of better aircraft engines. The differences between Curtiss and the Wrights, inflamed by outsiders venting personal antagonisms, were so deep that they could never be healed, for the men who had transcended the ties that had bound their species to earth could not transcend their emotions. Flying or walking, men, in the end, were only human.

For years, Europe was far more interested in aviation than was the United States. When the First World War broke out in 1914, only eleven years after the Wrights' first flight, the French Army had 1,500 planes and was able to requisition 500 more from private use. The German Army had 1,000 planes and a civilian reservoir of 450 more. In marked contrast, in 1917, the U. S. Army had only 55 planes, 51 of which were obsolete, and four obsolescent. The aviation section of the Signal Corps had only sixty-five officers. Thirty-five could fly and only five could have met combat conditions. In the fourteen years that had elapsed since the flight at Kitty Hawk, a total of fewer than two hundred airplanes had been built in the United States.

At the end of the First World War, the United States Air Force had forty-five squadrons and 767 pilots who had spent 35,000 flying hours in missions over the lines. The airplane of 1920 was far different from the machine which had been used for reconnaissance in 1914. These improvements were due mostly to Anthony Fokker of Holland, De Havilland of England, and the excellent French designers. The airplane was well launched in its career towards perfection in which men of many nations played their part, and the Wright brothers were figures of history.

The Wrights in their years of fame: (left to right) Orville, Katherine and Wilbur.

EVOLUTION OF THE WING

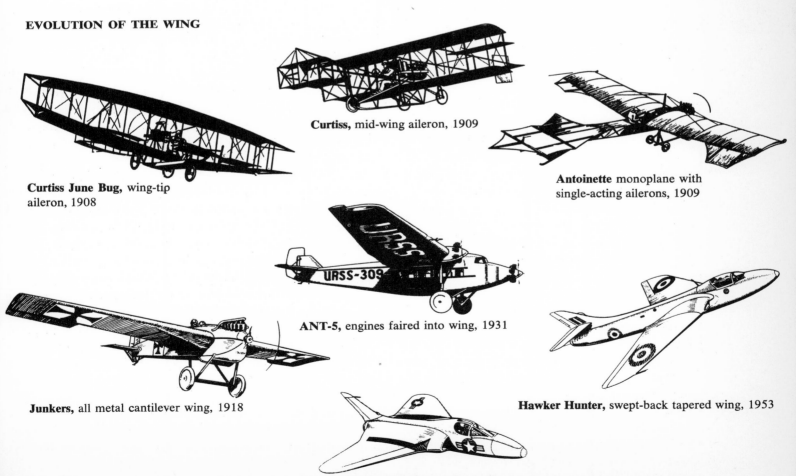

Curtiss, mid-wing aileron, 1909

Curtiss June Bug, wing-tip aileron, 1908

Antoinette monoplane with single-acting ailerons, 1909

ANT-5, engines faired into wing, 1931

Junkers, all metal cantilever wing, 1918

Hawker Hunter, swept-back tapered wing, 1953

Douglas F4D Skyray, modified delta-wing fighter, 1953

George Ellery Hale, looking at the sun's image through the 60-foot-tower telescope at Mt. Wilson in 1907.

GEORGE ELLERY HALE

1. EXPLORER OF THE SUN

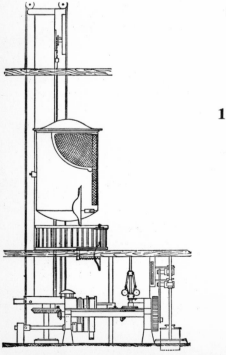

Passenger elevators, the first is shown above, became necessary with the growth of the American cities. Hale's father established the family fortune in the elevator business. George Hale was one of Chicago's rich young men.

Looking through the eyepiece of the Princeton instrument, a seventeen-year-old boy was awed by the apocalyptic vision of huge tongues of flame leaping out from the rim of the sun. The speed of the solar flames was almost 250 miles a second, Professor Charles Young told him. They could soar to heights of almost half a million miles.

The year was 1885, the boy was George Ellery Hale, and the sight was one he never forgot. It determined his career; and his career determined the course of American astronomy.

George Hale was an unusual boy, the son of unusual parents. During the years when Chicago's new industrial rich were living lives of exaggerated ostentation, William Ellery Hale and his wife Mary had far different values. George had the kind of mechanical toys that his contemporaries—Robert Millikan and Lee de Forest—could only dream about; and if the Hales had been different people, George would simply have been a spoiled rich child. However, he had a passionate interest in learning and his parents did everything to encourage him. When the boy's interest widened to include astronomy, a small telescope was purchased. George was intense, quick, and consumed with impatience to make still more rapid progress, but his father laughed, telling him not to try to get everything done yesterday. Nevertheless, Hale's father managed to get him, when he was fourteen, a second-hand refractor built by the great Alvan Clark.

When the telescope was mounted, and the moon and planets brought into focus, Hale was beside himself with excitement, and he had that sure sense of recognition that comes to those men who finally find their life work. He knew of the work on solar spectra and astro-photography that was just beginning at Harvard, and young Hale was one of the earliest enthusiasts. He became an amateur astrophysicist. His visit to Princeton was to lead him into one special branch of astrophysics—the study of the sun.

From 1886 to 1892, George Hale studied physics at MIT but spent most of his time as a volunteer assistant to E. C. Pickering at the Harvard Observatory. All this time, though, in the back of Hale's mind, was the soaring image of the flames shooting out of the sun.

No naked eye could see the sun's flames. Young at Princeton had shown Hale a special device to make them visible on the sun's rim, but Hale knew that these swirls of fire flickered and raced over the face of the entire sun. A more ingenious instrument than Young's was needed, and the principle of it came clear to Hale in 1889 when he was a senior at MIT, home on vacation, riding on a trolley in downtown Chicago.

Here was the problem: the sun was composed of incandescent atoms of the various elements in gaseous form. To an observer on earth, the light from the sun would be a mixture of all the radiations; but if a way could be found to distinguish between the radiation from the lighter elements of the surface and the heavier ones below, the different layers of the sun could be explored for their chemical composition.

In Hale's youth, the distribution of the elements in the sun was not known except that in 1868 Janssen, the French astronomer, had found hydrogen in the outermost layer. What Hale wanted was a "filter" that would transmit only the light from hydrogen and so produce a picture of just the outermost layer from which the giant flames came.

One of the characteristic lines of hydrogen was a unique red emitted by no other element. If every line in the sun's spectrum could be blotted out except this one red line, then Hale would be getting only the light from the solar prominence.

Riding on the trolley that day, Hale, the MIT senior, conceived the idea of placing behind a spectroscope prism an opaque screen with a narrow opening in it just wide enough to pass the one red hydrogen line which was contained in the sun's spectrum. If the entire apparatus were slowly moved across the rim of the sun, an observer would see only the portions of the hydrogen flame across which the spectroscope was sweeping. If the spectroscope oscillated rapidly back and forth, the image would appear continuous; and the naked eye would be seeing the entire form of the ever changing flames.

Before George Hale had entered MIT, his father had given him a complete spectroscopic laboratory. Now, in 1890, when Hale completed his course at the Institute, his father also bought him a telescope with a 12-inch refractor and housed it in a building with a dome and room for a complete library. This impressive array was the Kenwood Observatory. Such a gift for a twenty-two-year-old boy just out of college was something that could happen only in 1890 Chicago— but Hale set to work immediately on his new conception for solar exploration.

Hale married that June; and in the spring of the following year began his active work with the spectroheliograph. On May 7, 1891, he made his first successful photographs of the solar flames, and went on to discover that, in addition to hydrogen, the flames showed the presence of calcium. While an improved spectroheliograph was being built, he and his wife went abroad. Hale was only twenty-three but he was received by astronomers with great respect.

On a cold winter day in Chicago, January, 1892, Hale took solar photographs which gave remarkable information: the entire sun was covered with burning calcium clouds which seemed to be closely connected with sun spots. Other photographs enabled him to make spectral analyses of these darker portions that had erupted from deeper levels of the sun.

When the University of Chicago was founded in

1892 with funds from John D. Rockefeller, Hale, already one of the most brilliant young American astronomers, was invited to join the faculty. Two 40-inch discs of optical glass, enormous for that time, which had been ordered by the University of Southern California were on the market because USC lacked funds to complete the purchase. Hale wanted them for the University of Chicago. With his background and reputation, he was able to approach several wealthy businessmen for their support. Charles T. Yerkes, the traction magnate whose checkered career was to form the basis for Theodore Dreiser's novel *The Financier,* agreed to put up the money. No provision was made for either a building or other equipment to house the telescope and maintain a staff. Nevertheless, Hale set up the Yerkes Observatory and took on the responsibility of raising the rest of the necessary funds.

He felt responsible not only to the donors, but also to the strong staff of astronomers and physicists he had gathered. Many expenses were paid out of his own pocket. The Yerkes Observatory became world famous by 1900, but the continuous drive to raise funds was an enormous burden on Hale who was essentially a retiring man.

Hale's oldest daughter, Margaret, suffered from repeated attacks of bronchitis and asthma and had to be taken out to the milder climate of Pasadena in 1903 by Mrs. Hale.

George Hale joined his family in December of that year and, with a small portable telescope, climbed through uncut forest to the 6,000-foot summit of one of the magnificent mountains just south of the city. The air was clear, the view inspiring. Observations that night convinced him that a large telescope on this site should give remarkable results. In spite of his own weariness with raising endless money, Hale stood all alone on the summit of Mt. Wilson and began plans for the greatest observatory the world had ever known.

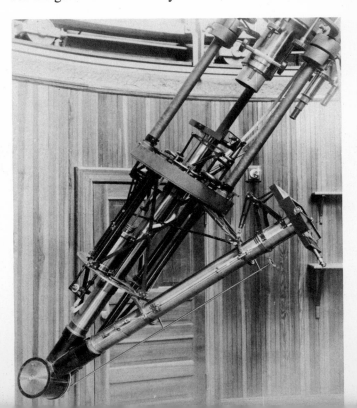

The spectroheliograph assembled at Kenwood in the 1890's for George Ellery Hale became a world-famous instrument. It established the presence of calcium in the solar surface.

The 100-inch Hooker telescope was housed by Carnegie. Hale gathered America's best astronomers at Mt. Wilson.

2. GIANT TELESCOPES

The room was dark except for the long cone of light from the magic lantern. On a white screen, pictures were cast of different portions of the heavens—nebuli, galaxies, planets whirling in discs of dust. A man's voice, uncultured, but awed, described each picture in terms of fantastic numbers. Distances were measured in millions and billions of miles; temperatures were announced that could mean only hell.

At length the lights went on in the drawing room of the Scottish castle of Andrew Carnegie. Lloyd George sat stunned, then he said slowly, "Never in my life have I been so entranced!"

These pictures had come to Carnegie from a California mountain top thousands of miles away where, every night, in a domed white building, men worked the quarries of star-fire in the sky. The Observatory lights could be seen for miles around and Alfred

Noyes wrote:

> By night it joined the company of heaven,
> And, with its constant light, became a star.

The Observatory was a tie between Noyes's poetry and the four-square prose of a diary entry made long before by young Andrew Carnegie in 1868 in the St. Nicholas Hotel in New York:

"Thirty-three and an income of $50,000 per annum! Beyond this never earn—make no effort to increase fortune but spend the surplus each year for benevolent purposes. Cast aside business forever, except for others. Settle in Oxford and get a thorough education, making the acquaintance of literary men— this will take three years active work—pay especial attention to speaking in public. Settle then in London and purchase controlling interest in some newspaper or live review and give the general management of it attention, taking a part in public matters, especially those connected with education and improvement of the poorer classes."

Palomar Observatory seen at night. The open shutter shows the 200-inch Hale telescope named after one of America's greatest scientific organizers.

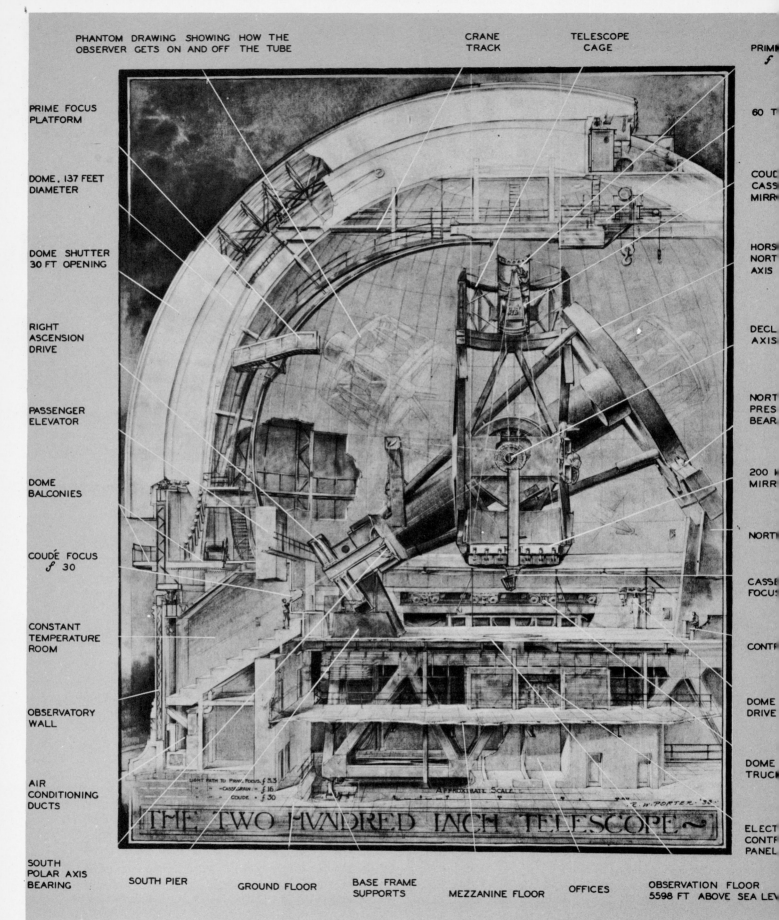

PHANTOM DRAWING SHOWING HOW THE
OBSERVER GETS ON AND OFF THE TUBE

CRANE
TRACK

TELESCOPE
CAGE

PRIM

PRIME FOCUS
PLATFORM

60 T

DOME. 137 FEET
DIAMETER

COUD
CASS
MIRR

DOME SHUTTER
30 FT OPENING

HORS
NORT
AXIS

RIGHT
ASCENSION
DRIVE

DECL
AXIS

PASSENGER
ELEVATOR

NORT
PRES
BEAR

DOME
BALCONIES

200 I
MIRR

COUDÉ FOCUS
f 30

NORTI

CONSTANT
TEMPERATURE
ROOM

CASS
FOCU

CONTR

OBSERVATORY
WALL

DOME
DRIVE

DOME
TRUCI

AIR
CONDITIONING
DUCTS

LIGHT PATH TO PRIM. FOCUS. f 3.3
CASSEGRAIN f 16
COUDÉ f 30

APPROXIMATE SCALE

R. W. PORTER '33

THE TWO HVNDRED INCH TELESCOPE

ELECT
CONTR
PANEL

SOUTH
POLAR AXIS
BEARING

SOUTH PIER

GROUND FLOOR

BASE FRAME
SUPPORTS

MEZZANINE FLOOR

OFFICES

OBSERVATION FLOOR
5598 FT ABOVE SEA LEV

The astronomer using the 200-inch telescope sits above the instrument in the area marked "prime focus" (left).

The immensity of the observatory can be seen in this photograph of the instrument pointing north.

3. THE 200-INCH TELESCOPE AT PALOMAR

Andrew Carnegie underestimated himself. He retired at sixty-three, not thirty-five. In his year of retirement, his income was 460 times $50,000 a year—$23,000,000. He was the first owner of great wealth to present himself as only a trustee for the public, and his example established a pattern for the use of wealth which was followed by Rockefeller, Ford, Huntington and others.

Andrew Carnegie was the fourth wealthy man to help George Hale advance American astronomy. The first had been his father; the second had been Yerkes; the third was Hooker of Pasadena who donated the 100-inch mirror and finally, there was Carnegie, the richest of them all. On January 19, 1911, the trustees of the Washington Carnegie Institution received a brief letter from Carnegie stating that he was adding another ten million dollars to his endowment to be earmarked for the Mt. Wilson Observatory.

Hale gathered and trained the men who were to be among the world's leading astronomers. Mt. Wilson became one of the intellectual centers of the scientific world and in the early 1930's Albert Einstein came to America specifically to study the newest data in astrophysics as background for the developments in his own theoretical work. In spite of the enormous responsibilities, strains and pressures on Hale, he considered his own greatest contribution to educational organization to be his part in the establishment of the California Institute of Technology.

In his early years at Mt. Wilson he had been asked to help plan the future policy of Throop Institute in Pasadena which had a small endowment for an art school, manual training, and other applied courses to meet local needs. Hale suggested a curriculum based on his own experience, and through his prestige, gathered some of the most outstanding scientists in the country. It was Hale who brought Robert Millikan from the University of Chicago to head the school, now transformed into the California Institute of Technology. He was also responsible for the formation of the Huntington Library and Art Gallery.

Hale was able to raise huge sums of money all his life because he had been born familiar with huge sums of money. To a scientist from a more modest background, an important project might be discarded in the planning stage because the costs seemed prohibitive. Hale knew who had the money and he went and got it, not because he admired bigness, but because he felt that science should not be shortchanged.

If Scott Fitzgerald was right when he said that the rich are different, then Hale was science's ambassador to that other "world." His huge installations at Mt. Wilson advanced science but also imposed a pattern on science. Hale thought of scientific teamwork as the cooperation between individuals—he did not foresee the day when the individual scientist would become only a unit in the larger, more impersonal "team."

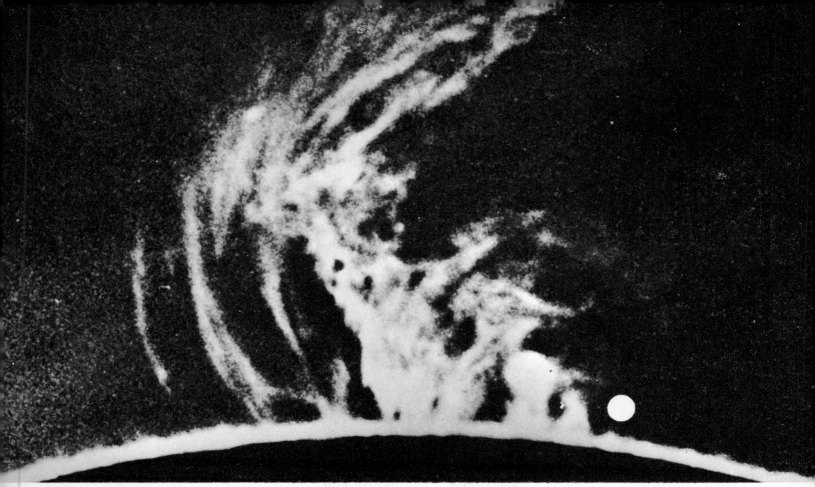

Solar prominences from the sun leap to 140,000 miles. The technique of solar photography was Hale's great achievement. His spectroheliograph was invented when he was less than thirty. The white disc shows the relative size of the earth.

4. THE SUN'S ATMOSPHERE

To an observer far outside of the earth's atmosphere, the sun is a white-hot ball with gigantic red and violet flames streaming over its surface, whirling in gigantic cyclones and tornadoes. Sometimes clots of fire shoot off into the black void which is the sky.

This is the appearance of the sun. Its atmosphere changes as one penetrates to the core, but the outermost regions consist of flaming hydrogen, helium, and calcium. Hydrogen, the lightest element in nature, gives off the reddish glare. The violet flame is incandescent calcium vapor, twenty times as heavy as hydrogen. These comparatively massive molecules float in the outer envelope on the tremendous outward pressure of radiation emitted from the core of the sun. The calcium atoms are eternally attempting to fall toward the interior of the sun, but twenty thousand times a second the calcium atoms are pelted with photons of radiation which keep the atoms back up in the outermost solar atmosphere.

The flames of the sun were first noticed by the English amateur astronomer, Francis Baily. He was observing an eclipse of the sun on July 8, 1842, from the upper floor of the University of Pavia when he saw the moon "suddenly surrounded with a. . .bright glory similar to that which painters draw around the heads of saints. . .but the most remarkable circumstance. . .

was the appearance of three large protuberances apparently emanating from the circumference of the moon (with) the appearance of mountains of prodigious elevation; their color was red tinged with lilac or purple."

George Hale was able to see these leaping flames in broad daylight when Professor Young of Princeton showed him the primitive Princeton spectroheliograph. Hale's devouring interest in the sun led him to discover the nature of these flames. Then he discovered how they were connected with the dark spots which moved with changing shapes across the face of the sun. The study of the sun spots—some larger than the earth itself—led him to prove that the sun was itself magnetic.

Joseph Henry had proven that the dark areas on the sun—the sun spots—were areas of comparative coolness. Later research established that each dark area was like the "eye" of a terrestrial storm—a vortex of a swirling solar disturbance in which streams of flaming hydrogen and calcium gas poured out into higher levels of the sun's atmosphere. Because these gases were expanding, they were cooled; and although their temperatures were enormously high on any earthbound scale, they were still so much cooler than the rest of the sun's surface, that they appeared black by comparison.

In 1908, Hale studied the sun in terms of the revo-

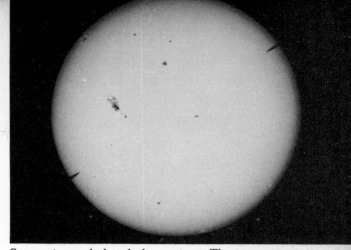

Sun spots are dark only by contrast. The temperatures are thousands of degrees.

The spectroheliograph of the 150-foot tower telescope lies deep in a shaft.

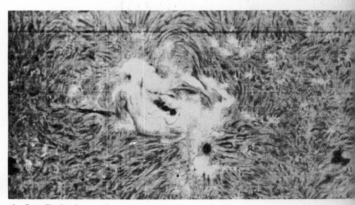

A detailed view of a sun spot shows the whirling motion of gas on the solar surface.

lutionary electron work by J. J. Thomson. Hale reasoned this way: the flaming hydrogen and calcium were electrified. Therefore free electrons in enormous numbers must be present in the solar atmosphere. The spiraling motion around each vortex must create huge sheets of electric current which in turn should develop powerful magnetic fields.

To test his theory, that same year on Mt. Wilson Hale examined an image of the surface of the sun that was 6.7 inches in diameter. He scrutinized every section of this disc through the slit of a 30-foot spectroscope. In certain areas—the sun spot regions—his delicate instruments recorded that the characteristic spectral lines of the sun seemed slightly broadened. There were many possible explanations for these small changes, but only a dozen years earlier Pieter Zeeman had demonstrated that magnetic fields altered the spectrum of the various elements in a highly characteristic way. Hale decided to test his deduction by repeating Zeeman's experiment.

"No time was lost in making the test," he wrote. "Two iron lines in the red part of the sun spot's spectrum. . .were first examined. The first day's observations were inconclusive. But on the second day. . .definite results were obtained. . . When observed with a large magnet in the laboratory, each line behaved as it did in the sun. It soon became certain, after many searching trials, that *magnetic fields existed in all the sun spots examined."*

This was an exquisite piece of research. Starting with premises based on his own observations and those of others, Hale had made a radical deduction. When subjected to direct experiment, the deduction was proven correct. Hale's work was particularly dramatic because he was dealing with cosmic forces. Against the inconceivable power radiated every second by the sun, a human being is physically powerless. Nevertheless the human mind was able to cross the million-mile void and stand unscorched while observing the nature of flames that soared out for hundreds of thousands of miles.

Hale, in retirement, organized a world-wide chain of observers to watch the sun twenty-four hours a day, so that if an observer at Greenwich saw the beginning of a sun spot toward evening he could alert observers in the United States who would chart the progress of the solar tornado from stations across the continent, and in turn pass it over for observation to astronomers in Japan, Australia, and the Soviet Union. Such stations were set up around the world.

Hale was not only a leader of astronomical studies in the United States, he was an organizer on a world scale.

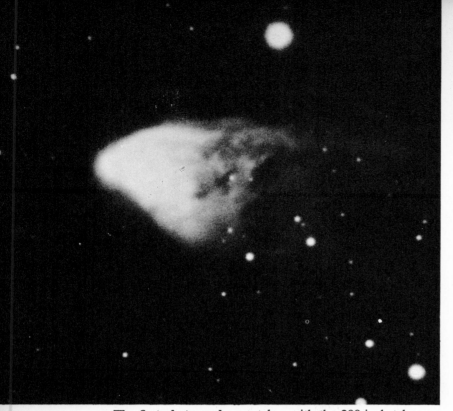

The first photograph ever taken with the 200-inch telescope shows one of the nebulae found by Mt. Wilson's Hubble.

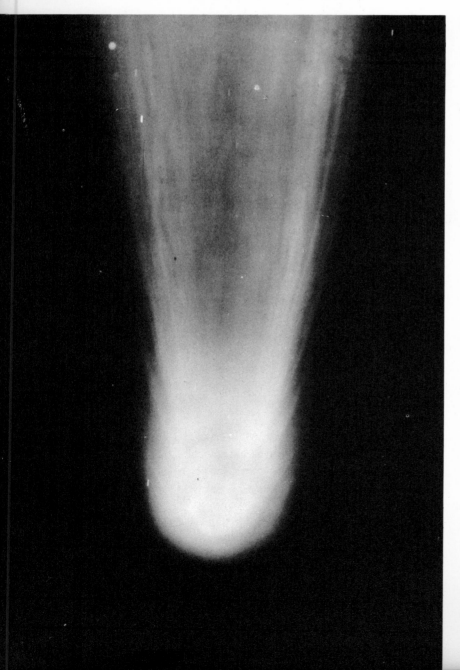

5. THE STARS

George Hale spent his life studying the sun because of his interest in the stars—the sun is the star that is closest to the earth.

By the dawn of the twentieth century, when Mt. Wilson was first established, this was the information that was known about the sun: its diameter, 864,000 miles; its mass, 331,950 earths; its temperature, 2000° C. in the outermost layer, rising to 6000° C. deeper in the atmosphere, and much higher at the core; its distance from the earth, 93,000,000 miles; and its chemical composition at the outermost levels. What was not known was the law which explained why the sun continued to shine, where it came from in the past, what it would be in the future.

In spite of man's ignorance, however, the amount of knowledge about the sun accumulated within a comparatively few decades of the nineteenth century was truly remarkable. One of the main desires of astronomers was to gather the same kind of information about the stars. As for the chemical composition of the stars, the spectroscope had given astronomers the same kind of information generally as it had about the sun. What was not known were the number of stars in the sky, their distances from each other and from the earth, and their sizes. About their future and past, again, nothing more was known than about the history and future of the sun.

In 1838, Bessel measured the apparent motion of a nearby star called 61 Cygni which was just visible to the naked eye. Its shift in the sky was infinitesimally small—exactly as if a man had to measure the displacement of one inch over half a year of a glowing pinhead eight miles away—which meant, on a cosmic scale, by Bessel's trigonometrical calculations, that the star Cygni was forty trillion miles away. Yet 61 Cygni was one of the nearest stars.

Bessel's method was so complicated in detail that the distances of only sixty stars had been calculated by the time Mt. Wilson began its observations.

Far out in the night sky, there was a faint point of light that glowed and dimmed regularly every few days. Spectrographs detected a periodic approach and recession. The first thought was that the point must be a pair of stars—one bright and one dark—rotating in a giant merry-go-round.

Then calculation showed that this was impossible. Another theory was tried. This time the star—a single one—was said to be pulsating—expanding and contracting like some giant lung of light. The spectrographic signs of approach meant that the expanding surface of the ball was coming towards us, recession meant the ball's contraction. Other evidence confirmed this theory.

The periods of fluctuation were as little as a day

The head of Halley's comet, one of the best known in Western history, was photographed in 1910 on the 60-inch telescope.

and a quarter for certain of these stars, called Cepheids, while others pulsed in rhythm that was as long as 127 days.

One of Pickering's disciples at the Harvard Observatory in 1912—Henrietta Leavitt—found many such pulsing stars out in a distant cluster called the Magellanic Cloud. She made a deduction that was to lead to a second and completely ingenious method of measuring stellar distances:

These stars were assumed to pulsate according to their intrinsic brightness. The brighter the star, the more slowly it pulsed.

Leavitt's explanation was exploited by a young newspaper man who became a biologist and then an astronomer—Harlow Shapley. At Mt. Wilson, Shapley made use of a highly exquisite refinement of a technique devised a century earlier by Count Rumford. To measure the comparative light intensities of two candles, Rumford arranged their distances from him until they appeared equally bright. If one candle was four times as bright as another it had to be placed twice as far away. On the other hand, when he knew the intensities of the candles, he could use the light as a measure of distance. Shapley used Cepheids in our own constellation as his "standard candle" and gained information about eighty-six other clusters. He was also able to measure the extent of our galaxy—the Milky Way, a flat disc of stars with a radius of 10,000 light years and only 1,000 light years deep. Edwin Hubble showed in 1924 that the great Andromeda nebula—a faint patch of light to the naked eye—was 900,000 light years away.

At Mt. Wilson, teams of astronomers took their turns using the giant telescopes, so that many researches were being carried out at the same time. E. E. Barnard, a Tennessee photographer who had discovered the fifth satellite of Jupiter, was charting the new regions of the sky brought into view by the increasing apertures of the giant telescopes. W. S. Adams was comparing spectrographic plates to prove that the brightness of certain lines on the photographic plate varied with the temperature of the light source, whether the source was an electric arc five feet away, or a distant star. Using this spectrographic method, Adams established still a third way of estimating stellar distances; and with this method, by 1915, he had made over two thousand determinations.

In the middle 1920's Edwin Hubble made a detailed study of stellar spectra and came up with these startling possibilities: either every star in the universe is moving away from us so that we live in an exploding universe; or else the speed of light is not the constant that everyone has assumed; or thirdly, there exists a cosmic dust whose existence has so far gone undetected. The final answer is yet to be found.

W. S. Adams solved one of the most perplexing problems and his answer was to lead, several decades later, through a chain of reasoning to a brilliant theory by Arnold Bethe of the constitution of stars. Bethe's equation, in turn, was to lead to the man-made star—the hydrogen bomb.

Traveling with the speed of light for eight years, seven months, and two weeks from the earth would take one to the star Sirius, which is twenty-six times as bright as the sun. In 1844, Bessel observed the motion of Sirius and concluded that it was traveling in an elliptical orbit. Newtonian mechanics demanded that some other body, undetectable at that time, must be causing Sirius to move—the unseen Companion of Sirius. Eighteen years later, Alvan Clark, the great American telescope maker, actually saw the Companion. It was assumed that the Companion was a feebly glowing red star.

In 1914, Adams at Mt. Wilson examined the dark Companion through a spectrograph and discovered that it was not dark at all, but bright, glowing white, almost as bright as the sun. It had appeared dark only by comparison with the brilliance of Sirius. Yet the total amount of light from it was only 1/360th of the sun, so that it was a glowing ball with a radius only 1/19th of the sun. It was smaller than our nearby planet, Uranus, and only somewhat larger than the earth, which gave the fantastic answer that the dwarf companion was the densest thing man had ever come across—each cubic inch of the companion weighed about a ton. In 1914, the discovery was incredible.

However great were the results of Mt. Wilson's work, George Hale was ridden by his feeling that he must continually justify the sums of money donated by individuals and institutions. He had raised money for the observatories like a fiery widow bullying contributions from rich relatives to send her adored sons to the best schools—a hundred thousand from one for a giant glass mirror, a hundred and fifty thousand from another for its polishing and mounting, a quarter of a million from a third for the control machinery and domed housing.

Just as the great Egyptian tombs were named after the pharaohs who built them, so the giant telescopes bore the names of the nineteenth-century millionaires—Lick, Yerkes, Snow, and Hooker. Hale had to retire at fifty-three, although he lived until he was seventy in 1938. He wore himself out because he tormented himself needlessly. It was not Andrew Carnegie, or Hooker, or Yerkes who made American astronomy possible; it was George Ellery Hale and his followers—Shapley, Hubble, Tolman, Humason, Adams and others—who gave the donors an opportunity to affix their names as footnotes to the great scientific tradition of the civilized world.

Lee de Forest, student of Gibbs, Ph.D. Yale, 1899, was voted the "ugliest and freshest man of his class."

LEE DE FOREST

1. THE ARDENT SPIRIT

In the spring of 1889 a sixteen-year-old boy sat down to an old typewriter and very gravely wrote to his father what he couldn't bring himself to say aloud.

"DEAR SIR: Will you favor me with your ear for a few moments? I wish to state my desires and purposes. I intend to be . . . an inventor, because I have great talents in that direction . . . If this be so, why not allow me to so study as to best prepare myself for that profession?"

The boy was wild to enroll in the Sheffield Scientific School rather than the Arts course at Yale University, as his father and grandfather had done before him.

"I write this with no ill will, but thinking that it is time to decide and choose my studies accordingly. Your obedient son,

LEE DE FOREST

"P.S. This machine beats Mr. Silsbey's all to flinders."

Lee de Forest was born on August 26, 1873, to Mary and Henry Swift de Forest. His father was the minister in the First Congregational Church of Council Bluffs, Iowa, graduate of Yale University and the Andover Theological Seminary.

Six years later the De Forests and their three children moved to Talladega, Alabama, where Dr. de Forest had been appointed director of an American Missionary Association School "open to all of either sex, without regard to sect, race, or color," which in the South meant that it was a school for the children of the newly freed slaves. Lee de Forest was one of the few white students.

The boy was fascinated by everything about him. He saw a blast furnace and then built a model out of an old ashcan; his compressed air supply was an old-fashioned bellows from the family heirlooms. He saw a locomotive and then built one of his own out of packing cases, sugar barrels, kegs, and a tin can for a whistle. He thought it was beautiful. He played ball with the other boys; swam in the creek, learned to play the cornet, subscribed to the *Youth's Companion,* and learned from the advertisements in the magazine how to win a fortune in a thousand different ways. On rainy days he loved to stretch out on the living room floor and sketch the intricate details of pistons and valves for the great engines of his dreams.

For two generations there had been a special scholarship at Yale for members of the De Forest family. At sixteen, Lee knew that he wanted to use the scholarship to go to the Sheffield Scientific School, and after his pleading letter, Dr. de Forest finally gave in. It meant another year's preparation, and Lee was sent to Dwight L. Moody's Mount Hermon Boys' School in Massachusetts, where he learned no science.

A typical Sunday was noted in the boy's diary when he went to hear "Dwight L. Moody preach on the five parts of repentance: conviction, confession, contrition, and—I can't remember the other two. Fine bean dinner at 2:30 and pie! pie!!"

He fell in love; spent the summer vacation selling *King's Handbook of the United States;* saved forty dollars by half starving himself. He was accepted at Yale, then worked his way out to the World's Columbian Exposition of 1893 by selling *What Can A Woman Do?* At the Exposition, he got a job as a chair pusher. "When my patrons asked me what they

should visit, invariably I would steer them into Machinery Hall."

For the whole summer of 1893 the fair was De Forest's home. Every spare moment he had he spent studying the models, the machines, engines, and the pretty girls. "Little then did I imagine," he writes, "that eleven years later, at the next great World's Exposition, this chair pusher's name would emblazon the loftiest tower."

His four years at Yale were happy, hungry, and full of hard work. He fell in love again, almost as a matter of course; and he kept on inventing gadgets. At one point he wrote in his diary, "I thought out the essentials for an underground trolley system, as I had just read in the *Scientific American* of a $50,000 prize offered for the best design. I felt so supremely happy I could have shouted. I vowed to give $5,000 to the Lord if I won the prize." But in spite of all his activity, he continually berated himself in his diary for his failures. "I don't improve all my opportunities, always resolving to do better, but too often repeating folly. I lack the individuality of character my life's work demands—fool!"

At Commencement in 1896 he was deeply moved and wrote in his diary, "Our days of preparation are over. They may have been inadequate, but we have *lived* these days, and the way in which we meet the rubs and buffetings of life will show how well. Yet be fortune what it may, you will ever find true hearts in '96 who hold—deep-graven—love and loyalty for Shef and Yale." His class voted him the nerviest and the homeliest man in the class.

The following fall he began graduate courses under J. Willard Gibbs, who had already become a legendary figure. "I can fervently say that it was Willard Gibbs's influence and inspiration which so firmly resolved me . . . to prepare myself for that project in research and invention which I had determined should

Volunteers for the Spanish-American War included De Forest who temporarily left physics to became a bugler.

be my life's work."

De Forest selected a doctoral problem in the recently discovered Hertzian waves. He wrote to Nikola Tesla, another of his idols, pleading for a job, but Tesla had no room for him.

De Forest broke his graduate studies to volunteer during the wild war fervor of 1898. His aspiration was to be a bugler, which would give him a horse, two red stripes on his pants legs, and no guard duty. Before the battery could move, the war was over, and De Forest returned to Yale.

In his last year he became familiar with Marconi's work in wireless and saw at once the system's weakness.

De Forest took his doctorate in 1899 and spent the summer in Council Bluffs. Once again he fell hopelessly in love. With his heart beating sweetly, he went to Chicago and found work with the Western Electric Company, but both the love affair and the job went badly. His independence of mind continued to divert him from routine telephone problems.

One day his superior said to him, "Look here, De Forest, you'll never make a telephone engineer. As far as I'm concerned you can go to hell in your own way. Do as you damn please!"

De Forest then gave up any pretense at telephone research and devoted himself eight hours a day to his own interest: wireless. Finally he found a job that seemed to promise him everything that he had wanted. His diary has this entry:

"April 8, 1900—At last, at last, after long planning, years of study, and weeks of patient, weary waiting, I have the opportunity offered for the work that I have chosen, experimental work in wireless telegraphy!"

De Forest worked as a chair pusher in the 1893 Exposition to earn money for Yale. At the St. Louis Fair, his own name was up in lights.

THE BEGINNING OF WIRELESS

For half a century before Marconi, experiments had been made with sending messages by electricity but without wires. Electricity can be conducted through many media, including water and air. "Wireless" communication means the use of these other media as conductors, saving the cost and removing the inflexibility of a permanent wire network. First attempts were to use rivers and lakes as water conductors. With the discovery of high frequency waves by Hertz, the air was added to the "wireless" domain. Modern wireless communication then began.

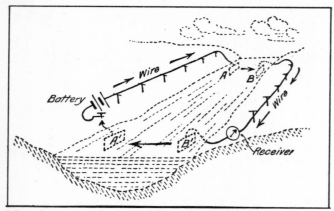

Morse's system of telegraphing across a canal used metal plates (A, A', B, B') submerged beneath the water. When the key to (A') was pressed, current from the battery flowed along the left-bank wire and then from plate (A) through the water to plate (B). The right-bank wire completed the circuit through the receiver and plates (B') and (A'). A lot of current was lost by diffusion in the water.

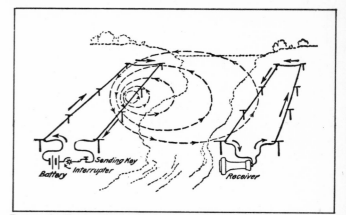

Preece in England, about the same time, used a more advanced scheme. Two huge loops of wire, hundreds of feet on a side, were set up as neighboring stations. Interrupted current in one loop induced magnetic forces, shown by dotted lines, which affected the neighbor circuit. Here the magnetic forces induced electric currents that reproduced the original signals.

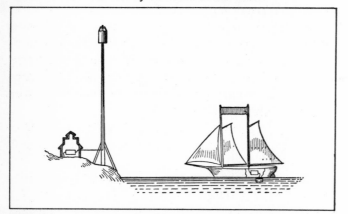

Edison patented a "wireless" system in which electrostatic charges in one tower induced a similar charge in another or in an antenna on a ship at sea. It worked over very short distances. For this reason, Edison held a prior patent on the "aerial" which he sold to Marconi, even though Marconi's aerial was more useful.

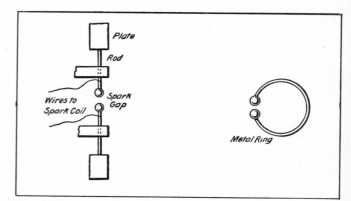

Hertz's famous oscillator and receiver of "radio" waves were very simple. The sender (left) was a spark gap loaded with two metal plates which acted like a condenser. Sparks in the gap radiated high frequency waves. When the second spark gap (right) and the ring were of the right size, the spark was reproduced without any wire connection.

MARCONI'S CONTRIBUTION

Guglielmo Marconi thought of using Hertz's waves as a way to send messages, which was possible if the sparks were turned on and off according to a code. His first system depended on a Branly-type coherer and then he developed a magnetic detector in which (a) was an iron wire band kept in rotation by pulleys (e), (e) through coils (c) and (b) which received the signal from the aerial wire (A). Magnets (d, d) kept the iron tape in proper condition to make the signal from the aerial through (b) induce an increased signal in the telephone coil (c). Marconi had the assistance of Lodge and Fleming, two brilliant physicists.

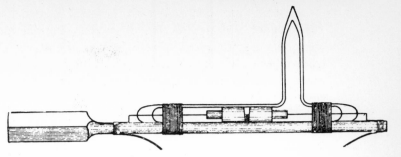

2. THE EARLY DECADES OF WIRELESS

Wireless telegraphy began with Guglielmo Marconi who was twenty in 1894. Only eight years had elapsed since Hertz's discovery of radio waves, but in that short time many other discoveries had been made. Branly in France and Popoff in Russia, investigating electricity in the atmosphere, had both found that a distant spark could affect loosely-packed metal filings. Metal particles pressed together had a high resistance to direct current, but a spark could momentarily lower the resistance. Investigators of atmospheric electricity made a circuit consisting of a battery, a vial of metal filings, and a telephone receiver. Atmospheric electricity could be detected by clicks in the telephone receiver.

Oliver Lodge, an electrical engineer, was, in 1894, the first to conceive that such a vial, which he called a coherer because the spark made the metal particles cohere momentarily, could be used as a laboratory detector for Hertzian waves. Lodge was seeking a greater understanding of electromagnetism and, in the scientific tradition, applied for no patent.

Marconi decided to apply Lodge's coherer to the art of signaling by means of Hertzian waves. He made mechanical improvements in Lodge's device and went one step further: he attached one end of the coherer to a wire extending high into the air and the other end to the ground. By means of this "aerial wire" he was able to transmit Morse code over a distance of nearly two miles in 1896.

That same year he went to England, his mother's native country, with letters of introduction to influential people. Marconi, himself, was independently wealthy. Several impressive demonstrations, including transmission up to eight miles, allowed him to get enough backing to form the British Marconi Wireless Telegraph Company. To investors, remembering the introduction of the telephone only twenty years earlier, it seemed as if new fortunes were about to be made overnight.

From the outset, Marconi made a point of associating with himself the most talented electrical engineers and inventors of his time. By 1900, there were seventeen professional engineers working for Marconi in England, and his two chief consultants were Oliver Lodge and Ambrose Fleming. In December, 1901, Marconi attempted to send a signal from England to a station in Newfoundland. His aerial was a wire connected to a kite. On the twelfth of December, the three dots of the letter "S" came through after weeks of static, but trans-Atlantic wireless communication was still many years away. Marconi concentrated on ship-to-shore apparatus.

Marconi's first detector was a tube of iron filings which "cohered" and conducted when radio waves passed.

De Forest's first receiver was the "responder": a point of platinum dipping into solution. Direct current caused a non-conducting bubble to form, but radio waves broke it.

AUGUST 16, 1902.

THE DE FOREST SYSTEM OF WIRELESS TELEGRAPHY

For several months now a regular interchange of wireless telegraph messages has been maintained by the De Forest Wireless Telegraph Company between their stations near the Battery in New York, and at Staten Island.

The history of the inception of the new system is interesting. In 1899 the inventors began the search for a new receiver for use in wireless telegraphy, one possessing that much desired quality of auto-sensitiveness. From the first the necessity for tapping the old coherer to restore it to sensitiveness, the complicated apparatus thus involved, the uncertainty of its action, and the slow speed of word-transmission necessitated, has called for a better, simpler, quicker receiver than that of Branley's.

Starting on this quest various principles were tried, at first without satisfactory results. The device lacked either sensitiveness or reliability. None of the so-called "auto-coherers" filled the bill. During the year following Dr. De Forest carried on his researches in this field in the laboratory of Armour Institute, kindly tendered him for this purpose. There he received the assistance of E. H. Smythe, of the Western Electric Company, and the responder is the result of their combined effort.

The new receiver, or "responder" as it is aptly called, depends on an electrotypic principle for its action. The field of investigation was entirely new, no data existed on the subject, and the present state of com-

De Forest's pioneer work in wireless was attracting public attention within only three years after he left Yale.

A fourteen-year contract with Lloyd's, signed in 1901, called for the erection of wireless stations all along the English coast. The British Admiralty contracted for equipment for thirty-two ships. Marconi operators remained on the Marconi company's payroll.

The important patents of the Marconi system included Oliver Lodge's invention of a tuning system, Marconi's tuning dial, the aerial, the Fleming diode detector—which was an adaptation of Edison's discovery of twenty years before—and Marconi's magnetic detector which replaced the coherer.

Marconi's competition in Germany were the two systems of Professor Ferdinand Braun, and that of Rudolf Slaby and Count von Arco which were merged by command of the Kaiser into a single corporation: *Telefunken. Telefunken* set up stations on Long Island and offered to sell sets outright to the United States Navy. Marconi refused to make any installations except on a rental basis.

Marconi and *Telefunken* both concentrated on radio telegraphy. The transmission of the human voice—radio telephony—was pursued only by Americans in the early years.

When Lee de Forest took his first wireless job in 1899, he was already considerably behind another American, Reginald Fessenden, who made three important contributions.

Instead of the coherer, Fessenden developed the "electrolytic detector" which was a fine platinum wire resting on the surface of an acid. Direct current in the platinum wire formed a gas bubble which cut off the flow of any further current. When the alternating current of a wireless signal passed through the wire, the bubble burst. The instantaneous flow of current could then be heard in a telephone receiver. Fessenden's detector remained the standard of sensitivity for a decade until De Forest's great invention replaced it.

Fessenden's second contribution was his plan to use high-frequency waves that were inaudible to the human ear, but could travel great distances. His "heterodyne" worked this way: a signal of 200,000 cycles was of course too high to be heard, but when the receiving set mixed this signal with one of 201,000 cycles generated within the set itself, the result was the *difference* between the two frequencies—an audible note of 1,000 cycles. Fessenden planned to superimpose audible messages on a high frequency "carrier" to be subtracted at the receiving end, but Fessenden's arc generator developed so much extraneous noise that his plan was not feasible until a decade later when De Forest's invention made the "heterodyne" principle a reality.

Fessenden's third contribution was the use of the high-frequency alternator which remained in use for fifteen years when another adaptation of De Forest's invention made these great installations obsolete.

Fessenden broke with his company, which eventually was sold to Westinghouse. Finally, the rights were transferred, in the early 1920's, to the newly formed RCA for 450,000 shares of RCA preferred and an equal amount of RCA common; but Fessenden had been dead for many years.

De Forest first appeared in the picture in 1900. Marconi, *Telefunken,* and Fessenden were already in strong patent positions. In the five years before 1906, De Forest took out thirty-four patents which were of general interest but none was truly fundamental.

That first job in 1900 was with a wireless pioneer named Johnson; but De Forest left him in less than a year to strike out on his own. He borrowed one thousand dollars to build wireless equipment to report the International Yacht races of 1901 for the Publishers' Press Association. He planned to bring an electrolytic receiver of his own design called a "responder" to public attention. The attempt ended in failure; the apparatus was so delicate that it was out of order more often than it worked.

In 1902, De Forest met Abraham White, a stock promoter. White organized the American De Forest Wireless Telegraph Company, authorized to raise three million dollars by issue of common stock. The War Department gave him an experimental order for the Signal Corps, and the Navy, anxious to become independent of foreign wireless companies, also gave him an order. The United Fruit Company built a De Forest radio chain between Costa Rica and Panama.

In the meantime, White, the president of the company, had issued lush prospectuses and erected ninety stations across the country, most of which never sent a message. In 1907, De Forest discovered that his directors were looting the treasury by selling all assets to a dummy company. De Forest resigned, taking with him only those patents which were pending and formed a new corporation called the De Forest Radio Telephone Company to be capitalized at two million dollars. The Navy immediately ordered twenty-seven sets for a round-the-world flotilla.

In 1910, De Forest staged the first musical radio broadcast in history from the Metropolitan Opera House with Caruso. He also transmitted daily programs of music which were received by an ever-growing number of amateur operators.

In 1911, the government went on a crusade against wireless stock promoters and the De Forest company, unable to raise further funds, crashed. To recoup his losses, De Forest decided to concentrate on an invention which he had patented back in 1906. This was the invention which Nobel Laureate I. I. Rabi was later to describe as "ranking with the greatest of all time."

Lieutenant Weaver, Flag Officer under Admiral Evans, using the De Forest Radio Telephone on board the U.S. Flagship *Connecticut* in 1907. In the first decade of the 20th century, the U.S. had only foreign radio manufacturers to choose between, Marconi of England and Slaby-Arco of Germany, until De Forest came along. The U.S. adopted his systems to be free of foreign dependence.

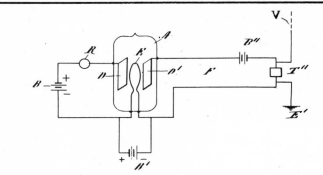

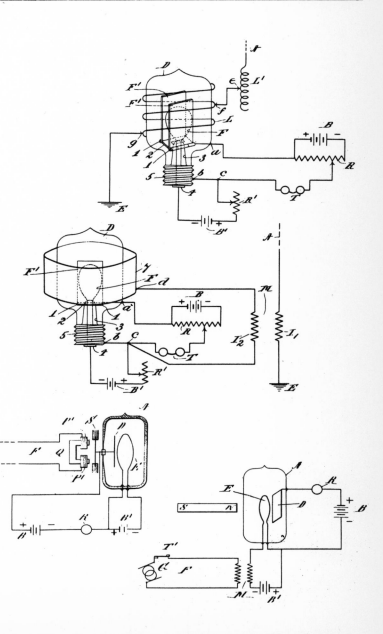

The "audion" was patented by De Forest in 1907, and was one of the century's most important inventions.

De Forest's vacuum tube patent drawings show a wide variety of methods for impressing a radio signal on the third electrode.

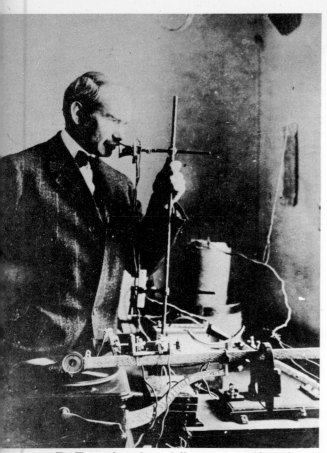

De Forest broadcast daily programs of music and news a decade before Westinghouse's KDKA.

The audion, shown on the panel, was invented just when De Forest took up radio telephony.

3. THE AUDION

From the very beginning of his work in wireless, De Forest kept seeking for more and more efficient means to detect radio waves. He tried improving the various forms of detectors then in general use, coherers and electrolytic detectors, and so he knew their unreliability and weakness better than most men.

The device which De Forest finally developed did not come to him in any single burst of conception, but in a step-by-step process over a period of years. In spite of his advanced training at Yale, De Forest was not familiar with the Edison effect. In the days before the general acceptance of the existence of the electron, the Edison effect was scarcely known outside of the immediate circle of Edison workers.

De Forest's first experiment in this field dated back to a September evening in 1900 when he investigated the effect of Hertzian waves on the flame of an ordinary Welsbach burner. De Forest had known that a gas flame could conduct electricity. Although his experiment with the Welsbach burner gave questionable results, he was convinced that in incandescent gases he would sooner or later find a good detector for Hertzian waves. Because he lacked the money required for such a research, he concentrated on the electrolytic responder. This he developed to a point where it competed successfully with the devices of other inventors.

During exciting promotional ups-and-downs in a New York whose description could be compounded out of O. Henry and James Huneker, he still found time to return again and again to his experiments on gases. In 1903, in New York, he rigged up a Bunsen burner in which the flame played on two platinum electrodes, one of which was connected to an aerial wire and the other to the ground through a telephone receiver. He was able to receive wireless signals from a ship in New York bay.

"It was perfectly obvious that the gas flame would be an impractical device on shipboard, so I next sought to heat incandescent gases directly by means of electric current."

He made an experiment using the carbon filament lamp, but it was a failure. In 1903, he had another bulb built that contained a carbon filament at one side and a platinum plate nearby. De Forest planned to connect the plate to a high voltage source while the radio waves were to ionize the gases in the bulb and thereby make the internal resistance follow the variations of the radio signal. To increase the effect on the gas in the bulb, De Forest wrapped a piece of tin foil around the outside. This third electrode was connected to the antenna and carried the incoming signal.

"I then realized that the efficiency could be still further enhanced if this third electrode were introduced *within* the (bulb) . . ." This bulb was the same as the previous one, with the addition of another little platinum plate to replace the tin foil that had been wrapped outside.

This is how De Forest understood what was happening in his tube: He assumed that the loop of carbon filament was giving off electrons because De Forest was one of the early believers in the electronic theory of matter. These electrons were bombarding the gas in the bulb and creating electrically charged atoms-ions. This ion current flowed to the platinum plate connected to the high voltage battery. Radio waves from the aerial, impressed on the other platinum electrode, influenced the flow of the ion current so that it duplicated the signal.

De Forest next realized that this control electrode would be still more effective if it were put *between* the filament and the collecting plate.

"Obviously, this third electrode should not be a solid plate. Consequently, I supplied McCandless with a small plate of platinum, perforated by a great number of small holes. This arrangement performed much better than any preceding it, but . . . to simplify . . . the construction I decided that the interposed third electrode would be better in the form of a grid, a simple piece of wire bent back and forth, located as close to the filament as possible."

This proved superior to any detector that had ever functioned before, even in its crudest state. The filament was heated by a six-volt battery and the high voltage used was twenty-two volts. This three-electrode tube—the "triode"—was the prototype of the billions of radio tubes that have since been built.

His patent was still pending when De Forest broke with White, and he was allowed to take it with him when he formed his new company. His experiments had all been performed in secret and at night, and he continued to keep the triode hidden in a small wooden box with the connections outside. When he felt that he finally had it working, he passed the earphones—the "cans"—over to his assistant, who listened and, startled by the power of the incoming signal, said, "My God, Doc, hear those signals! What you got in that box?"

His name for the device was the "audion." He sold them wax-sealed in boxes to the Navy Bureau of Equipment in Washington. The Navy operators, to boost their phenomenal output still further, heated the filaments above the rated operating temperature and burnt them out. The chief clerk decided the tubes were at fault and passed out this order to Navy operators: "No more audions; use your old detectors."

The audion of De Forest was by later standards a feeble and fractious instrument, but it was the best that could be made at that time. Just as Edison's incandescent lamp would have been impossible without the invention of Sprengel's vacuum pump, so De Forest was handicapped by the fact that his audion was invented three years before the Gaede high vacuum pump and a decade before Langmuir's diffusion pump. The early De Forest "vacuum" tubes would be considered "gas-filled" by a later generation unfamiliar with the conditions of the early days of wireless.

Several years were required for him to explore all the possibilities of the vacuum tube.

When his North American Wireless Company went into bankruptcy in 1911, he took a salaried engineering job on the Pacific coast with the Federal Telegraph Company. In the meantime, he had married unhappily, and two fortunes had gone down the drain. Three hundred dollars a month a continent away from scenes of recent unhappiness seemed, to a heartsick man, a welcome solution.

In San Francisco, he made intensive experiments on the amplification possibilities of the audion. He tried circuit after circuit. He would set a loudspeaker in the window of his laboratory and walk away as far as he could until he had reached a threshold of audibility. When he had obtained a circuit that gave him "two block gain," he wrote East to a friend, John Stone, who aroused the interest of A. T. & T. In the fall of 1913, the Telephone Company paid fifty thousand dollars for the telephone amplifying rights of audion. As a "repeater"—a device that could take a feeble signal and pass it along highly amplified—the audion promised to replace the special circuits of Michael Pupin. A year later, in October, 1914, Western Electric paid ninety thousand dollars for the radio rights to the audion, then renegotiated for whatever rights were left. The final Western Electric price was a quarter of a million dollars.

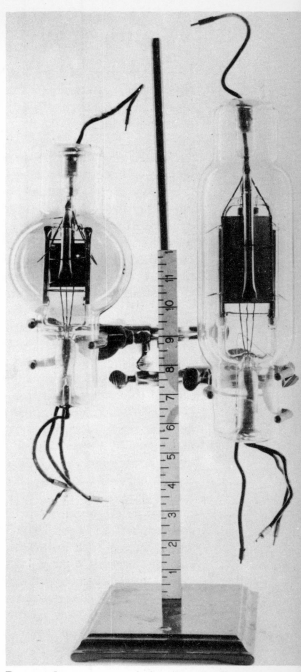

Power tubes were soon designed on De Forest's audion idea. Once the tube was in the hands of the strongly-manned corporation laboratories of the Telephone Company, General Electric, and Westinghouse, research and development on every facet of vacuum tube construction made rapid progress. Hundreds of millions of dollars were spent. The result was a fabulous variety of vacuum tubes designed for a fabulous variety of purposes. Electronics became one of the great industries of the century with an economic value to the United States alone of two billion dollars.

4. THE UBIQUITOUS
VACUUM TUBE

During the years of the First World War, radio research was conducted in military secrecy. The audion was improved, new uses were found for it, new circuits were designed, and an entirely new field of engineering was developed.

Shortly after the war, three of the great electric companies bought out American Marconi and pooled their own radio communication patents to form a new company—Radio Corporation of America—to be devoted to wireless telephony and telegraphy. No sooner had the baptismal papers of the new giant been filled out, than the public discovered radio and turned everything upside down.

The kind of program which De Forest had sent out before 1910 was being repeated for amateurs by Frank Conrad of the Westinghouse research labs under amateur license KDKA; and this time the informal program caught on. Overnight, it seemed, about ten million Americans rushed to the stores to buy the kind of galena-crystal radio receiving sets which had become obsolete almost a decade earlier. Advice to amateur set builders which began to appear in 1912 in Marconi's *Wireless World* was now published in every newspaper and syndicated as widely—in the early 1920's—as columns on etiquette and advice to the lovelorn.

Then within another few months, the public discovered, as if it had just been invented the day before, that there was such a thing as a "radio tube" which could be used as a far more sensitive detector than the crystal. Manufacturers filled the stores with commercially built radio sets, on the face of which were three tuning dials—as patented by Marconi at the turn of the century. By the mid-1920's, an improved version used a single tuning dial from Reginald Fessenden's NESCO, just as if that, too, had not been available for years and years.

With the new entertainment broadcasting, Westinghouse discovered that it owned a gold mine in its rights to manufacture radio receivers "for amateur use," no part of this right having been sought by RCA at its founding, at which Westinghouse had been a participant. In self-defense, RCA formed a subsidiary corporation—the National Broadcasting Company—to be devoted purely to entertainment broadcasting. Within a decade, this new subsidiary proved to be a far greater source of income to RCA than the wireless telephone and telegraph. Fessenden, Marconi, and almost every other pioneer in wireless communication had thought only in terms of transmission and exchange of information. It was the public who discovered that radio would entertain it.

Once again there was dramatic confirmation of the economic law that fifteen or twenty years usually pass between the development of an invention and its evolution into a form where the public will adopt it.

De Forest and David Sarnoff of American Marconi insisted that they had always asked for some type of home receiver which would bring to the American home the finest music available. Neither of them, however, had ever advocated an advertising billboard combined with a non-stop vaudeville show. Herbert Hoover saw very clearly the evils of commercially sponsored radio and put up a valiant but losing fight against it.

In the financial battles and mergers of the 1920's, De Forest turned his back on radio. The large companies no longer had any need for him and he was too independent a personality to become merely a salaried employee. A second marriage had ended disastrously, and his life was out of joint. Looking for new fields, he turned to the possibility of a talking motion-picture, which he called the phonofilm.

From 1923 to 1926 he offered the system to one studio after another, and everywhere met with the answer that the public did not want talking pictures.

De Forest's contribution to sound film was that he was the first to work out a practical method of photographing the sound wave on the same film that carried the picture. An earlier system suggested by Edison was simply a phonograph record played simultaneously with a motion picture.

In 1926, Warner Brothers, facing failure, decided to gamble its existence on talking pictures. They used the archaic record method, but the public was delighted, and a new scramble was on for the rights to talking picture methods. This time, however, De Forest was up against companies far too powerful for him to fight. Western Electric and the Telephone Company successfully outmaneuvered him and although phonofilm was a serviceable system, it never achieved the commercial recognition which it deserved.

By 1930 Lee de Forest, in his late fifties, a man still retaining the independence from a day that was gone forever, was working in his own private laboratory in California looking for new fields that had been overlooked by the giant companies which had been created in part by his invention of the triode.

For the first time, he married happily.

During the next twenty years, there was no diminution in the rate at which he applied for patents; he was granted over three hundred. Many of them were commercially successful, but none of them approached in importance the magnificent universality of the triode. This was no reflection on Lee de Forest, for the triode was invention on a magnitude that may be touched only two or three times in a century.

Talking pictures was another interest of De Forest. He developed the process called "phonofilm" in which the sound track was photographed on the same film with the picture. Producers did not believe in sound movies.

From and For
those who help themselves

Experimenters' Experiences

FIRST PRIZE TEN DOLLARS
A Galena Detector Which Has Given Excellent Results

I have found that the Galena detector, which I am about to describe, has given better results than any I have used.

As shown in the accompanying diagram, the base is made of oak, or other

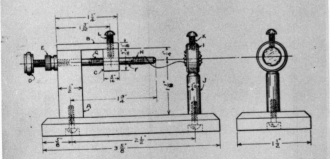

hard wood, and can be constructed to suit the size of cabinet. Brass upright A, having dimensions ½" by ¼" by 1¾", is drilled to receive adjustment screw D. Nut E is taken from a dry battery and is soldered in line with hole. B is a piece of brass ¼" by ⅜" by 1¼", and is tapped at one end to receive set screw L. This is soldered to top of A, as shown in the sketch. C is a piece of brass 7/16" by ¼" by

¼", drilled at the center to receive pin F. Another hole is drilled in the top of the pin hole to receive the set screw, and is soldered to piece C. F is a pin 2 by ½ inches, which slides back and forth and is kept in tension by spring G and set screw L. G is a small spring which keeps a pressure on the pin. H is a piece of No. 36 B and S copper wire used to make contact with the galena. I is a round brass nut screwed onto brass stud H, and is tapped on top to receive set screw. The set screw is used to hold the detector mineral in place. J is a piece of brass ½" by ¼" by ¾", to hold the galena holder.

Screws and parts can be made according to the supply of material on hand in the shop.

EDW. DORST, New York.

Radio amateurs were plentiful a decade before the public discovered crystal sets, and so was advice to set makers.

Lee de Forest's life was long, stormy, and full of disappointments. Only in later years did he find happiness.

Irving Langmuir (center) in the early years of the General Electric Research Laboratory. Willis Whitney, the director, leans on folded arms to inspect one of W. D. Coolidge's early X-ray tubes. The year is 1912.

IRVING LANGMUIR

1. A TALENT FOR SERENDIPITY

In the huge Parisian crowds that watched the funeral cortege of the great scientist, Pasteur, stood a young American schoolboy. The silent mourning of a hundred thousand people for the death of his god reaffirmed his desire to be a scientist, and was to remain one of the most moving experiences of his life. Irving Langmuir was to fulfill his ambitions. He became one of the first Americans to appear in a new role—the industrial researcher in pure science; and he was to be the first American industrial scientist to win the Nobel prize.

Langmuir was born in 1881 in the genteel Brooklyn that was a meadow of small, tree-lined, church-steepled towns. From comfortable houses, set deep in green lawns, men rode to offices in the city across the river on horse-cars and steam trains. Irving Langmuir's father was the kind of man who affably made and lost modest fortunes with the calm assumption that the next fortune was waiting just around the corner. Irving was entered at one of the local Brooklyn public elementary schools, but when he was eleven, the family moved to Paris to accompany the oldest son Arthur, who wished to study chemistry in Germany.

Irving was enrolled in one of the small boarding schools in the suburbs of Paris, described by André Gide in The Counterfeiters. Langmuir was the only foreigner in the school and did poorly because he rebelled against what he considered the "absurdly rigorous discipline." His father was friendly with the director, however, and the boy was allowed to go his own way. An understanding instructor encouraged him to teach himself the use of logarithms and trigonometry.

He was a boy who could pour tremendous vitality into any particular interest. When he wasn't cross-examining his adored older brother on chemistry, he was pounding into the head of his younger brother, Herbert, every fact on electricity he came across. His mother once said, "The child gets beside himself with enthusiasm, and shows such intelligence on the subject that it fairly frightens one."

The family returned to the United States when Arthur completed his doctorate, and Irving was sent to the Chestnut Hill Academy in Philadelphia. He was driven by his passion for science. On his own, he worked through a book on calculus in six weeks. At fourteen he entered Pratt Institute in Brooklyn, and at seventeen, the Columbia School of Mines to study engineering. He took his Ph.D. at the University of Göttingen in 1906. The Stevens Institute of Hoboken, founded by the grandson of old John Stevens, gave him the post of chemistry instructor, and there, for a while, the whirlwind rested.

At the end of his third year at Stevens, instead of taking one of his usual mountain vacations, he decided to spend a summer in the new laboratories of General Electric at Schenectady. Those few months stretched out to cover the rest of his career, for he happened to go to General Electric at a time in his own life and the life of the General Electric labs when he was to be exactly the right man at the right time in the right place.

By 1900, through ruthlessness, enterprise, and the imperial support of J. P. Morgan, General Electric had combined the Edison patents with those of the New England electrical manufacturing firm of Thomson-Huston to become one of America's greatest corporations. The directors knew that the company could maintain its competitive position only if it continued to offer new products and services. So far they had been able to capitalize on knowledge gathered by academic scientists during the whole of the nineteenth century. General Electric executives, A. G. Davis and E. W. Rice, decided that the company must itself contribute to this pool of fundamental scientific knowledge. A new type of industrial laboratory was required, and Willis R. Whitney was brought from the MIT faculty to serve as director.

When Langmuir first went up to Schenectady in 1909, he had a very distorted idea of what he would find. In spite of the publicity given to GE's new laboratory, Langmuir expected to be assigned to some routine application. To his surprise, Whitney told him to spend as much time as he pleased visiting the laboratories to find out what kind of problems were being studied. Then whenever he was ready, he was to go to Whitney and tell him how he himself would like to spend the summer months. "When I joined the laboratory," Langmuir said, "I found that there was more 'academic freedom' than I had ever encountered in any university."

While Langmuir was studying the laboratory, Whitney studied Langmuir. Whitney watched his work over the summer months and knew that he had found a rare combination of insight and wonder—of literalness and imagination.

The short-term research which Langmuir picked for himself that summer was to lead in many directions:

(1) to marked improvement in the ordinary domestic lighting bulb;

(2) to the perfection of the triodes in which De Forest had pioneered;

(3) to the development of the theory of why elements combine in chemical combination;

(4) to the development of the special two-dimensional universe of the surface and its applications to chemistry, physics, and biology;

Charles Steinmetz, early worker in high-frequency alternating currents was one of General Electric's most colorful figures. A militant Socialist, a grower of orchids, he protected his individuality behind the façade of the "eccentric genius."

The physics laboratory of the Pratt Institute in Brooklyn when Langmuir was a student there from 1895 to 1897.

(5) to the explanation of the remarkable phenomenon known as catalysis;

(6) to such meteorological experiments as the seeding of clouds to make rain.

Throughout his long career, Langmuir never undertook a research with a practical goal in mind. All of his useful results were simply by-products of investigations into the most fundamental questions of nature. Whenever Langmuir was asked why he had started a certain line of research his answer was always, "Because I was curious, I guess"; and when asked why he carried it out, he replied, "For the fun of it."

Two centuries ago, Horace Walpole gave a name to "the art of profiting from unexpected occurrences"— *serendipity.*

Langmuir's talent in serendipity over fifty years gave him "fun," honorary degrees, medals, and the Nobel prize. To the world, Langmuir gave more provocative leads to new fields of knowledge than any other contemporary American.

For all these happy things GE paid the bill and lost nothing by it. As a result of its own laboratory developments, General Electric, a private American corporation, was richer and more powerful in 1954 than a combination of many of the great pre-World War I European kingdoms and empires, whose hussars and lieutenants were cutting such dashing figures in Vienna, Berlin, and Paris, when Irving Langmuir, in a high starched collar and tight-cuffed trousers, stepped off the train in 1909 at Schenectady, U. S. A.

Lamp research at GE led Langmuir (right) to studies of surface chemistry, atomic structure, and vacuum pumps.

2. THE LITTLE WORLD WITHIN A GLASS BALL

"When I first went to GE in 1909," said Langmuir, "a large part of the laboratory staff was busily engaged in the development of drawn tungsten wire." Tungsten made superior filaments for incandescent lamps. It could be heated to extremely high temperatures, 3100° C., and therefore gave off a far more brilliant light than any other metal.

Dr. Coolidge, the General Electric X-ray expert, had developed a method for drawing tungsten into wires, but the hard, brittle metal presented a thousand problems to investigators. Langmuir's curiosity was aroused because the laboratory had been able to make only three filaments that operated successfully under alternating current. The others had become brittle and broken.

Because of Langmuir's doctoral work on gases, he guessed that one of the possible causes of tungsten filament failure was the abundance of gas trapped in the metal during manufacture. He told Whitney that this was the problem he would like to attack. Actually Langmuir's decision was determined by his discovery that the General Electric laboratories possessed vacuum apparatus far superior to any he had ever seen, and the tungsten filament research would be a good way to familiarize himself with these new techniques.

Beginning almost at random, he took one of the tungsten filament incandescent lamps and connected it to an extremely sensitive low-pressure measuring device—the recently developed McLeod gauge. He wanted to see if there would be any increase in the gas content within a lighted lamp.

Within a couple of days the McLeod gauge showed that the bulb was filled with an amount of gas equal to seven thousand times the volume of the filament—a staggering result. More than that, there was no indication that the production of gas was going to stop. He had started out to see if the heated filament could possibly exude gas. He had discovered so much gas that it had to be coming from a source far larger than any hair-sized wire.

"What I really learned during that summer was that glass surfaces which have not been heated a long time in vacuum, slowly give off water vapor; and this reacts with a tungsten filament to produce hydrogen.

"It was the universal opinion among the lamp engineers . . . that if only a much better vacuum could be produced in a lamp, a better lamp would result . . . however, I really didn't know how to produce a better vacuum, and instead proposed to study the bad effect of gases by putting gases in the lamp. I hoped that in this way I would become so familiar with these effects of gas that I could extrapolate down to zero gas pressure and thus predict, without really trying it, how good the lamp would be if we could produce a perfect vacuum."

Working for three years, he was finally able to say that the tungsten filament tended to evaporate electrons at a rate that was dependent only on its own temperature and had nothing to do with the amount of gas that was present. Therefore the idea of a perfect

A pliotron tube of 250 watts was shown to Sir J. J. Thomson, "father of the electron," by Langmuir and Coolidge during

vacuum making a perfect lamp was wrong. As a result he was able to go directly contrary to the established belief. He filled his lamps with nitrogen, producing a more brilliant light and a stronger bulb than had ever been produced before. This lamp, because of its efficiency, saved American light users one million dollars a night in light bills.

Stemming from this same research—the effect of gases on burning filaments—Langmuir was able to predict that De Forest's triodes would operate with undreamed-of sensitivity if he could attain the vacuum which the lamp engineers had once thought necessary for ordinary incandescent lamps.

To achieve such a vacuum Langmuir invented a vacuum pump one hundred times more powerful than any previous pump; and with it he was able to create a vacuum that was almost one billionth of the pressure of the atmosphere. Remembering the water vapor trapped in the glass walls of lamps, he invented a special oven—to bake the glass vacuum tubes while they were being evacuated. The so-called "hard" vacuum tube used in all radios is the result.

Langmuir improved the De Forest audions not only by increasing their vacuum; he also tried filling them with great quantities of gas. In these tubes, torrents of current were created when the gas was bombarded by the electrons boiling off the filament. Before Langmuir grew tired with tube research, he developed a variety of tubes to fit all ranges of current—from micro-

The thyratron, one of the tubes developed by GE, delivered power through heavy discharges of a gaseous atmosphere.

microamperes to the great surges that flowed through transmitting tubes that were almost as tall as a man.

In 1907, when Lee de Forest applied for his patent on the triode, the staff of the GE labs at Schenectady consisted of forty scientists and engineers and fifty-five technical assistants. Ten years later, the GE research staff had been increased to a total working force of three hundred men.

Research leaders like Langmuir, Coolidge, and Whitney, surrounded by able staffs, left little room for the individual inventor working alone in his own workshop. Yet the power of the research team, in the end, depended on the imagination of the team director. As long as men like Langmuir could be attracted to the corporation laboratories, the research teams would be sure to find some practical application of his work. From the point of view of dividends, Langmuir's type of pure research more than paid for itself.

Langmuir's most fruitful result from his filament research for tubes and lamps came about by accident. When he was testing tungsten for its electron-emitting powers, he happened to pick up one that had been prepared by Coolidge for a special purpose. In Langmuir's testing apparatus, this particular filament produced electrons with an abundance he had never seen before. He found that the tungsten had been impregnated with thoria—an oxide of thorium. When Langmuir investigated further, he found that the filament behaved best when the tungsten was coated with a layer of thoria—*no more than one molecule thick.*

Just at the moment when science was trying to understand Einstein's four-dimensional universe, Langmuir went off pioneering into the contradictions, complexities, and beauties of the hitherto unexplored two-dimensional world.

World War I. The pliotron was one of the numerous forms of multi-element tubes that followed De Forest's lead.

A trough of water covered with films of oil gave Langmuir exhaustive information about the structure of molecules.

3. THE MONOMOLECULAR FILM OF OIL

"I started to work in the General Electric laboratory in 1909 on high-vacuum phenomena in tungsten filament lamps and began introducing different gases into the bulb to see what would happen, just to satisfy my curiosity. . . . I put nitrogen, hydrogen and oxygen into a bulb and heated the filament to 3000° C. . . . Some very extraordinary things happened. One was that the oxygen formed into a film on the surface of the filament. It was held so tenaciously that it could stand heating up to 1500° for years, and you could not reduce it with hydrogen. . . . I found several other situations of a similar kind. I found that a single layer of thorium atoms on tungsten could increase the electron emission from a tungsten filament in vacuum one hundred thousand fold."

In 1909, when Langmuir started his work, the existence of molecules was far from being generally accepted. Millikan's experiments had not yet been performed, yet Langmuir already believed that "the proof was conclusive that atoms and molecules were perfectly real things. Then I said, if that is so, go the whole limit in treating this idea."

Langmuir experimented with the behavior of insoluble substances on the surface of a liquid. They were simply films of grease floating on top of a pan of water, but Langmuir was able to translate his observations into penetrating statements about the size and shape of the molecules in the film, and their chemistry in general.

A drop of an oily substance, when placed on the surface of water, can behave in one of two ways: it can either remain as a compact blob, or spread out over the water surface in an extremely thin film. It was Langmuir's idea that the film would continue to spread until it became one molecule thick. The adhesive force between the molecules would keep the film from spreading any further. His apparatus was a pan of water. On the surface of the water floated a light rod across the width of the pan. Once an oil film was formed, Langmuir moved this rod sideways along the pan and compressed the film. A dynamometer—an instrument that measured force—told him how much force had to be applied to compress the film; even the force could have been measured in terms of the weight of feathers. As he moved his barrier, he found that the area of the oil film could be reduced to a certain extent with practically no force being applied. However, as the area was further reduced, there came a point where there was considerable resistance. The dynamometer showed an abrupt increase in the amount of force that was required.

Langmuir's first experiments were performed with organic acids which were long hydrocarbon chains. These molecules varied in length from fourteen to thirty-four carbon atoms. To Langmuir, the most striking result was that the critical pressure was the same for all the acids—the length of the molecule made no difference!

Langmuir reasoned this way: The oily film was to be considered as a network of chainlike molecules, lying loosely side by side. The compression that met with no resistance was simply the straightening and aligning of the chains into a more orderly fashion. As the film was compressed still further, the chains were forced to stand on end to get into still smaller areas. Finally the crucial point was reached when *all* the molecules were upended and there was no longer any free space. The point of crucial pressure came, then, when the two-dimensional "liquid" was transformed into an incompressible two-dimensional solid.

His next concern was to find out why this happened. Some simple paraffin hydrocarbons, which were long chains of carbon atoms saturated with hydrogen, did not form films on water. They remained on the surface as tight little drops. He then discovered that if one of the *end carbon groups* of such a hydrocarbon were to be replaced with a group similar to an inorganic water-soluble acid or a base, a film would be formed.

"Just to picture the thing qualitatively, suppose you have a molecule which is a long hydrocarbon with carbon atoms in it and with a group on the end that has affinity for water, and you bring the molecule into contact with water. The end tends to go into the water . . .

"If you have a pure hydrocarbon without these groups . . . for example, petrolatum or Mujol, it forms little globules on the surface of the water.

"I am thinking of the molecules on the water as real objects. You see, the moment you start to draw a picture of them as the organic chemist does, you think of them as having shapes, lengths, volumes. . . . These chains of hydrocarbons are not to be looked on as rigid and inflexible chains, but as pieces of ordinary iron anchor chain. . . . The molecule . . . can assume different shapes, in which the carbon atoms always have a linear sequence. Therefore, when you compress the film . . . the chains must be vertical. The molecules will then occupy their smallest area; and the measure of that area enables you to calculate the cross-section of the molecules when they are squeezed together and extended to maximum length.

"Under those conditions, what do you expect? Well, first of all, when you increase the length of the chain by spreading a film composed of molecules having a longer hydrocarbon chain, this will not change the area of the film, but will change its thickness. Volume divided by area is the thickness, so you can calculate the thickness." However the thickness of the film was then the length of a molecule. "Total area divided by the number of molecules is the area covered by each molecule," said Langmuir, and in this way he was able to calculate the diameter of a *single carbon group* in the chain *with its water-soluble components*.

Such measurements, which were begun around 1917, gave Langmuir a deep insight into many molecular dimensions and new information about the groupings of molecules in complicated protein molecules.

Langmuir's power was his utter simplicity of outlook. With his small metal pan of water and simple measuring devices, he was able to get information that was later duplicated only by the most complicated X-ray apparatus and calculations. In the thirty-seven years that have passed since Langmuir's 1917 experiments, his techniques in this field are still the model for all contemporary work; in biological fields for the study of complicated viruses, in chemistry for the study of giant molecules, and in optics for the study of the nature of surfaces with the highest transmission of light.

In 1932, Irving Langmuir was awarded the Nobel prize in physics "for his discoveries and researches within the realm of surface chemistry."

1919 was not an unusual year for Irving Langmuir. With one research team, he was doing work on the design of vacuum tubes; with another group of assistants, he worked on chemical reactions at low pressures; with a third team, on the chemistry of surfaces; a fourth on the electric discharges in gases—and he still found time to publish one of the most important papers of the year on why chemical reactions took place, why atoms were able to form themselves into molecules.

JUNE 20, 1885.]   **Scientific American.**

EXPERIMENTS WITH SOAP BUBBLES AND FILMS.*

The true nature of a liquid film is comparable to that of a perfectly elastic and tightly stretched membrane. All liquids are bounded and inclosed by such a membrane, composed of the substance of the liquid

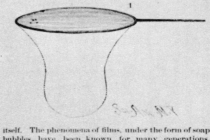

itself. The phenomena of films, under the form of soap bubbles, have been known for many generations. They were seriously studied by Sir Isaac Newton, and later by the scientist Dr. Plateau, of Belgium, a curious study for one, like the latter, afflicted with total blindness.

If a ring one or two inches in diameter, and provided with a handle, is dipped into a solution adapted for

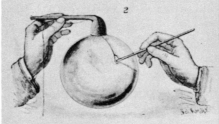

forming films, and is withdrawn, it will be found to be filled with a beautiful film, straight and firm, reminding us of the wing of a dragon fly, Fig. 1. If we blow against it, it will be driven out into a purse-like shape of very characteristic outline (see dotted line). If it be held between the mouth and a candle, it will screen the latter from strong blowing until it breaks, when the candle will be extinguished.

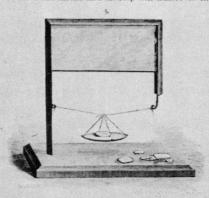

By particular management a hole of any desired size can be made in the side of a soap bubble. This is done by tying a small loop, less than the third of an inch, in the end of a silk thread, moistening it thoroughly with the solution, and hanging it over the bowl of a pipe just before blowing a bubble. As the bubble is blown, the end of the thread and the loop will adhere to it.

Then by touching the film within the loop, either with a hot wire or with a piece of blotting paper, the film

*From a lecture on "The Physics of Beauty," to be given in full, with many additional illustrations, experiments, and formulas, in SUPPLEMENT No. 135.

will break inside of the loop, which will fly open to its widest extent, Fig. 2. The bubble will immediately collapse, or by vigorous blowing may just be kept inflated. The blast from the hole is sometimes enough to extinguish a candle.

This shows that the film is elastic. To measure directly the tension exerted by an inflated bubble, a glass tube bent at a right angle may be attached to the end of a pipe stem. After blowing a bubble, the end of the glass tube may be dipped into water, when the depression will show the pressure, Fig. 3. It will be but a small fraction of an inch.

To measure the tension of the film per unit of surface, a little frame with grooved sides is employed. In the grooves a wire carrying a little scale pan slides freely up and down, Fig. 4. The wire is pushed home to the top of the frame and some of the solution introduced, either by dipping the top or by painting it in with a brush. Then by adding weights the film can be pulled down like a delicate curtain until the limit is reached, and it breaks.

By mounting a ring as a pendulum and filling it with

a film, Fig. 5, the retardation the latter exercises on its swing is quite striking.

Four of the rings may be mounted as a windmill, Fig. 6, and be made to turn several times by the breath until their perishable sails break one by one.

If a thread, well moistened with the solution, is laid across a ring containing a film, and the film is broken on one side of it, the thread will be suddenly snatched across the ring and be drawn up tightly against the opposite side. To facilitate manipulation, the ends of the thread may be fastened to the ends of a wire, or thin slip of wood. On drawing out the thread it will draw with it a curtain of film, and will assume the curve of the arc of a circle, Fig. 7. In this way the ring may be again filled with film and the thread be entirely removed.

A bubble may be blown, a moistened ring touched to

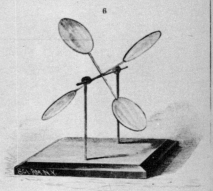

it, and the pipe pulled away, leaving the bubble adhering to the ring. The pipe may be again dipped, passed through the upper part of the bubble into its interior, and a second bubble may be blown thus in the interior of the first, Fig. 8.

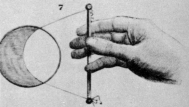

The study of thin films by Langmuir revived techniques that had not been used since the 1880's. Langmuir's method was a variation of that shown in Fig. 4 of the above article that ran in the *Scientific American*, 1885.

4. THE CHEMICAL BOND

Langmuir had been a graduate student when J. J. Thomson described atoms as spheres in which electrons were embedded like raisins in a pudding. The sphere was positively charged; the electrons were negative. Each element was characterized by a different number of electrons. Hydrogen had one, helium had two, lithium had three, and so on. Only a few decades earlier, the great Russian Mendeleyev had arranged the known elements in a certain sequence called the periodic table. Thomson was able to construct his "raisin pudding" model of the atom to fit Mendeleyev's table, but Thomson's model did not explain either radiation or chemical activity.

In 1911, two years after Langmuir began work for General Electric, an important experiment was performed at Cambridge by Ernest Rutherford, who was bombarding a metal foil with the alpha particles from a sample of radium.

If the Thomson model was correct, the tiny alpha particles would penetrate clear through the insubstantial atoms which composed the foil, except for a number which would be absorbed. To Rutherford's amazement, some of the alpha particles were being sharply deflected as if solid objects within the foil had been hit.

Rutherford then assumed that the positive charge of an atom, instead of being spread throughout a large sphere as Thomson had suggested, must exist as very small but massive concentrations in the center of each atom. According to Rutherford, this "nucleus" had to be one millionth of a millionth of a centimeter in diameter.

Niels Bohr enlarged upon Rutherford's theory by assuming that the electrons were in eternal motion, rotating in definite orbits around the positively charged nucleus, like planets around the sun. The electrons could instantaneously jump from one orbit to another and emit radiation.

While this Bohr-Rutherford model seemed to clarify many points for the physicist, Langmuir was aware in 1919 that it did not answer any questions as yet for the chemist.

A molecule consisted of atoms in chemical combination, but atoms tended to form only certain combinations. Carbon could combine with four hydrogens to form methane, or with two oxygens to form carbon dioxide. On the other hand, oxygen would combine with two hydrogens to form water. The number of hydrogen atoms with which an atom would combine was called its *valence*.

Hydrogen had a valence of one, oxygen had a valence of two, carbon had a valence of four, sodium and lithium also had valences of one, calcium and barium had valences of two. There were substances like sulphur and iron which could have several valences. When helium and argon were discovered, it was found that they had no valence at all—they could enter into chemical combination with no other elements. For that reason they were called "inert" gases.

In 1919 Langmuir suggested a model of the atom to suit the needs of chemists. In Langmuir's atom, as in that of Bohr and Rutherford, the nucleus was in the center. This nucleus was to be like the heart of a pearl, the center of concentric shells. Each shell could contain no more than a certain number of electrons. The innermost shell, according to Langmuir, had room for only two electrons. Hydrogen had only one electron, and so this shell was only half-filled—therefore hydrogen was chemically active because it would tend to attract an electron even if it was already part of another atom. This tendency to seek out one electron,

Linus Pauling, chemical theorist

according to Langmuir, was why hydrogen had a valence of one.

In helium, which had two electrons, this inner shell was saturated, and this explained why helium was inert.

Langmuir stated that once this inner shell of two electrons was saturated, an atom which had more electrons would begin to fill the next shell, which had room for eight electrons. Lithium, which had one more electron than helium, would then have only one electron in its outer shell which it could lose, and this explained why lithium was so active chemically. Neon, on the other hand, had two electrons in its inner shell, and eight electrons in the outer shell. Since neon, then, was saturated in both shells, it would, like helium, be inert.

Carbon had fourteen electrons, two in its innermost shell, eight in the second shell, and four in the third shell, which meant that there were still four open places. To fill these four open spaces, carbon could combine with four hydrogens or two oxygens. With this explanation, Langmuir ranged through all the compounds and reactions known to chemistry. Molecules that were composed of atoms which used each others' electrons to saturate their own shells were very stable. They required a lot of heat to break them up, and became gases at extremely low temperatures. Methane and CO_2 satisfied these requirements.

Langmuir's comprehensive work was, of course, modified by subsequent knowledge, but it broke trails for Linus Pauling of the California Institute of Technology, who carried on the exploration of the nature of the chemical bond.

Linus Pauling was able to explain the arrangement of the most complicated organic molecules; and showed, for example, that the straight chain theory was an oversimplification. The atoms of the giant organic molecules did not array themselves in the convenient two dimensions of paper representations, but were highly complicated three-dimensional structures. Pauling was able to extend the work even to the study of the structure of viruses.

Langmuir's intense love for mountaineering had aroused his interest in meteorology and the structure of clouds. This, in turn, led him to study the possibility of artificial snow- or rain-making in supercooled clouds. In the winter of 1945 he and an assistant made a number of experiments, introducing different crystals into supercooled air, to test the theory that a crystal could form the nucleus for a chain reaction condensation.

On July 21, 1949, the Army Signal Corps and the Office of Naval Research in New Mexico sponsored a test by Langmuir and his staff.

Langmuir's ground generator started releasing iodized smoke at five-thirty in the morning. Three hours later, a big cloud was seen to gather downwind from the generator. Radar screens showed rain drops within the cloud at 9:57, revealing that the chain reaction was taking place within the cloud. Very soon thereafter lightning flashed, thunder rolled, and the heavy rain fell over a wide area for several hours. Subsequent tests proved inconclusive because too much was expected.

According to his friends, Langmuir has always been the prototype of the popular conception of the "scientist." Everything that came to his notice immediately became the subject of intense speculation. To him, however tenuous the line of speculation, time spent in such a way never seemed wasted. He regretted only the time he spent in courtrooms defending patents.

"I feel as if I'd wasted half my life that way," he once said.

But even if that were literally true, the other half was so spent that America and the rest of mankind are deeply in his debt.

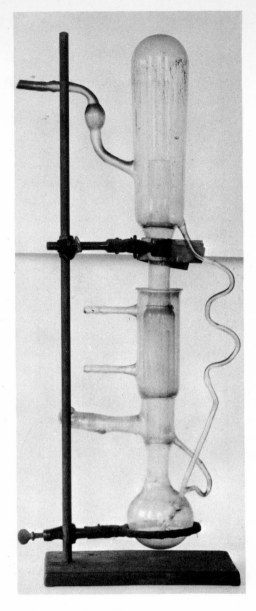

Without high-vacuum techniques there would be no radio, television, cyclotrons, radio location, nor much industrial chemistry. Langmuir's interest in high-vacuum work led him to GE in the first place, and while there he greatly furthered the art. His mercury vapor condensation pump, (left) designed in 1915, created vacuua that approached a one-hundred-millionth of an atmosphere. Because of its basic importance to so many fields of research, the mercury vapor diffusion pump must be considered as important to the 20th century as Maudslay's slide-rest was to the 19th. At the bottom is a flask of mercury which vaporizes up an interior column into the upper bulb. Condensation of the mercury concentrates gas molecules from the system to be evacuated (upper arm) so that they may be removed through the lower arm by a mechanical pump. Liquid mercury from the upper bulb flows back to the lower flask.

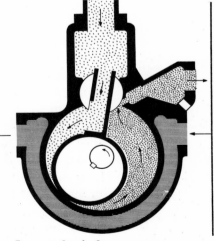

In a mechanical vacuum pump, gas from the system to be evacuated flows in at the top. A roller, mounted on an eccentric, rotates along a cylindrical wall and so concentrates the gas to a pressure higher than the atmosphere. Dots and arrows show what happens. The shaded area shows the direction of flow of a cooling fluid.

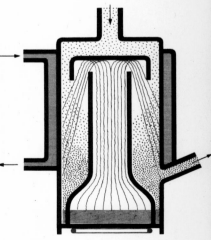

In a diagram of a mercury vapor condensation pump, the wavy lines traveling upwards and out show the paths of the mercury molecules. The dots, entering from above, represent molecules from the system to be evacuated. The downward motion of mercury causes collisions with the gas molecules, driving them down in heavy concentrations.

THE CHEMICAL INDUSTRY

1. LEO H. BAEKELAND
AND THE WORLD OF POLYMERS

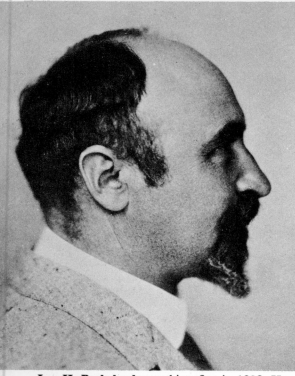

Leo H. Baekeland was thirty-five in 1898. He was one of the many foreign-born scientists who helped create American technology.

Baekeland's notebook shows his division of the famous reaction into four steps. "D/ Insoluble in all solvents . . . I call it Bakelite."

380

On an evening in 1889, one of the most brilliant young chemistry professors of Belgium, Leo H. Baekeland, attended a meeting of the New York Camera Club. He was a large exuberant man of twenty-six, visiting America on three accounts. He was on his honeymoon, on a traveling professorship, and on a government mission to study American institutions of higher education. At the Camera Club, he met and impressed Richard Anthony of the A. and H. T. Anthony Company—the largest photographic firm in the city. Without stating his intentions explicitly, Baekeland let Anthony know that he would not be at all averse to giving up his Ghent professorship and his government mission, if there were sufficient inducement to settle down and live in the United States.

The Anthony Company—later to become Ansco—had several technical problems that needed solving, and the young Belgian chemist who had recently invented a dry plate that could be developed in a tray of water seemed just the person. An offer was made, and Baekeland accepted, but the arrangement was not permanent; Baekeland could not be happy working for someone else.

To American industry in the '90's, chemistry was still largely an academic subject. If a manufacturer ran into a process problem that could not be worked out by his plant foreman, he might take his troubles to a consulting chemist. When Baekeland left Anthony in 1891, he had no definite plans except to open a consulting office and laboratory and, like a young doctor or lawyer, hope that clients would find his address. He engaged in so many fruitless projects that his money dwindled. Finally he became sick. Enforced idleness made him take stock. He was squandering himself, he realized. The thing to do was to concentrate on some one project that could pay off the fastest. The two years with Anthony had made him appreciate the importance of an invention he had projected eight years before when he had been only twenty—a photographic paper sufficiently sensitive to be printed by artificial light.

Focusing his energies, he perfected the process named *Velox*. This was 1893—a year of deep depression. Nevertheless he found a partner in Leonard Jacobi, and together they established the Napera Chemical Company at Napera Park, Yonkers, to manufacture the paper.

For some years, the going was hard because the professional photographers clung to the traditional method of printing by sunlight. However, the new and growing group of amateurs created by George Eastman proved a willing market, and the business finally prospered. In 1899, Baekeland received a letter from Eastman saying that he was impressed with *Velox*. "If you are interested in selling, come up to Rochester. We can talk it over and, I am sure, come to terms."

Like every ambitious man who is asked his price, Baekeland could not think of the figure. Riding out to Rochester, he decided that he would take twenty-five thousand dollars.

Courteously, Eastman ushered him into his office, showed him to a seat, and offered him a million dollars.

Starting the new century a millionaire at thirty-seven, Baekeland built a private laboratory for himself and devoted the next few years to studying electrochemistry, raising his family, and traveling abroad with his

wife and two children. This was 1906, the seventh year of the Automobile Age, and the trip was taken in a specially built Peerless limousine, upholstered with green leather and carrying on its roof the ten leather suitcases required for the young family's safari through France, England, and Italy.

In his book, *A Family Motor Tour through Europe,* he wrote: "I have met automobile parties of many descriptions, but I have not yet encountered any who had undertaken a long trip accompanied by children as we did."

When he got back to America, he threw himself intensively into the most elusive problem in chemistry of his time; he set out to duplicate a feat that had not been performed since the discovery of glass over three thousand years before.

The origin of glass is lost in history. Pliny wrote that some Phoenician sailors, shipwrecked with a cargo of Egyptian natron, a crude form of sodium carbonate, built a shelter using blocks of the soft white stone. A beacon fire was lit to cook meals. In the morning, the sailors found mysterious small clear beads in the ashes; glass had been formed from the combination of the alkali in the natron and the silicates of the sand. But this was a legend even in Pliny's day—the temperature for such a fusion was too high to be obtained from such a flame.

A material like glass that can be shaped under heat and pressure is said to be a thermoplastic. Glass has another property: the fundamental molecule combines with itself over and over to form a marvelously complicated structure. This is called a polymerization. Glass is not a crystalline structure, but an amorphous mass. Many polymers occur in nature—resin, amber, and the cellulose of vegetable fiber; but glass remained the only plastic polymer synthesized by man until Leo Baekeland attacked the problem.

In the early years of the nineteenth century, French chemists showed how chemical analysis could break down familiar substances into their constituent parts. Then Berthelot reversed the procedure. Instead of taking compounds apart, he *created* the familiar substances by bringing together their constituent parts. This he called *synthesis.* The most momentous synthesis in the history of chemistry was Woehler's creation of urea from the mineral compounds, ammonia and cyanogen. From the earliest days in Egypt, the land of Khem, the priests of Ammon Ra (who gave their name to ammonia as a substitute for the greatest bleaching agent in the world: the sun-god Ammon) were the first practitioners of the alchemical art (Al-Khem). Alchemy subsequently taught the doctrine that certain substances occurred in minerals in the ground, while others could not be created without the organic "life-force." Urea was one of these "organic" substances.

Berthelot synthesized other "organic" substances—vinegar, benzene, and many more—from mineral compounds. His express aim was "to do away with 'life' as an explanation wherever organic chemistry is concerned." His results were as profoundly disturbing to religious thought as Darwin's theory of organic evolution. However, over the years, chemical synthesis took on a popular meaning that was quite different from Berthelot's. "Synthetic" compounds were thought to be cheap substitutes, inferior to the natural product, instead of "man-made equivalents."

Baekeland's "synthetic" resin was designed to reproduce the most desirable qualities of amber, with the addition of many new properties that would make the synthesized substance more useful. Baekeland himself, however, did not suspect that he was about to start a revolution in the domain of substance.

The Baekelands cycled happily in their early days. In 1906, a millionaire, he and his family toured Europe happily in a green Peerless. On his return to America, he finished Bakelite and lived happily ever after.

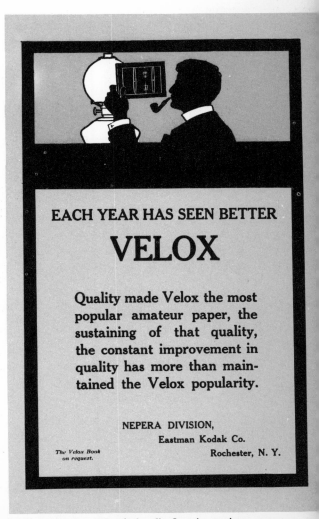

EACH YEAR HAS SEEN BETTER

VELOX

Quality made Velox the most popular amateur paper, the sustaining of that quality, the constant improvement in quality has more than maintained the Velox popularity.

NEPERA DIVISION,
Eastman Kodak Co.
Rochester, N. Y.

The Velox Book on request.

Velox paper was Baekeland's first invention. Eastman was said to have given him a million dollars for it at the turn of the century.

Leo Baekeland, D. Nat. Sc., D. Ch., D. Sc., D. App. Sc.

Baekeland's laboratory was in the basement of his home, later out in a backyard shed.

The first pressure oven—Bakelizer in which Baekeland tamed the phenol-formaldehyde reaction.

The first commercial batch of Bakelite was produced in this chamber, designed for pressure.

2. OXYBENZYL–METHYLEN–GLYCOLANHYDRIDE: BAKELITE

As a starting point, Baekeland picked two of the simplest and most available organic compounds—phenol and formaldehyde. Phenol—popularly known in the form of carbolic acid, a brownish, pungent-smelling liquid—is a pink crystalline powder in its pure form, melting at 41° C. with a boiling point of 182° C. Phenol is completely soluble in water, highly reactive, and is obtained in large quantities from the production of coal gas. Formaldehyde, a pungent gas, is the oxidized form of methyl alcohol. Baekeland knew that the two substances could react in a variety of ways. From experiments made in the previous twenty-five years, he knew that every combination of the two compounds had resulted in a brown, viscid, tarlike mass that was practically unanalyzable. Baekeland carefully repeated every experiment that had been made to be sure that he would commit all the known errors at the outset.

When the phenol and formaldehyde were mixed together and heated, a violent bubbling took place in the retort. The mixture became molten and then hardened to a solid mass with the consistency of fossilized sponge cake because of the never-ceasing bubbles. Every research worker on the problem had used a temperature less than the boiling point of water—high enough to get the reaction going—but low enough to keep the bubbling to a minimum.

After repeated experiments Baekeland made three major discoveries. The first was that the bubbling was a result of the reaction, in which gas was given off at a very high pressure. If he pumped air into the retort above the mixture *before* applying heat, the gas pressure in the bubbles was less than the pressure of the retort, and the bubbling was blocked for the same reason that charged water cannot bubble in a pressure-filled bottle. The solution remained crystal clear throughout the reaction.

Baekeland's second discovery was that the reaction was being driven at too low a temperature. If he raised the temperature to *twice* the boiling point of water, the reaction was completed within only a few minutes. The third way to control the reaction was the discovery that if he added dilute acid to the mixture of phenol and formaldehyde, the result was a thick clear liquid. If he added alkaline substances, the final product was a hard, clear, insoluble solid, resistant to acids and heat. He could therefore determine the hardness of his product beforehand by adjusting the acidity.

Once on the right track, he spent another two years studying every facet of the reaction. Finally he was able to produce batches of a substance that could not be softened by heat like resins, that would not shrink after being removed from the mold like celluloid, that could be machined with almost as high a degree of precision as brass. By that time his product was protected by four hundred patents.

Early in February, 1909, he demonstrated a number of Bakelite articles to members of the recently formed Chemists Club of New York. Some of his articles—cigarette holders and pipe stems—were substitutes for amber. Others were substitutes for porcelain in electrical applications, with the advantage that Bakelite was a better insulator and nowhere near as brittle.

At a meeting of the American Chemical Society, he described the history of the reaction and every detail of his own research.

"I take about equal amounts of phenol and formaldehyde and I add a small amount of alkaline . . . agent to it." With heat, "the mixture separates in two layers, a supernatant aqueous solution and a lower liquid," which could be thin, thick, or viscous, depending on how long he let the reaction go.

Whatever the consistency of this lower liquid, it was the first, or A, stage of the reaction. A was still soluble in most of the organic solvents.

Under further heat, A became something else—B—which did not dissolve in commercial solvents, but absorbed them. B swelled. With further heating, B became soft, but hardened on cooling. Because of this property, B could be molded into any desired shape.

When B was heated after it had been molded, it fused into a hard, homogeneous mass, called Bakelite C—the form in which Bakelite is known to the public. All of these steps had to be carried on under extremely high pressures, so that in the early days there was always the danger of explosion. Baekeland had worked out the design of his own ovens, however, and he was sure of his final product.

"It is very hard, cannot be scratched with the finger nail; in this respect it is far superior to shellac and even to hard rubber. It misses one great quality of hard rubber and celluloid, it is not so elastic nor flexible. As an insulator and for any purposes where it has to resist heat, friction, dampness, steam, or chemicals, it is far superior to hard rubber, casein, celluloid, shellac and, in fact, all plastics. In price also it can splendidly compete with all these.

"Instead of pouring liquid A into a glass tube or mold I may simply dip an object into it or coat it by means of a brush . . . and provide it rapidly with a hard brilliant coat of Bakelite, superior to any varnish and even better than the most expensive Japanese lacquer. . . . But I can do better, I may prepare an A much more liquid than this one . . . and I may soak cheap, porous soft wood in it . . . and let the synthesis take place in and around the fibers of the wood. The result is a very hard wood, as hard as mahogany or ebony . . ."

Bakelite's first commercial success was as an insulator in the electrical field where the plastic was reinforced with a wood filler to make it shock proof.

During the First World War, it was used for airplane parts, then for automobile parts. After the war, it went hand-in-hand with the fantastic growth of the radio industry.

Bakelite was the first of a long series of resins that were to shape the economy of America. For example, without the synthetic fabrics, the quantities of natural leather required for automobile upholstery covers would be so enormous that beefsteak would be priced at only a few cents a pound, or far more likely, automobiles would be fewer and more expensive. Because of the weight and strength of plastics (certain forms of which have greater tensile strength than steel), they were being used in every field of American manufacture less than two decades after Baekeland's discovery.

A survey of the history of world invention makes one point clear: if a certain useful machine has never been built because technology lacks an adequate material, then sooner or later that machine will be built because the material problem is bound to be solved. A second truth: the production of new materials makes hitherto undreamed-of mechanisms become theoretically possible. In this chain of the human conquest of the physical world—mechanism and material—Bakelite is one of the most important links.

Home radio in the 1920's boomed the domestic use of Bakelite.

Wireless in World War I had already proven Bakelite's insulating power.

Brass beds lacquered with Bakelite were advertised in the *Furniture World* in December, 1912.

Airplane propellers were successfully made from laminated canvas soaked in Bakelite.

3. CHEMISTRY, INDUSTRIAL GIANT

Just after dawn on a summer morning in 1916, the flat calm of Chesapeake Bay was broken by a patch of ripples. A moment later, the ripples turned into turbulence and then the surface broke with the silent, ghostly rising of the giant gray German submarine, *Deutschland,* which had evaded the entire British fleet and crossed the Atlantic to carry on trade with America. The submarine docked at Baltimore, and with gracious condescension, Americans were told that Germany had come to relieve our chemical famine with dyes and medicines. In return the Germans wanted only some rubber and nickel—a million dollars' worth. The World War was in its second year in Europe, and Americans were still too proud to fight, when the *Deutschland's* feat drove America into a frenzy of admiration.

Some Americans, stirred by the drama, cheered the Germans; others, more knowing, bitterly realized the economic trick that had been played on America for the preceding quarter century by the German chemical industry in combination with the German Foreign Office and General Staff.

The American chemical famine was no accident: it was part of German strategy. The major victim of that strategy, of course, was England, which had allowed herself to be betrayed by her own concept of free trade.

In the nineteenth century, the industry of synthesizing chemicals was started in England by James Muspratt, who set up a factory to manufacture soda ash, and by William Henry Perkin, who produced the first dye from coal tar. Then the newly consolidated German nation began building up its own industrial-

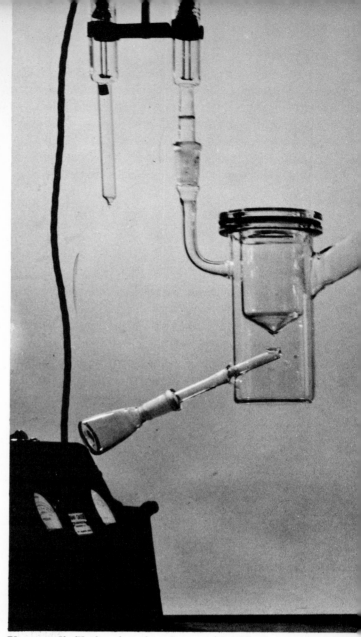

Vacuum distillation, based on Langmuir's diffusion pump, was on

ization by encouraging German scientists in every way. German businessmen received government aid to manufacture chemicals with the long-range view of making Germany independent of imports, against the coming days of continental war.

In the 1880's and '90's, Germans concentrated on reducing to industrial practice the chemical syntheses developed in French and English academic laboratories. German firms, amalgamated into non-competing cartels with state sanction, manufactured huge quantities of industrial chemicals and exported them to foreign nations with the express design of putting foreign competitors out of business. Because England operated according to the rules of classic capitalism, no tariff was placed on the import of basic chemicals, and the English chemical industry was destroyed by the state-subsidized German product. The same situation occurred in the United States. Americans were encouraged by low German prices to import German dyes and medicines in the finished state.

Arthur Amos Noyes was one of the chemists who marked America's coming of age in science. Wolcott Gibbs, Ira Remsen, Gilbert Lewis also contributed to the great transition. Their generation, contemporaries of Michelson and Millikan, were mostly educated in Europe. The next generation, their students, showed the beginning of a reversed trend.

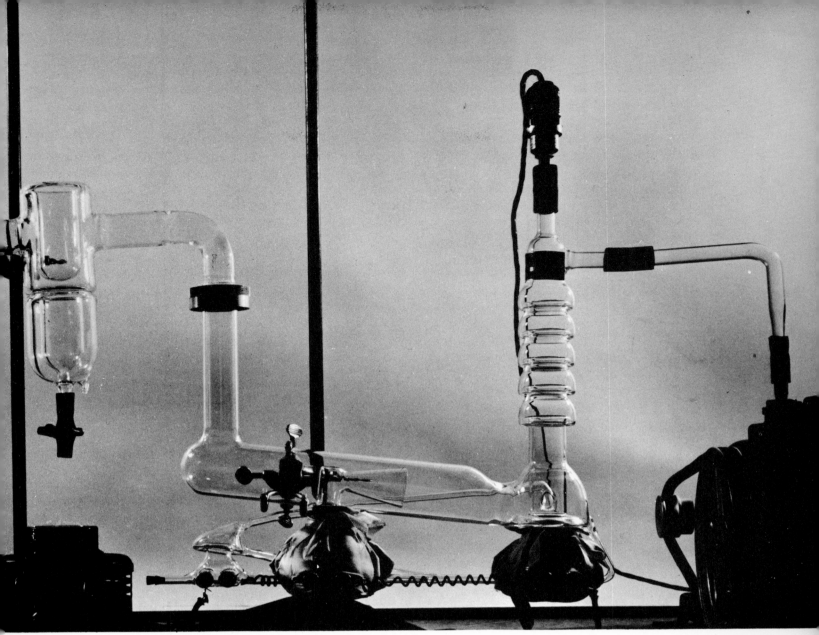

the research laboratory techniques reduced to billion-gallon industrial practice with the arrival of American chemical industry.

Americans had pioneered in many nineteenth-century fields of industrial chemistry—sulfite cellulose and artificial abrasives: carborundum, calcium carbide, alundum, aluminum—but whenever an American firm set up a plant for the production of a basic chemical from coal tars, it found itself undersold by the German product. Only seven small companies producing dyes remained in business in America by 1914.

The English were caught so badly by the outbreak of the war that they were still manufacturing their Boer War explosive: trinitrophenol—TNP—while the Germans were already in production of TNP's close chemical relation: trinitrotoluene—TNT—which was enormously superior as a disruptant in the warhead of explosive shells.

Under the pressures of war in 1914, the British began to build up a chemical industry from scratch. In the same years the Americans did nothing but try to negotiate through Switzerland for dribbles from the German vats. Prices of stored chemicals in America

soared to fantastic heights: twenty dollars' worth of chemicals sold for a thousand dollars; then, on being diluted ten to one, was sold again for twenty thousand dollars.

In 1917, when America entered the war, the same textile manufacturers whose preference for the German product had thwarted the growth of American chemicals brought pressure on the United States government for drastic action. The Alien Property Custodian seized all the German patents. These in turn were sold to a commission called the Chemical Foundation, which was financed by a public stock sale. The Chemical Foundation licensed any American manufacturer who would pay a small fee for the rights to German chemical processes. The proceeds from license sales were to be used for the advancement of chemical information in this country. As a result of this enforced boom in chemicals—even though many of the war-born companies collapsed with the coming of peace—chemistry became one of the industrial giants of America. The roster of names contained duPont, Dow, Eastman, American Cyanamide, National Aniline, and Union Carbide and Carbon.

Before the war, an American chemist with a Ph.D. was rarely seen working outside a university even though the American Chemical Society had seven thousand members in 1914. After the war, chemical engineering became a widespread American profession, and a Ph.D. was not much more than a minimum requirement for an industrial job.

New products appeared on the American market. Cellulose acetate, first produced by Count de Chardonnet as "artificial silk" in 1889, had been improved by the Dreyfus brothers in France and Arthur D. Little in the United States. During the war, the Dreyfuses had used their formula in England for the production of aircraft "dope"—a smooth, lacquer-like coating for the cloth wings of planes.

With the collapse of the aviation business after the war, the Dreyfus brothers came to the United States to operate a plant built for them by this government during the war years. They entered the field of synthesized textiles. To avoid the stigma of cheapness that had grown up around the idea of "artificial silk," they invented the name "Celanese."

DuPont undertook a long-range study of dyes and artificial rubber; Eastman concentrated on photographic chemicals, but the side reactions from their researches led them to develop their own textiles and industrial solvents.

Hercules Powder Company went into the field of synthetic resins. In time, most of the large American chemical companies found themselves competing with each other in the field of dyes, solvents, synthetic lacquers, and textile fibers.

By 1929, American annual production of rayon was one hundred million pounds.

The automobile companies, in an endeavor to find more durable paints, had to enter the field of varnishes and pigments. The oil companies, too, became part of the chemical industry, not only to improve their product, but to find profitable means of disposing of distillate fractions recovered from their cracking plants.

In 1940, the United States produced 250,000,000 pounds of synthetic plastics and 500,000,000 pounds of rayon—in both cases a 500 per cent increase during a decade of business depression.

The broadest attack on the problem of synthetic polymers was undertaken by duPont in 1928. Their 1934 result was a substance as truly revolutionary as Baekeland's discovery. For just as Bakelite filled needs that could not be met by celluloid or cellulose acetate, so nylon proved to have properties which no fiber ever before had equaled.

4. THE GIANT MOLECULES

Once the German Army hit its stride in August, 1914, the Allied Armies could only retreat, make a stand, die, retreat to a new stand, die again and fall back once more. During those terrible months, said Lord Moulton, director general of British Explosive Supplies, the Allied Armies were sustained by three American corporations—J. P. Morgan and Company, Bethlehem Steel, and E. I. duPont de Nemours—manufacturers of gunpowder and construction blasting compounds.

The standard of high explosives set by the Imperial German Army with TNT in 1914 forced the Allied nations to turn at once to the duPont Company, which had emerged from its Panama Canal Construction with a monthly production of 600,000 pounds. Only a few days after war was declared, Russia ordered close to a million pounds of TNT; France ordered eight million pounds of cannon powder; and the British and the Italians were not far behind. By the time the war in Europe was six months old, duPont had accepted contracts for close to fifteen times its production capacity, as well as for products it had never made before.

By April, 1918, the company's capacity was fifty-four times what it had been in 1914.

When the war ended, the number of munitions workers was reduced from 85,000 to 18,000, and canceled contracts added up to $250,000,000. The company, an overnight mammoth, faced collapse. In the crisis, the company desperately sought new fields in order to use the highly integrated production techniques that had been developed; and it began a campaign to absorb other companies which were already in operation in these fields. Along with this, went a parallel program to develop new projects. In outline, here is the record:

1918—Coal tar dyes and chemicals.

1920—Viscose rayon yarn undertaken by the outright purchase of American rights to French and English patents. The American product was given the name "rayon" in 1924 when it began to appear on the market, not only as a textile for wear, but as reinforcement for rubber tires.

1923—"Cellophane" cellulose film—by purchase of the American rights to the Swiss patent of Jacques F. Brandenberger. Cellophane and the machines for making it were ready in Switzerland in 1912.

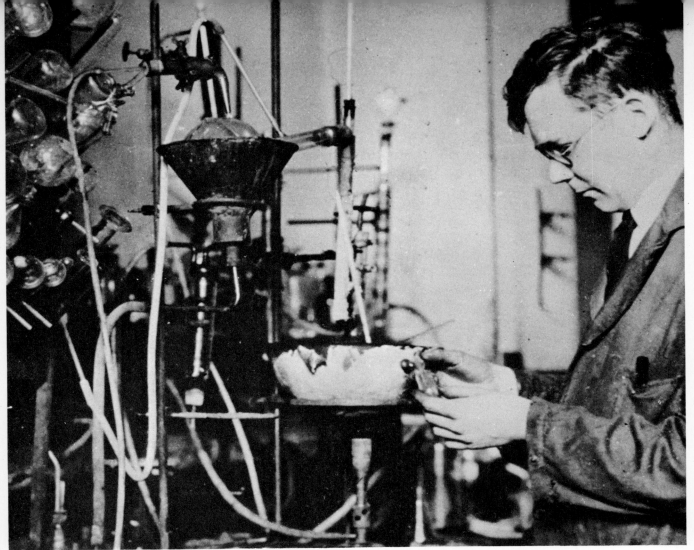

Dr. Wallace H. Carothers started his research in long chain polymers for duPont in 1927, and produced nylon.

1924—Synthetic ammonia—by the purchase of American rights to the French Claude process and the Italian Casale process.

1925—Industrial alcohol.

1928—Acetate rayon yarn by purchase. Hit textile market in beginning of depression, but by 1937 the National Resources Committee classed rayon as one of the six outstanding technical achievements of the century. 1937 rayon production in the United States six times greater than the consumption of silk.

In 1920, the United States produced five million pounds of synthetic plastics of all kinds. Ten years later, automobiles and radios had caused this production figure to be multiplied almost ten times.

By the late 1920's powder and explosives had become one of the smallest interests of the duPont Company. So far, however, the company had not pioneered in any field that had not been worked over before. Its laboratories, founded in 1911, were for development only.

In 1928, the company set up a far different type of laboratory. As director of fundamental research, duPont picked Dr. Wallace H. Carothers, at that time thirty-two years old. He had taught organic chemistry at Harvard and had done brilliant research on giant molecules. Carothers was a highly sensitive, moody perfectionist, who found his deepest relaxation in music. He was a scientist, deeply aware of a noble tradition.

Nineteenth-century chemists, in their search for simplicity in nature, concentrated on substances with simple molecular structure. Not until the end of the century was chemical theory strong enough to face the existence of an entire range of compounds that seemed to contradict all their accepted laws. Scientists, used to compounds like hydrochloric acid with a mass of thirty-six molecular units, were appalled by the complexity of molecules which, if they could believe their figures, ran to forty thousand units of mass. Cellulose nitrate weighed 10,000 units and common starch weighed 36,700.

Yet these giants had a fundamental simplicity. For example, starch had a basic molecular unit—called the *monomer*—that could be written as $C_6H_{10}O_5$; but this unit added on to itself hundreds of times over again to form a *polymer*. Proteins were also polymers and so were the resins. Baekeland had worked with a type of polymer, but the theory of polymers did not become clear until Carothers went at the problem with the same view as Berthelot.

5. CAROTHERS' FORMULA 66— DUPONT'S NYLON

Carothers, working in the duPont laboratories, intended to synthesize giant polymers starting with the simplest molecular structures.

First he had to work out the laws. He distinguished between two fundamental classes of polymers:

1. A-polymers are produced by addition. The unit molecules—the monomers—all identical, add on to each other to form chains that may be hundreds of monomers long. Sometimes the chains have elaborate branches.

2. C-polymers are formed when the basic molecules react chemically among themselves. C-polymers form long chains just as do the A-polymers, but the process is a *polycondensation* rather than addition.

Having studied the different dynamics of polymerization and polycondensation, Carothers and his staff began the synthesis of giant chain molecules starting from inorganic compounds.

On April 16, 1930, Carothers' assistant, J. W. Hill, recorded that his particular assignment resulted in the kind of chain condensation compound predicted by Carothers' theory.

A few weeks later, Hill reported again to Carothers that the reaction product could be drawn out into a fiber which was pliable and elastic. When cooled, the delicate fiber would stretch still further in his hand to several times its original length and then suddenly

become "fixed" when the chains of molecules had been pulled to their ultimate lengths and lay parallel to each other. The fiber's strength was surprising, but the temperature characteristics were poor. The substance softened in hot water and dissolved in the standard cleaning fluids.

Carothers at that time was interested only in proving the theory of polymerization from simple inorganic compounds, and the sample was put aside. He next turned to the polymerization of the hydrocarbons of acetylene and took the research up to the point where his results could be turned over to the development laboratories for the production of a synthetic rubber.

However, Carothers' staff was interested in the fiber problem, and now he caught their enthusiasm. He focused his attention on the condensation product of certain polyamides which had a molecular linkage very similar to the protein linkage in natural fibers like wool and silk. This linkage gave the synthetic fiber an elasticity equal to that of the natural substances. This great stroke was no accident: it was the aim of Carothers' theory.

On May 23, 1934, Carothers synthesized a super-polymer which he himself spun into fiber by squirting a hot solution of it through the tiny opening in a hypodermic needle. The thread that was formed was then cold-drawn to its full length and subjected to all the exacting tests which Carothers could devise. Over a million dollars had gone into the research when Carothers turned "polymer 66" over to the development laboratory where engineers, physicists, metallurgists, and cost accountants could study the problem of

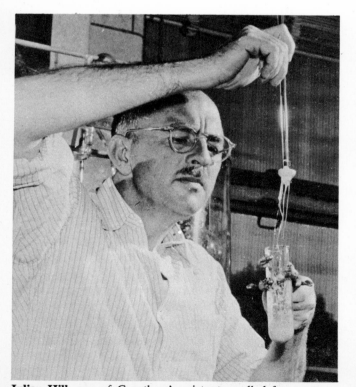

Julian Hill, one of Carothers' assistants, pulled from a test tube a stringy sample of material that was a forerunner of nylon. The slender filaments suggested threads.

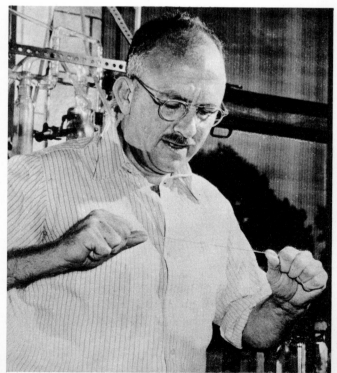

When pulled to a certain length, the material became tough and fixed, because all its molecules had been drawn into line. Hill's 1930 experiment proved Carothers' theory.

manufacture.

On October 27, 1938, duPont publicly announced the new product. For the first time in the history of the chemical industry, a synthetic was offered to the public, not as a substitute, but as a premium product, superior to natural fiber—and, therefore, the public must expect to pay a premium price. The first nylon products on the market sold out so quickly that the company's faith was more than justified.

Carothers was a scientist whose goal was a deeper understanding of nature. To him, it was the proof of his theory that counted. The commercial success would have been only a secondary satisfaction if he had lived to see it. One year before the public announcement, he ended his life at the age of forty-one.

In his short lifetime he had proven that the trepidation felt by nineteenth-century chemists at the possibility of giant molecules was needless. Carothers had shown that these structures conform to the simplicity of nature.

Thirty-five years had elapsed between the time that Leo Baekeland did his work on Velox and the time that Carothers went into the laboratories of the duPont Company. In those years America had become a very different country, and the chemical industry was as radically transformed.

In the 1890's, Baekeland was still able to go into business for himself on a modest scale, live the life of an enterprising individual, and with wit, luck, and shrewdness make a fortune for himself.

In 1928, Carothers had only this choice besides university teaching—to go to work for a giant corporation at a salary and sign an agreement that all of his patents would be turned over to his employer. Carothers' product, valued at billions of dollars, would have earned him no particular income commensurate with his contribution. The individual had been absorbed by the group. The product was known as duPont nylon; the name of Carothers was known only to specialists.

On the other side of the picture, it must be said that it is very improbable that a man of Carothers' temperament would ever have gone into business for himself either in 1895, 1905, or any other time. Moreover if he had gone into business to manufacture nylon himself, he could never have gathered the enormous resources required to support the staff of expert scientists in collateral fields who solved the subsidiary problems that arose.

In all likelihood, Carothers as an individual would have spent at least fifteen years to achieve what he was able to do in four. The team approach of the huge corporation laboratories gave society useful results more quickly and more surely than any other way—once an imaginative individual had shown the direction in which to go.

In the 1930's, "rugged individualism" glittered in political slogans that might have been emotionally useful on the campaign platform, but the phrase had no place in most industrial, chemical, or electrical laboratories, or in the factory where mass production was the epitome of teamwork, or in very few other facets of what had become the highly mechanized American scene.

Viscose rayon threads are formed when one solution is extruded into another under pressure. Acetate rayon threads are formed when another solution is sprayed into air.

New Silk Made on Chemical Base Rivals Quality of Natural Product

Du Ponts Patent Process of W. H. Carothers for Full Synthetic Creation—Fiber Will Stretch Far—Cost Yet to Be Known

Copyright, 1938, by Science Service.

WASHINGTON, Sept. 21.—A new artificial silk, superior to natural silk or any synthetic rayon in its fineness, strength and elasticity has been patented here by the late W. H. Carothers, chemist of the E. I. du Pont de Nemours Company.

For the past month, du Pont officials have maintained a complete silence, in the face of many rumors, as to the nature and properties of a new fiber which was superior to silk and potentially could run silk off its last existing market in the hosiery field. News of this new fiber, without details, leaked into chemical circles.

Completely synthetic in their origin, the new fibers can be easily drawn to a size only one-tenth the diameter of a natural silk filament, or in the extreme case, to only one-seventy-fifth the diameter. Yet it shows a tensile strength equal or better than that of silk. In some cases the fibers are 150 per cent stronger than silk.

"The elastic recovery of these fibers under moderate elongations was very remarkable," the patent states, "and in this respect was much superior to existing artificial silks."

Described as 'Lustrous and Silky'

The fibers are "lustrous and silky in appearance" and are almost completely insensitive to moisture. When made into fabrics, the synthetic fiber fabric possesses a far better elastic recovery than natural silk.

In the new patent, fiber experts at the National Bureau of Standards here believed they had noted

the long-awaited and very important announcement.

The Carothers patent (No. 2,130,948) with fifty-six broad and basic claims describes the production of fibers from long chain amine compounds. These are prepared by reacting diamines and dibasic acids. Out of this reaction come acid salts which are crystalline solids having fairly definite melting points.

Eight specific ways of creating the new fibers are described. A typical reaction is a mixture of 14.8 parts of penta-methylene-amine, 29.3 parts of sebacic acid and 44 parts of mixed xylenols.

Penta-methylene-amine is known as cadaverine and can be derived from ammonia. In nature it is formed as a decay product of the chemical known as lysine, which occurs in many proteins and is present in serum albumen and in the fibrin from clotted blood. Lysine is essential to nutrition.

Can Be Stretched Up to 700%

Sebacic acid is, chemically, a dibasic acid which can be prepared by heating castor oil soap with sodium hydroxide. Dr. Carothers was among those scientists who had previously shown that it is possible not only to form ring compounds of dibasic acids but also—and probably the important point in the new patent—to create long linear molecules in chain formation.

The mixed xylenols used in the process are the solvents for the complicated amine and the dibasic acid. Means are provided in the patent for the recovery of these solvents.

The first public announcement of nylon was made in 1938, about a decade after Carothers began his research. Carothers had killed himself the year before.

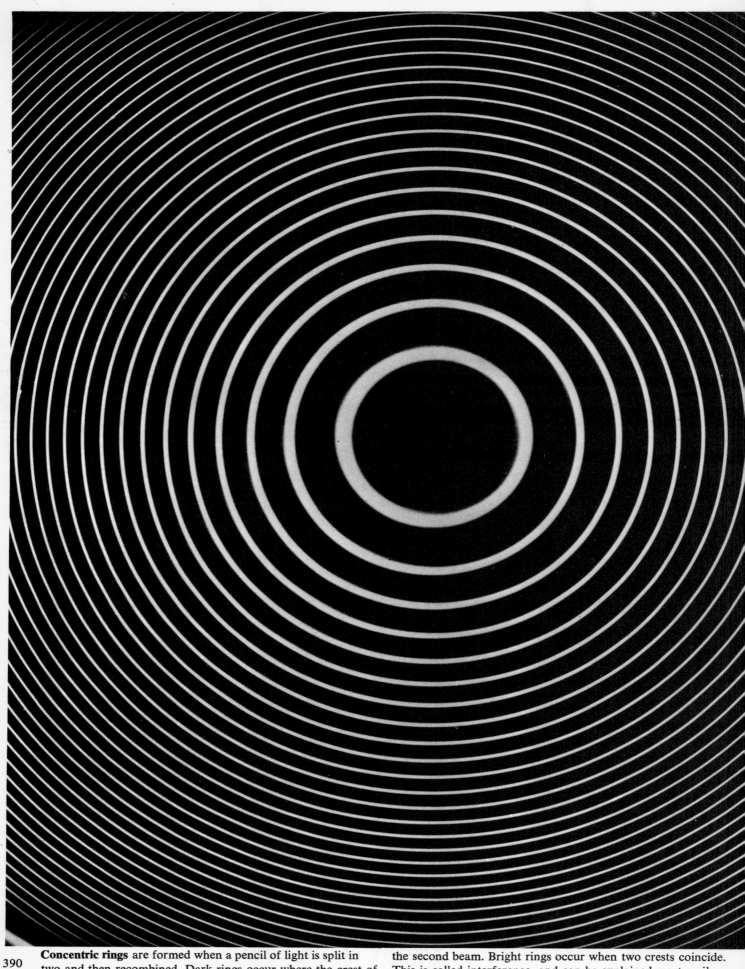

390 **Concentric rings** are formed when a pencil of light is split in two and then recombined. Dark rings occur where the crest of a wave in one beam is canceled by a trough of another wave in the second beam. Bright rings occur when two crests coincide. This is called interference, and can be explained most easily by assuming that light consists of waves.

PART SEVEN

The New Dimension

The receding wave leaves only a mark of bubbles along the shore that tells nothing of the swirl, roar and surge of the water that has come and gone. In the same way, newspapers and stories written in a past time give only the most indirect indication of the shape of things as they were. The Golden Twenties were *not* golden; the Era of Wonderful Nonsense was neither wonderful nor nonsense.

If statistics have any meaning, the decade before the stock market collapse of 1929 was a period of hard times for most Americans. After a brief land boom immediately following the war, the farmers' position was one of continuing crisis. Nor were other Americans very much better off. At the time, the Brookings Institution said that "a family income of $2,000 may be regarded as sufficient to supply only the basic necessities," but sixty per cent of American families lived on less than $2,000 a year. The newspapers of the time, stressing prize-fights, cross-channel swims, murder trials, and love-nest raids, played up what most people wanted to *read* about, not what they were actually doing.

The war had enormously increased America's productivity, and with the swing back to peace, finished goods began to pile up in huge inventories, far larger than the demand. For that reason, American business laid its greatest stress on selling—high pressure selling, if necessary—for the goods had to be moved. It was no accident that the air was full of salesmen's slogans, that the heroes of the popular magazine stories were bright young salesmen, or that salesmen became the heads of corporations. "The business of America," said Calvin Coolidge, "is business." And there could be no business without sale. The salesmen ran at full speed, selling everything to each other, hustling as fast as they could, and the Depression loped grimly along, always only one step behind. Babbitt, the hero of Sinclair Lewis' wryly compassionate novel, had a right to stop and ask himself what life was all about.

The great wave of speculation in corporate common stocks was only a postponement of what was long overdue in 1926; but again, the bull market was no accident. It was based on hysterical faith in the boundless future of corporate business, which in turn was due to the frenzy of self-hypnotism into which salesmen lashed themselves at sales meetings, Booster meetings, and the thousand and one forms of conventions of Go-Getters. It was nurtured by the stock market promoters arranging "mergers" between companies for the quick profits in stock flotation, without any concern for the productive capacity of the resulting hybrids. Yet anyone who looked askance at all the shenanigans was fixed with a gimlet eye and warned, as in Dos Passos' *The Big Money,* "not to monkey with the buzz saw."

Only 5 per cent of all Americans had annual incomes between $5,000 and $10,000 a year and only 2.3 per cent had incomes over $10,000. The pressures on the Great American Sales Force were so great that it is no wonder they wanted to get away from themselves after business hours and read about trivia; and because they were faced with the need to make daily sales records or get another job, it is also no wonder that they read longingly about the men who broke all-time records in home runs, in the prize ring, or flew airplanes further or faster than anyone else had ever done.

Another escape from the daily financial pressures of a tottering economy was the promise, made to America somewhere around 1925, that millions could be made overnight simply by investing in the common stock of the great corporations. The frenzy for selling sold the idea that the American corporation was a magical device, almost a divine thing, and for three years the public beat its worshiping head in adulation against the god's feet. The murderous bruises on the public forehead in 1929 showed that beneath the gilt-edged blue chips the god was brass.

A long hard look was taken at the god in 1932 when Adolph A. Berle, Jr.,

Technological unemployment, which worried Walter Hunt when he invented the sewing machine, has now extended to the offices.

INTERFERENCE RINGS

The most important discoveries in physics during the first quarter of the twentieth century showed that light and matter were not as different as had been thought. For over a century, all optical phenomena had been explained by the wave nature of light; then Heinrich Hertz and Arthur Compton each discovered new optical phenomena, both of which could be explained only by assuming that light consisted of particle-like packets of energy. However the interference pattern of light shown on the preceding page indicates the existence of light waves. A similar interference pattern, shown on the opposite page, again produceable only by waves, was created by a stream of solid matter—electrons—fired through a vial of crystals. It therefore followed that solid matter, of subatomic size, at least, also must possess a wave nature. The realization during the 1920's of this duality in nature—particle and wave—proved far more important to the future than any of the political, sporting, or financial events that filled the newspaper columns of the time.

and Gardiner C. Means published *The Modern Corporation and Private Property,* which stated that by 1930 half of the national wealth was owned by corporations, of which half again was owned by only two hundred companies. By that time, twelve million Americans were out of work and they had lost their reverence for any form of man-made god; they were simply bewildered, desperate, frightened individuals. This nation had been founded on the revolutionary doctrine that the rights of the individual were supreme. However, some time after the Civil War, the ranks of American individuals had been increased in a novel way. The Fourteenth Amendment to the Constitution of the United States protected the Negroes—freed by the Thirteenth Amendment—by preventing any state from abridging "the privileges or immunities of citizens of the United States, nor shall any State deprive any person of life, liberty, or property without due process of law." In 1894, Justice David Brewer, in the case of *Regan vs. Farmers' Loan and Trust Company,* culminated a series of judicial decisions by coming out flatly with the statement that the Fourteenth Amendment applied to corporations; in other words, corporations were also individuals.

Invention may be defined as the novel combination of known means to achieve results never attained before by such a method. Invention is not limited to the field of mechanical contrivances. There may be social, political, or economic inventions. Mechanical inventions have always had to meet the test of usefulness. Social, political, and economic inventions must meet the same test. The political invention created by the Articles of Confederation did not work and had to be discarded. Similarly, John D. Rockefeller's form of business aggregation, called the "trust," only half met the need for the large integrated business organization that was demanded by "The American System of Manufacture"—mass production. The holding company, on the other hand, by its fluidity, was able to meet all these needs and so found a congenial home in the industrial life of America. That it used its strength to beat that home into a shape more receptive to its existence cannot be denied; but the fact remains that the corporate form of amalgamation succeeded where the trust had failed.

The entire decade of the 1930's was spent by Americans demanding that if the corporations *had* to be classed as individuals, let them act a little more like *people.* No one in the 1930's objected to corporations as such. Two-thirds of American corporations—which might include a corner candy store, a hat shop or a steel mill—earned less than $5,000 a year. For such enterprises, the corporate form was merely a legal convenience. On the other hand, A. T. & T. was equivalent to over eight thousand "small" corporations and controlled more wealth than existed within twenty-one states combined. In the same class were Standard Oil of New Jersey, U. S. Steel, General Motors, and the Consolidated Gas Company of New York.

It was apparent, though, that the large corporation was here to stay and the lawbooks of the 1930's bristled with laws defining the limits within which they had to operate. What was not widely apparent was that the social habits of behavior inherent in "corporation living" could not help but spread and become the accepted standards of even those Americans who classed themselves as "self-employed." A man born in 1900 was shocked to read that two hundred companies had come into possession of 49.2 per cent of America's corporate wealth by 1930. His daughter, born in 1930, looked askance in 1954 when the point of this consolidation was raised. "Wasn't it always this way?" she asked in innocence.

The role of science and invention in America had always been to increase the well-being and the rights of the individual. Since corporations were individuals, science and invention could do the same for them—and did.

Electron interference pattern, (see caption on facing page)

The Compton effect diagramed above shows how light of a certain frequency (gray ball at left) collides with an electron (dark ball center) and gives it motion shown by the arrow. Conservation of energy demands that after the collision, the energy of light is decreased by the amount given to the electron, hence the longer wave length.

The photo-electric effect also demands that light be considered according to the laws of particles. Light (from left) collides with a bound electron and gives it enough forward momentum to knock it out of the atom. The loops enclosing the arrows show the probability of the electron's passage through any point on the loop.

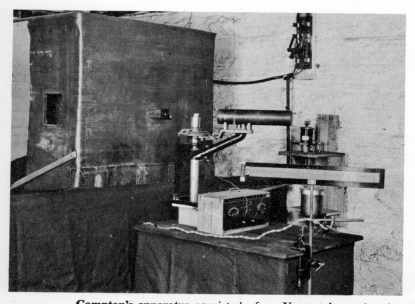

Compton's apparatus consisted of an X-ray tube enclosed in the shield as the photon source, and an angular detector (horizontal cylinder) of the deflected photons.

ELECTRONICS

1. PIECES OF LIGHT

The classical wave theory of light died hard, not because anyone had a vested interest in its survival, but because it successfully explained every phenomenon of light except one: the photo-electric effect which made sense only if light consisted of tiny packets of radiation. Not until 1923 did science come across a second phenomenon that could be explained only by the particle theory of light. The discoverer was Arthur H. Compton, aged thirty-one.

The centers of population had moved westward in the United States from the Atlantic seaboard, and so the majority of twentieth-century physicists, like the majority of Americans, were born and raised in the continental area west of the Appalachians and east of the Rockies—the Mississippi valley. Compton was born in Wooster, Ohio, in 1892 when A. A. Michelson was already world famous and Robert Millikan, an advanced graduate student. Compton grew up in physics when the new quantum theories no longer seemed as radical as they had at first. To men of Michelson's generation, the years after 1900 seemed a time

Arthur H. Compton, chancellor of Washington University from 1945 to 1953. His famous experiment was done in Chicago in 1924. He was given the Nobel prize in 1927.

of transition into uncertainty from a world of stability. To Compton and his generation, twentieth-century physics meant exciting pioneering in new worlds of knowledge.

Compton took his doctorate at Princeton in 1916, and then worked for a time on the short-lived project at the Westinghouse Laboratories under C. E. Skinner, who was trying to create, within a corporation framework, a laboratory devoted to pure science similar to those of the universities. At Westinghouse, at this time, the project was too expensive for the company to bear, and the directors began to get impatient for practical results. Not until the growth of the radio industry, after 1920, were the Westinghouse Laboratories under S. M. Kintner to prove a fruitful contributor to the storehouse of technological information. By that time Arthur Compton had left the company to become head of the physics department at Washington University in St. Louis, Missouri. Three years later, Michelson called him to the Ryerson Laboratory at Chicago where Compton came across the effect that was to make him the third American to receive the Nobel prize for physics.

Compton was studying the reflection of X-rays from crystal surfaces with an X-ray spectroscope which, like the prism spectroscope for visible light, could measure wave lengths and frequencies. While radiating carbon with X-rays of a particular frequency, he found that at certain angles the reflected X-rays had a different frequency—lower than the frequency of X-rays striking the crystal. If this had happened with visible light, it would be as though a beam of pure yellow had been reflected from a mirror as red. There was no explanation to be found in the classical electromagnetic theory of light.

Compton at once made this assumption: the X-rays were individual particles of radiant energy. The amount of energy could be calculated—as Einstein had done for photo-electricity—by multiplying the frequency by Planck's constant, the number determined by Millikan with the "vacuum machine shop" a few years earlier.

Compton assumed further that the X-ray light particles had collided with individual electrons. When one rolling billiard ball collides with another ball, some of the energy of the first ball is imparted to the second. By analogy, Compton deduced, when the X-ray photon collided with one of the electrons in a carbon atom, the photon must have lost part of its energy to make the electron move faster. Since the energy of the X-ray photon was dependent directly on its frequency, the change in energy would have to result in a change in frequency.

Compton first subjected his hypothesis to the test of numerical calculation using as his mathematical model the simple case of billiard ball-like particles. The calculation checked exactly with his experimental result. Further experiment confirmed him brilliantly.

Classically, an electromagnetic light wave traveling through space gradually spreads its energy. Photons behave very differently. Compton's analogy runs this way: "There once was a sailor on a vessel in New York harbor who dived overboard and splashed in the water. The resulting wave after finding its way out of the harbor, reached the harbor in Liverpool. Here another sailor was swimming beside his ship. When the wave reached him he was surprised to find himself knocked by the wave up to the deck. . . . There is now no need to imagine an ether such as was necessary to propagate waves, for the inertia of these (light) particles will carry them with undiminished speed to the remotest part of the universe without any such connecting medium and without loss of energy."

Later, the "Compton effect" was actually found to occur in the visible regions of light by the Indian physicist, C. V. Raman.

Compton was awarded the Nobel prize in 1927 along with C. T. R. Wilson of England who used his cloud chamber to corroborate Compton's theory. Where Compton had observed the energy decrease in X-rays bombarding electrons, Wilson observed the energy increase of electrons bombarded by X-rays.

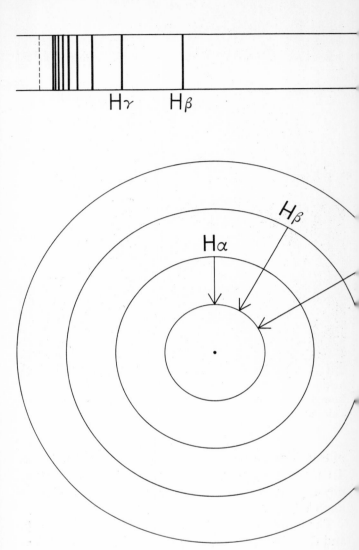

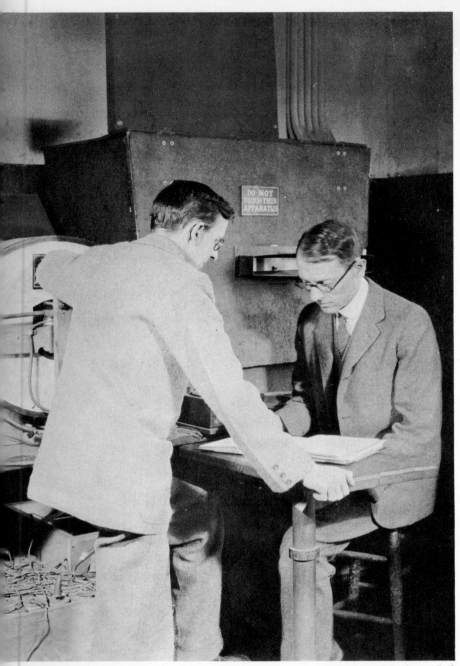

C. J. Davisson and L. H. Germer of the Bell Telephone Laboratories demonstrated the wave nature of matter in 1927.

The Bohr theory of the atom in diagram form shows four possible circular orbits for a hydrogen electron. The electron may fall from any outer orbit into the inner one and release energy in the form of light. Above the atom is a diagram of the spectra showing the emitted lines.

2. WAVES OF MASS

The proof that light waves can act like particles seemed to reduce physical phenomena to the simple proposition that both radiation and matter had a granular structure. However, shortly after Compton performed his experiment, the French physicist De Broglie was asking this question: If waves can behave like particles, why can't particles of matter behave like waves? He was asking this question, incidentally, in the dark Proustian splendor of his Paris mansion where, as the Duc de Broglie, he lived with his brother the

Prince de Broglie, also a physicist, and a sister who was one of the great ladies of French society.

The 1913 Bohr theory of the atom required electrons to rotate around a nucleus in certain fixed orbits without explaining why only these orbits could exist. Bohr had selected his orbits only because they gave the right answer. De Broglie in 1924 considered electron orbits by concentrating on the behavior of taut wires. Such a wire could vibrate only with the "standing waves" such as are set up in harp and piano strings under vibration. The wave length of the standing waves is determined by the length of the wire. De Broglie's next consideration was this: if, instead of the wire

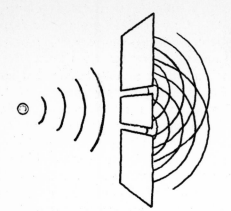

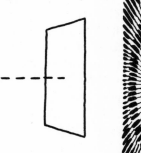

Interference bands (right) can be formed by waves from a point source (left) passing through two parallel slits (center). Each slit acts as a new source of light. Overlapping of wave fronts determines light or dark bands on the screen.

Circular interference pattern (right) by diffraction of electrons passing through a screen (center) from an electron gun (left). Like the two slits (above), the crystals of the screen act as new sources of waves.

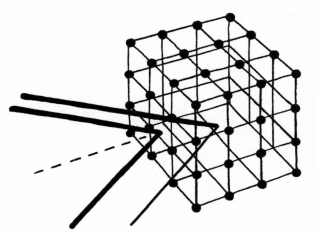

A crystal lattice may act like a three-dimensional grating for electrons. Reflection from two different layers means that the original beam is split in two and then recombined, fulfilling the conditions for interference.

being fixed at both ends, suppose it to be a ring, then exactly the same pattern of standing waves would be imposed upon it. Other wave lengths simply could not exist unless the size of the ring were changed.

De Broglie assumed that the rotating electron was a kind of standing wave of electricity passing around the nucleus. These standing waves of electricity were assumed to have a wave length which depended on the speed with which the electron was moving. Therefore, if the velocity of an electron were known, its wave length could be calculated; then, when the wave length was known, one could calculate the size of the orbit which would permit standing waves of that particular

length. The higher the velocity, the shorter the wave length. De Broglie found that the orbits determined by his theory had exactly the same size as those that had been imposed on the Bohr theory. De Broglie's theory had this distinct advantage over Bohr's theory: Bohr's theory had been contrived to fit the experimental data that came from the study of spectra; De Broglie's theory was a natural consequence of the behavior of the electron. Bohr's theory was arbitrary; De Broglie's was not.

De Broglie's theory received its confirmation three years later in 1927 in the Bell Telephone Laboratories from C. J. Davisson and L. H. Germer.

3. THE ELECTRON MICROSCOPE

The Bell Company had a tradition of research that dated back to its founder, Alexander Graham Bell. Bell's assistant during the years of the telephone's development, Thomas A. Watson, continued on with the telephone laboratory after Bell followed other interests. Watson's engineering laboratory was expanded by his successor, Hammond V. Hayes. At the same time, the Bell System's manufacturing branch—Western Electric—also developed research laboratories devoted to telephone engineering. In 1912, the laboratories of Western Electric and the Telephone Company underwent an historic change in the treatment of engineers and the approach to research.

Dr. Frank Jewett, who was responsible for the change, said, "I . . . discovered that the method that was being followed in rewarding engineers for their technical accomplishments was not satisfactory. The situation was an outgrowth of the conditions in the telephone industry in the 1880's and 1890's. This had been the 'era of the inventor' when it was vital to the future of the company to control the basic patents in the telephone art. In order to stimulate invention, the Western Electric Company had offered a reward of one hundred dollars for every patent issued. And this practice had continued into a period when the Bell Telephone System had become firmly established ahead of all rivals and the need for patents was no longer acute. The engineers would get together from time to time to discuss some new development in which they were all interested. Each man would then go off by himself and try to develop the idea in secrecy to the point where a patent application could be made. Moreover, wherever it was possible to make a number of divisional patent claims, instead of one broad claim, this was done, even though a patent on one broad claim would usually be more valuable to the company."

Jewett put an end to the reward on a per-patent basis—it had outlived its usefulness and was acting as a stimulant to divisiveness.

With a dozen years of experience in successfully running a research organization, the American Telephone and Telegraph Company in 1925 set up another laboratory—a non-profit corporation owned jointly with General Electric—call the Bell Telephone Laboratories. The purpose of these new laboratories was exactly the same as those which had been tried by Skinner almost a decade earlier at Westinghouse. Where Westinghouse had failed, the Telephone Company now succeeded.

In the telephone company laboratories, Clinton Joseph Davisson, who was forty-five, and Lester Halbert Germer, thirty, were doing physics research under ideal conditions, as free from pressure for "immediate and practical" results as if they were in a large, handsomely-endowed university laboratory. Their work included research in x-rays and crystallography. They were both men of enormous competence, but so far neither one had made a contribution that could be considered to have major importance.

Their famous experiment, as very often happens, grew out of an accident. They had been experimenting with nickel as a possible target for an X-ray tube, bombarding the nickel with high-speed electrons. The beam of electrons was focused on different faces of the nickel crystal and the number of electrons reflected at different angles was measured. The entire apparatus was, of course, mounted in a vacuum tube.

One day the tube cracked and air rushed in. The crack was sealed and the apparatus pumped out. Langmuir's vacuum technique had become standard laboratory practice and the entire system was heated during pumping to remove all air molecules which might have adhered to the surfaces of the various parts. During this heating the nickel crystal was not only "outgassed," but its structure was changed to what was probably a higher degree of uniformity. When the electron bombardment was resumed, Davisson and Germer found results very different from what they had obtained before.

Instead of getting "specular" reflection—the regular bouncing back which one would expect from throwing elastic balls against a hard wall—they found a *higher intensity of reflection at certain angles and lower intensity at others.*

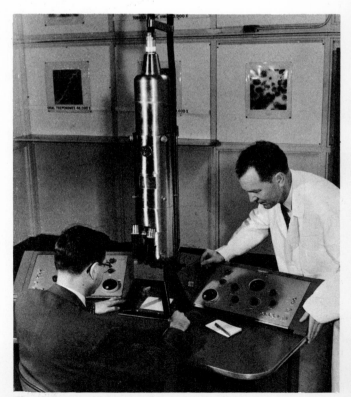

The electron microscope (above) uses the wave properties of the electron to achieve magnifications up to 200,000, which is a hundred times the power of optical microscopes. The binocular eyepiece views a fluorescent screen.

In terms of classical physics, this made no sense at all. To Davisson and Germer, it looked as if their reflection patterns were exactly what would happen when very short waves were being diffracted from the face of a finely lined grating. One could consider the smooth crystalline face of the nickel as a grating only if one could believe that the electron had a wave length of the same order as X-rays. Until that moment, De Broglie's theory had been only a mathematical curiosity. De Broglie had stated that the wave length of an electron depended on the velocity. In the apparatus of Davisson and Germer, electron velocity could be carefully controlled.

The results were irrefutable: different velocities for electrons produced exactly the diffraction patterns that were predicted for waves. These results were repeated independently the following year by G. P. Thompson of England and Kikuchi in Japan.

The sharp line of difference between matter and radiant energy was growing fainter and fainter. The 1913 quantum theory of Bohr was replaced by the 1924 wave theory of De Broglie and modified by Heisenberg and Schroedinger. Two years after Davisson and Germer's confirmation of the wave theory of matter, De Broglie was awarded the Nobel prize. Davisson received the prize ten years later.

One direct result of the Davisson-Germer experiment that proved of enormous value was the development of the electron microscope which can "see" objects as small as individual protein molecules. The electron microscope today plays an important role in virus and metallurgical research.

HOW THE ELECTRON MICROSCOPE WORKS

The lenses of an electron microscope are magnetic fields. At the very top of the diagram at the left is the electron gun which shoots out a very fine pencil of charged particles. These diverge as they travel downwards until they pass through the area of the first magnetic field which bends them back into convergence and brings them to a focus. At this point, the object is placed. Where the object is dense, many electrons are absorbed; and the electron beam thus bears the imprint of the material it has traversed. A second magnetic field now diverges the beam of particles, spreading it out so that the image is magnified. A third magnetic field, called the projection coil, brings the magnified beam to a focus on a fluorescent screen which is viewed through an eyepiece. A wave is affected only by an object which is several times larger than the wave length. Sound waves are neither blocked nor affected by objects a few inches in diameter. Visible light cannot "see" objects smaller than a ten-thousandth of an inch. Electrons and hard X-rays have wave lengths in roughly the same range, but electrons are more affected by the solid media they traverse than X-rays and are therefore ideally suited to fine microscopy.

Influenza virus (spheres) magnified 60,000 times. Rudenberg first conceived the instrument to identify the virus of poliomyelitis, from which his son was suffering. RCA engineered the microscope to its present high standard.

4. TELEVISION

In spite of the years of labor of De Forest, Langmuir and other men, in spite of the fortunes that had been made and lost in wireless promotion since 1900, there were only thirty licensed broadcasting stations in the United States in 1922, sixteen years after De Forest applied for his patent on the triode. The art of radio was still in its infancy; yet 1922 was the year when fifteen-year-old Philo Farnsworth stayed after school in the small, dusty ranch town in Idaho, and drew blackboard diagrams to explain to his chemistry teacher a possible system for electronic television.

The idea of television was not new in 1922 any more than the idea of an airplane had been new in 1895 when the Wright brothers first became interested in flying. Farnsworth had read a popular science magazine account of the work done by Boris Rosing in Russia in the early 1900's. Rosing was the first to attempt a television system that used a cathode ray tube in which the electron beam struck a fluorescent screen and made a picture from a moving pinpoint of light. Since this was before De Forest developed the triode as a means to amplify feeble currents, Rosing had succeeded only in receiving a small blurred image by wire across his laboratory.

The popularly written article gave Farnsworth no technical electrical details, but it led him to speculate about a system to register a moving picture by electronic means and transmit it by radio. The plan he explained to his teacher in 1922 was already far beyond Rosing's achievement.

In 1926 Farnsworth was an office boy on a Salt Lake Community Chest Drive under George Everson. A chance conversation led Farnsworth to reveal his inventive hopes. More impressed by the boy than by the idea, Everson took him out to San Francisco to have the idea appraised by engineers. The report was so favorable that Everson organized a syndicate led by Jess McCargar of the Crocker First National Bank and raised twenty-five thousand dollars to underwrite the development. The signing of the organization papers was held up when Farnsworth admitted that he was not yet twenty-one. Everson had to call Farnsworth's mother long distance for permission to be her son's guardian. The first major contract in the television industry, therefore, bore the signature of an "infant."

Any television system works on this general principle: the picture to be transmitted is divided into a mosaic of tiny squares of light or dark. Reading from one side to the other, line beneath line, the light intensity of each little square is radio-signaled to the receiver which reassembles them in their original order and reproduces the original picture.

To do this electronically, again certain general principles must be followed. The original picture is focused into a highly-evacuated tube in which there is a screen of a few square inches, covered with photoelectric material. Areas of brightness in the picture become areas of heavy photoelectric current; darker areas give off feebler currents. The differing measure of these currents can be transmitted by radio. At the receiving end, these pulses of current create spots of light or darkness on a fluorescent screen.

The heart of Farnsworth's system lay in his camera—called the "image dissector." The picture, transformed into photoelectrons, was moved by magnetic

Television microscopy is one of the many fields of application explored by Vladimir Zworykin, television pioneer.

Zworykin of RCA invented the iconoscope, an electronic camera for television. His patents date back to the 1920's.

coils in front of a fixed electrical probe—back and forth, up and down—and the probe scanned the picture in terms of current falling on itself.

The first crude demonstration witnessed by Farnsworth's backers was late in the summer of 1928, after sixty thousand dollars had been spent. The picture was divided into almost 150 lines, the entire picture being completely scanned thirty times a second.

During the early thirties, the clarity of Farnsworth's image increased and Philco took over the development. Farnsworth put on a demonstration for the Franklin Institute, producing a clear moving image on a screen slightly larger than a square foot. Two years later, two hundred and fifty thousand dollars had been spent and Philco gave up, realizing that commercial television was still a long way off.

Farnsworth's backers were unable to sell the patents to RCA and Paramount in 1938 because the expenses of the development had pushed the price to over a million dollars. The syndicate then decided to start commercialization by themselves and bought the Capehart Corp. of Fort Wayne, Indiana, for their manufacturing plant. The war, in 1941, put an end to any immediate prospects for commercial television and the company went into the production of radar devices.

However, their patent position in television was so sound that their only rival in the field was the patent structure of RCA built upon the work of Vladimir Zworykin. Farnsworth's start in television dated from a brief popular article that described the work of Boris Rosing. Zworykin's connection with Rosing had been much closer: as a graduate student, before the Russian Revolution, he had been Rosing's assistant.

Zworykin came to America and, in 1920, joined the Westinghouse staff just at the point when it was being reorganized to undertake radio research. There was no interest in television and he resigned. In February, 1923, only a few months after Farnsworth's first blackboard demonstration out in Idaho, Zworykin found a sympathetic ear in Samuel Kintner, the new manager of the Westinghouse research department. Zworykin got permission to go ahead, but not until five years later, in 1928, was he able to work out the principles for his television camera called the "iconoscope." This was as revolutionary a conception as Farnsworth's.

In Zworykin's system the picture to be transmitted was shone into a disc of mica covered with pinpoint islands of photo-electric material. A narrow electron beam, no wider than any of the dots, scanned this mosaic, detecting the feeble or intense emissions.

The importance of Zworykin's work was recognized by David Sarnoff of RCA which, in 1930, took over the radio research laboratories of GE and Westinghouse. For the first time, Zworykin received large-scale assistance. By 1939, $9,253,723 had been spent on developing television by RCA—nine times the amount put up by Farnsworth and his backers.

Zworykin and Farnsworth had both been pioneering in the same field, and though their points of view were different, it was inevitable that the two companies had to reach a cross-licensing arrangement.

During World War II, techniques of instrumentation perfected E. E. Armstrong's system of frequency modulation which was admirably suited for television's ultra-high frequencies. By the end of the war, television was able to go commercial in a state that was technically far advanced when compared with radio broadcasting twenty-five years earlier.

Cathode ray tubes, descendants of Crookes' tube, are the basic tool of modern electronics. At the far left is an electron gun, and immediately adjacent is the region where the electron intensity is modulated by an incoming signal. Two sets of deflection plates, at right angles to each other, make the beam sweep up and down, across and back.

The one-man, fully mechanized, push-button, entirely automatic factory, as imagined unhappily by artist Joseph Low.

THE SECOND INDUSTRIAL REVOLUTION

Originally, mechanical invention gave extra hands to undermanned America in its war against the wilderness. Once started, the flow of invention never ceased. Long after the geographical frontiers had been reached, settled, and heavily populated, the productivity of the American individual continued to increase until by 1900 each American each year was turning out more consumer goods than he had the year before. In the decade between 1939 and 1948 the per capita productivity of Americans increased thirty-two per cent. A large part of this is said to be due to the development of the electronics industry.

By 1951, the electronics industry in the United States was estimated at two and a half billion dollars, five times as large as it had been in 1940. Its growth rivaled that of American chemistry. In 1940, the half-billion-dollar American electronics industry had been mostly devoted to the manufacture of radio tubes and receiving sets. A decade later, television and radio accounted for two billion dollars, the remaining half billion was spread over a wide variety of industrial applications so profound in their ultimate meaning that the leading theorists of the design of electronic equipment predicted that the accelerating application of electronics would create a second Industrial Revolution—as wide-reaching in social effect as the steam engine in the preceding century.

De Forest's triode turned out to have as many applications as the lever. During World War II every nation involved on both sides developed systems of radio location. The American system was called radar—radio detection and ranging—and traced its inception back to 1926 when Breit and Tuve observed the reflection of short-wave radio signals back from the ionized upper layer of the earth's atmosphere.

Michelson's apparatus for measuring the speed of light was so delicate that only a master experimentalist could operate it. The 1950 radio-locater, whether mounted on an airliner, a battleship, an air field, or a ferry boat, measured the speed of light by electrical means and required little more training than was needed to drive an automobile.

The principle of the radio-locater is this: a transmitter sends out a radio signal in pulses of high-frequency radiation. These pulses travel in a straight line with the speed of light and are reflected by solid objects. The transmitter is coupled with a receiver that picks up the reflected pulse. The time taken for the pulse to go out and return, multiplied by the speed of light, gives the distance to the object and back. The instrument itself does the calculation, and the operator reads off the distance of the reflecting object. After the war, in which radar proved of inestimable value, it seemed almost anticlimactic when some U. S. Army Signal Corps workers aimed a radar apparatus at the moon. The signal returned within a few seconds and the moon's position was measured with an accuracy undreamed of before.

Twenty years is said to be the average time for a new mechanical invention to find its market. Fifty years is about the average time taken for the most specialized research equipment in "pure" physics to become a standard industrial tool.

Fifty years passed between the time of Joseph Henry's experiments and the introduction of the practical alternating-current transformer in the 1880's. Bunsen and Kirchoff's famous spectroscopic experiments of the 1860's foreshadowed the use of the spectroscope by the commercial laboratories beginning with the 1920's. The 1950's began to see industrial applications for the instruments that had been devised for the physical researchers of the early 1900's—the experiments which revolutionized phys-

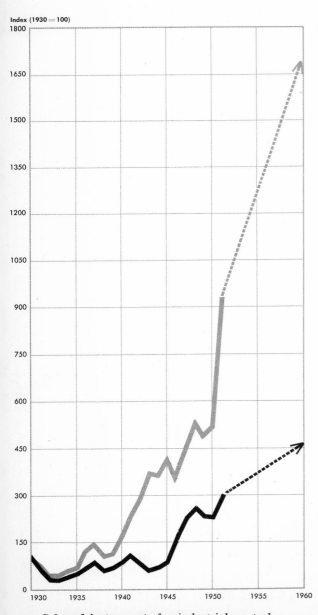

Index (1930 = 100)

Sales of instruments for industrial control (upper line) have increased far more rapidly than outlay for U.S. plant equipment.

ics with the introduction of the electron.

Forty years of cosmic ray research since 1911 developed a variety of ingenious electronic techniques for counting the electric impulses detected by Geiger counters. The Geiger counter, purchasable in the sporting goods establishment of Abercrombie and Fitch in 1950, started life as a detector of high-energy invisible particles—either those emitted by radioactive substances or cosmic rays. The Geiger counter, usually a few inches long, is a gas-filled tube consisting of a cylinder with a wire along its axis. A high-energy particle passing through such a tube creates a momentary flurry of ionization in the gas which is detected as an electrical impulse. Counting circuit techniques became highly developed. Circuits were needed which could not only add pulses at the rate of a million a minute, but could simultaneously subtract those pulses which did not fall into certain categories. Moreover, other counting circuits could be designed to detect every tenth, thousandth or ten thousandth pulse, as the experimenter required.

While physicists were developing these "coincidence" and "anti-coincidence" counters, their circuit techniques were being used to develop elaborate electronic computing machines which could add and subtract numbers, in the form of electric pulses, with such rapidity that even a multi-numbered multiplication, repeated addition, could be performed faster than by other means. Complicated integrations, a more complicated form of addition, could also be performed, as well as long division, repeated subtraction, and differentiation, which is a highly complicated subtraction.

Special forms of these electronic pulse-counting computers were used during the Second World War for range-finding by radar, and after the war, in more complicated forms, by the Census Department for its compilations of statistics, by insurance companies,

The McMurrey Refining Company near Tyler, Texas, is an examp

and by a variety of other industrial firms in payroll, marketing, and inventory compilations.

It is in this area that Norbert Wiener of MIT, one of the pioneers in the theory of electron control circuits, saw the greatest social impact by the art of electronics. Two years after the appearance of Wiener's *The Human Use of Human Beings, Fortune* magazine said, in January, 1952: "There is now no doubt that the United States is on the threshold of an era in which mass production techniques will be applied to the routine processing of paper work on the same scale that such techniques have been applied to the manufacture of goods . . . Perhaps the major block to fast

The control panel (below) represents the sequence of operations, each step having its own panel unit.

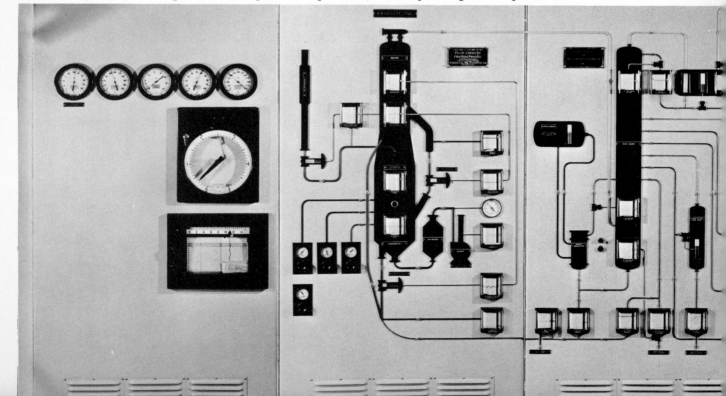

machine control of a continuous process. Only a few men run it.

the *click* of the broken circuit was the signal to start a second reaction; and this system was followed down the line from the introduction of raw material to the finished product.

In many plants, every stage of production was monitored by electron circuits. The functions of the specialized plant foremen and technical workers were being replaced by electrical circuits. Mechanization was being advanced to the point where it needed a new name—automation.

The introduction of steam power replaced the muscular power of unskilled labor. The introduction of electronics, Wiener said, threatens the next higher level of workers—the skilled man who receives his salary for his judgment. Great shifts in employment will have to be made. In the nineteenth century these shifts were disastrous, indirectly causing wars and revolutions. In the twentieth century, technologists warned that unless American society made a conscious effort to cushion the effects of this shift, only the most dire social consequences could result to negate the undeniable long-range benefit. The electronic replacement of skilled human judgment in the 1950's is only the beginning; but with the past as guide, the future may be guessed.

"It is perfectly clear," wrote Wiener, "that this will produce an unemployment situation in comparison with which . . . the depression of the thirties will seem a joke . . . thus the new industrial revolution is a two-edged sword. It may be used for the benefit of humanity, assuming that humanity survives long enough to enter a period in which such benefit is possible. If, however, we proceed along the clear and obvious lines of our traditional behavior, and follow our traditional worship of progress and the fifth freedom—the freedom to exploit—it is practically certain that we shall have to face a decade more of ruin and despair."

development of business computers is the human, or more specifically the accountant, mind."

The office staff of America increased from three to eight million from 1920 to 1952. Wiener predicted that this "elimination of excessive clerical steps" could result in the same kind of economic dislocation that came when the steam engine was introduced to eliminate "excessive human physical labor."

During the years that computers were penetrating the American business office, electronic devices were being used in many stages of industrial processes. In chemistry, electronic circuits were designed to turn off a reaction when it had reached a certain stage, and

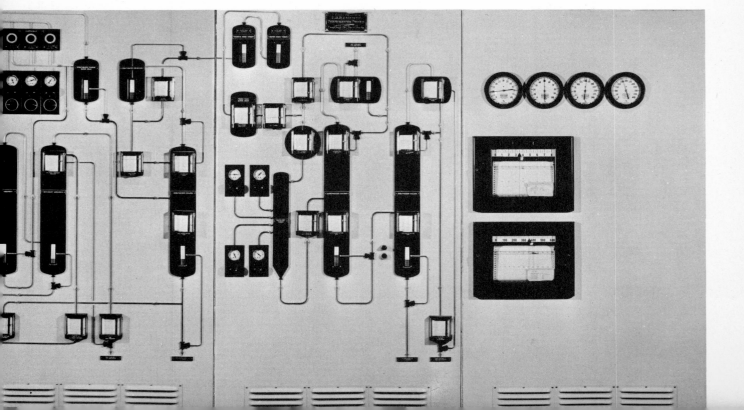

The mass spectrometer, shown above in principle, separates atomic nuclei of different weights. If a mixture of many nuclei is ejected from a common source (left) all with the same velocity, a magnetic field pointing into the plane of the paper will make them curve in arcs of different radii. At the far right, separate collectors capture the fractions that are sorted out. The existence of isotopes was demonstrated by such an apparatus. It became a tool for the large-scale separation of isotopes of uranium to produce fissionable uranium 235.

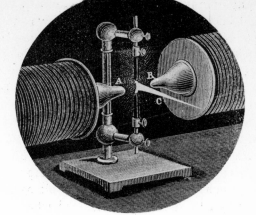

Deflection of charged particles was shown to 19th-century physics students by placing an arc between the pole pieces (A, B) of a magnet. A flame of charged particles (C) shot out at 90°.

NUCLEONICS

1. UNFASHIONABLE PHYSICS

Less capricious than the changes in fashion of women's clothing, but just as real, are the changes in popularity of the various fields of scientific research. When certain fresh lines of inquiry seem more obviously promising than others, scientists all over the world swarm in to see what nuggets of new information can be picked. Older fields of inquiry fall out of favor.

In the first three decades of the twentieth century, most physicists were busily trying to explain the world of atomic matter in terms of the two immutable particles: the negatively charged electron and the comparatively ponderous, positively charged proton. The nuclei of atoms were considered to be tightly packed conglomerations of protons and electrons (although no explanation was offered as to how these could exist so close together without exploding), while around each such nucleus electrons rotated in rigorously prescribed orbits. Interest focused on these outer electrons and their behavior; chemical combination depended on them only, and the theories of Bohr, Schroedinger, and De Broglie were devoted to this exterior structure. Until 1930, the favorite instrument of physics research was the spectrograph; ninety per cent of each issue of *The Physical Review* was devoted to spectrographic analyses of the exterior structure of atoms. Another approach to this same problem was being developed by I. I. Rabi, whose "molecular beam" technique would eventually win him a Nobel prize. The study of the nucleus was pursued by very few people; nuclear physics was decidedly unfashionable.   One man who did not follow the popular trend was Ernest Rutherford of Cambridge University, who had studied radioactivity almost from its first discovery. He had received the Nobel prize with Soddy in 1908 "for his investigations into the disintegration of elements and the chemistry of radioactive substances." He observed the effect of radioactivity on various gases.

Rutherford's apparatus was very simple: a sample of radioactive material was placed inside a small box. A pinhole in one wall of the box passed a fine stream of radioactive emanation. This box could be moved along the length of a gas-filled cylinder in which it was placed. A thin metal foil formed a "window" at one end of this cylinder; and just outside this window was a small fluorescent screen which gleamed with pinpoints of light every time it was struck by the particles in the radioactive emanation.

The experiment consisted of moving the box through the gas-filled cylinder away from the fluorescent screen until no pinpoints of light could be seen. This distance was called the "range" of the particles in that particular gas. In 1919, Rutherford discovered that the "range" in nitrogen was considerably longer than for any other gas; so much longer that the experiment did not make sense. When he checked his results carefully, he found that the fluorescent screen was being pinpointed with light by particles that were not part of the radioactive emanation at all, but by protons.

Rutherford therefore made this assumption: when alpha particles collided directly with nitrogen nuclei, an entirely new nucleus was created which was unstable and disintegrated into a form of oxygen and ordinary hydrogen. It was this ejected hydrogen which he was detecting in the form of high-speed protons. This historic experiment was the first man-made nuclear transmutation.

In spite of the importance of Rutherford's work, very few of the younger physicists were inspired to leave the fashionable fields of atomic physics. Nevertheless, a small number of physicists continued to work on transmutations. Information was slowly amassed that suddenly revealed its meaning in 1932, an explosive year in physics. Three new types of elementary particles were discovered—the neutron, the deuteron, and the positron.

Early that year, Botha and Becker in Germany bombarded a plate of beryllium with alpha particles. A very high energy radiation was produced and thought to be gamma rays. The Joliot-Curies repeated the experiment and allowed the radiation to fall on paraffin which had a high carbon content. The irradiated paraffin produced high energy protons. But the Joliot-Curies, like the Germans, still ascribed the cause to gamma rays. The same experiment was repeated a third time by Chadwick in England, one of Rutherford's disciples. Chadwick refused to accept gamma rays as the agency for the expulsion of protons from paraffin. He demonstrated that the only way to explain what was happening was to make the revolutionary assumption that the beryllium, bombarded by alpha particles, was producing a new particle that had the same mass as the proton but no electrical charge. There had never been, in nature, a fundamental particle that was electrically neutral, but subsequent experiment that same year proved Chadwick's contention, and in 1935 he received the Nobel prize for his discovery of the neutron.

In 1929, a California physicist, E. O. Lawrence, had become impatient with the primitiveness of nuclear research. Physicists had to borrow bits of radioactive material from cancer hospitals, and these could be borrowed for only a few hours at a time. Out in California, over the next few years, Lawrence perfected an instrument which would produce concentrated streams of elementary particles without the cost of elaborate high-voltage installations. The instrument, because of the circular path which the projectiles had to follow, was subsequently called the cyclotron.

In 1932 the astronomical study of hydrogen spectra seemed to indicate certain anomalies which could be explained only if there were still another unknown form of hydrogen. Harold C. Urey of Columbia University made an exhaustive study and that year announced the existence of "heavy" hydrogen or deuterium. Its nucleus, twice as heavy as the proton of ordinary hydrogen, seemed to be a combination of a proton and the recently announced neutron of Chadwick. This indicated that the atomic nucleus was composed only of protons and neutrons. The puzzling question of nuclear electrons was answered: there were none. The neutron solved the most pressing problem of the nucleus. The study of atomic spectra suddenly became unfashionable, the spectrographs were turned over to undergraduate students, and nuclear physics suddenly became high style. Before the end of the year, however, the promised clarity was confused by the discovery of still a third particle, the positron.

Several years before, a brilliant young English theoretical physicist, Dirac, had developed a new theory of the electron that promised great results, but had one serious flaw. This weakness in the theory could not be removed no matter how hard Dirac and others tried to revise his equations. The attempted doctoring of Dirac's theory came to a halt in 1932 when Carl Anderson of California announced the results of some cosmic ray studies.

The flaw in Dirac's theory was that it demanded the existence of a positive electron. The flaw turned out to be the theory's greatest triumph, for that year Carl Anderson found the particle in nature. Although the positron's existence satisfied Dirac's equation, at the moment it satisfied nothing else, and physicists were unable to accommodate it until Robert Oppenheimer of California came up with the theory of "pair production." A photon passing close to a nucleus could spontaneously transform itself into an electron and a positron. Cloud chamber experiments proved Oppenheimer correct and also showed that the reverse could happen: a positron and an electron, when very close, could annihilate each other and become a single packet of radiant energy.

In 1932, Adolf Hitler was catapulting to power in Germany, Franklin D. Roosevelt was elected President of the United States, but the events that were to have the most far-reaching effects on human history took place in physics laboratories. The throb of vacuum pumps and the squeal of chalk moving on blackboards were to prove more insistent than the blare of radio loudspeakers.

The first two cyclotron chambers ever built were tried just after classes reassembled from the Christmas holidays of 1929 at the University of California. They were designed for a magnet with a 4-inch pole piece. The first one (left) was made of window pane, brass scrap, and sealing wax. The improved model was a collapsed laboratory flask silvered on the inside. Prof.

E. O. Lawrence was looking for a means to obtain high-energy nuclear particles using small installations and low voltages. Twenty-five years later, the descendants of these original models were among the most massive, most expensive, and complicated devices ever built for scientific research. Like the giant telescopes, cyclotrons helped develop the "research team" in science.

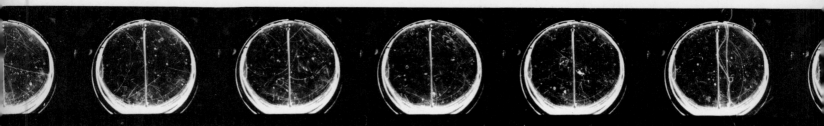

Cloud chamber photographs, made at ten-second intervals, reveal the tracks made by charged nuclear particles.

2. THE CHEMISTRY OF THE NUCLEUS

Irene and John-Frederic Joliot-Curie had missed out on the discovery of the neutron in 1932, but just two years later they stumbled on something equally important. They were bombarding a thin disc of nonradioactive aluminum with alpha particles. By accident, their radioactivity recorders remained in operation near the aluminum even after they had removed the alpha particle source. To their surprise, the instruments showed that some kind of emanation was still coming from the aluminum foil.

Their first guess was that the aluminum had somehow become contaminated, but that possibility was soon discarded. They then tested the emanation and found an even greater surprise—the aluminum disc was giving off none of the three types of ordinary radioactive rays, but was producing *positive* electrons, the very positrons which had been discovered two years earlier.

The Joliot-Curies repeated their experiment and found the same result. For the first time in the history of science, an element had been made radioactive in the laboratory. Ever since Becquerel's discovery in 1896 it had been assumed that radioactivity existed in a very few massive elements. Now, it seemed, radioactivity could actually be induced. The discovery that positrons played a role in nuclear transformations was equally important.

They went further and tried to understand what must have happened: the alpha particle—helium—had not only collided with an aluminum nucleus, it must have stuck to it and *combined* with it to form something that was different from either one. The nature of the newly created nucleus could be guessed by counting up the particles that had combined—it had to be phosphorus. The aluminum foil was dissolved in hydrochloric acid, and chemical tests proved the presence of traces of phosphorus. When the aluminum and phosphorus-bearing fractions were completely separated, it was found that all the radioactivity went along with the phosphorus fraction. This was proof of their contention. They also found

that the synthesized radioactive phosphorus was continuing to disintegrate—it was changing into silicon.

At about this time, E. O. Lawrence in California began to use the cyclotron for heavy radiation of a large number of elements. He and his co-workers were able to create and identify radioactive sodium, iodine, and many others. All of these "artificial" radioactive substances lost their radioactivity very quickly—some in a matter of seconds, some in a matter of days. It now became clear why light radioactive elements had never before been found in nature. They must all have existed at some time long past. Their radioactive lives were so short, however, that they had all disappeared eons ago. The only radioactivity still left on earth was in the very long-lived elements like uranium, thorium, and radium.

Lawrence's experiments with the cyclotron consisted of bombarding the natural elements with protons. Popular newspaper accounts made them sound like experiments in destruction. Actually, since the proton is one of the fundamental building blocks of the nucleus, these were experiments in *construction*. Physicists were adding nuclear blocks, one at a time, to see the differences created by each addition. Newspaper accounts stressed the lethal-sounding high voltages, almost as if bigness itself were the aim, as if the various cyclotron laboratories were engaged in a mammoth contest to out-voltage each other. The truth was that these high voltages were required to make the protons penetrate the enormous barriers of the nucleus.

Over a period of five years, from 1934 to 1939, the information amassed by the cyclotrons and similar devices amounted to a richly detailed story, and it was possible to discern some of the fundamental laws which governed the structure of the nucleus, and how nuclear particles combined. Nuclear chemistry had come into being.

It was apparent that the nucleus was composed of protons and neutrons tightly packed together. The force that held these particles in combination was unknown. But physicists were able to say how much energy was required to put a nucleus together. By the same token, this was the amount of energy that could be released if the nucleus were to be taken apart. The actual calculation was ordinary arithmetic.

The simplest nucleus was hydrogen—only one proton. The next simplest was "heavy" hydrogen—one proton and one neutron. The sum of their masses as free particles was 2.0171 units. The mass of the two in combination as the "heavy" hydrogen nucleus was 2.0147 units, which meant that the *combination was lighter than the sum of the separate particles* by .0024 units. Another way of saying it is that .0024 units of mass had been *annihilated* when the two had come together. This number—the slight discrepancy between the two weights—was one of the most revealing numbers in nature; it was the *direct measure of the energy required to bring a neutron and proton into combination.*

This kind of nuclear bookkeeping was then applied to helium which consisted of two protons and two neutrons. The process was continued for every element known, and in every case the nucleus was lighter than the sum of the particles it contained.

It was found that the nuclei requiring the greatest amounts of energy—and therefore the most stable— were those of intermediate weight. The heaviest elements and the lightest proved to be the most unstable in theory, as they were in actual fact.

Besides the unknown nuclear force which held the particles together, there was another force tending to disrupt them. This was the simple law of electrical repulsion.

The larger the nucleus, the more particles it contained, the more important became this disruptive force. The theory said that there would be a critical size to the nucleus beyond which this force of disruption would be even more powerful than the force holding the particles together. Any nucleus with a diameter larger than this would explode.

Calculations showed that this limit was reached by the most massive elements—uranium and thorium. Because they were on the verge of disruption, they were highly unstable. Every so often, said the theory, one of these nuclei would have to eject enough mass from itself to come down to a safer limit of size. These ejected particles were those which had been called the "radioactive emanations"; and by 1939, "natural" radioactivity—of radium, uranium, and thorium—at last was seen to be nothing more than this explosive self-regulation of unstable nuclei.

In 1939, over forty-five years of study of radioactivity had been completed; and at last a true semblance of order seemed about to emerge.

At least in physics, there was the same sense of serenity about the future as physicists had felt in 1893—before Becquerel, Roentgen, and J. J. Thomson had pulled the foundations from beneath everything that was enshrined in belief. There was, however, this difference: in 1939, physicists were not operating under incorrect information—they just did not know that their correct information was loaded.

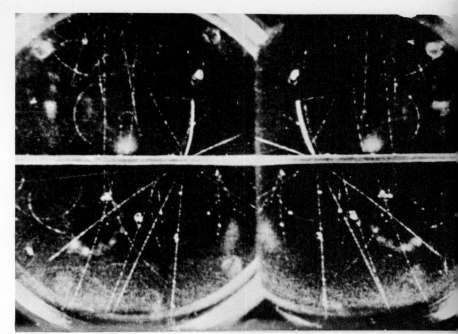

The meson, a nuclear particle having mass intermediate between the electron and the proton, was found in these cloud chamber pictures by Anderson and Neddermeyer in 1936.

Million-volt X-rays were used to fragment atomic nuclei. Such enormous voltages were required to overcome the forces which hold the atomic nucleus together. Men learn how things are put together only by taking them apart.

411

Spiral nebula in *Coma Berenices* seen edge on. Stars are the crucibles for the chemistry of nuclear particles.

3. STAR LIFE

Radioactivity of the heavy elements was not the only question that was clarified by the studies of nuclear chemistry in the decade of the 1930's. Another great success was the brilliant explanation advanced for the constitution of the stars.

By 1939 it was possible to explain the evolution of stars in such a way that one could offer answers to the following questions:

1. Which stars are old and which stars are new?

2. Where does a star get the energy which it radiates?

3. How does the sun shine?

The names of American astrophysicists who worked out most of these solutions were Arnold Bethe of Cornell, George Gamow, and Edward Teller of George Washington University. Other Americans were Zwicky and Critchfield. Important contributions were made by Von Weizacker of Germany and Landau of Russia.

It was in 1939 than Gamow and Teller added the

last pieces to the puzzle; and their information made it possible to tell the story of the stars from the beginning.

Every star begins, so runs the theory, with a mass of cool gas containing all the known elements, but mostly hydrogen. This mass may be four times that of the sun, but spread in a vast cloud far more rarefied than the earth's atmosphere.

Due to the force of gravitation, this nebulous floating mass imperceptibly begins to contract. Since the atoms of the cloud collide with each other more and more frequently, this slow contraction over eons raises the temperature of the massive gas cloud and it begins to glow faintly in the midnight darkness of star-lit space.

The outer atmosphere of such a gassy star would still seem almost a vacuum to an earth dweller. At the very center, however, the temperature may climb to a million degrees, which is where the range of nuclear chemistry begins. Most of the electrons of the atoms in this hot center zone have been ripped away, leaving only the nuclei.

Nevertheless, even at a million degrees, the only particles with sufficient energy to react with each other are the protons—the hydrogen nuclei. They collide at terrific speeds. Instead of bouncing apart like billiard balls as they did at lower temperatures, they begin sticking together to form the heavy hydrogen nucleus—the deuteron, emitting positive electrons as a by-product.

When enough heavy hydrogen has been created, the protons begin to attack it too. Protons collide with the deuterons to form helium, a violent reaction that gives off radiation. Radiation on the way out of the star loses energy through billions of "Compton effect" collisions and so, from the outside, the star still appears a dull red.

When the escaping radiation becomes sufficiently intense, the pressure of this light on the outer layers of the gas cloud cancels out the contracting force of gravitation, and contraction ceases.

For millions of years, perhaps, the red giant holds its size while the hydrogen furnace glows in the interior. When the deuterium is finally consumed, radiation ceases, and the star contracts again. The temperature climbs from a million to ten million degrees, where now another nuclear reaction begins to take place.

At this high temperature, the protons have enough energy to smash deep into the core of the lithium nucleus, seven times as heavy as hydrogen. Now the protons stick to lithium nuclei, and the resulting unstable mass bursts apart into two helium nuclei, again giving out tremendous radiant energy. Once again the contraction of the red giant—much brighter now—comes to a halt until all the lithium is consumed.

Then for the third time, the slow contraction begins, causing still higher temperatures, and the protons at the core hurtle back and forth with greater energies than before. They soon begin to attack the elements next heavier than lithium—beryllium and boron. The smashing of the beryllium produces lithium and helium; the smashing of boron produces carbon. It is in this state that the star begins to pulsate, swelling and contracting in regular waves as the outward pressure of radiation oscillates against the contracting force of gravitation. In this state, the star is in the Cepheid class.

When this reaction first begins, the oscillation takes place very rapidly; but as the temperature climbs, the pulsations slow down. These were the stars used as "standard candles" by Harlow Shapley, and the 1939 theories of nuclear chemistry gave brilliant support to what had been only a shrewd guess decades earlier.

Cosmic eons pass for the star in this state, but eventually the light elements like lithium, boron, beryllium are also consumed, and the great contraction continues. In terms of mass, the next elements to be vulnerable to the attack of the smashing protons are carbon and nitrogen; yet when the triggering temperature is reached, an entirely new type of reaction takes place. Instead of the heavier elements being consumed by hydrogen, it has now become the turn of the hydrogen—using carbon and nitrogen as catalysts—to be itself consumed to form helium.

In this stage, the temperature of the star's core is twenty million degrees. Its outer appearance is no longer red and diffuse. It glows hard, brilliant, whitish yellow, and has contracted to a hundredth of its original size. During the length of the carbon-nitrogen cycle, contraction completely ceases; and the star glows for billions and billions of years until all the hydrogen is consumed.

This is the main period of a star's life; our sun is in this stage right now and it is the last stage of a star before its ultimate slow death. After the hydrogen is consumed, the white-hot star contracts still further until it shrinks to the point where the particles are crushed together to form a neutral "stone" of inconceivable density. The Dark Companion of Sirius, which aroused so much interest at the turn of the century, is just such a dying star—only a little over twice as large as it will be at the end.

With all the innocence of a judge signing a death warrant, unaware that eventually it is to be used on himself, physicists in 1939 discussed the theoretical case of the dying Companion as the end result of the kind of explosions that could be created by nuclear chemistry. To physicists, explosive nuclear chemistry made perfect sense on the sun and in the distant stars; but to a man, that year, they all believed that "it can't happen here."

Enrico Fermi, born in Rome 1901, Nobel Laureate 1938 when he came to the United States. He was already one of the world's leading physicists when he began research into the possibilities of a nuclear chain reaction.

THE
CHAIN REACTION: 1

"On January 16, 1939, Niels Bohr of Copenhagen, Denmark, arrived in this country to spend several months in Princeton, New Jersey," wrote Henry Smyth in his book, *Atomic Energy for Military Purposes,* and was particularly anxious to discuss some abstract problems with Einstein. Just before Bohr left Denmark, two of his colleagues, German refugees O. R. Frisch and L. Meitner, had told him their guess that the absorption of a neutron by a uranium nucleus sometimes caused that nucleus to split into approximately equal parts with the release of an enormous amount of energy.

With that guess, the drums of history began to roll. Bohr went to Princeton and told J. A. Wheeler what Frisch and Meitner had said. Wheeler discussed it with others as an interesting development in nuclear physics. The laboratory gossip spread to New York within the next few days, where it was discussed in the seminar rooms and faculty offices of Columbia University. To Enrico Fermi, a short, quick-moving man with suave gray eyes and a sudden, shy smile, the news had a special meaning.

A few years earlier, Fermi had performed some experiments for which he had been able to give only a tentative explanation.

The ordinary chemical properties of atoms and molecules depend on the number of electrons rotating about each nucleus. This number, in turn, depends on the number of protons in the nucleus. If an extra neutron were added to the nucleus, the mass would be increased by one unit, but the chemical properties would be unchanged; the new heavier nucleus is an "isotope" of the old one. If, on the other hand, a proton were added to a nucleus, not only did the mass change by one unit, but an additional electron was now needed to balance the added positive charge. This additional electron made the chemical properties of the new atom very different from what they had been before. The new atom is not an isotope, but another element; an added proton means transmutation.

In 1934, Fermi had bombarded some heavy radioactive nuclei and thought that he had created several elements heavier than uranium—elements that had not existed in nature. Fermi had called them *trans-uranic* elements. In the light of Bohr's 1939 news, it occurred to Fermi that instead of creating trans-uranic ele-

ments, he had split the uranium nucleus into halves just as Frisch and Meitner had suggested. Such a nuclear explosion ought to be accompanied by a number of other nuclear fragments—perhaps other neutrons.

That very year, 1939, physicists like George Gamow were saying that the public was wrong to expect that usable energy could ever be released from atomic nuclei by bombardment in cyclotrons. While a single collision between a neutron and a nucleus could release relatively large amounts of energy, much more energy was lost by other neutrons that hit nothing at all. The cyclotron bombardments had only academic interest. Usable nuclear energy would be a possibility only in the unlikely event that a reaction would be found where several neutrons were produced for every collision that took place. Only in that way could every nuclear collision release enough neutrons to create several more collisions and so on—in a chain reaction.

As soon as Fermi heard the report from Princeton, he sensed that the "unlikely event" was at hand. He discussed the matter with John Dunning and George Pegram and arranged for a preliminary experiment to be made at once. He then went down to Princeton to speak personally to Bohr, an old friend, with the understanding that they would go to Washington where, on January 26th, the American Physical Society was scheduled to hold its winter meeting. Dunning remained behind at Columbia to make the preliminary experiment. Dunning, then in his thirties, was a Montana radio engineer turned physicist. He worked around the clock in the Pupin Laboratory for several days and performed the first experiment in America that demonstrated the actuality of this nuclear split—called *fission*.

Dunning arrived in Washington toward the end of the conference and read his report. To dramatize his finding, newspapers printed their usual descriptions of nuclear experiments: if a certain small amount of uranium were to undergo fission, an explosion could occur that would blast a crater as wide as the distance between New York and Patchogue, Long Island. This time the typewriters beat out a rhythm that jibed with the fateful drumbeat no one yet could hear.

However, Dunning did not have any evidence that neutrons were being emitted with each reaction; and this was exactly what Fermi still wanted to know.

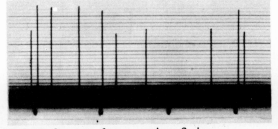

Pulses of energy from uranium fission recorded on an oscillograph.

Three other laboratories attempted the same experiment, and three weeks later *The Physical Review* contained four other articles on the subject. By the end of 1939, over one hundred scientific papers on nuclear fission appeared in America alone.

The first controlled chain reaction of nuclear fission was put into operation in Chicago under Fermi's lead on December 2, 1942. The lattice arrangement of uranium and graphite was called the "pile."

Nuclear reactors, ten years later, at Brookhaven, were already mammoth installations. The wall (left) shields a great "pile." The round clamped doors shut out neutrons. The open door (lower left) permits experimentation.

2. THE PILE

Fermi, in cooperation with Leo Szilard, Herbert Anderson, a graduate student, and Walter Zinn, a part-time researcher, began experiments to determine whether or not there was a fruitful emission of neutrons with each fission. If there were only one per fission, the reaction would just sustain itself. If there were two neutrons, the chain reaction was possible. Other laboratories undertook similar experiments. By June, 1940, the pooled knowledge actually could describe the various types of fission, the energy needs for the neutron to make this fission take place, and—more important—that the number of neutrons emitted per fission were, in the official government report made in 1945: "between one and three."

In the meantime, the government had been approached as early as March, 1939, when George Pegram of Columbia arranged for Fermi to discuss the matter with the Navy. The Navy expressed interest, but nothing more. Leo Szilard approached Einstein in July, and Einstein, in turn, sent a communication to President Roosevelt. In November of that year, a meeting took place between several scientists and representatives of the ordnance divisions of the armed services—Colonel Adamson and Commander Hoover.

Money began to be appropriated in small amounts by the government, and the project became secret. In November, 1940, forty thousand dollars was assigned to Columbia for research on the materials and conditions necessary for a controlled chain reaction—a nuclear power plant.

By the following summer, 1941, an elaborate cubic structure of uranium and graphite had been set up at Columbia, a "pile" eight feet on a side. Seven tons of uranium oxide were sealed in iron containers. They were disposed in blocks among the array of carbon bricks which served to slow down the neutrons until they had the right energy to be captured. The research team was led by Fermi. His assistants were Herbert Anderson, Walter Zinn, George Weil, and Bernard Feld. They reported that their pile could not be made self-generating without greater purity of materials. Their work was checked by a Princeton team under S. K. Allison.

Six months later, in January, 1942, the Columbia and Princeton teams were both moved to Chicago where they combined forces. On the floor of a squash court under the west stands of Stagg Field of Chicago University, a new pile was built with improved materials containing six tons of uranium. On December 2, 1942, the complicated array of monitoring instruments told the scientists that something unusual was happening. The random click of the counters came faster and faster. The pile was actually operating. For

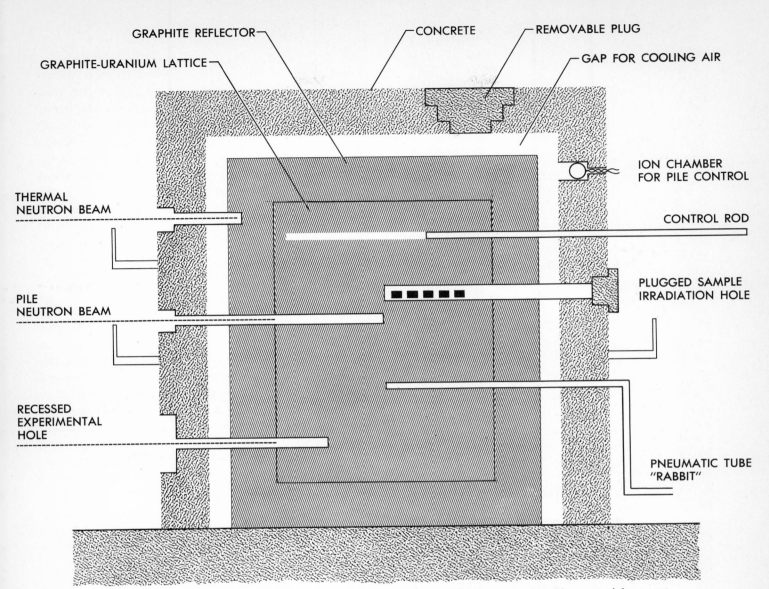

GRAPHITE REFLECTOR

GRAPHITE-URANIUM LATTICE

CONCRETE

REMOVABLE PLUG

GAP FOR COOLING AIR

THERMAL NEUTRON BEAM

ION CHAMBER FOR PILE CONTROL

CONTROL ROD

PILE NEUTRON BEAM

PLUGGED SAMPLE IRRADIATION HOLE

RECESSED EXPERIMENTAL HOLE

PNEUMATIC TUBE "RABBIT"

Uranium and graphite form the heart of the experimental pile shown in the diagram. Slow neutrons are captured by the nuclei of one of the uranium isotopes which explode, giving off several fast neutrons. The graphite slows these fast neutrons up enough so that they can be captured again.

A control rod of neutron-absorbing material can cut down the reaction when an ion chamber shows the rate is too high. There are openings into the pile for researchers to test the fast (pile), or the slow (thermal) neutrons. The pile is air-cooled, and encased within concrete walls.

the first time in the recorded history of this planet at least, human beings were producing power in the same way that energy was produced in the stars. The first yield was only half a watt, then in ten days, the power output was 200 watts; later it was to be measured in kilowatts.

The chain reaction worked. The theory of fission was clear. The materials were available to build a bomb. All that was needed was two billion dollars worth of the most brilliant engineering in the history of science.

From Chicago the main effort now moved elsewhere—to California, to Tennessee, to Hanford, Washington. The most important names in American science were added to the roster of active participants: I. I. Rabi, Harold Urey, J. A. Wheeler, the two Comp-

ton brothers, James Conant, J. R. Oppenheimer, E. O. Lawrence, Lee DuBridge, and E. Teller. On July 16, 1945, a news release from the U. S. War Department said:

"Mankind's successful transition to a new age, the Atomic Age, was ushered in July 16, 1945, before the eyes of a tense group of renowned scientists and military men gathered in the desert lands of New Mexico to witness the first end results of their $2,000,000,-000 effort. Here in a remote section of the Alamogordo Air Base, 120 miles southeast of Albuquerque, the first man-made atomic explosion, the outstanding achievement of nuclear science, was achieved at 5:30 A.M. of that day. Darkening heavens, pouring forth rain and lightning immediately up to the zero hour, heightened the drama. . . .

3. MAGNIFICENT, STUPENDOUS AND TERRIFYING

"This phase of the Atomic Bomb project, which is headed by Major General Leslie R. Groves, was under the direction of Dr. J. R. Oppenheimer, theoretical physicist of the University of California. He is to be credited with achieving the implementation of atomic energy for military purposes.

"Final assembly of the atomic bomb began on the night of July 12, in an old ranch house. As various component assemblies arrived from distant points, tension among the scientists rose to an increasing pitch. . . . During the final assembly, a bad few minutes developed when the assembly of an important section of the bomb was delayed. The entire unit was machine tooled to the finest measurement. . . . The insertion was partially completed when it apparently wedged tighter and would go no farther. Dr. Bacher, of Cornell, however, was undismayed and reassurred the group that time would solve the problem. In three minutes' time . . . the assembly was completed without further incident.

"On Saturday, July 14, the unit which was to determine the success or failure of the entire project was elevated to the top of a steel tower. All that day and the next, the job of preparation went on . . . amid lightning flashes and peals of thunder. . . . Tension reached a tremendous pitch in the control room as the deadline approached. . . . With twenty minutes to go, Dr. S. K. Allison took over the radio set and made periodic time announcements.

"The time signals, 'minus twenty minutes, minus fifteen minutes,' and so on and on increased the tension to the breaking point. . . . Dr. Oppenheimer and General Farrel held their breaths . . . praying with the intensity of the moment. . . . At 'minus 45 seconds' robot mechanisms took over, and from that point on the whole great complicated mass of mechanism was in operation without human control. Stationed at a reserve switch, however, was a soldier scientist ready to attempt to stop the explosion should the order be issued. The order never came.

"Dr. Oppenheimer, on whom had rested a heavy burden, grew tenser as the last seconds ticked off. He scarcely breathed. He held onto a post to steady himself. For the last few seconds he stared directly ahead and then when the announcer shouted 'Now' and there came this tremendous burst of light followed shortly after by the deep growling roar of the explosion, his face relaxed into an expression of tremendous relief. Several of the observers back of the shelter to watch

The fireball of an atom bomb explosion emerges through the clouds during an experimental test of a nuclear bomb at Eniwetok. In the foreground is a hilly island.

The post-war synchrotron at California Institute of Technology gives subatomic particles 500 million electron-volts of energy.

the lightning effects were knocked flat by the blast.

"The effects could well be called unprecedented, magnificent, beautiful, stupendous and terrifying. The lightning effects beggared description. The whole country was lighted by a searing light with an intensity many times that of the midday sun. It was golden, purple, violet, gray and blue. It lighted every peak, crevasse, and ridge of the nearby mountain range with a clarity and beauty that cannot be described. . . . Thirty seconds after, the explosion came, the air blast pressing hard against the people and things, to be followed almost immediately by the strong, sustained, awesome roar which warned of doomsday and made us feel that we puny things were blasphemous to dare

Cosmic ray bursts can be produced terrestrially in cloud chambers. The black horizontal bars (above) are lead plates. Near the center top can be seen the downward track of a single powerful particle. Traversing six plates, it collides with a nucleus in the seventh, creating a shower of subatomic particles, which in turn create secondary showers.

The cosmotron at Brookhaven National Laboratory gives protons 2.3 billion electron-volts of energy. In the foreground, a Van de Graaf generator injects the protons into the ring.

tamper with the forces reserved to the Almighty.

"Immediately thereafter, a huge multi-colored surging cloud boiled to an altitude over 40,000 feet. Clouds in its path disappeared. Soon the shifting substratosphere winds dispersed the now gray mass.

"The test was over, the project a success.

"The steel tower had been entirely vaporized. Where the tower had stood there was a huge, sloping crater. . . . To examine the nature of the crater, especially equipped tanks were wheeled into the area, one of which carried Dr. Enrico Fermi, noted nuclear scientist."

The first news to the public came on the electrifying summer day when a nuclear bomb was dropped on Japan. But neither that day, nor the day, years later, when a hydrogen bomb was set off on a Pacific atoll, marked the dawn of the new era in world history; war and destruction go back to a time before the saber-toothed tiger.

The day to be remembered is December 2, 1942, when a group of scientists working under Enrico Fermi, Nobel Laureate, showed that uranium nuclear fission could be made to yield useful power for the benefit of the human race. The explosions in the Pacific, bigger and bigger, louder and louder, were all digressions; and sooner or later man's path will be retraced to retrieve all the possibilities that were made plain that winter day in the west stands of Stagg Field.

	1910	1920	1930	1940	1950
PROFESSIONAL PERSONS	4.4	5.0	6.1	6.5	7.5
PROPRIETORS, MANAGERS AND OFFICIALS	23.0	22.3	19.9	17.8	16.3
CLERKS AND KINDRED WORKERS	10.2	13.8	16.3	17.2	20.2
SKILLED WORKERS AND FOREMEN	11.7	13.5	12.9	11.7	13.8
SEMISKILLED WORKERS	14.7	16.1	16.4	21.0	22.4
UNSKILLED WORKERS	36.0	29.4	28.4	25.9	19.8

Trades in America have changed importance in the past fifty years. The percentage of professionally trained men has doubled. With mechanization, the number of unskilled workers has halved, the number of semi-skilled workers has increased by fifty per cent. With mechanization has gone concentration of economic power; and the rise of great corporations has cut down the number of independent proprietors and managers by fifty per cent.

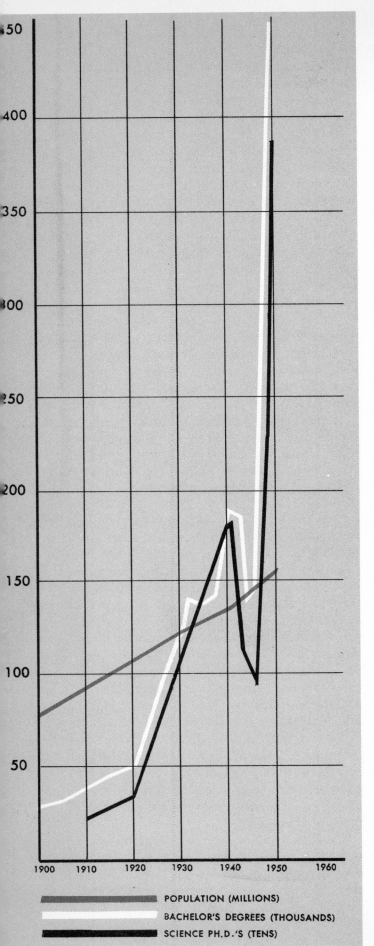

450

400

350

300

250

200

150

100

50

1900   1910   1920   1930   1940   1950   1960

▬▬▬▬▬▬ POPULATION (MILLIONS)
▬▬▬▬▬▬ BACHELOR'S DEGREES (THOUSANDS)
▬▬▬▬▬▬ SCIENCE PH.D.'S (TENS)

Science degrees in America
have increased
in number at a far greater rate than the
rise in population in the same years.

THE TWENTIETH CENTURY— THE HALFWAY MARK

I submit that we of the mid-twentieth century have been moving forward to a considerable degree because of the momentum accumulated in the days of the amateur and the lone inventor. . . . Whether there will continue to be a favorable cultural atmosphere for the exceptional man with really new ideas in science I have some doubt.

—DR. JAMES B. CONANT

"At the beginning of 1950," wrote Bruce Bliven, "many newspapers and magazines . . . published elaborate reviews of the years since 1900, liberally illustrated with the quaint costumes of the McKinley era, with bicycle parades, barber shop quartets with handlebar mustaches, and the earliest automobiles struggling along the main highways deep in mud. None of them, so far as I am aware, discussed what seems to me to be the most significant fact about the changes of the past half century—the alteration in the moral climate from one of overwhelming optimism to one which comes pretty close to despair."

One might well ask: why the despair? If one of the goals of America was to make living physically easier for the individual through science and invention, then surely that goal was closer to attainment for more people than at any time before in the history of the civilized world.

By 1950 the engineering problems of mass production had been largely surmounted in the industries that fed, clothed, and housed the populace. The individual moved easily all over the continent in mass-produced conveyances. When sick, he was cured by mass-produced medicines. The fruits of science and invention were everywhere at hand, yet critics of the times said that life had become drab, colorless, and stereotyped. In the old days, ran one complaint, the rich drove around in Isotta-Fraschinis, Hispano-Suizas, and Rolls-Royces; the poor drove around in Model T Fords. One could tell who was who. Today, say the advertisements at least, everyone drives a Buick. Nevertheless, the 1954 Buick (in all price ranges) comes in a greater variety of styles and colors (also mass-produced) than manufacturers ever dreamed possible in 1900. With vitamin-enriched, mass-produced foods, American children are inches taller, grow to be adults pounds heavier, and live years longer than in 1900.

Entertainment was mass-produced in 1954, yet much of it came to a fairly high standard; and every individual had his choice of looking at his television set, playing a recording of some music he preferred, or reading the best fiction (printed in units of 200,000 copies) written by his contemporaries, for twenty-five cents. He could also pursue an ancient form of entertainment and spend some time with his friends. Clothes were made by machines (in units of a hundred thousand) but in 1954 garments were better made and styled for more people than in 1900. In every conceivable way, physical living in the 1950's was infinitely easier than it had been half a century before.

Then why the despair? Was it because the 1950's were seeing the fulfillment of prophecies made a century earlier—that the end result of science and invention would be the machine's mastery over man and that the very uniformity of every article that came to hand would take all the zest and variety out of life? That, alone, could not explain the despair, because household labor-saving devices, food, clothing, and homes are merely tools with which life is lived. Rembrandt's paint brushes could not have been very different in kind from El Greco's or Picasso's or Mondrian's; yet with these very similar tools and pigments, these painters portrayed very different pictures of life. Beethoven, Elgar, and Gershwin had used the same limited number of musical notes and composed highly individualized music, each in his own image. Uniformity in tools can never make for uniformity in product as long as there is diversity in humankind.

But did that diversity still exist in America in the 1950's as it had in the early years of the century? Was the 1950 American the same individualist his grandfather had been?

"A lot of companies in my industry were started in the early years of the century as one-man shows," said a corporation president to Frederick Lewis Allen in 1952. "There was a fellow with an idea and some capital and the business was his personal business. . . . Then the thing grew, and in the twenties the sales problem was uppermost and this man was succeeded by a big salesman. Later we began to see the importance of research, and a research man, or at any rate, a research-minded man, would get the nod. But now research has become so complicated that it's a specialty and what you need is a team of people each one of which knows one or more of these various specialties, and the chief thing required of the head fellow is that he be able to keep this team working as a well-balanced unit. He's got to be a good captain of the team. As chairman, I don't pretend really to know what the research people are doing; it's my job to keep them going in harmonious balance with the rest of the outfit."

This stress on the "team" would have been puzzling to an individual American businessman at the turn of the century, but in the 1950's, it had become so much the order of things that it was the subject of study for sociologists, anthropologists, and psychologists who told the story of the "group thinking" junior executive American: how he lived, thought, dressed, and married as a result of being part of a society in which every second American adult was on the payroll of a corporation and highly sensitive to what people "in his shop" thought about him.

According to David Riesman's study, *The Lonely Crowd,* the 1900 man was being replaced by another type who was better suited to "a society in which the problems not only of mere subsistence, but also of large-scale industrial organization and production have been for the most part surmounted." The 1950 model was the man trained to get along with the "group," who knew what the group expected and wanted. His values were the group's values, his goals were the group's goals. The voice that directed him came not from within himself but from others—he was an "other-directed" man.

Adult working Americans were used to the idea of being subordinate to someone else, used to being a member of someone else's staff, no matter how many people were members of *his* staff, used to "getting along" with others, used to "playing safe" so that there would be no black mark against him when the time came for him to advance one step upward. Adult working Americans had become hierarchy-conscious to an extent that far surpassed the old simple classification of "rich, poor, and middle class." And in this hierarchy-consciousness, the only kind of diversity that was absolutely safe was a diversity just like everyone else's diversity.

Was this new personality pattern the result of a brilliant plot hatched by diabolical minds in the pay of the giant corporations? Actually, such a development is not to the interests of any group that has to draw upon its ranks for future leadership. In one interview after another, corporation heads revealed to W. H. Whyte of *Fortune* magazine that they were alarmed at the new dispensation. Certainly one man ought to be able to work along with another, but "somewhere along the line he's got to be himself, too!"

A submissive man is a self-deprived man. "All human beings want and need intervals of feeling personally powerful," wrote Margaret Halsey, in *The Folks at Home.* "They want and need power over their environment . . . power to develop their talents in whatever direction those talents want to go. But for all his society's magnificent conquests of Nature, the one thing the mid-century American has not got is the feeling of personal power."

This lack, characteristically and traditionally, could well be the reason for the feeling of despair. For such a situation, neither science nor invention can offer a cure.

If the statistics are correct, corporation heads could not reverse the trend even if they tried. It is not the machine that has mastered man—it is the social organization created by man to run the huge aggregates of mass-producing machinery which seems to have enforced the pattern that has mastered man. Not technology, but the sociology of technology. It is useless to talk of going back to the "good old days" of cottage industry. Who in the 1950's wants oil lamps and outdoor plumbing, to have half one's children die at birth, to work fourteen hours a day, to be old at forty-five?

Is America doomed to be populated only by "other-directed" men? No. Nor are the "other-directed" men born that way. Normal, healthy babies grow up "group-oriented" only because in that way lies the most tangible rewards. Let rewards be offered for individualism, and the country will swarm with individualists. It is the lesson of history that this had better be done. Submissiveness is far too expensive to the health of society.

For one thing, it has resulted in the acceptance of legislative and executive directives that would have been inconceivable as recently as two decades ago. "If a nineteenth-century American were introduced to the Atomic Age," wrote Leon Svirsky in 1950, "he would certainly be astonished to learn that atomic energy is merely a semi-clandestine military project almost entirely divorced from the ordinary life of mankind . . . Hiroshima made the atom a political and psychological phenomenon as well as a physical one. Yet non-scientists for the most part have shied away from trying to understand it. The new physics gives them a headache as well as a sick feeling in the pit of the stomach. This is deplorable on every count: not only has the reluctance to face the atom removed atomic policy from the democratic process, played into the hands of the alarmists and demagogues, and given rise to all sorts of unreasonable fears, but it is entirely unjustified."

This refusal to examine atomic policy has harmed American science by curtailing the freedom of American scientists to communicate with scientists abroad. Yet, if this freedom had not existed in 1939, America would never have had the information to initiate such a development as nuclear energy. Who knows what information is not being made available to America today? American scientists try vainly to explain that most security demands are more harmful to America than to any possible enemy. They know that the phenomena of nature cannot be kept secret. Today people laugh at the ancient Pythagoreans who tried to hide the truth, so shattering to their religious dogma, that the ratio of the circumference of a circle to its diameter could not be expressed as the ratio of whole numbers. The world discovered that it was an irrational number, and said, "So what?"

American science has a superb tradition of experimentation, but until the day arrives when America develops theoreticians of the caliber of Willard Gibbs, it will continue to depend on men trained in Europe. Julian Schwinger of Harvard and Richard Feynman of Cal Tech give every promise of being brilliant, but two are not enough. Information in science is at least a two-way trade.

Great scientific theories and great inventions are acts of creation and, like the composition of great music, the writing of great poetry, the painting of great pictures, they are the work of human beings of intense individuality, the very quality that the American republic was founded to enshrine. It is the potential that is latent in every American. Its suppression, however temporary, may well be the reason for the 1950 American despair; its eventual release may well be America's greatest, most joyous victory.

ACKNOWLEDGMENTS

My debt runs high to the many people who helped me with this book. Wherever I went for assistance, whether to friends, to scholars in the field, to libraries, museums, universities, or to private collections, I found generosity and willingness to help. As a visitor to the world of scholarship, I was met with courtesy and patience. As an author, I was given every conceivable aid by my publishers.

First and foremost, I am indebted to my wife, Helen, for her sympathetic understanding, hard work, and encouragement through two trying years.

Then I am indebted to two close friends, Lee Wright and Albert Leventhal—between them, they suggested that I write this book in the first place; they then made it possible for me to do so; and finally they gave me continual support while I wrote it. Lee Wright's editorial supervision was indispensable.

Paul Jensen's artistic taste and talent are responsible for the book's handsome appearance. As the layout editor, he worked along with me from the very beginning. His sympathy for my text, appeciation for my pictures, and editorial suggestions were all invaluable. Almost half the picture captions were written by him from my notes.

Eloise Knapp Hay was my research assistant and secretary. To the work, she brought tact, an appreciation and talent for scholarship, and devotion to every task that came to hand. In her secretarial capacity, she was assisted by Anne Davies. Special research was done by Ann Satterthwaite. The detailed correspondence required for such a project was performed by Lou Ashworth. The final manuscript, picture credits, and many other last-minute details were taken care of by Sophie Sorkin and Barbé Tirtoff.

Leonard Gelber of New York University read the entire manuscript—pictures and text—with the eyes of the professional historian. Wherever possible, he checked every statement, date, and inference for authenticity with his scholar's sense of responsibility. Whatever errors remain in the text were made in areas outside Dr. Gelber's domain.

Most of the pictures in the first half of the book were made from photographs taken for me by Thomas E. Bailey, then at the Massachusetts Institute of Technology. He worked tirelessly to give me the best reproductions of which the Institute's excellent equipment was capable. Most of the second half of the book was made from photographs made for me at the Fogg Museum of Harvard University by James Ufford and James West, who also set perfection as their standard. Additional photographic work was done by Thomas Comey of the Photostat Department of Widener Library; by Edwin B. Luce of Worcester, Mass.; and by Philip Mosher and Lorraine Armitage of Vineyard Haven, Mass.

One of my strongest supports in this project was Howard Mumford Jones of Harvard University. Without his friendship, the task would have been ten times as difficult. Besides making me feel at home in Cambridge, and in addition to the many long discussions we had together which allowed me to capitalize on his broad scholarship and creativity, he turned over to me and my assistants his own study in Widener Library for almost half a year. Later, Robert Haynes, the Library's assistant director, very kindly arranged for me to have the Charles Eliot Norton Study in Widener Library where this book was completed.

In fact, I am deeply indebted to the entire staff of Widener Library and the other libraries of Harvard. From Keyes Metcalf, the director, I received many favors. Foster Palmer and Thomas O'Connell of the library staff were continually helpful, as were Carolyn Jaspers and William Jackson of Houghton Library. Mrs. E. I. Tulloch of the Chemistry Library made many items available to me, and Robert Lovett helped me in the use of the Baker Library of the Business School.

At Harvard also, I was greatly helped by I. Bernard Cohen's advice and kindness. Out of his own vast scholarship in the history of science, Dr. Cohen gave me many leads, corrected many of my misconceptions, and made himself continually available.

Julian Schwinger gave me many hours discussing contemporary work in physics, and Norman Ramsay gave me an experimentalist's point of view of the same developments. Harlow Shapley recalled the early years at Mt. Wilson, and reminisced about Hale, Millikan, Michelson, and Langmuir. I also owe thanks to Dorrit Hoffleit of the Harvard College Observatory.

My own research began at the Hayden Library of the Massachusetts Institute of Technology, where Vernon Tate, the director, generously extended to me the facilities for visiting scholars. Robert Booth, assistant director, gave me active personal help day after day, interested himself in the project, and introduced me to the many people at the school who could be of assistance to me.

At M.I.T., Sanborn Brown generously allowed me to draw on his great collection of material on Count Rumford. Warren Ogden permitted me to use his extensive bibliographical studies on the history of engineering and mechanical invention, and even presented me with one of the rare copies of Butterworth's *Rise of the Industrial Arts*. Norbert Weiner, in many interviews, ranged through his wide interests for me and gave me many new insights. Elting Morison helped me with many historical questions. Jane Lawson made innumerable suggestions that were embodied in the book, did extensive research whenever called upon, and was helpful in a thousand other ways.

At the Boston Public Library, John M. Carroll gave me many privileges. Lorraine Sullivan made extensive searches for me in the Science Division. All the patents reproduced in the book were secured for me from Boston Public Library's Patent Division by Louis Polishook.

Clarence Brigham of the American Antiquarian Society in Worcester gave me access to the society's twenty-six miles of stacks, and his own personal guidance through them as well as through the collections of pictures, manuscripts, and ephemera. Hope Gilson, of the society's staff, helped me with the many tedious tasks of securing reproductions and keeping references and credits in order. I am also indebted to Clifford Shipton.

Walter Muir Whitehill of the Boston Athenaeum always received my requests graciously and I never came away empty-handed. He was particularly helpful in nautical matters.

Ernest Dodge and Charles Copeland of the Peabody Museum of Salem gave me detailed information on Bowditch and the clipper ships, and went to particular trouble to get me the original McKay plans of the "Lightning."

Romana Javits gave me much time and advice at the New York Public Library Picture Collection, and Bella Landauer herself helped me to select the items which I have used from her remarkable collection at the New York Historical Society.

At Yale University, I am indebted to the late John Marshall Phillips and to Lamont Moore of the Art Gallery, to Henry Fuller and Marjorie Wynne of the Sterling Library, and to Stephen Kezerian of the News Bureau.

Dennis Flannagan of *The Scientific American* performed more favors for me than I can enumerate; and the entire files of the magazine were placed at my disposal.

Robert G. Fiedler of the California Institute of Technology must have gathered over a hundred pictures for me from various sources.

The following corporations gave me invaluable assistance from their historical records: Electric Boat Division of the General Dynamics Corporation, the Ford Motor Company, Armour and Company, Westinghouse Electric, Eastman Kodak, Remington Rand, Bakelite, E. I. du Pont De Nemours and Company, Radio Corporation of America, Bausch and Lomb, General Electric, Bell Telephone Laboratories, Swift and Company, General Motors, and the Petroleum Institute.

In addition to those mentioned before, I drew on the following museums: the Smithsonian Institution, the National Air Museum, the Addison Gallery of American Art, the Missouri Historical Society, the Metropolitan Museum of Art of New York, the West Point Museum, the School of Art of the Syracuse University, the Wadsworth Atheneum, the American Museum of Photography, the Confederate Memorial Literary Society, the Museum of the City of New York, the Library of Congress, and the Museum of Modern Art of New York.

Besides the universities and institutions listed above, I owe thanks to these: the University of Chicago, the Case Institute of Technology, the University of California, the Yerkes Observatory, Washington University, and the Mount Wilson and Palomar Observatory.

Finally, in the gathering of the material, I must thank these individuals: Lee de Forest, Mr. and Mrs. Edwin Grabhorn, Frank H. Woods, Jr., Ethel M. Kelly, Laurence A. Fleischman, Ralph G. Van Name, Lynde P. Wheeler, Sir Charles Darwin, Mrs. A. Agassiz, Clark Millikan, Don Masson, George Baekeland, and Dorothy Giles.

From first to last, the ten thousand details of the physical production of the book were handled with taste, skill, and sympathy by Tom Torre Bevans and his assistant, Rosalie Barrow. Without these two, there would have been no book. I must also thank Kay Jerman and Eve Metz for their assistance at the end.

PICTURE CREDITS

KEY TO PICTURE POSITION: [T] = top; [C] = center; [B] = bottom; [L] = left; [M] = middle; [R] = right; and combinations, for example [TC] = top center.

78 [BL] Courtesy Yale University Art Gallery
[TR] Butterworth, *Rise of Industrial Arts*

79 Diderot and D'Alembert, *Encyclopédie*

80 [all] Hubert, P. G., *Men of Achievement*

81 [TL] Buckingham, J. S., *Travels in the Southern States of North America*
[TCL] Dow, George Francis, *Slave Ships and Slaving*
[TR] Trollope, Mrs. Frances Eleanor, *Domestic Manners of the Americans*
[B] Peabody Museum of Salem

82 [TL, CL] Steel, David, *The Elements and Practise of Rigging and Seamanship*
[BL, BR] Diderot and D'Alembert, *Encyclopédie*

83 [BL] Davidson, *Life in America*
[BR] *New Haven Colony Historical Society*

84 [T] White, George S., *Memoir of Samuel Slater, the Father of American Manufacture*
[BL] Brown, John Howard, *Lamb's Textile Industries of the United States*

85 [T] White, George S., *Memoir of Samuel Slater, the Father of American Manufacture*
[CR] Brown, John Howard, *Lamb's Textile Industries of the United States*
[BR] Keir, Malcolm, *The Pageant of America*

86 [TL] White, George S., *Memoir of Samuel Slater, the Father of American Manufacture*
[CL] Keir, Malcolm, *The Pageant of America*
[BL] New York Public Library Print Collection, Alexander Anderson

87 [all] White, George S., *Memoir of Samuel Slater, the Father of American Manufacture*

88 [BL] Brown, John Howard, *Lamb's Textile Industries of the United States*
[all others] Hunt, Freeman, *Lives of American Merchants*

89 [T, BR] New York Public Library Print Collection, Alexander Anderson
[TR] Keir, Malcolm, *The Pageant of America*
[CR] New York Public Library, Bella Landauer Collection, Bank Note Engravings

90 [B] New-York Historical Society

92 [all] New York Public Library Print Collection, Alexander Anderson

93 [T] Library of Congress, Robert Kerr, "Custom House"
[all others] New York Public Library Print Collection, Alexander Anderson

94 Aero Service Corporation

96 [TL] National Portrait Gallery, E. A. Duyckinck
[BL, BR] Audubon, Maria R., *Audubon and His Journals*

97 Audubon, Maria R., *Audubon and His Journals*

98 [TL, BR] Agassiz, Elizabeth Cary, *Louis Agassiz: His Life and Correspondence*
[BL, CR] Harvard University, Houghton Library

99 [all] Holden, Charles Frederick, *Louis Agassiz, His Life and Work*

100 [all] Fremont, Brevet Captain J. C., *The Exploring Expedition to the Rocky Mountains in the Year 1842, and to Oregon and North California in the Years 1843–44*

101 [BL] Library of Congress
[all others] Fremont, Brevet Captain J. C., *The Exploring Expedition to the Rocky Mountains in the Year 1842, and to Oregon and North California in the Years 1843–44*

102 [TL] University of Chicago Libraries
[BL] Beaumont, William, *Experiments and Observations on the Gastric Juice*

103 [TL, TR] Beaumont, William, *Experiments and Observations on the Gastric Juice*
[B] William L. Clements Library, *Four Letters of Alexis St. Martin*

104 [BR] Packard, Francis Randolph, *The History of Medicine in the United States*
[all others] Figuier, Louis, *Les Merveilles de la Science*

106 Figuier, Louis, *Les Merveilles de la Science*

107 [BR] Figuier, Louis, *Les Merveilles de la Science*
[all others] Massachusetts General Hospital, *The Semi-Centennial of Anesthesia*

108 [all] Urbain, Georges and Boll, Marcel, *La Science et Ses Applications*

109 American Antiquarian Society, *Conversations on Chemistry in Which the Elements of That Science are Familiarly Explained and Illustrated by Experiments and Plates*

110 Smithsonian Institution, *Collected Works of Joseph Henry*

111 [all] Guillemin, Amédée, *Le Monde Physique*

112 [TL] New-York Historical Society, Currier, "Explosion of the U.S.S. Princeton"
[BL] Smithsonian Institution, *Collected Works of Joseph Henry*
[BR] *Century Magazine*, 1888

113 [BL] Smithsonian Institution, *Collected Works of Joseph Henry*
[R] The Frederick H. Meserve Collection, New York

114 [T] New-York Historical Society, H. R. Robinson, "Hard Times"
[B] Old Print Shop, New York

116 Syracuse University, Samuel F. B. Morse, "The Louvre"

117 [TR] Addison Gallery of American Art, Phillips Academy, Andover, Mass., S. F. B. Morse, "Self Portrait"
[BR] New York Public Library Picture Collection

118 [TR, BR] Reid, James D., *The Telegraph in America*
[BL] Figuier, Louis, *Les Merveilles de la Science*

119 [TL, BL] Reid, James D., *The Telegraph in America*
[TR] Figuier, Louis, *Les Merveilles de la Science*

120 [T, BL] Lardner, Dionysus, *The Museum of Science and Art*
[BR] Reid, James D., *The Telegraph in America*

122 [TL] *Appleton's Cyclopedia of American Biography*
[TR] New York Public Library Picture Collection
[CL, BL, BR] *Shaffner's Telegraph Manual*

123 [BL] New-York Historical Society
[all others] Harvard University, Widener Library, *Davis' Catalogue of Apparatus*

124 [TL] New York Public Library Picture Collection, #199
[BL] U. S. Patent Office

125 Goodyear, Charles, *Gum-Elastic and Its Properties*

126 [all] McCabe, J. D., *Great Fortunes and How They Were Made*

127 Museum of Fine Arts, Boston, Karolik Collection

129 [TL, TR] Goodyear, Charles, *Gum-Elastic and Its Properties*
[B] Boston Public Library

130 [TL] Singer Sewing Machine Company
[TR] *Knight's American Mechanical Dictionary*
[BR] Iles, George, *Leading American Inventors*

131 [all] U. S. Patent Office

132 [TL] Iles, George, *Leading American Inventors*
[BL, BR] Parton, Lemuel, *Elias Howe and the Sewing Machine*

133 [all] Parton, Lemuel, *Elias Howe and the Sewing Machine*

134 [all] Singer Sewing Machine Company

135 Singer Sewing Machine Company

136 [T] Metropolitan Museum of Art, New York
[BL] New York Public Library Picture Collection

138 [TL] Boston Atheneum, John Neagle, "Pat Lyon at the Forge"
[CL] New York Public Library Picture Collection
[BL] Butterworth, *Rise of Industrial Arts*

139 [T] American Museum of Photography, 338 South 15 Street, Philadelphia
[B] New York Public Library, Bella Landauer Collection, Bank Note Engravings

140 [TL] *Harper's Weekly*
[CL] U. S. Patent Office
[BL] Byrn, Edward W., *The Progress of Invention in the Nineteenth Century*

141 American Antiquarian Society

142 [B] Chicago Historical Society

144 [B] New-York Historical Society

145 Library of Congress

146 [T] Brown, William H., *History of First Locomotives in America*
[B] Museum of Fine Arts, Boston, Karolik Collection

147 [T] Brown, William H., *History of First Locomotives in America*
[all others] Tredgold, Thomas, *A Practical Treatise on Railroads and Carriages*

148 [all] Old Print Shop, New York

149 Old Print Shop, New York

150 [T] Dempsey, G. Drysdale, *Treatise on Locomotives*
[BL, BR] Clark, T. C., *The American Railway*

151 [TL, CL] Old Print Shop, New York
[BL] U. S. Patent Office

152 [T] Old Print Shop, New York
[all others] Clark, T. C., *The American Railway*

153 [T] Baltimore and Ohio Railroad
[B] Brown, William H., *History of First Locomotives in America*

154 [TL, BL] Dempsey, G. Drysdale, *Treatise on Railroad Practise*
[TCL] Bryant, William Cullen, *Picturesque America*
[BCL] Stevens Institute

155 Old Print Shop, New York

156 [TR, TL] Beaufoy, Mark, *Nautical and Hydraulic Experiments*
[BL] Griffiths, John W., *Treatise on Marine and Naval Architecture*

157 [all] Griffiths, John W., *Treatise on Marine and Naval Architecture*

158 [TL] McKay, Richard C., *Some Famous Sailing Ships and Their Builder, Donald McKay*
[CL] New-York Historical Society, Bella Landauer Collection
[BL] New York Public Library Print Collection, Alexander Anderson
[TR] Peabody Museum of Salem

159 [all] Peabody Museum of Salem

160 New York Public Library Picture Collection

161 [TL] New York Public Library, Bella Landauer Collection, Bank Note Engravings
[all others] *Harper's Monthly*, 1851

162 [T, B] Old Print Shop, New York
[CL, CR] New York Public Library, Bella Landauer Collection, Bank Note Engravings

163 U. S. Patent Office

164 Crocker Art Gallery, Sacramento, Charles Nahl, "Sunday Morning at the Mines"

166 [TL] New York Public Library, Stokes Collection
[CL, BL, BR] Old Print Shop, New York

167 [BL, BR] Old Print Shop, New York

168 [all] American Petroleum Institute, New York

169 [TR] Figuier, Louis, *Les Merveilles de la Science*
[BR] Oil Industry Information Committee

170 Figuier, Louis, *Les Merveilles de la Science*

171 American Petroleum Institute, New York

172 [T] Metropolitan Museum of Art, New York, Robert Dudley, "Awaiting the Reply"
[BL] Lossing, Benson S., *History of City of New York*

173 [BCR] New York Public Library
[all others] Figuier, Louis, *Les Merveilles de la Science*

174 [TL] *Illustrated London News*, 1858
[TR] Figuier, Louis, *Les Merveilles de la Science*
[B] New York Public Library Picture Collection

176 *Illustrated London News*, 1865

177 [TL] Figuier, Louis, *Les Merveilles de la Science*
[TR, B] New York Public Library Picture Collection

178 Confederate Museum, Richmond, Va., Conrad Wise Chapman, "White Point Battery Charleston, S. C.—1863"

180 [T] *Gardner's Photographic Sketchbook of the War*
[B] *Pictorial War Record, Battles of the Late Civil War*

181 Miller, Francis Trevelyan, *The Photographic History of the Civil War*

183 [T] *Gardner's Photographic Sketchbook of the War*
[CR] Leslie, Frank, *Historical Register of the United States Centennial Exposition, 1876*
[BR] *Pictorial War Record, Battles of the Late Civil War*

184 [all] Figuier, Louis, *Les Merveilles de la Science*

185 [BL] Figuier, Louis, *Les Merveilles de la Science*
[TR, BR] *Harper's Weekly*, 1859

186 *Harper's Weekly*, 1859

187 [T] The Museum of Modern Art, New York
[BL] *Scribner's Monthly*, 1889
[BR] Miller, Francis Trevelyan, *The Photographic History of the Civil War*

188 Putnam County Historical Society, John Ferguson Weir, "The Gun Foundry"

190 [all] Leslie, Frank, *Pictorial History of the War*

191 [TR] U. S. Patent Office
[BR] Byrn, Edward W., *The Progress of Invention in the Nineteenth Century*

192 [TL, CL] Gilmore, Q. A., *Charleston Harbor in 1863*
[BL] Leslie, Frank, *Pictorial History of the War*

193 Putnam County Historical Society, Rossiter, "Picnic on the Hudson"

194 [L] U. S. Patent Office
[TR] Farrow, Edward S., *Military Encyclopedia*

195 [TL] Farrow, Edward S., *Military Encyclopedia*
[R] U. S. Patent Office

196 [all] Leslie, Frank, *Pictorial History of the War*

197 [all] *Harper's History of the Great Rebellion*

198 [T] Leslie, Frank, *Pictorial History of the War*
[B] Lossing, B. S., *Our Country—A Household History from the Discovery of America to the Present Time*

200 [TL] De Chasseloup-Laubat, *Les Marines de Guerre Moderne*
[CL, BL] *Harper's History of the Great Rebellion*

201 [all] *Harper's History of the Great Rebellion*

202 New Haven Colony Historical Society, Warren Sheppard, "Monitor and Merrimac"

203 Missouri Historical Society, St. Louis, Thomas Burridge, "Osage—U. S. Gunboat"

204 [all] *Scribner's Monthly*, 1890

205 [TR] Reed and Simpson, *Modern Ships of War*
[B] *Harper's History of the Great Rebellion*

206 [T] Leslie's *Pictorial History of the War*
[all others] *Harper's Weekly*, 1865

207 [TL] Leslie, Frank, *Pictorial History of the War*
[TR] *Scribner's Monthly*, 1889
[CR] Gilmore, Q. A., *Charleston Harbor in 1863*
[BR] *Harper's New Monthly Magazine*, 1897

208 [TL] Leslie's *Pictorial History of the War*
[CL] *The Confederate Soldier in the Civil War*
[BL] Gilmore, Q. A., *Charleston Harbor in 1863*

209 [T] Confederate Museum, Richmond, Va., Conrad Wise Chapman, "Charleston Bay and City—1863"
[C] *The Confederate Soldier in the Civil War*

210 [TL] *The Confederate Soldier in the Civil War*
[B] Confederate Museum, Richmond, Va., Chapman, "The David"

211 [TR] Leslie's *Pictorial History of the War*
[B] Confederate Museum, Richmond, Va., Chapman, "The Hunley"
[C] General Dynamics Corporation Electric Boat Division, Submarine Library

212 *L'Illustration*, 1893

214 [TR] *Leslie's Illustrated Newspaper*, vol. 42
[TL, B] *Harper's Weekly*, vols. 20, 22

215 Ingram, J. S., *The Centennial Exposition*

216 [all] Leslie, Frank, *Historical Register of the United States Centennial Exposition, 1876*

217 [TL] *L'Illustration*, 1893
[TR] Leslie, Frank, *Historical Register of the United States Centennial Exposition, 1876*

218 [T] *Illustrated Catalogue of the Centennial*
[BL] *Harper's Weekly*, vol. 20
[BR] Leslie, Frank, *Historical Register of the United States Centennial Exposition, 1876*

219 [BR] *Leslie's Illustrated Newspaper*, vol. 42
[T, BL] Leslie, Frank, *Historical Register of the United States Centennial Exposition, 1876*

220 [TL] *Leslie's Illustrated Newspaper*, vol. 42
[TR] *Harper's Weekly*, vol. 20

221 [all] *Harper's Weekly*, vol. 12

222 [T] *Leslie's Illustrated Newspaper*, 1877
[all others] Clark, T. C., *The American Railway*

223 [TR, CR] U. S. Patent Office
[BR] *Appleton's Cyclopedia of Applied Mechanics*

224 [all] New York Public Library Picture Collection

PICTURE CREDITS

225 [all] *Leslie's Illustrated Newspaper*, 1877
227 [T] *Harper's Weekly*, vol. 12
[CL, CR] Clark, T. C., *The American Railway*
[BL] U. S. Patent Office
[BR] *Harper's Weekly*, vol. 38, 1894
228 [TL] Remington, Frederic, *Drawings*
[BL] Wooster, Owen, *Jimmyjohn Boss*
229 [all] Armour and Company
230 *Harper's Weekly*
231 [all] U. S. Patent Office
232 [all] *Harper's Magazine*, 1882
233 [TL, CL] *Harper's Magazine*, 1882
[BL] U. S. Patent Office
234 [TL] *Scribner's Magazine*, 1892
[TR] U. S. Patent Office
[C] *Illustrated Catalogue of the Centennial*
Takes Command
[B] Giedeon, Siegfried, *Mechanization*
236 [TL, TR] Giedeon, Siegfried, *Mechanization Takes Command*
[CL] Byrn, Edward W., *The Progress of Invention in the Nineteenth Century*
[BL] Byrn, Edward W., *The Progress of Invention in the Nineteenth Century*
[RC] *Illustrated Catalogue of the Centennial*
237 [TR] Byrn, Edward W., *The Progress of Invention in the Nineteenth Century*
[TL] Giedeon, Siegfried, *Mechanization Takes Command*
[BR] Benjamin, Park, *Modern Mechanism*
238 New York Public Library Picture Collection
240 [all] *Scribner's Monthly*, 1897
241 [T, C] *Scribner's Monthly*, 1897
[BR] Benjamin, Park, *Modern Mechanism*
242 [all] *Harper's Magazine*, vol. 88, 1893–4
243 [all] *Harper's Magazine*, vol. 88, 1893–4
244 [TL, B] Leslie, Frank, *Historical Register of the United States Centennial Exposition, 1876*
[TM, TR] *Illustrated Catalogue of the Centennial*
245 Leslie, Frank, *Historical Register of the United States Centennial Exposition, 1876*
246 In author's possession
247 [CR] New York Public Library, Bella Landauer Collection, Bank Note Engravings
[TR, BR] *Appleton's Cyclopedia of Applied Mechanics*
248 [all] Buchanan, Robertson, *Millwork and Other Machinery*
249 [all] Buchanan, Robertson, *Millwork and Other Machinery*
250 Collection of Mr. and Mrs. Laurence A. Fleischman, Detroit, Thomas Anshutz, "Steelworkers: Noontime"
251 [TR] Leslie, Frank, *Historical Register of the United States Centennial Exposition, 1876*
[all others] *Illustrated Catalogue of the Centennial*
252 [TL] *North American Review*, June, 1888
[CL] Ingram, J. S., *The Centennial Exposition*
[BL, TR] Remington Rand, Inc.
[BR] *Illustrated Phonographic World*
253 [TR] *Illustrated Catalogue of the Centennial*
[all others] *North American Review*, June, 1888
254 [TL, CL, TM, TR] Benjamin, Park, *Modern Mechanism*
[BL] [BR] *Illustrated Phonographic World*
255 [all] *Illustrated Phonographic World*
256 [TL] Leslie, Frank, *Historical Register of the United States Centennial Exposition, 1876*
[BL] *Harper's Weekly*, vol. 12
[TR] Benjamin, Park, *Modern Mechanism*
257 Butterworth, *Rise of Industrial Arts*
258 Westinghouse Corporation
259 [TR] New York Public Library Picture Collection
[TL] *Scribner's*, 1897, "The American Railway"
[CL] *Scribner's Monthly*, 1889
260 Westinghouse Corporation
261 [TL] *Harper's Weekly*, 1885
[TR, CR, BR] *Harper's Monthly*, vol. 93
[BL] Byrn, Edward W., *The Progress of Invention in the Nineteenth Century*
262 Museum of the City of New York, W. Louis Sonntag, Jr., "The Bowery at Night"
264 [TL, TR] Figuier, Louis, *Les Merveilles de la Science*
[CL, BR] Hoffleit, Dorrit, *Some Firsts in Astronomical Photography*
[BL] *London and Edinburgh Philosophical Magazine*, June, 1840
265 [all] Figuier, Louis, *Les Merveilles de la Science*
266 [TL] Eastman Kodak Company
[BL] Museum of Modern Art, New York, O'Sullivan, T. H., "Ancient Ruins in the Canyon de Chelle"
267 [TL, TR] Figuier, Louis, *Les Merveilles de la Science*
[BR] U. S. Patent Office
268 [T] *Scientific American*, 1885
[BL] Eastman Kodak Company
269 *Scribner's Monthly*, 1889
270 [CL, BR] Eastman Kodak Company
[BL] *Scribner's Monthly*, 1889
271 Eastman Kodak Company
272 [TL] *Annals of the Astronomical Observatory of Harvard University*
[TR] Guillemin, Amédée, *The Heavens*
[BL] *Harper's Weekly*, vol. 13
[BR] *Philosophical Journal of London*
273 [all] *Harper's Weekly*, vol. 13
274 [T, CL] Hoffleit, Dorrit, *Some Firsts in Astronomical Photography*
[BL] *Harper's Weekly*, vol. 13
275 [TR] Hoffleit, Dorrit, *Some Firsts in Astronomical Photography*
[BR] *Harper's Weekly*, vol. 22
276 [BCL] Goldberg, Leo, *Atoms, Stars, and Nebulae*
[all others] Harvard College Observatory
277 [TR] *Rowland, Henry, Collected Works of*
[BR] Byrn, Edward W., *The Progress of Invention in the Nineteenth Century*
[BL] Harvard College Observatory
278 [TL] Figuier, Louis, *Les Nouvelles Conquêtes de la Science*
[BL] Bell, Alexander G., *Visible Speech as a Means of Communicating Articulation to Deaf Mutes*
279 [TR] The Bettman Archive, New York
[BR] Bell, Alexander G., *Visible Speech as a Means of Communicating Articulation to Deaf Mutes*
280 [all] *Bell, Alexander G., Deposition of*
281 [TR, R3, BR] Figuier, Louis, *Les Nouvelles Conquêtes de la Science*
[C] Bell, A. G., *Upon the Production of Sound by Radiant Energy*
282 [TL, CR] *Leslie's Illustrated Weekly*, 1877
[BL] Figuier, Louis, *Les Nouvelles Conquêtes de la Science*
283 [CR] Figuier, Louis, *Les Nouvelles Conquêtes de la Science*
[TR] [BR] *Harper's Monthly*, vol. 93
285 [TL, TR] Guillemin, Amédée, *Electricity and Magnetism*
[BL] *Harper's Weekly*, 1881
[BR] Bell, A. G., *Upon Electrical Experiments to Determine the Location of the Bullet in the Body of the Late President Garfield*
286 [TL, BL] Figuier, Louis, *Les Nouvelles Conquêtes de la Science*
[CL] Culver Service Photos, New York
287 New York Public Library Picture Collection
288 [all] Figuier, Louis, *Les Nouvelles Conquêtes de la Science*
289 [BL] *Journal of Society of Arts*, May, 1879
[BM] *Appleton's Cyclopedia of Applied Mechanics*
[BR] *Harper's Weekly*
290 [T] Edison Company
[CL, CR] Figuier, Louis, *Les Nouvelles Conquêtes de la Science*
[BR] New York Public Library Picture Collection
291 [TL] New York Public Library Picture Collection
[TR] *Harper's Weekly*
292 [TL] *Harper's Weekly*, 1877
[BL, TR, CR] Byrn, Edward W., *The Progress of Invention in the Nineteenth Century*
294 [TL] Fleming, J. A., *Fifty Years of Electricity*
[BR] Guillemin, Amédée, *Electricity and Magnetism*
295 [CR, B] Muybridge, Edward, *Animal Locomotion*
[top 4] Holmes, Oliver Wendell, "The Human Wheel, Its Spokes and Felloes," *Atlantic Monthly*, May, 1863
296 [T] Muybridge, Edward, *Animal Locomotion*
[all others] *Scribner's Monthly*, vol. 18, 1895
297 [TR] U. S. Patent Office
[BR] Byrn, Edward W., *The Progress of Invention in the Nineteenth Century*
298 Yale University Library
299 *Harper's Weekly*, vol. 1
300 Yale University Library
301 [TR] *Scribner's Monthly*, vol. 18, 1895
[BR] *Illustrated London News*, 1876
302 [all] *Illustrated London News*, 1876
305 Ralph Van Name
306 *Scientific American*
307 *Scientific American*, Dec., 1949
309 University of Chicago Library, Department of Special Collections
310 [all] Guillemin, Amédée, *Le Monde Physique*
311 [all] *Harper's Magazine*, vol. 43, 1871
312 [TL] *American Journal of Science*, 1878
[TR, CR] *Astronomical Papers of American Ephemeris*
[B] University of Chicago
314 [TR] Michelson, A. A., *Light Waves and Their Uses*
[all others] *American Journal of Science*, 1881
315 [TL] *American Journal of Science*, 1881
[TR] Michelson, A. A., *Light Waves and Their Uses*
316 Mt. Wilson and Palomar Observatories
317 [TL] Michelson, A. A., *Light Waves and Their Uses*
[TM] Mt. Wilson and Palomar Observatories
[TR] *Scribner's Monthly*, vol. 18, 1895
318 David Eisendrath, courtesy *Scientific American*, May, 1950
320 Permission Auto Manufacturers' Ass'n.
321 [all] Permission Auto Manufacturers' Ass'n.
322 [TL] Permission Auto Manufacturers' Ass'n.
[TR] Figuier, Louis, *Les Merveilles de la Science*
323 [TL] Figuier, Louis, *Les Merveilles de la Science*
[TR] *Harper's Weekly*, vol. 12
324 [all] Permission Auto Manufacturers' Ass'n.
325 [BL] Homans, J. E., *Self-Propelled Vehicles*
[BR] Sloss, R. T., *The Book of the Automobile*
326 Permission Auto Manufacturers' Ass'n.
327 [T] Permission Auto Manufacturers' Ass'n.
[CR, BR] Homans, J. E., *Self-Propelled Vehicles*
328 [TL] Courtesy Clark Millikan
[BR] *Harper's Weekly*
329 [TL] White, William Allen, *Court of Boyville*
[BR] *Scribner's Monthly*, vol. 18, 1895
330 [TL, CL] *Harper's Monthly*, 1904
[BL] *Philosophical Magazine and Journal of Science*, Oct., 1897
331 *The Electrician*, 1895
332 *Comptes Rendus des Séances de l'Académie des Sciences*, Feb., 1896
333 [all] *Harper's Monthly*, 1904
335 [TR] Courtesy Clark Millikan
[BR] California Institute of Technology
336 California Institute of Technology
337 [all] California Institute of Technology
338 [TL] California Institute of Technology
[TR] *The Physical Review*, Jan., 1916
339 [all] *The Physical Review*, 1916
340 Brown Bros., New York
341 National Cash Register Company, Dayton, O.
342 [T] *Scientific American Supplement*, 1910
[BL] Brown Bros., New York
343 [all] Smithsonian Institution
344 [all] Chanute, Octave, *Progress in Flying Machines*
345 [TR] Chanute, Octave, *Gliding Experiments*
[all others] Chanute, Octave, *Progress in Flying Machines*
346 U. S. Patent Office
347 U. S. Patent Office
348 *Air Progress*; copyright Street and Smith
350 California Institute of Technology
351 [T] International News Photos
[B] *Air Progress*, copyright Street and Smith
352 [TL] Mt. Wilson and Palomar Observatories
[BL] Kennedy, William Sloane, *Wonders and Curiosities of the Railway*
353 University of Chicago
354 Mt. Wilson and Palomar Observatories
355 Mt. Wilson and Palomar Observatories
356 Mt. Wilson and Palomar Observatories
357 [all] Mt. Wilson and Palomar Observatories
358 Mt. Wilson and Palomar Observatories
359 [all] Mt. Wilson and Palomar Observatories
360 [all] Mt. Wilson and Palomar Observatories
362 [TL] Courtesy Lee de Forest
[B] *Harper's Magazine*, vol. 88, 1893
363 *Harper's Weekly*, 1898
364 [BL] Fleming, J. A., *Fifty Years of Electricity*
[all others] Hogan, J. V. L., *Outline of Radio*
365 [TR] Fleming, J. A., *Electric Wave Telegraphy*
[CR] Courtesy Lee de Forest
[BR] *Scientific American*, 1902
367 [T, BL] Courtesy Lee de Forest
[C, BR] U. S. Patent Office
368 [all] Courtesy Lee de Forest
369 Courtesy Lee de Forest
371 [BL] *Wireless Age*, 1914
[T, BR] Courtesy Lee de Forest
372 General Electric Research Laboratories
373 [TR] General Electric Research Laboratories
[CR] *Harper's Magazine*, 1886
374 [all] General Electric Research Laboratories
375 General Electric Research Laboratories
376 General Electric Research Laboratories
377 *Scientific American*, June, 1885
378 California Institute of Technology
379 [TR] General Electric Research Laboratories
[BL, BR] Eric Mose, courtesy *Scientific American*, May, 1950
380 [all] Bakelite Corporation
381 [TR, CR] Bakelite Corporation
382 [all] Bakelite Corporation
383 [BL] Bakelite Corporation
[all others] Mumford, John Kimberly, *The Story of Bakelite*
384 [T] K. Chester, courtesy *Scientific American*, May, 1950
[BL] California Institute of Technology
387 E. I. du Pont de Nemours, Inc.
388 [all] E. I. du Pont de Nemours, Inc.
389 [BL] American Viscose Corporation
[BR] E. I. du Pont de Nemours, Inc.
390 National Bureau of Standards, courtesy *Scientic American*, Sept., 1953
392 *The New York Times*, May 8, 1954
393 R. C. A., courtesy *Scientific American*, Sept., 1953
394 [BL] Washington University News Bureau
[all others] James Egleson, courtesy *Scientific American*, March, 1952
395 Washington University News Bureau
396 [TR] James Egleson, courtesy *Scientific American*
[TL] Bell Telephone Laboratories
397 [all] Gilbert d'Andrea, courtesy *Scientific American*, May, 1948
398 Radio Corporation of America
399 [BL] Radio Corporation of America
[R] Irving Geis, courtesy *Scientific American*, Oct., 1950
400 [all] Radio Corporation of America
401 Irving Geis, courtesy *Scientific American*, Oct., 1950
402 Joseph Low, courtesy *Scientific American*, Sept., 1952
403 Sara Love, courtesy *Scientific American*, Sept., 1952
404 [all] Bernard Hoffman, courtesy *Scientific American*, Sept., 1952
406 Westinghouse Corporation, courtesy *Scientific American*, Feb., 1949
407 Guillemin, Amédée, *Le Monde Physique*
409 University of California, Radiation Laboratory
410 *Scientific American*
411 [all] California Institute of Technology
412 Mt. Wilson and Palomar Observatories
414 University of Chicago
415 John R. Dunning, Columbia University, courtesy *Scientific American*
416 [TL] University of Chicago
[BL] Brookhaven National Laboratory
417 James Egleson, courtesy *Scientific American*, Aug., 1953
418 Atomic Energy Commission, courtesy *Scientific American*, Oct., 1949
420 [TL] California Institute of Technology
[BL] W. B. Fretter, University of California, courtesy *Scientific American*, March, 1952
421 Brookhaven National Laboratory
422 Eric Mose, courtesy *Scientific American*
423 Adolph Brotman, courtesy *Scientific American*

BIBLIOGRAPHY

ACKERMAN, C. W. *George Eastman.* Boston: Houghton Mifflin Co., 1930

ADAM, NEIL KENSINGTON. *The Physics and Chemistry of Surfaces.* London: Oxford University Press, 1938.

AGASSIZ, ELIZABETH CARY. *Louis Agassiz: His Life and Correspondence.* Boston: Houghton Mifflin Co., 1885.

AGASSIZ, LOUIS. *Contributions to the Natural History of the United States.* Boston: Little, Brown & Co., 1857.

AGASSIZ, LOUIS. *Lake Superior: Its Physical Character, Vegetation and Animals.* Boston: Gould, Kendall & Lincoln, 1850.

AGASSIZ, LOUIS. *Recherches sur les poissons fossiles.* Neuchâtel, 1833–1843.

ALLEN, FREDERICK LEWIS. *The Big Change.* New York: Harper & Brothers, 1952.

American Journal of Science and Arts, The. PROFESSOR BENJAMIN SILLIMAN AND BENJAMIN SILLIMAN, JR., EDS. New Haven, 1818–1845.

American Journal of Science, The. JAMES D. DANA AND B. SILLIMAN, JR., EDS. Second Series. New Haven, 1846–1870.

Annals of the Astronomical Observatory of Harvard College. Cambridge: Metcalf & Co., 1856.

Appleton's Cyclopaedia of American Biography. J. G. WILSON AND J. FISKE, EDS. New York: D. Appleton & Co., 1888.

Appleton's Cyclopaedia of Applied Mechanics. PARK BENJAMIN, ED. New York: D. Appleton & Co., 1881.

Appleton's Dictionary of Machines, Mechanics, Engine Work and Engineering. New York: D. Appleton & Co., 1866.

Arts and Crafts in New York, 1726–1776, The. New York: New York Historical Society, 1938.

AUDUBON, MARIA R. *Audubon and His Journals.* New York: Charles Scribner's Sons, 1897.

BAEKELAND, LEO H. "A Family Motor Tour Through Europe," *The Horseless Age* (New York), 1907.

BAILEY SOLON I. *The History and Work of the Harvard Observatory.* New York: McGraw-Hill Book Co., 1931.

BARBER, H. L. *Story of the Automobile.* Chicago: A. J. Munson and Co., 1917.

BARBER, J. W. AND HOWE, HENRY. *Historical Collection of the State of New York.* New York: S. Tuttle, 1842.

BARTHOLDI, FREDERIC AUGUSTE. "The Statue of Liberty Enlightening the World." *North American Review* (New York), 1885.

BATHE, GREVILLE AND DOROTHY. *Oliver Evans.* Philadelphia: Historical Society of Pennsylvania, 1935.

BEAUFOY, MARK. *Nautical and Hydraulic Experiments.* London: H. Beaufoy, 1834.

BEAUMONT, WILLIAM. *Experiments and Observations on the Gastric Juice.* Facsimile ed. Cambridge: Harvard University Press, 1929.

BELL, A. G. *Upon Electrical Experiments to Determine the Location of the Bullet in the Body of the late President Garfield.* Washington: Gibson Bros., 1882.

BELL, A. G. *Upon the Production of Sound by Radiant Energy.* Washington: Gibson Bros., 1881.

BELL, A. G. *Visible Speech as a Means of Communicating Articulation to Deaf Mutes.* Washington: Gibson Bros., 1872.

BILLINGTON, RAY ALLEN, LOEWENBERG, BERT JAMES AND BROCKUNIER, SAMUEL HUGH, *The United States, American Democracy in World Perspective.* New York: Rinehart & Company, Inc., 1947.

BLIVEN, BRUCE. *Twentieth Century Unlimited.* Philadelphia: J. B. Lippincott Co., 1950.

BORTH, CHRISTY. *Pioneers of Plenty.* New York: Bobbs-Merrill Co., 1939.

BOWDITCH, NATHANIEL. *New American Practical Navigator.* Newburyport: Edward M. Blunt, 1802.

BRANLY, EDOUARD. *Le télégraphie sans fils.* Paris: Payot & Cie., 1922.

BROWN, SANBORN. "Benjamin Thompson: The Caloric Theory of Heat," *American Journal of Physics,* New York: 1950.

BROWN, SANBORN. "Benjamin Thompson: Discovery of Convection Currents." *American Journal of Physics,* New York: June, 1947.

BROWN, SANBORN AND SCOTT, KENNETH. "Benjamin Thompson, International Informer." *New England Quarterly,* Brunswick, Maine: March, 1948.

BROWN, SANBORN AND STEIN, ELBRIDGE W. "Benjamin Thompson and the First Secret Ink-Letter of the American Revolution." *Journal of Criminal Law and Criminology of Northwestern University* (Cleveland), 1950.

BROWN, WILLIAM H. *History of the First Locomotives in America.* New York: D. Appleton & Co., 1874.

BUCHANAN, ROBERTSON. *Millwork and Other Machinery.* London: John Weale, 1841.

BUCKINGHAM, J. S. *Eastern and Western States of America.* London: Fisher & Sons, 1842.

BYRN, EDWARD W. *The Progress of Invention in the Nineteenth Century.* New York: Munn, 1900.

CARNEGIE, ANDREW. *Autobiography of.* Garden City: Doubleday, Doran & Co., 1920.

CATLIN, GEORGE. *Letters and Notes on the Manners, Customs and Conditions of the North American Indians.* London: Chatto and Windus, 1842.

CAVEN, R. M. *Joseph Priestly.* London: Institute of Chemistry of Great Britain and Ireland, 1933.

Century Magazine, The. New York: The Century Co., 1881–1893.

CHANUTE, ACTAVE. *Gliding Experiments.* Reprinted from the *Journal of the Western Society of Engineers,* Chicago, 1897.

CHANUTE, OCTAVE. "Progress in Flying Machines," *The American Engineer and Railroad Journal* (New York), 1894.

CHASE, CARL T. *The Evolution of Modern Physics.* New York: D. Van Nostrand Co., 1947.

CLARK, ARTHUR H. *The Clipper Ship Era.* New York: G. P. Putnam's Sons, 1912.

CLARK, DUGALD. *The Theory of the Gas Engine.* New York: D. Van Nostrand Co., 1882.

CLARK, T. C. *The American Railway.* New York: Charles Scribner's Sons, 1897.

COHEN, I. B. *Benjamin Franklin's Experi-*
ments. Cambridge: Harvard University Press, 1941.

COHEN, I. B. *Proceedings American Philosophical Society,* New York: American Philosophical Society: June, 1952.

COHEN, I. B. "In Defense of Benjamin Franklin." *Scientific American* (New York), August, 1948.

COLDEN, CADWALLADER D. *Memoir Prepared at the Request of the Committee of the Common Council and Presented to the Mayor of the City at the Completion of the New York Canals.* New York: Davis, 1825.

Comptes Rendus. The Proceedings of the Meetings of the Academy of Sciences. Paris: Gautier-Villars et Fils.

Confederate Soldiers in the Civil War, The. BEN LA BREE, ED. Louisville: *The Courier-Journal,* 1895.

COOLEY, THOMAS M. *The American Railway, Its Construction, Development, Management and Appliances.* New York: Charles Scribner's Sons, 1897.

CORBIN, DIANA FONTAINE MAURY. *Matthew Fontaine Maury.* London: Sampson Low et al., 1888.

COULSON, THOMAS. *Life of Joseph Henry.* Princeton: Princeton University Press, 1950.

CROWTHER, J. G. *Famous American Men of Science.* New York: W. W. Norton & Company, Inc., 1937.

DAVIDSON, MARSHALL. *Life in America.* Boston: Houghton, Mifflin Co., 1951.

DE FOREST, LEE. *Father of Radio.* Chicago: Wilcox & Follett, 1950.

DEMSEYS, G. DRYSDALE. *The Practical Railway Engineer.* London: J. Weale, 1847.

DEMPSEY, G. DRYSDALE. *Rudimentary Treatise on the Locomotive Engine.* London: J. Weale, 1857.

Deposition of Alexander Graham Bell. New York: Bell Telephone Company, 1908.

DEVENS, R. M. *Our First Century.* Springfield, Mass.: C. A. Nichols & Co., 1880.

DICKERSON, H. W. *Robert Fulton, Engineer and Artist.* London: John Lane, 1913.

DONNAN, F. G. "The Influence of J. W. Gibbs on the Science of Physical Chemistry," *Journal of the Franklin Institute* (Philadelphia), September 17, 18, 19, 1924.

DUNBAR, SEYMOUR. *A History of Travel in America.* Indianapolis: Bobbs-Merrill Co., 1915.

DUNLAP, ORRIN E., JR. *Radio's Hundred Men of Science.* New York: Harper & Brothers, 1944.

DUTTON, WILLIAM S. *Du Pont, One Hundred and Forty Years.* New York: Charles Scribner's Sons, 1942.

DUYCKINCK, EVERT A. *National Portrait Gallery of Eminent Americans.* New York: Johnson, Fry & Co., 1861.

EDDINGTON, A. S. *Stars and Atoms.* New Haven: Yale University Press, 1927.

EDISON, THOMAS ALVA. *Diary and Sundry Observations of.* D. D. Runes, ed. New York: New York Philosophical Library, 1948.

Electrician, The. London: 1862–1952.

ELLIS, EDWARD S. *Youth's History of the United States From the Discovery of America by the Northmen to the Present Time.* New York: Cassell & Co., 1887.

ELLIS, GEORGE E. *Sir Benjamin Thompson, With Notices of His Daughter.* Boston: American Academy of Arts and Sciences, 1870.

EVANS, OLIVER. *The Young Millwright and Miller's Guide.* Philadelphia: Pub. by Oliver Evans, 1795.

EVERSON, GEORGE. *The Story of Television.* New York: W. W. Norton Company, Inc., 1949.

FARROW, EDWARD S. *Military Encyclopedia.* 3 vols. New York: Pub. by Edward S. Farrow, 1885.

FIGUIER, LOUIS. *Les merveilles de la sci-*
ence. Paris: Furne, Jouvet & Cie., 1876.

First Century of the Republic, The. T. D. WORLSEY, ED. New York: Harper & Brothers, 1876.

FLECK, H. RONALD. *Plastics, Scientific & Technological.* London: Temple Press Ltd., 1943.

FLEMING, J. A. *Electric Wave Telegraphy.* London: Longmans, Green, 1906.

FLEMING, J. A. *Fifty Years of Electricity.* London: Wireless Press, 1921.

FLORY, PAUL, J. *Principles of Polymer Chemistry.* Ithaca: Cornell University Press, 1953.

FRÉMONT, J. C. *The Exploring Expedition to the Rocky Mountains in the Year 1842, and to Oregon and North California in the Years 1843–44.* Washington: Gales & Seaton, 1845.

FULTON, ROBERT. *Torpedo War and Submarine Explosives.* New York: W. Eliot, 1810.

FULTON, ROBERT. *A Treatise on the Improvement of Canal Navigation.* London: I. & J. Taylor, 1796.

GASS, PATRICK. *Gass' Journal of the Voyages and Travels of Lewis and Clark.* Philadelphia: Mathew Carey, 1811.

GIBBS, J. WILLARD. *Scientific Papers of.* New York: Longmans, Green, 1906.

GIEDION, SIEGFRIED. *Mechanization Takes Command.* New York: Oxford University Press, 1948.

GILMORE, Q. A. *Charleston Harbor in 1863.* New York: D. Van Nostrand Co., 1865.

GOLDBERG, LEO. *Atoms, Stars and Nebulae.* Philadelphia: Blakiston Co., 1943

GOODYEAR, CHARLES. *Gum Elastic and Its Varieties.* New Haven: Pub. for Author, 1853–55.

GRAY, ASA. "Louis Agassiz" in *The Andover Review.* New York: Houghton, Mifflin Co., January, 1886.

GREELEY, HORACE, CASE, LEON, ETC. *The Great Industries of the United States.* Hartford and Chicago: 1874.

GRIFFITHS, JOHN W. *Treatise on Marine and Naval Architecture.* New York: D. Appleton & Co., 1853.

GUILLEMIN, AMÉDÉE. *Electricity and Magnetism.* S. P. THOMPSON, ED. London: The Macmillan Co., 1891.

GUILLEMIN, AMÉDÉE. *The Heavens.* London: Richard Bentley, 1868.

GUILLEMIN, AMÉDÉE. *Le Monde Physique.* Paris: Librairie Hachette, 1882.

HALE, GEORGE ELLERY. *The Depths of the Universe.* New York: Charles Scribner's Sons, 1924.

HALE, GEORGE ELLERY. *The New Heavens.* New York: Charles Scribner's Sons, 1922.

HALE, GEORGE ELLERY. *Signals From the Stars.* New York: Charles Scribner's Sons, 1931.

HALE, GEORGE ELLERY. *Study of Stellar Evolution.* Chicago: University of Chicago Press, 1908.

HALE, GEORGE ELLERY. *Ten Years Work of a Mountain Observatory.* Washington: Carnegie Institution of Washington, 1915.

HALE, GEORGE ELLERY, AND FOX, PHILIP. *Rotation Period of the Sun.* Washington: Carnegie Institution of Washington, 1908.

HALL, CAPTAIN BASIL, R. N. *Forty Etchings Made with Camera Lucida in North America.* Edinburgh: Cadell & Co., 1829.

HARLOW, ALVIN F. *Old Wires and New Waves.* New York: D. Appleton-Century, 1936.

Harper's New Monthly Magazine. New York: Harper & Brothers, June, 1897.

HAYNES, WILLIAM. *This Chemical Age.* New York: Alfred A. Knopf, 1942.

HENDRICK, BURTON J. *Life of Andrew Carnegie.* Vol. II. Garden City: Doubleday, Doran & Co., 1932.

HENRY, JOSEPH. *Collected Works of.* Washington: Smithsonian Institution, 1886.

HOFFLAIT, DORRIT. *Some Firsts in As-*

tronomical Photography. Cambridge: Harvard College Observatory, 1950.

HOGAN, J. V. L. *Outline of Radio*. Boston: Little, Brown & Co., 1923.

HOLDER, CHARLES FREDERICK. *Louis Agassiz, His Life and Work*. New York: G. P. Putnam's Sons, 1893.

HOLMES, OLIVER WENDELL. "The Human Wheel, Its Spokes and Felloes," *Atlantic Monthly*, May, 1863. Reprint published Boston: Ticknor & Fields, 1870.

HOMANS, J. F. *Self-Propelled Vehicles*. New York: Theo. Audel and Co., 1908.

HOWE, HENRY. *Memoir of Most Eminent American Mechanics*. New York: Derby & Jackson, 1858.

HUBERT, P. G. *Men of Achievement*. New York: Charles Scribner's Sons, 1894.

HUBERT, P. G. *Men of Achievement: Inventors*. New York: Charles Scribner's Sons, 1913.

HUNT, FREEMAN. *Lives of American Merchants*. New York: Derby and Jackson, 1858.

HUSBAND, JOSEPH. *The Story of the Pullman Car*. Chicago: A. C. McClurg & Co., 1917.

HUTCHINSON, W. T. *Cyrus Hall McCormick*. New York: The Century Co., 1935.

ILES, GEORGE. *Leading American Inventors*. New York: Henry Holt & Co., Inc., 1912.

Illustrated Catalogue of the Centennial Exhibition, The. New York: John Filmer, 1876.

INGRAM, J. S. *The Centennial Exposition*. Philadelphia: Hubbard Bros., 1876.

JACKSON, FREDERICK TURNER. *The Frontier in American History*. New York: Henry Holt & Co., Inc., 1920.

JAFFE, BERNARD. *Crucibles*. New York: Simon and Schuster, Inc., 1930.

JAFFE, BERNARD. *Men of Science in America*. New York: Simon and Schuster, Inc., 1946.

JAFFE, BERNARD. *Outposts of Science*. New York: Simon and Schuster, Inc., 1935.

JAMES, WILLIAM. "Louis Agassiz," *Harvard Graduates' Magazine* (Cambridge), June, 1897.

JENSEN, PAUL. *The Fireside Book of Flying Stories*. New York: Simon and Schuster, Inc., 1951.

JONES, A. D. *The American Portrait Gallery*. New York: Henry Miller, 1869.

JOSEPHSON, MATTHEW. *The Robber Barons*. New York: Harcourt, Brace & Co., 1934.

KANE, JOSEPH NATHAN. *Walter Hunt, American Inventor*. New York: 1935.

KAPLAN, A. D. H. AND KAHN, ALFRED E. "Big Business in a Competitive Society," *Fortune Magazine* (New York), February, 1953.

KELLY, FRED C. *The Wright Brothers*. New York: Harcourt, Brace & Co., 1943.

KIRKLAND, EDWARD C. *A History of American Economic Life*. New York: F. S. Crofts and Co., 1934.

Knight's American Mechanical Dictionary. New York: Hurd & Houghton, 1877.

Lamb's Textile Industries of the United States. E. OVERTON FOSTER, ED. Boston: J. H. Lamb, 1916.

LANE, R. W. *Henry Ford's Own Story*. New York: Ellis O. Jones, 1917.

LANGLEY, SAMUEL PIERPONT. *Memoir on Mechanical Flight*. 2 vols. C. H. MANLY, ED. Washington: Smithsonian Institution, 1911.

LANGMUIR, IRVING. *Phenomena, Atoms and Molecules*. New York: Philosophical Library, 1950.

LARDNER, DIONYSIS. *The Museum of Science and Art*. London: Walton & Maberly, 1856.

LESLIE, FRANK. *Historical Register of the United States Centennial Exposition, 1876*. New York: Frank Leslie's, 1877.

LESLIE, FRANK. *Pictorial History of the War*. New York: Frank Leslie's, 1862.

LESSING, LAWRENCE P. "The Electronics Era." *Fortune Magazine* (New York), July, 1951.

LEUPP, FRANCIS E. *George Westinghouse*. Boston: Little, Brown & Co., 1918.

LEWIS, CHARLES LEE. *Matthew Fontaine Maury*. Annapolis: U. S. Naval Institute, 1922.

London and Edinburgh Philosophical Magazine. London: John Taylor. June, 1840.

MABEE, CARLTON. *The American Leonardo —A Life of Samuel F. B. Morse*. New York: Alfred A. Knopf, 1943.

MAURY, MATTHEW F. *Explanation and Sailing Directions to Accompany Wind and Current Charts*. Washington: W. A. Harris, 1858.

MCCABE, J. D. *Great Fortunes and How They Were Made*. Cincinnati: 1870.

MCCLURE, J. B. *Edison and His Inventions*. Chicago: Rhodes & McClure, 1879.

MCKAY, LAUCHLAN. *The Practical Shipbuilder*. New York: Collins, Keese & Co., 1839.

MCKAY, RICHARD C. *Some Famous Sailing Ships and Their Builder, Donald McKay*. New York: G. P. Putnam's Sons, 1928.

MACKENSIE, CATHERINE. *Alexander Graham Bell*. Boston: Houghton, Mifflin Co., 1928.

MACLAURIN, RUPERT. *Invention and Innovation in the Radio Industry*. New York: The Macmillan Co., 1949.

MARCOU, JULES. *Life, Letters and Works of Louis Agassiz*. New York: The Macmillan Co., 1896.

MICHELSON, A. A. *Light Waves and Their Uses*. Chicago: University of Chicago Press, 1903.

MICHELSON, A. A. *Studies in Optics*. Chicago: University of Chicago Press, 1927.

MILLIKAN, R. A. *The Autobiography of*. New York: Prentice-Hall, Inc., 1950.

MILLIKAN, R. A. *Electrons (+ and −). Chicago*: University of Chicago, 1935.

Miracle at Kitty Hawk—Letters of Wilbur and Orville Wright. FRED C. KELLY, ED. New York: Farrar, Strauss & Young, 1951.

MIRSKY, JEANETTE AND NEVINS, ALLAN. *The World of Eli Whitney*. The Macmillan Co., 1952.

MONTROSS, LYNN. *War Through the Ages*. New York: Harper & Bros., 1944.

MORISON, SAMUEL ELIOT. *The Maritime History of Massachusetts*. Boston: Houghton, Mifflin Co., 1921.

MORRIS, EDMUND. *Derrick and Drill*. New York: James Miller, 1865.

MORSE, SAMUEL F. B. *His Letters and Journals*. E. LIND MORSE, ED. Boston: Houghton, Mifflin Co., 1914.

MUSCHAMP, EDWARD A. *Audacious Audubon*. New York: Brentano's, 1929.

MUYBRIDGE, EDWARD. *Animal Locomotion*. Philadelphia: J. B. Lippincott Co., 1888.

Naval Encyclopaedia, A. Philadelphia: L. R. Hamersly, 1881.

NEVINS, ALLAN. *Ford: The Times, The Man, The Company*. New York: Charles Scribner's Sons, 1954.

NEWHALL, BEAUMONT. *The History of Photography*. New York: The Museum of Modern Art, 1949.

"Office Robots," *Fortune Magazine* (New York), January, 1952.

PACKARD, FRANCIS RANDOLPH. *The History of Medicine in the United States*. Philadelphia: J. B. Lippincott Co., 1901.

Pageant of America, The. New Haven: Yale University Press, 1927.

PARRINGTON, VERNON. *Main Currents in American Thought*. Vol. III. New York: Harcourt, Brace & Co., 1930.

PARTON, JAMES. *History of the Sewing Machine*. Reprinted from *Atlantic Monthly*, May, 1867.

PAULING, LINUS. *The Nature of the Chemical Bond*. Ithaca: Cornell University Press, 1940.

Photographic History of the Civil War. FRANCIS TREVELYAN MILLER, ED. New York: Review of Reviews, 1911.

Physical Review, The. Vol. VII, No. 1. Ithaca: The American Physical Society, January, 1916.

Popular History of American Invention, A. WALDEMAR KAEMPFFERT, ED. New York: Charles Scribner's Sons, 1924.

PRESCOTT, GEORGE B. *The Speaking Telephone, Electric Light and Other Recent Electrical Inventions*. New York: D. Appleton & Co., 1879.

PRIESTLY, JOSEPH. *Experiments and Observations on Different Kinds of Air*. London: 1781.

PRIME, S. I. *Life of Samuel F. B. Morse*. New York: D. Appleton & Co., 1875.

PROUT, HENRY G. *A Life of George Westinghouse*. New York: Charles Scribner's Sons, 1922.

REED, SIR EDWARD J. AND SIMPSON, EDWARD. *Modern Ships of War*. New York: Harper & Brothers, 1888.

REID, JAMES D. *The Telegraph in America*. New York: John Polhemus, 1886.

REIGART, J. FRANKLIN. *Life of Robert Fulton*. Philadelphia: Henderson & Co., 1856.

REMINGTON, FREDERIC. Drawings. New York: R. H. Russell, 1897.

RICHTMEYER, F. K. *Introduction to Modern Physics*. New York: McGraw-Hill Book Co., 1934.

RICKARD, T. A. *A History of American Mining*. New York: McGraw-Hill Book Co., 1932.

RIESMAN, DAVID. *Faces in the Crowd*. New Haven: Yale University Press, 1952.

RIESMAN, DAVID. *The Lonely Crowd*. New Haven: Yale University Press, 1950.

ROBINSON, WILLIAM MORRISON, JR. *The Confederate Privateers*. New Haven: Yale University Press, 1928.

ROE, JOSEPH WICKHAM. *English and American Tool Builders*. New Haven: Yale University Press, 1916.

ROE, JOSEPH WICKHAM. *Interchangeable Manufacture in American Industry*. A Newcomen Address, August, 1939. Newcomen Society, Birmingham, Alabama, printed by The Birmingham Publishing Company, 1939.

ROWLAND, HENRY A. *The Physical Papers*. Baltimore: Johns Hopkins Press, 1902.

RUKEYSER, MURIEL. *Willard Gibbs*. New York: Doubleday, Doran & Co., 1942.

RUMFORD, COUNT. *Collected Works of*. Boston: American Academy of Arts and Sciences, 1870.

ST. MARTIN, ALEXIS. *Four Letters of*. Ann Arbor: William L. Clements Library, 1937.

St. Nicholas. Vol. XI, part 2. New York: The Century Co., 1884.

SCHLUETER, ROBERT E. "A Short Biographical Sketch of Dr. William Beaumont." Address before medical staff and resident Sisters at St. Anthony's Hospital. St. Louis: December 9, 1935.

SEELIG, MAJOR G. "Biographical Sketch of William Beaumont." Weekly Bulletin. Vol. XXVIII, Nos. 13–14. December 8 and 15, 1933. St. Louis Medical Society, 1933.

Semi-Centennial of Anaesthesia, The. Boston: Massachusetts General Hospital, 1897.

Sky and Telescope. Cambridge: Harvard College Observatory, June, 1947.

SLEEMAN, CHARLES. *Torpedoes and Torpedo Warfare*. Portsmouth: Griffin, 1889.

SLOSS, R. T. *The Book of the Automobile*. New York: D. Appleton & Co., 1905.

SMILES, SAMUEL. *Lives of Boulton and Watt*. London: J. Murray, 1865.

SMITH, E. F. *Chemistry in America*. New York: D. Appleton & Co., 1914.

SMITH, E. F. *Chemistry in Old Philadelphia*. Philadelphia: J. B. Lippincott Co., 1919.

SMITH, E. F. *Priestly in America*. Philadelphia: P. Blakiston, 1920.

STEEL, DAVID. *The Elements and Practice of Rigging and Seamanship*. London: Published by author, 1794.

STEWART, CHARLES B. *Lives and Works of Civilian and Military Engineers of America*. New York: D. Van Nostrand Co., 1871.

STRUIK, DIRK. *Yankee Science in the Making*. Boston: Little, Brown & Co., 1948.

SWARD, K. *The Legend of Henry Ford*. New York: Rinehart & Company, Inc., 1948.

SWIFT, R. B. *Who Invented the Reaper?* Chicago: Published by the author, 1897.

TAUSSIG, F. W. *Inventors and Money-Makers*. New York: The Macmillan Co., 1930.

TAYLOR, H. S., LAWRENCE, E. O. AND LANGMUIR, I. *Molecular Films, the Cyclotron and the New Biology*. New Brunswick: Rutgers University Press, 1942.

"Technology: The Instrument Frontier," *Fortune Magazine* (New York), December, 1952.

THORPE, T. E. *Joseph Priestly*. New York: E. P. Dutton, 1906.

TRAIN, ARTHUR, JR. *The Story of Every Day Things*. New York: Harper & Brothers, 1941.

TREDGOLD, THOMAS. *A Practical Treatise on Railroads and Carriages*. New York: Bliss and White, 1825.

TURNBULL, DOUGLAS. *John Stevens, An American Record*. New York: The Century Co., 1928.

TURNER, FREDERICK JACKSON. *The United States, 1830–1850, The Nation and Its Sections*. New York: Henry Holt & Co., Inc., 1935.

USA, The Permanent Revolution. EDITORS OF *Fortune* AND RUSSELL DAVENPORT. New York: Prentice, Hall, Inc., 1951.

United States Centennial Commission International Exhibition, 1876, The Official Catalogue. New York: John R. Nagle & Co., 1876.

United States Centennial Commission International Exhibition, 1876, Reports and Awards, The. FRANCIS WALKER, ED. Philadelphia: J. B. Lippincott Co., 1877.

URBAIN, GEORGES AND BOLL, MARCEL. *La science et ses applications*. Paris: Librairie Larousse, 1933.

VAIL, ALFRED. *The American Electro Magnetic Telegraph*. Washington: J. & G. S. Gideon, 1845.

VAN DOREN, CARL. *Benjamin Franklin*. New York: Viking Press, Inc., 1938.

VERY, EDWARD W. *Navies of the World*. New York: John Wiley & Sons, 1880.

WEINER, NORBERT. *The Human Use of Human Beings*. Boston: Houghton, Mifflin Co., 1950.

WESTCOTT, THOMPSON. *Centennial Portfolio*. Philadelphia: Thomas Hunter, 1876.

WESTCOTT, THOMPSON. *Life of John Fitch*. Philadelphia: J. B. Lippincott Co., 1857.

WHEELER, LYNDE PHELPS. *Josiah Willard Gibbs*. New Haven: Yale University Press, 1951.

WHITE, GEORGE S. *Memoir of Samuel Slater, Father of American Manufacture*. Philadelphia: 1836.

WHITE, HARVEY E. *Classical and Modern Physics*. New York: D. Van Nostrand Co., 1940.

WHITE, WILLIAM ALLEN. *The Court of Boyville*. New York: McClure, Phillips & Co., 1902.

WHITNEY, ELI. *Correspondence of Eli Whitney Relative to the Invention of the Cotton Gin*. M. B. HAMMOND, ED. New York: *American Historical Review*, 1897.

WILSON, H. W. *Ironclads in Action*. Samson Low, et al., 1896.

WILSON, J. M. *Masterpieces of the Centennial International Exhibition*. 3 vols. Philadelphia: Gebbie & Barrie, 1876.

Wireless Age. New York: Marconi Publishing Co., 1914.

WISTER, OWEN. *Jimmyjohn Boss*. Illus. Fred Remington. New York: Harper & Brothers, 1900.

WOLF, RALPH F. *India Rubber Man*. Caldwell, Idaho: Caxton Printers, Ltd., 1939.

WRIGHT, ORVILLE. *How We Invented the Airplane*. FRED C. KELLY, ED. New York: David McKay Co., Inc., 1953.

INDEX

Italicized page numbers are caption references

ABOUT THE AUTHOR

MITCHELL WILSON's career has won him acclaim in two widely separated fields. His novel, *Live with Lightning,* was a nationwide best-seller and a Literary Guild selection. He is himself a physicist and inventor. As assistant to Enrico Fermi, he developed many of the devices and techniques used in cosmic ray research.

Born in New York in 1913, Mr. Wilson took degrees at Columbia University and New York University. He taught for a short while at the College of the City of New York and then spent several years in industrial research. During this period he wrote several novels and short stories. Finally, he realized that he must decide between the two absorbing careers—science and writing—and chose writing. His most recently published novel is *The Lovers*.

Mr. Wilson now lives on Martha's Vineyard with his wife and two daughters.